RESEARCH & ENGINEERING APPLICATIONS IN ROCK MASSES
VOLUME 2

PROCEEDINGS OF THE 26TH U.S. SYMPOSIUM ON ROCK MECHANICS
SOUTH DAKOTA SCHOOL OF MINES & TECHNOLOGY / RAPID CITY
26-28 JUNE 1985

Research & Engineering Applications in Rock Masses

Edited by
EILEEN ASHWORTH
South Dakota School of Mines & Technology, Rapid City, South Dakota

VOLUME TWO

A.A.BALKEMA / ROTTERDAM / BOSTON / 1985

*The texts of the various papers in this volume were set individually
by typists under the supervision of each of the authors concerned.*

For the complete set of two volumes, ISBN 90 6191 500 3
For volume 1, ISBN 90 6191 601 1
For volume 2, ISBN 90 6191 602 X

Published by: A.A.Balkema Publishers, P.O.Box 1675, 3000 BR Rotterdam, Netherlands

Distributed in USA & Canada by: A.A.Balkema Publishers, P.O.Box 230, Accord, MA 02018

Printed in the Netherlands

Table of contents

VOLUME ONE

Preface   V

Organizing committee   VII

Sponsors   VIII

US National Committee   IX

Previous symposia proceedings   XI

Award winners for 1984

Abstracts of award winning research papers:

Background   3

The Basic Research Award I   4

The Basic Research Award II   5

Case Histories Award   6

Student Masters' Thesis Award   7

1 *Slope stability*

Study on rock slope protection of toppling failure by physical modelings   11
Deeswasmongkol Niyom & S.Sakurai

Nomograms for the assessment of toppling failure in rock slopes   19
P.Choquet & D.D.B.Tanon

Geotechnical investigation and appraisal of face stability in jointed rock mass in
surface mining   31
R.N.Singh & A.El-Mherig

The characteristics of coal measures slope instability in British surface coal mines   41
R.N.Singh, B.Denby & D.J.Brown

Rock mechanics in surface mining – An update   49
C.O.Brawner

2 Geological and empirical evaluation of rock properties

A comparison of some approaches to the classification of rock masses for geotechnical purposes
J.E.Udd & H.Wang   69

Influence of geological factors on the mechanical properties of rock in the Palo Duro Basin
D.M.Cregger, D.H.Corkum, A.O.Gokce & J.H.Peck   79

A new rock classification method for design purposes
N.Turk & W.R.Dearman   81

Analysis of the elastic and strength properties of Yucca Mountain tuff, Nevada
R.H.Price & S.J.Bauer   89

Pillar design for frozen placers
Frank J.Skudrzyk   97

3 Numerical modeling of fractured rock

A simplified modelling strategy for describing rockmass behaviour around stope faces in deep hard-rock gold mines
Richard K.Brummer   113

The kinematics of block inter-penetrations
Gen-hua Shi, Richard E.Goodman & John P.Tinucci   121

Equivalent continuum of large scale modeling for rock masses: An alternative approach
Emmanuel Detournay & Christopher St.John   131

Seismic stability of fractured rock masses with the distinct element method
Jean-Pierre Bardet & Ronald F.Scott   139

Rock motion modeling of oil shale cratering experiments
E.Gorham-Bergeron   151

4 Subsidence

Subsidence prediction for Saskatchewan potash mines
C.Steed, W.F.Bawden, A.M.Coode & P.Mottahed   163

Numerical modelling of the behavior of overburden rock masses associated with longwall mining
H.J.Siriwardane   171

Subsidence over a room and pillar mine in the Appalachian coal province and the use of subsidence predictive methods — A comparative analysis
T.Z.Jones & K.K.Kohli   179

Computer modeling of the surface effects of subsidence control methods
Keith A.Heasley & Lee W.Saperstein   189

Surface subsidence resulting from longwall mining in central Utah — A case study
A.J.Fejes   197

5 Rock mass characterization in deep boreholes

Applications of borehole-acoustic methods in rock mechanics
F.L.Paillet   207

Borehole measurements in extreme environments   221
Richard K.Traeger

Fracture detection and evaluation using new wireline methods   227
Richard A.Plumb, Alain Brie & Kai Hsu

6 *Applied numerical modeling*

2-D and 3-D finite element analyses of room-pillar mining systems with flat and
rolling coal seams   231
S.T.Wang, L.M.Galloway & G.E.Blandford

Comparison of numerical modeling with predictions from laboratory tests and
field observations of deformation in a potash mine in Sergipe, Brazil   239
Alvaro Maia da Costa & Charles Fairhurst

Salt pressures on defense high-level waste packages   251
D.P.Nelson & A.F.Fossum

Modeling with infinite elements in the study of stress field and heat diffusion at
the contour of underground excavations   259
M.Cravero, G.Iabichino, G.Carosso & G.P.Giani

Fuzzy methodology in tunnel support design   269
Charles Fairhurst & Dezhang Lin

7 *Problems associated with weak rock*

Cross hole seismic investigation for characterization of the rock foundation at
the site of a large rock fill dam   281
T.L.By

Design procedures of large underground openings in weak rock   289
Daniel E.Hokens

Mine inundations   297
D.E.Nicholson

Building embankments with shale   305
M.W.Oakland & C.W.Lovell

Test procedures for salt rock   313
M.B.Dusseault, D.Mraz, J.Unrau & C.Fordham

8 *Hydraulic fracture*

Pseudo-three-dimensional fracture growth modeling   323
John D.McLennan & John C.Picardy

An improved model for fluid-driven cracks in jointed rock   333
R.J.Shaffer, A.R.Ingraffea & F.E.Heuze

Hydraulic-fracture growth in dipping anisotropic strata as viewed through the
surface deformation field   341
Gary R.Holzhausen, C.S.Haase, S.H.Stow & George Gazonas

The sizing of a hot dry rock reservoir from a hydraulic fracturing experiment   355
George Zyvoloski

Determination of rock mass deformation modulus during hydraulic fracturing   363
S.A.Dischler & K.Kim

9 Constitutive modeling of rock, rock masses and joints

Nonassociative constitutive laws for Algerie granite 377
P.E.Senseny & J.R.Simonson

Constitutive modeling of rock joints with dilation 387
Michael E.Plesha

A constitutive law for shear behavior of rock joints 395
R.Janardhanam & William F.Kane

A comparison of hydrostatic-stress and uniaxial-strain pore-volume compressibilities using nonlinear elastic theory 403
Mark A.Andersen & Frank O.Jones, Jr.

10 Ground support

Effects of moisture on anchorage capacity of expansion shell rock bolts 413
Yoginder P.Chugh

Evaluation of roof bolt tension measuring techniques 425
H.N.Maleki, M.P.Hardy & C.J.H.Brest van Kempen

The influence of monolithic permanent roadside support upon coal rib pillar design in longwall mining 439
A.K.Isaac & A.R.Payne

Liner support for excavations through strong jointed rock masses 447
R.F.Cook & R.W.McCrae

A new aspect in tunnel closure interpretation 455
A.Guenot, M.Panet & J.Sulem

11 Fracture mechanics

Fracture parameters of Fontainebleau sandstones: Experimental study using a high temperature controlled atmosphere double torsion apparatus 463
M.Darot, Th.Reuschlé & Y.Gueguen

Formation and stability of steeply dipping joint sets 471
John Kemeny & Neville G.W.Cook

Time-dependent microcracking in plutonic rock due to heat from a nuclear-fuel waste vault 479
B.J.S.Wilkins, Y.Liner & G.L.Rigby

The modelling and measurement of super-conducting rock joints 487
Nick Barton, Axel Makurat, Gunnar Vik & Fredrik Løset

Fracture toughness testing of coal 497
G.C.Kirby & C.J.Mazur

12 Model verification

Physical and numerical simulations of fluid-filled cavities in a creeping material 507
Dale S.Preece & Herbert J.Sutherland

Calculation of laboratory stress-strain behavior using a compliant joint model 515
Duane A.Labreche

Measurement and calculation of the mechanical response of a highly fractured rock 523
S.J.Bauer, R.K.Thomas & L.M.Ford

Comparison between predicted and measured stresses in an underground coal mine 531
L.J.Wardle & K.E.McNabb

Energy analysis of hydraulic fracturing 539
J.Shlyapobersky

13 *Poster session A*

Use of the Schmidt hammer for rock and coal testing 549
K.Y.Haramy & M.J.DeMarco

Study on estimating geostresses by the Kaiser effect of AE 557
K.Michihiro, T.Fujiwara & H.Yoshioka

Effects of contact area of an interface on acoustic wave transmission
characteristics 565
L.R.Myer, D.Hopkins & N.G.W.Cook

Crustal stress and rock pressure are determined from the shape of the weak plane 573
Liren Yu & Guangping Cui

In situ stress indications around Lake Ontario 575
E.N.Lindner

Moisture adsorption rate and strength degradation of Illinois shales 591
Sathit Tandanand

Penetrometer to determine the mechanical properties of rocks 601
T.Cyrul & A.B.Szwilski

A note on the implementation of a continuum finite element approach for
stress analysis in jointed rock 613
James R.Carr

The effect of hydraulic-fracture growth on free oscillations of wellbore pressure 621
Gary R.Holzhausen & Richard P.Gooch

Coupled finite element/boundary element analysis for nonlinear fluid flow in
rock fissures and fissure networks 633
D.Elsworth

On the use of a single shape function for the integral equation of a plane crack
under normal loading 643
M.J.Bouteca & S.M.Tijani

Finite element modeling of rock breakage mechanism 651
R.H.Haghighi, C.J.Konya & R.G.Lundquist

Finite element analysis of the Stress Control Method 659
Shosei Serata, Shiann-Jang Chern, Mauro Foglia & Tetsuya Nakamura

Field application of fracture mechanics analysis to small rock slopes 667
Thomas M.Tharp & D.Todd Coffin

Rock wedge stability analysis on a personal computer 675
L.W.Abramson

VOLUME TWO

14 Underground mine design

The application of numerical models in coal rib pillar design at longwall panels 685
A.R.Payne & A.K.Isaac

Longwall design improvement in coal mines using finite element analysis 693
Bruce H.Gardner, Frederick Carr & Edward Martin

Yield pillar usage in longwall mining at depth — No.4 Mine, Brookwood,
Alabama 695
Michael Gauna, Kenneth R.Price & Eddie Martin

Strength of mine pillars 703
James E.Russell

15 Seismic and acoustic emission/microseismic studies

Structural stability monitoring using high-frequency microseismics 707
Richard C.Repsher & Bernard J.Steblay

Determining peak stress history using acoustic emissions 715
D.J.Holcomb, & R.J.Martin, III

Directional acoustic emission activity in response to borehole deformation in
rock masses 723
Robert J.Watters & Amir M.Soltani

Location of acoustic emissions during fracture of slightly anisotropic granite 731
C.H.Dowding, L.Samama, S.P.Shah & J.F.Labuz

Propagation of acoustic waves through cracked rock 739
Robert W.Zimmerman & Michael S.King

16 Field testing for nuclear waste

Thermal-cycle testing of the G-Tunnel heated block 749
Roger M.Zimmerman, Michael L.Wilson, Mark P.Board, Michael E.Hall
& Robert L.Schuch

Analysis of a loading test on a large basalt block 759
Roger D.Hart, Peter A.Cundall & Michael L.Cramer

The use of field data to evaluate and improve drift response models for the
Waste Isolation Pilot Plant (WIPP) 769
Harold S.Morgan, Charles M.Stone & Raymond D.Krieg

In-situ load-deformation characterization of the CSM/OCRD jointed test block 777
A.M.Richardson, W.Hustrulid, S.Brown & W.Ubbes

Mechanical response of jointed granite during shaft sinking at the Canadian
Underground Research Laboratory 785
T.Chan, P.A.Lang & P.M.Thompson

17 Heat and fluid flow

Measurement methods for thermal transport properties of rocks 797
T.Ashworth, David R.Smith & E.Ashworth

Preliminary evaluation of alterant geophysical tomography in welded tuff 807
A.L.Ramirez & W.D.Daily

Thermal convection through a system of rigid idealized fissures 817
Gaurav Rajen & F.A.Kulacki

Effect of stress on permeability of coal 831
Satya Harpalani & Malcolm J.McPherson

Permeability property effect on saturated-unsaturated seepage flow analysis
in rock 841
Hidenobu Yoshida, Takashi Matsumoto, Kenji Aoki & Yuzo Ohnishi

18 In situ testing results and interpretations

Observations of borehole deformation modulus values before and after extensive
heating of a granitic rock mass 851
W.C.Patrick, J.L.Yow, Jr. & M.C.Axelrod

The influence of rock mass fracturing on the measurement of deformability by
borehole expansion tests 859
Bernard Amadei

In-situ determination of elastic coefficients of rock mass 869
Pan Li-zhou

Some laboratory and field deformation modulus results and their application
to a practical problem 873
D.P.Richards & W.A.Hustrulid

A strategy for future laboratory rock mechanics programs 883
B.M.Butcher & A.K.Jones

19 Rock drilling and cutting

A review of waterjet excavation research 895
David A.Summers

Mechanics of rock-bit interaction at elevated temperatures 905
Mario G.Karfakis & Robert W.Heins

20 Poster session B

A Monte Carlo method for studying thermal conductivity and thermal
anisotropy in aggregates 917
Larry J.Van Stone

An experimental determination of mixed and forced convection heat transfer
coefficients in a modeled nuclear waste repository 925
Rodney L.Osborne & Richard N.Christensen

Theoretical background to the development of a computer code for the
modeling of seam-like deposits 927
J.P.E.Moris & K.I.Oravecz

Rock mass classification by fuzzy sets 937
V.U.Nguyen & E.Ashworth

The asymmetric stress distribution around a slotted cylinder in a poroelastic medium 947
E.P.Fahrenthold & J.B.Cheatham, Jr.

Detection of yield and rupture of underground openings by displacement monitoring 957
S.M.Maloney & P.K.Kaiser

Geostatistical approach to roof fall prediction 967
T.Cyrul & Kot F.Unrug

Mine subsidence hazard detection technique for Pennsylvania's anthracite coalfields 977
Swapan Bhattacharya, Madan M.Singh & Noel M.Moebs

Application of geophysical exploring methods for observing rock failure in the mining of coal seams menaced by water-bodies 985
Liu Zongcai, Sun Zhengpeng, Gao Hang, Li Baiying, Yu Shijian, Li Jiaxiang & Zeng Ruihua

Stresses and strains on the common boundary surface and strength of composite rock masses acted by three-dimensional compressive stresses 993
Tan Xue Shu, Xian Xue Fu & Cao Wei

Blast induced subsidence in the craters of nuclear tests over coral 999
Donald E.Burton, Robert P.Swift, H.David Glenn & Jon B.Bryan

A blocky physical model of longwall caving under strong roof conditions 1007
M.B.Wold

Finite element techniques for the determination of rock salt material properties from in situ and laboratory penetrometer data 1015
Stephen Niou, Shiann-Jang Chern & Shinji Kikuchi

The application of a personal computer in a rock mechanics data acquisition system 1023
Zbigniew Hladysz & Charles A.Kliche

Evaluation of a large sample triaxial test facility: A progress report 1033
Malcolm J.Reeves

21 Instrumentation

Some recent developments in vibrating wire rock mechanics instrumentation 1043
Piyush K.Dutta

Application of holographic interferometry to in-situ stress measurement 1055
Douglas R.Schmitt, Jay D.Bass & Thomas J.Ahrens

An apparatus for the study of the behavior of rocks under three dimensional loading 1057
Akhtar S.Khan & Fersheed K.Irani

The use of the pressuremeter to evaluate the strength-deformation characteristics of soft rocks 1067
Robert C.Bachus

A borehole instrument for measuring mining-induced pressure changes in underground coal mines 1075
Eric R.Bauer, Gregory J.Chekan & John L.Hill, III

22 In situ case histories

Pore pressure effects on the minimum principal stress direction in shallow tar sands   1087
Daniel D.Bush & Nick Barton

Problems associated with near surface in-situ stress measurements by the overcoring method   1095
P.Garritty, R.A.Irvin & Ian W.Farmer

In situ rock stress measurements in French coal mines: Relation between virgin stresses and rock bursts   1103
R.Revalor, J.Arcamone, JP.Josien & JP.Piguet

Implications about in situ stress at Yucca Mountain   1113
S.J.Bauer, J.F.Holland & D.K.Parrish

Topography, stresses, and stability at Yucca Mountain, Nevada   1121
Henri S.Swolfs & William Z.Savage

23 Rock blasting

Insitu measurement of blast damage underground by seismic refraction surveys   1133
Paul N.Worsey

Statistics – A key to better blast vibration predictions   1141
Amitava Ghosh & Jaak J.K.Daemen

Seismic characterisation of rock masses before and after mine blasting   1151
R.P.Young & J.J.Hill

Predicting grain size distribution of blast material based on rock fabric information   1159
Dirk van Zyl

24 Underground excavation

Field measurements of rock displacement in deep shafts in quartzite with high in situ stress   1163
M.J.Beus & J.K.Whyatt

Development of a geo-numerical model as an aid in stope design   1173
R.Pakalnis, H.D.S.Miller & T.Madill

An in situ technique for the assessment of failure in coal pillars   1181
James J.Snodgrass & David A.Newman

ICBM deep basing construction planning study   1189
Patrick D.Lindsey

25 New stress measurement methods

Insights into the relationship between wellbore breakouts, natural fractures, and in situ stress   1199
Lawrence W.Teufel

In situ stress evaluation from borehole breakouts – Experimental studies   1207
Bezalel C.Haimson & Courtney G.Herrick

Determination of in-situ stresses in the floor of a diatomite quarry 1219
Richard M.Nolting, Glenn M.Boyce & Richard E.Goodman

In situ stress measurements in stratified hard rock formations 1227
Krishnan Shrinivasan & Shosei Serata

Predicting the in-situ state of stress using Differential Wave Velocity Analysis 1235
N.-K.Ren & P.J.Hudson

26 Physical modeling

A study on the validity of stress measurements in jointed crystalline rock 1247
Scott Brown, William Hustrulid & Archie Richardson

Load response of modelled underground structures 1255
Khosrow Bakhtar, Alan Black & Robert Cameron

Physical model study of a longwall mine 1261
Duk-Won Park & Dwayne C.Kicker

Modeling of coal mine roof reinforcement 1273
H.C.Pettibone, S.M.Dar & T.W.Smelser

Investigation of equivalent materials for physical modeling of Utah coal seams 1281
H.Moon & V.J.Hucka

Author index 1289

Papers for which no written text was available at the time of publication

In situ physical properties measurements in boreholes
Jeff Daniels
Short paper presented as part of the panel discussion in the Rock mass characterization in deep boreholes session

Yield pillar design and evaluation for a longwall mining system
H.N.Maleki, J.F.T.Agapito, Bob Lauman & Marc Wangsgard
Paper presented in the Underground mine design session

Rock drilling and mechanical excavation research – A review
Levant Ozdemir
Paper presented in the Rock drilling and cutting session. Written version to be included in a US National Committee for Rock Mechanics report

Single plane of weakness theory applied to chip volume and rate of penetration
J.F.Evers
Paper presented in the Rock drilling and cutting session

Blasting research – A review
Darrell D.Porter
Paper presented in the Rock blasting session. A written version is to be included in a US National Committee for Rock Mechanics report

The rock mechanics associated with bi-level mining system at two Saskatchewan potash mines
P.Mottahed & B.W.Schmitke
Paper presented in the Underground excavation session

14. Underground mine design

Chair: Z.T.BIENIAWSKI
The Pennsylvania State University, University Park, USA

Cochair: W.HUSTRULID
Colorado School of Mines, Golden, USA

The application of numerical models
in coal rib pillar design at longwall panels

A.R.PAYNE & A.K.ISAAC
Department of Mineral Exploitation, University College, Cardiff, UK

1 INTRODUCTION

The rib pillars left between adjacent longwall panels are intended to protect the gateroads from harmful stress abutments, with a reduction in pillar width generally requiring an increase in strength of the gateroad support system.

Wilson (1972) using the 'yield zone' hypothesis, formulated a pillar width design procedure on the assumption that at the point of fracture of its core, the yield zones meet and increased roof lowering over the pillar results with severe gateroad closure. The hypothesis has been successfully applied for wide pillars but not those less than 10m in width which have little or no solid core.

In designing support systems for gateroads, Whittaker (1977) used the 'detached block' theory, associated with the presence of a ribside 'break', in which the roadside pack has to resist the weight of a block of strata equivalent to the waste caving height and the distance from the ribside 'break' to the waste caving line.

Smart et al (1982) in designing packs for dual life gateroads, developed the 'roof beam tilt' approach resulting in an underground subsidence profile. The pack has to be stiff enough to resist excessive roof tilt while not exceeding the strength of roof and floor strata.

Numerical model simulation provides one method of investigating the effect of separate support elements to be evaluated together. One such model is being applied to several gateroad locations in the South Wales Coalfield, U.K. for comparison with strata and support displacement and stress measurements obtained from underground investigations.

2 THE FINITE DIFFERENCE NUMERICAL MODEL

A finite difference numerical model developed by Mayer (1981) aims to predict support system deformation at underground excavations in 'soft' coal measures strata. The model is comprised of a main iterative program with several accessory programs for failure and analysis, displacement and stress plotting.

The strata is simulated by a matrix or mesh of mass nodes interconnected by hypothetical springs via stress nodes, with Young's Modulus, Poisson's Ratio and density of the strata describing the properties of the 'springs' and mass nodes. The matrix is loaded by applying a stress to the top nodes. The displacements for each mass node are calculated in each iteration until 'equilibrium' or 'convergence' has been obtained from which the vertical and horizontal stress at each point is determined. The elasto-plastic behaviour of yield zones around excavations is simulated by altering the Young's Modulus and Poisson's Ratio of the nodes which have failed according to the triaxial failure criteria of the strata. The new Young's Modulus is evaluated from the triaxial failure criteria on the amount of work done on the node in failing it, while Poisson's Ratio is increased to its maximum value as the strata has assumed to have lost all cohesive strength.

2.1 Input Parameters

The parameters required by the model are divided into four types:
    (i)   model configuration parameters which define the geometric configuration of the strata to be modelled;
    (ii)   model control parameters which define the model features to be employed to simulate the specified situation;
    (iii)   solution parameters which control the iterative procedure to solve the finite difference equations;
    (iv)   physical property parameters which define the physical properties of all the material within the model area and the load applied to the model.

The first three input parameters can be assessed by considering the aims and location of the modelling exercise. However, the physical property parameters for the proximate strata, coal and support system have to be evaluated for each individual application.
    (1)   Proximate strata: These are obtained from 10m long cores taken from roof and floor strata of the gateroad; the core is divided into lithological units and prepared core specimens from each unit are allocated to uniaxial or triaxial compression tests. By averaging the results in each unit, a representative set of properties for each unit is obtained.
    (2)   Coal and Seatearth: These properties are obtained using the same method as for proximate strata except that problems in coring these in situ generally require large bulk samples to be collected and cored in the laboratory.
    (3)   Gateroad Support: The elasticity of the support elements is obtained from laboratory tests of models, cylindrical samples and pack materials
    (4)   Caved Waste: The mechanics of waste caving is a complex process, but for simplification, two assumptions have been made. Firstly caving occurs to a height of 2h above the coal seam, h being the extracted height, while secondly, the angle of caving is a constant 45°. The properties are then evaluated by taking into account where the material originates from the strata immediately above the seam.
    (5)   Loading of the top nodes: The loading on top nodes has been estimated as the product of the average density above the area to be simulated, and the depth of the workings, assuming a uniform loading 10m above the excavation. Recently when modelling narrow rib pillars with caved waste on both sides, modelling has commenced from the surface.

2.2 Modelling Procedure

Having obtained physical property values, consideration is then given to the mesh densities desirable in different parts of the model. In general, greater densities are required in regions of greater distortion, such as the immediate vicinity of an excavation. A value of about 0.5m between nodes has been found to be satisfactory for the final mesh in most simulations. This should include all areas in which the excavation under investigation are thought to have measurable effects to the surface or otherwise.

On achieving the required mesh, failure analysis is conducted using the set of programs referred to previously. Program FAIL determines the failed nodes, while program YOUNG'S the new Young's Moduli. The procedure is repeated until the model 'stabilises' when no new nodes fail so that the complete effects of stress redistribution around the excavation have taken place. This process simulates the gradual extension of a yield zone. Comparisons between model simulation and in situ results are then possible for evaluation of the authenticity of the model in both absolute displacement and stress values, and also characteristic deformation.

3   INVESTIGATIONS OF THE TAFF MERTHYR COLLIERY SUPPORT SYSTEM

Research locations for the work have been Taff Merthyr and Lady Windsor Collieries in the central part of the South Wales Coalfield, although only Taff Merthyr results are reported in the Paper. Investigations were conducted at permanent sites for detailed deformation data, and along gateroad length to establish the representative nature of the site data.

Permanent instrumentation sites provided measurements of support and strata behaviour in the vicinity of and remote from the gateroad. The main parameters measured and instrumentation used are included in an accompanying paper of this Symposium (Isaac and Payne, 1985).

3.1   Field Investigation

At Taff Merthyr Colliery, 200m wide longwall retreat coalfaces with dual life gateroads are used for maximum extraction of the Seven Foot Seam (Figure 1(a)). The Seven Foot Seam dips 4° to the South West, with the faces working down dip and extracting 1.45m of the 1.80m seam section, at a depth of approximately 550m. The geology consisted of a medium strength mudstone roof interbedded with siltstones, with a soft seatearth layer overlying weak mudstone floor strata. A rectangular gateroad (5.0m × 2.3m) with a 5m coal pillar and dummy road system, was used with connections every 20m. The predriven B20 Tailgate was initially supported by steel roof bars on steel or wood props. 25m ahead of the advance of B20 Face, extra supports were installed to protect the gateroad from the effects of the front abutment zone. A monolithic pack or hardwood cogs were installed on the pillarside of the gateroad, with the dummy road supported by hardwood cogs and steel roof bars.

Two investigation sites were installed in B20 Tailgate, viz., T.B.1.1, a comprehensively instrumented site 200m from the face entry, and T.B.1.2, a satellite site, for convergence recorder and roof inclination measurements, at 320m. The support system and instrumentation used are shown in Figure 1(b).

Analysis of the deformation of dual-life gateroads has been divided into four phases, depending on the position of the first and second faces relative to the site. The phases are defined as:

Phase 1: time-dependent behaviour associated with development and standby period;

Phase 2: (a) high activity behaviour of the front abutment zone for 20-50m ahead of the first face, and (b) high activity behaviour after passage of the first face for approximately 100m of face advance;

Phase 3: time-dependent deformation awaiting end of first face and commencement of second face operations;

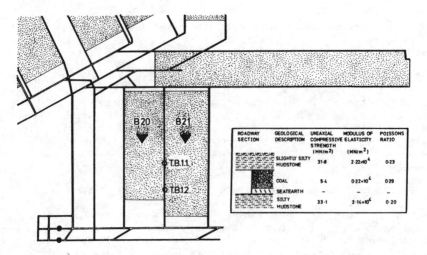

ROADWAY SECTION	GEOLOGICAL DESCRIPTION	UNIAXIAL COMPRESSIVE STRENGTH (MN/m²)	MODULUS OF ELASTICITY (MN/m²)	POISSONS RATIO
	SLIGHTLY SILTY MUDSTONE	31·8	2·22×10⁴	0·23
	COAL	5·4	0·22×10⁴	0·29
	SEATEARTH	–	–	–
	SILTY MUDSTONE	33·1	2·14×10⁴	0·20

(a) Mine layout and geotechnical date

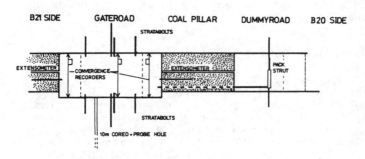

DISPLACEMENT MEASUREMENT

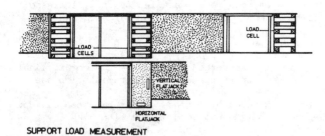

SUPPORT LOAD MEASUREMENT

(b) Gateroad seven foot seam, support system and instrumentation at Site T.B.1.1

Figure 1. Taff Merthyr Colliery, South Wales Coalfield, U.K.

Phase 4: high activity behaviour of front abutment zone ahead of second face.

Vertical closure is shown in Figure 2(a) illustrating the higher rates of closure (6.4mm/m advance) associated with the front abutment stress and waste consolidation behind the face. The onset of the front abutment occurred 15m ahead of the face with a total gateroad vertical closure of approximately 20% of original height. Maximum closure was recorded in the centre due to considerable floor heave. However, dummy road closure at 40% indicated that this may have absorbed some of the floor heave from the tailgate. Total closure on passage of the second face was approximately 40%, with the effects of the front abutment zone being approximately 125m ahead of the face.

The graph also shows increased closure on the pillarside compared with the ribside, until the effect of the second face, where the trend started to reverse.

This is confirmed by roof beam inclinations which show a tilt firstly towards B20 or pillarside, from the B20 abutment zone which reversed on the onset of B21 abutment. A maximum value of 210 minutes was recorded towards the pillar during Phase 3. Ribside and pillar extrusion measured using the multi-reference point extensometer show a total of 88mm movement of the ribside with a yield zone depth of 3.5m, while the pillar yielded a total of 80mm.

As the face side pillar provided the majority of support, support load development was generally low, rising to a maximum of 2 MPa in the dummy road and only 1 MPa in the gateroad. However, lateral pressure on the pillar support did reach a maximum of 2 MPa indicating the lateral strength of the support element (Figure 2(b)).

The proposed characteristic deformation behaviour is shown in Figure 2(c), demonstrating the maintenance of roof beam and support integrity, and considerable floor heave which was controlled by dinting.

3.2 Model Simulation

The model has been applied to both locations referred to (Payne, 1985). However, before making direct comparisons between the model and in situ results, it is necessary to consider the relationship between them. The model being entirely elastic, cannot simulate time-dependent deformation as experienced in Phase 2 of a single life gateroad, and Phase 3 of a dual-life gateroad. Thus only closure and loads before these phases can be simulated and all comparisons presented below are based on this premise.

Investigation site T.B.1.1 was modelled as shown in Figure 3(a). An initial mesh density of 2.0m was reduced in 2 stages to 0.5m where failure analyses commenced. Due to the very weak nature of the strata, 'stabilisation' was finally achieved after 12 successive analyses. Relative displacements and the failure produced at 'stabilisation' are shown in Figure 3(b),(c) respectively. Table 1 compares the in situ results at the end of Phase 2 with those of the model giving the difference and error percentage.

In situ closure far exceeds that simulated, indicating the problems of elastically modelling weak plastic strata. Negligible floor heave was predicted, while from survey levelling the largest amount of vertical closure was attributed to it. Roof closure compared well as shown by the change in roof beam inclination. Pillar extrusion and support lateral loading are also compatible, demonstrating that the failed strata modelling assumption operates well for coal. The pillar acted as a prestressed pack which needed no consolidation and only yielded slowly as it failed and was extruded into the gateroad. Some control had been provided by the lateral strength of the supports.

STAGE 1
After Development

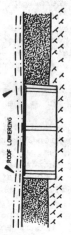

Initiation of Ribside Extrusion

STAGE 2
After First Face Operations

Pack Compression allowing Roof to pivot over Ribside
Foundation Failure allowing Floor Heave and Cog Displacement

STAGE 3
Infront of Second Face Operations with Repairs

Roof Lowering due to Ribside Extrusion
(Ribside Break contained)

(c) Characteristic deformation behaviour

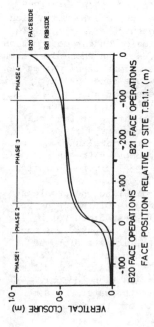

(a) Vertical closure

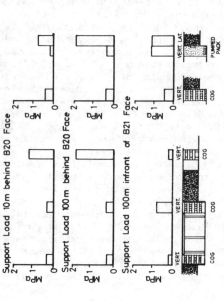

(b) Support load development

Figure 2. In situ results

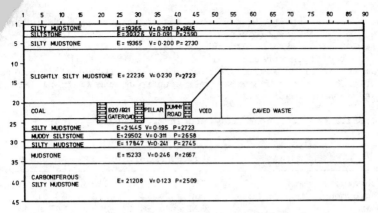

(a) Model configuration and strata properties

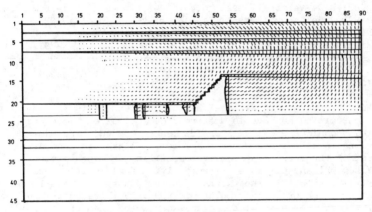

(b) Relative displacement

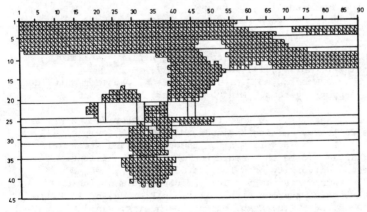

(c) Failure pattern

Figure 3. Model Results

The problem of weak strata in the modelling technique is confirmed by the failure plot which has large-scale floor failure. Tensile fracturing and flow of floor strata into the excavation possibly confined failure to the top floor strata (~ 5m).

Apart from the in situ large scale floor movement, the model simulated characteristic deformation behaviour well with roof beam tilt, pillar extrusion and support loading.

Table 1. T.B.1.1 comparison of model and in situ results, final simulation

	In situ	Model	Diff.	% Accuracy
B20 Side Convergence (mm)	318	100	-218	-68.5
B21 Side Convergence (mm)	260	64	-216	-77.1
Dummy Road (mm)	624	226	-298	-47.8
Roof Beam Inclination (mins)	48'	30'	-18'	-37.5
Flat Jack 1 B20 Side Vertical (MPa)	0.30	0.28	-0.02	- 7.1
Flat Jack 2 B21 Side Vertical (MPa)	0.40	0.38	-0.02	- 5.2
Flat Jack 3 B20 Side Lateral (MPa)	1.80	2.20	0.4	+22.2
Extrusion Pillar (mm)	88	92	6	+ 6.8
Extrusion Ribside (mm)	80	19	-61	-76.2

4 CONCLUSIONS

The finite difference numerical model has shown flexibility in modelling different mining methods in different geological environments. The modelling technique provides a useful means of predicting gateroad conditions in situations where small coal pillars are used as an integral part of the support system, for modelling the interaction between the support and pillar simultaneously. Problems still exist with weak strata, especially seatearths, as the plastic or tensile failure cannot yet be properly simulated. However, these areas can be identified even though absolute amounts cannot be predicted. Future development of the model must attempt to simulate these soft rock strata characteristics and/or encourage the development of a rheologically-based modelling technique.

REFERENCES

Wilson, A.H. 1972. An hypothesis concerning pillar stability. Mining Engineer, No.141, 131, June, 409-417.
Whittaker, B.N. & Woodrow, C.J.M. 1977. Design loads for gateside packs and support systems. Mining Engineer, No.189, 136, Feb, 263-275.
Smart, B.G.D., Isaac, A.K. & Roberts, D. 1982. Pack design criteria for Betws Colliery. Mining Engineer, No.250, 142, July, 15-22.
Mayer, A.D. 1981. The development of theoretical and stochastic modelling as an aid to the prediction of strata behaviour. Ph.D. Thesis, University of Wales, Cardiff.
Isaac, A.K. & Payne, A.R. 1985. The influence of monolithic permanent roadside support upon coal rib pillar design in longwall mining. Proc. 26th U.S. Symp. on Rock Mechanics, Rapid City, South Dakota.
Payne, A.R. 1985. Longwall coal pillar deformation behaviour. Ph.D. Thesis, University of Wales, Cardiff.

Longwall design improvement in coal mines using finite element analysis

BRUCE H.GARDNER
Serata Geomechanics Inc., Richmond, California, USA

FREDERICK CARR & EDWARD MARTIN
Jim Walter Resources Inc., Birmingham, Alabama, USA

1 Overview

This study presents an application case example of a new method of mine design improvement for longwall developments in underground coal mines. The method draws together three distinct elements of technique -- finite element simulation, stress control via yielding pillars, and specialized techniques for geomechanical behavioral monitoring of underground openings. These techniques are combined to improve the benefits of longwall mining by appropriately altering the design geometry of associated pillars and gate roadways. The gains thus achieved include increased safety, decreased costs of artificial support for the gate roadways, increased rates of recovery, and increased rates of advance.

This method is applied at the Jim Walter Resources coal mines near Tuscaloosa, Alabama, which provide the case examples for this presentation.

2 Background

The impetus for the development of this method began in the early 1980s, when severe ground control problems emerged in a deep coal mine in the Black Warrior coal basin. Floor heave vertical convergence rates typically producing 100% roadway closure less than one year after excavation severely hampered the #5 mine operation. A program of roadway deformation monitoring was instituted to chart the patterns of floor heave with respect to time and spatial position in the mine. Mine #5 utilized a room and pillar mining pattern, not yet supporting longwall development. Experiments using a stress control, yield pillar mining pattern were instituted. Both 3-entry and 4-entry yield pillar time control designs were tested. These tests were highly successful. Floor heave was essentially eliminated in the stress control protected rooms.

3 Yield pillar longwalling

Concurrently, at Mines #3, #4, and #7, longwall extraction was already underway. The tailgate roadways in these developments were sustaining severe damage from the stress thrown off by the excavation of preceding longwall panels. Both the danger to personnel and the high cost of artificial support in the tailgates presented major operational problems.

Enlargement of the stiff pillars bounding the gate roadways, sufficient to stabilize those gates, would prohibitively reduce rates of recovery and advance. On the basis of the Mine #5 experience, an alternating pattern of yield pillars and support pillars was tested. Substantial improvements in tailgate stability resulted. The benefits included not only gains in safety, plus reduced investment in artificial support, but increased rates of recovery and advance as well.

4 Finite element analysis

Further design changes, including reductions in yield pillar and/or support pillar widths, could further enhance the benefits enumerated above. However, field trials of appropriate combinations and permutations of such design changes would involve a prohibitive degree of risk and cost.

Finite element analysis is used, instead, to search the space of such possible design improvements for those excavation geometries which exhibit the most desirable deformation characteristics. However, to be applicable to modelling the pillar yielding, stress control process, the FEM code used must implement an advanced type of constitutive model. This constitutive model must be capable of simulating the time-dependent, non-elastic material behavior upon which the stress control process depends. The REM (Rheological Finite Element Method) code was utilized in this study. The constitutive laws it implements are well-developed in those areas of viscoplastic, deterioration, failure, and post-failure behavior by which the yield pillar phenomenon arises.

5 Design improvement method

The method of this study involves the development of a preliminary REM model of the coal mine ground. The preliminary model uses results of previous triaxial testing and stress measurement work to set up the material property parameter and initial stress inputs to REM. This model is then calibrated using the available deformation data -- total vertical convergence, immediate floor strata expansion, etc. -- from openings in the mine. The systematic procedure by which this calibration is conducted is presented. Later, when more comprehensive in situ and laboratory property and stress data become available, the "preliminary model" is converted into a "site-specific model", by reconciliation to these new data. The model is applied to improving the design of pillar support for the longwall tailgates. The resulting design alterations are presented and discussed. The rates of advance, recovery, and artificial support investment associated with the original versus the later, computer-aided, longwall pillar designs are contrasted. Field data on the actual performance of the various longwall designs is compared to the corresponding finite element simulation predictions. The overall method involving the FEM simulation for coal longwall design improvement is evaluated on the basis of these comparisons.

Yield pillar usage in longwall mining at depth
No. 4 Mine, Brookwood, Alabama

MICHAEL GAUNA, KENNETH R.PRICE & EDDIE MARTIN
Jim Walter Resources, Brookwood, Alabama, USA

1 ABSTRACT

Jim Walter Resources No. 4 Mine extracts coal at 610 to 670 m (2000 to
2200 ft) of depth. Yield pillar designs utilizing 6.1 and 7.6 m (20
and 25 ft) wide pillars alongside the longwall headgate entry were
established in two adjacent longwall gate sections. The experimental
yield pillar-abutment pillar areas were formed for comparison to equal
size chain pillar gate road designs. Data was collected through monitoring roadway deformational behavior during longwall mining. The
information obtained indicates a 6.1 m (20 ft) yield pillar width is
appropriate for No. 4 Mine. Data illustrates that yield pillars in
conjunction with abutment pillars offer improved roadway stability and
improved resource recovery. Results from the experimental areas
have led to yield pillar designs being used to establish gate roads
and main air courses.

2 INTRODUCTION

No. 4 Mine began operation in 1976 as a deep shaft mine situated 64 km
(40 mi) southwest of Birmingham, Alabama, in a previously unmined portion of the Black Warrior Coal basin. The mining system consists of
continuous miner units used to develop main air courses and longwall
gate sections for mechanized retreat longwall mining.

2.1 Mine geology

A high grade bituminous coal is extracted from the Mary Lee and Blue
Creek seams. A 0.3 to 0.9 m (1 to 3 ft) rock layer, lithologically
ranging from a carbonaceous shale to a sandy shale, separates the two
coal seams. Continuous miner sections normally extract the Mary Lee
seam, rock layer, and Blue Creek seam which results in mining heights
ranging from 2.1 to 3.4 m (7 to 11 ft). Longwall mining only extracts
the Blue Creek coal which ranges from 1.2 to 2.1 m (4 to 7 ft) in
thickness. Approximately 10.7 m (35 ft) of shaley sandstone overlies
the Mary Lee seam. A fire clay - shaley sandstone floor underlies the
Blue Creek seam. The coal being mined lies far from coal surface out-
crop at a depth of approximately 610 m (2000 ft) and liberates
significant quantities of methane while being mined.

2.2 Gate section pillar design

No. 4 Mine stress conditions coupled with weak coal seam mechanical
properties require substantial pillars to protect roadways from the
stresses imposed by longwall mining. Four entry longwall gate designs
have been presently adopted to meet mine ventilation requirements
during longwall gate road development. Initially, it was determined
that four entry gate section designs should consist of three - 35 X 35
m (115 X 115 ft) pillars of equal size situated across the section. The
total width of gate section excavation encompassed 130 m (425 ft)
including the 6.1 m (20 ft) roadway widths. Longwall stresses transferring across these pillars cause roadway damage to the tailgate of the
next panel. Tailgate roadway reinforcement cost approximately $196 per
m ($60 per ft) of entry. It was deemed necessary to reduce the 130 m
(425 ft) total gate section width and reduce tailgate support costs to
improve resource recovery and improve cost efficiency of longwall
mining. To accomplish these improvements JWR wished to establish yield-
abutment-yield pillar gate section designs.

2.3 Yield pillar-abutment pillar design

According to Serata, three pillar types exist: yield, critical, and
abutment pillar. A yield pillar is excavated sufficiently small so that
it has failed when mined (Serata, 1976). Ground control is achieved by
the overburden stresses transferring to abutment pillars which flank the
yield pillars (Cummins and Given, 1973). Abutment pillars must withstand
the stresses imposed upon them and the roof must be capable of arching
or spanning over the yield pillar region. Placing yield pillars alongside large abutment pillars is an accepted concept in gate section
design (Euler, 1979). Critical pillars represent a pillar size between
yield and abutment pillars where the pillar is sufficiently strong to
accept stress. However, critical pillars are incapable of resisting
cover load for an extended period of time. Critical pillars should not
be placed in the gate road design which are initially stable when first
excavated. Adverse roadway damage could result after longwall stresses
are placed upon the critical pillars.
   Yield pillar sizing was based on theory developed by Dr. A.H. Wilson
(Wilson, 1977; Carr and Wilson, 1983; and Martin and Carr, 1984). Wilson
(1977) presents equations for determining yield zone widths for differing strata conditions. Martin and Carr(1984) determined that yield zone
calculations for strong roof and floor conditions are appropriate for
yield pillar calculations in the Warrior Coal basin.
   A potential yield pillar width of 7.0 to 10.3 m (23 to 34 ft) can be
calculated for No. 4 Mine. Experimental yield pillar test areas were
developed prior to committing an entire section to a given design as
shown in Figure 1. The decision was made to initially experiment with
7.6 m (25 ft) pillars. Results obtained while monitoring led to the
development of an additional experimental area with 6.1 m (20 ft)
pillars.
   Abutment pillars should control stresses imposed by longwall mining.
Calculations indicate that abutment pillars approximately 54.9 to 61.0
m (180 to 200 ft) in width and 70.1 m (230 ft) in length should provide
for satisfactory ground control. The abutment pillars established in
the experimental areas are larger than the calculated design size.
Therefore, yield pillar response should not be influenced by adverse
roadway deterioration caused by an improperly sized abutment pillar.

696

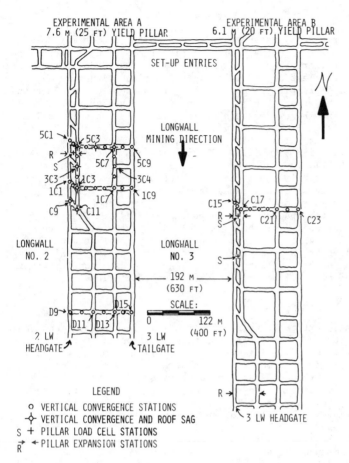

Figure 1. Yield pillar experimental areas.

3 YIELD PILLAR EXPERIMENTAL AREAS

The experimental areas were constructed by transitioning four entry
nearly equal size pillars into a four entry yield-abutment-chain pillar
configuration as shown in Figure 1. Roadways were monitored during
development and during longwall panel extraction. The first experimental
area (A), formed to evaluate 7.6 m (25 ft) wide pillars, encompassed
274 m (900 ft) of panel development between the second and third
longwall panels on the east side of No. 4 Mine. The second experimental
area (B), formed to evaluate 6.1 m (20 ft) wide pillars, encompassed
488 m (1600 ft) of panel development between the third and fourth longwall panels. These areas offered the first opportunity to evaluate
yield pillars alongside total extraction mining at Jim Walter Resources.
Longwall No. 2 mined the panel west of area A from August to November
1983. Longwall No. 3 mined the panel between area A and B from August
to October 1984.

697

3.1 Pillar dimensions and roadway support

Test area A was originally excavated with two - 38.1 X 33.5 m (125 X 110 ft) and one - 28.3 X 33.5 m (93 X 110 ft) pillars positioned across the section. Unequal pillar sizes result from a transition made at the start of the gate section. Test area B was originally mined with three - 35 X 35 m (115 X 115 ft) pillars positioned across the section. In both areas, yield pillars were established alongside the headgate belt roadway by transitioning the two western chain pillars into a yield pillar-abutment pillar design. In area A, yield pillars were 7.6 m X 32 m (25 X105 ft) with abutment pillars 68.6 X 70.1 m (225 X 230 ft). In area B, yield pillars were 6.1 X 32 m (20 X 105 ft) with abutment pillars 64 X 70.1 m (210 X 230 ft). The eastern chain pillars remained unchanged in both areas in order to fix the location of the outer roadways for the entire length of longwall panel. Roadway widths are 6.1 m (20 ft).

Roof support consisted of 1.2 m (4 ft) mechanical anchor roof bolts on 1.2 m (4 ft) center spacing. Rib support consisted of 1.8 m (6 ft) mechanical anchor - angled rib bolts installed into the pillars on approximately 1.2 m (4 ft) spacings. Supplementary rib line wood post were also installed in the headgate belt entry to contain rib sloughing in yield pillar and chain pillar areas. Tailgate roadway supplementary support consisted of steel fiber reinforced concrete cribs.

4 EXPERIMENTAL AREA INSTRUMENTATION

Roof sag stations, vertical convergence (roadway closure) stations, and pillar dilation (pillar horizontal expansion) stations proved to be the most useful long term monitoring devices. Roadway deformational behavior demonstrated the roadway response to high stresses and pillar load transfer. Jim Walter Resources and the University of Alabama, Mineral Engineering Dept. in a joint project placed vibrating wire stressmeters within pillars in the experimental areas. These gauges were useful in monitoring yield pillar loading. However, stressmeters could not be relied upon for long term monitoring in larger pillars. Front abutment pressures from longwall extraction destroyed the majority of the gauges before the face advanced adjacent to the stressmeter location.

4.1 Roof sag extensometers

Seven roof sag stations were placed at vertical convergence stations (see Figure 1) to measure bed separation between the roof of the entry and an anchor positioned 3.0 m (10 ft) into the overlying strata. All roof sag stations exhibited minimal bed separation which is normal for this portion of No. 4 Mine. Roof sag data indicates that roadway closures are primarily attributable to floor heave.

4.2 Vertical roadway convergence

Conventional pillar convergence stations D9 to D15 were established across the section as shown in Figure 1. These stations measured roadway deformation caused by longwall stresses in the region south of the abutment pillars. Figure 2 illustrates the roadway closure profiles generated by advancement of No. 2 longwall west of these stations and by advancement of No. 3 longwall east of these stations. As No. 2 longwall passed the line of convergence stations, closures of approximately 0.20 m (8 in) were observed at stations D10 and D11. Vertical convergence continued as No. 2 longwall advanced. As No. 3 longwall mined past the stations, closures ranged from 0.91 m (36 in) at D15 to 2.90 m (114 in) which represents total closure, at station D10. For clarity, only measurements for five specific days are shown on Figure 2.

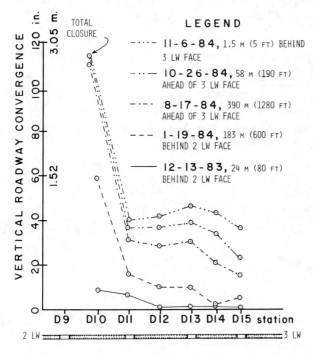

Figure 2. Vertical convergence profile along stations D9 to D15 in the conventional pillar area.

Yield pillar convergence stations 5C1 to 5C9 were also established across experimental area A (see Figure 1). Figure 3 illustrates convergence profiles along 5C1 to 5C9. Convergence in the vicinity of station 5C3 progressed as No. 2 longwall advanced. Convergence continued after No. 3 longwall mined past the test area. However, closure did not exceed 0.36 m (14 in) in the entry east of the 7.6 m (25 ft) pillar. In comparison, the area monitored by station D10 showed total closure in a chain pillar region of similar distance from No. 2 longwall gob. The tailgate roadway of No. 3 longwall monitored by station 5C9 and 1C9 indicate closures of approximately 0.13 m (5 in) as No. 3 longwall passed. This relects the more stable tailgate condition when compared to the 0.91 m (36 in) of convergence which occurred at D15 in the conventional pillars south of the abutment pillars. In test area B roadway convergence is similar to that found in area A. Measurements between stations C15 to C23 in area B are similar to measurements between 5C1 to 5C9 in area A at similar longwall face positions.

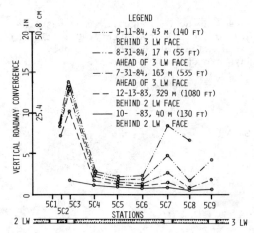

Figure 3. Vertical convergence profile along stations 5C1 to 5C9 in yield pillar experimental area A.

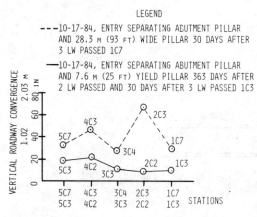

Figure 4. Convergence profiles for entries east and west of the abutment pillar in experimental yield pillar area A.

Figure 4 illustrates the improved roadway condition achieved by placing a yield type pillar alongside an abutment pillar. A convergence profile is plotted between station 1C3 and 5C3 along the entry separating the abutment pillar and 7.6 m (25 ft) yield pillar. After approximately 363 days after No. 2 longwall passed and approximately 30 days after No. 3 longwall passed, 0.23 to 0.53 m (9 to 21 in) of convergence was measured between stations 1C7 and 5C7 along the entry separating the abutment pillar and the 28.3 X32.0 m (93 X 105 ft) pillars. Approximately 30 days after No. 3 longwall passed, closures ranged from 0.71 to 1.70 m (28 to 63 in) between 1C7 and 5C7. This indicates that the 28.3 m (93 ft) wide pillars are allowing more rapid roadway deterioration.

700

4.3 Pillar horizontal dilation and yield pillar stress

Comparisons were made to assess if the pillar rib side of 6.1 or 7.6 m
(20 or 25 ft) wide pillars were significantly less stable than the rib
side of 35 X 35 m (115 X 115 ft) pillars. East and west ribs of
pillars were monitored with dilation stations where movement was measured
between a fixed reference point in the entry and a station placed on the
rib surface of the pillar. The pillars studied were located immediately
alongside the headgate belt entry as shown in Figure 1.
  Data indicates no significant difference exists in lateral pillar
expansion for the three pillar sizes studied. Pillar lateral movement
varied from 20 to 32.5 cm (8 to 12.8 in) for the west ribs (rib side
towards the panel) as the longwall face passed the dilation stations.
East rib sides (on the opposite side of the pillar away from the panel)
experience less lateral movement as the wall passes with values
ranging from 3.6 to 10 cm (1.4 to 4.0 in). It's concluded that added
adverse rib deterioration with yield pillars would be minimal when
compared to the rib displacement presently occurring with the conventional square pillars while longwall mining.
  Vibrating wire and hydraulic load cells were installed in the yield
pillars in test areas A and B at the positions shown in Figure 1. Gauge
data indicates that the 7.6 m (25 ft) pillar did not begin to yield
until No. 2 longwall face was approximately 91m (300 ft) from the gauge
location (Park, Sanford, Simpson, and Hartman, 1984). Load cell readings indicate that the 6.1 m (20 ft) pillar was yielding immediately
after it was formed by initial mining. As No. 3 longwall mined past
the 6.1 m (20 ft) pillars, readings continued to decrease or remain
stable.

4.4 Experimental area conclusions

Yield pillars in conjunction with an adequately designed abutment pillar
significantly improved roadway conditions when compared to gate road
designs utilizing nearly equal size pillars. A 6.1 m (20 ft) yield
pillar width is appropriate for No. 4 Mine. Yield pillar sizing
criteria found in mining texts may oversize yield pillars. For example,
the SME Mining Engineering Handbook suggests a 9.1 (30 ft) minimum
yield pillar width for a depth of 610 m (2000 ft). Also, experience
with the tailgate roadway of No. 3 longwall has shown that abutment
pillar tailgate cribbing can be reduced to approximately 25% of the
cribbing cost found necessary in areas having equal size pillars.

5 YIELD PILLAR MINE DESIGN

A 6.1 m (20 ft) yield - 61.0 (200 ft) abutment - 6.1 m (20 ft) yield
pillar four entry gate section design now exists at No. 4 Mine. This
configuration, with adjustments in abutment pillar sizes, has been
adopted at other JWR coal mines. This design reduces the total gate
section width from the 129.5 m (425 ft), required with the original
design, to 97.5 m (320 ft) which improves resource recovery. Also, less
excavation is now required to advance the entire section.
  Figure 5 illustrates mining projections used at No. 4 Mine. Longwall set up entries are now established with a yield pillar plan which
increases longwall recovery by allowing the lengthening of panels. This
design has been successfully applied on three panels. In addition, all
submain entries and most main entries have been converted to yield -

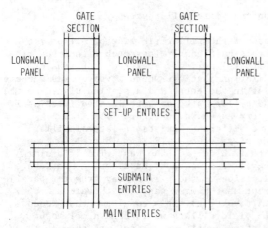

Figure 5. Yield pillar - abutment pillar mining
projections showing entry center lines.

abutment - yield pillar designs which increase resource recovery and
improve ground control when compared to designs employing equal size
pillars. Presently, over 9.2 km (5.8 mi) of yield pillar entries have
been completed using the designs shown in Figure 5. Serata Geomechanics
has been asked to perform finite element computer analysis to aid in
determining optimum abutment pillar sizes. Ground response will
continue to be studied to assure pillars are properly designed.

REFERENCES

Carr, F. & A.H. Wilson 1982. A New Approach to the Design of Multi-
    Entry Developments for Retreat Longwall Mining. Second Conference on
    Ground Control in Mining, West Virginia University, July:1-21.
Cummins, A.B. & I.A. Given (ed) 1973. SME Mining Engineering Handbook.
    American Institute of Mining, Metallurgical, and Petroleum Engineers,
    p. 13-100 - 13-103.
Euler, W.J. 1979. Improving Longwall Entry Development and Operation.
    Mining Congress Journal, May: 21-27.
Martin, E. & F. Carr 1984. Control of Floor Heave in Coal Mines. Second
    International Conference, Stability in Underground Mining. Society of
    Mining Engineers of AIME: 13-33.
Park, D., R.L. Sanford, T.A. Simpson, & H.L.Hartman 1984. Pillar
    Stability And Subsidence Study At A Deep Longwall Coal Mine. Second
    Annual Workshop, Generic Mineral Technology Center, Mine Systems
    Design and Ground Control-Reno, Nevada.
Serata S. 1976. Stress Control Technique - An Alternative to Roof
    Bolting?: Mining Engineering, May: 51-56.
Wilson, A. H. 1977. The Effect of Yield Zones on the Control of Ground,
    Sixth International Strata Control Conference, September: 52-93.

Strength of mine pillars

JAMES E.RUSSELL
Texas A & M University, College Station, USA

ABSTRACT

Bieniawski (1984) notes that the strength of mine pillars depends on three factors: i) the size effect whereby the strength of the material is reduced, ii) the shape effect generally included in the form of the width-to-height ratio, and iii) the effect of the properties of the pillar material. Numerical studies are convenient for studying the strength of mine pillars because the influence of each of these factors can be studied. However, such studies have relied on fractional reduction of the strength of deformation properties to account for the size effect. In this paper, the size effect is studied using an elastic-plastic material model employing the empirical strength criterion for rock masses published by Hoek and Brown (1980) as the yield criterion. A convential finite-element code with a Mohr-Coulomb material model is used for the calculations by forcing the local equivalent Mohr-Coulomb envelope to be tangent to the curved empirical envelope. The equivalent angle of internal friction, Φ_e, and cohesion, COH_e, now depend on σ_3, the minimum principal stress according to the following equations:

$$\Phi_e = 2 \ [\arctan(\sqrt{q}) - \pi/4]$$

$$COH_e = [\sigma_{1s} - q\sigma_3]/[2\sqrt{q}]$$

where $q = 1 + m/\{2\sqrt{[m(\sigma_3/\sigma_c) + s]}\}$,
and m, s, and σ_{1s} are respectively the parameters for, and the strength calculated from, the Hoek and Brown empirical model. Because the cohesion and friction angle now depend on the minimum principal stress in each element, they must be updated for each interaction within each load or displacement increment. The increased nonlinearity of the problem naturally slows down the computation. The procedure described provides a means to employ what appears to be the most universal empirical strength model for rock masses in a finite-element code capable of handling shape effects and the redistribution of stress upon the onset of local yielding or failure. Other post-failure paths such as perfectly brittle have not yet been investigated.

REFERENCES

Bieniawski, Z.T. 1984. Rock mechanics design in mining and tunneling, p. 193. Rotterdam: A.A. Balkema.

Hoek, E. and E.T. Brown 1980. Empirical strength criterion for rock masses, J. Geotech. Eng. Div., ASCE, J. T. 9, p. 1013-1035.

704

15. Seismic and acoustic emission/microseismic studies

Chair: H.REGINALD HARDY, Jr.
          The Pennsylvania State University, University Park, USA
Cochair: R.PAUL YOUNG
          Queen's University, Kingston, Canada

Structural stability monitoring using high-frequency microseismics

RICHARD C.REPSHER & BERNARD J.STEBLAY
Department of the Interior, Bureau of Mines, Denver Research Center, Colorado, USA

1 INTRODUCTION

The Bureau of Mines through in-house and contract research has developed a technique and related equipment to nondestructively monitor the
structural stability of underground openings and detect precursors to
stress-related failures such as roof separation, coal outbursts, and
roof falls, both large and small. By detecting and analyzing the high-
frequency rock noise produced by the changing of stress conditions
occurring as a result of active mining or local tectonic activity, the
structural stability of the opening can be determined.

2 TECHNIQUE DESCRIPTION

All naturally occurring materials emit acoustic emissions when subjected to an increase in structural loading. Geologic materials produce
these emissions when load changes are applied. Metal fatigue and failure research studies using this technique have been ongoing for many
years, and successful studies have been carried out using frequency
ranges of acoustic emissions (AE) in the megahertz range. Only recently have failure studies been carried out in geologic materials using
the high-frequency spectrum. The Bureau of Mines research program has
identified that the optimum frequency range for rock is between 36 and
150 kHz. In this frequency range the acoustic emissions can be analyzed for their relationship to the structural stability of the material.
These acoustic emissions can be characterized as elastic vibrations
emitted from the material undergoing deformation. These emissions are
sinusoidal, with periods ranging from a few microseconds to a hundred
ms. The source of these emissions is believed to be microfractures
that originate in a very small volume of rock in the vicinity of the
sensor. Normally these signals are not the high-frequency component of
actual physical dislocations, commonly referred to as "rock noise,"
which is in the audible frequency range, but are very small-scale displacements that result from the changing load conditions in the vicinity of the sensor that are indicative of the change in structural loading in the surrounding rock mass. The high-frequency component of
acoustic emission is detectable if the source is close enough to the
sensor, and one such instance will be discussed.

3 SYSTEM DESCRIPTION

The high-frequency microseismic monitoring system used is portable, battery operated, and designed to operate in an underground environment. The unit is self-contained with a single sensor and preamplifier that is coupled to the mine roof. A single enclosure contains the electronics and batteries to continuously record and display the incoming data. The electronics are contained in modules with different although integrated functions.

1. Detector Module: This unit amplifies and filters the incoming acoustic emissions from the preamplifier and conditions the signal for detection and processing of the signal. Gain and threshold adjustments are provided to accommodate the varying underground environments that may be encountered during data collection (i.e., coal vs hard rock). The detector module output is sent to the processor module for digital processing.

2. Processor Module: All data processing functions and recorder output routines are performed in this module. The on-board microprocessor controls and generates all signals, recorder scaling, and data displays.

3. Indicator Module: Provides audible and visual indications of anomalous stress conditions. The levels for these warnings are programmable within the processor module and are indicative of high-stress conditions or that a preset ratio level has been exceeded, indicating the structure is undergoing a failure. These indicators are useful when monitoring structural stability, but are commonly disabled when gathering information on rates of loading or when not specifically monitoring for failure.

4. Battery Module: The electrical power to operate the system is contained in this module. The battery is removable and provides 7 to 10 days of continuous operation. A battery charger and spare battery are included in the complete system. The entire package weighs approximately 25 lb.

The monitoring system is designed with an adjustable threshold level to detect the incoming acoustic emissions. The microprocessor cumulatively counts (for a 1-min time period) each discrete emission that exceeds the preset threshold level (fig. 1) and also measures the amount of time the signal exceeds the preset threshold. This time is also cumulatively summed for the identical 1-min time period as the event count. Both of these values are stored in the microprocessor, where a numerical ratio (also referred to as the "Stress Factor") of the cumulative time over threshold per total event count value is determined for each minute. The event count and ratio values are output by the system for recording purposes. The time-over-threshold is a unitless clocking value; however, it can be interpreted as an index of the energy released by the structure with time. It represents the approximate area "under the curve" of an acoustic event, which is an accepted method to estimate the energy released during an event.

In data analysis the event count is used as a measure of the rate of change of stress, while the ratio value (stress factor) is the indica-

tor of the structure's ability to adjust to the changing stress
conditions that mining produces. During periods of normal structural
adjustment, the ratio value remains in a fairly constant range (50-
500). Prior to a stress-related failure, the value dramatically
increases, then drops to a normal value. This ratio spike is a precursor to a structural failure and is the point in time when the mechanics
of the failure are occurring, as distinguished from the manifestation
(physical happening) of that failure.

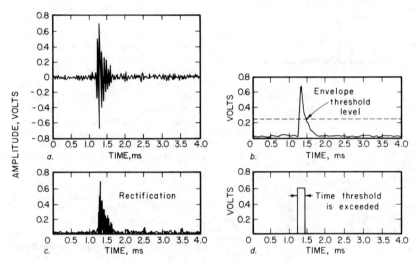

Figure 1. Typical waveform package and processing.

The monitoring technique and equipment have provided precursors to a
variety of stress related failures including roof falls (large and
small), face pushes, outbursts, pillar spall, and rapid floor heave.

4   RESULTS AND DATA ANALYSIS

The initial research effort by the Bureau of Mines was to develop a
Roof Fall Warning System that could provide warnings for roof falls in
underground coal mines. To gather this type of information, retreat
mining operations were used for data collection. This mining method
provides frequent, large roof falls necessary for documentation. If
precursors to this type of fall of ground could be obtained, the likelihood of success in room-and-pillar operations would be enhanced.
Figure 2 shows data collected in a retreat mining operation. The sensor was located about 200 ft from the active mining where a pillar was
being split. The roof adjacent to this pillar had not fallen and spanned approximately 100 ft on each side. At 11:56 am, an anomalous
stress factor was noted. Fifteen minutes following this precursor, the
entire rock mass fell with no audible warning. The stress factor had
remained below 500 for several hours preceding this event, indicative
of normal structural adjustment in the area. This type of data has
been collected on many occasions and lends credence to the ability of
the equipment and technique to provide precursors to large roof falls.

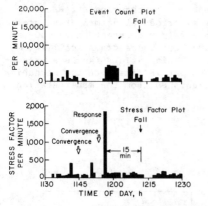

Figure 2. Precursor to large roof fall.

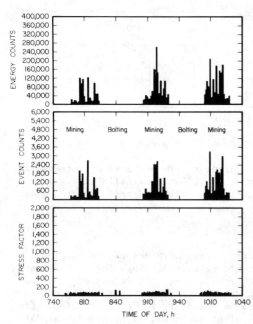

Figure 3. Normal activity for mining bolting cycle.

The research effort was extended to determine the potential application to small roof falls, those involving less than 300 pounds of material.

During a typical mining sequence in a room-and-pillar coal mining operation, active mining is followed by roof bolting of the exposed roof. When the bolting is completed, active mining com-mences with this repetitive cycle. Figure 3 represents data obtained during this cycle where normal structural adjustments are occurring. The event count rises with the removal of support, decreases as the structure is redistributing the load change, remains low during the bolting phase, and then increases again as mining continues. The ratio (stress factor) indicates a normal and stable condition. The question often arises about whether the monitoring system is responding to the mining equipment operation. The system is NOT "hearing" the mining machine, as the system does not respond to any frequency less than 44 kHz, which is well above the range normally generated by the mining equipment, and the event count does not rise until the coal pillar is removed (generally 1 min or more after the machine is cutting coal), not when the machine is started up. This figure represents several hours of data and just two mining cycles. General data collection is normally for an entire shift of many mining cycles. Figure 4 is another data set from a room-and-pillar operation where a mining cycle starts at 7:33 am and ends at 8:17 am. The stress factor indicates a normal structural adjustment to this mining. However, at 8:22 the event count started to rise, but there was no mining activity at the time. The roof bolting procedure had not been completed. At 8:25 there was an anomalous stress factor value of 2000, indicative of a structural failure. Seven minutes later a small roof fall (less than 100 lb material) occurred between previously installed roof bolts.

710

This type of data has been gathered from several sites and is an in i-cation that the technique is useful in providing precursors to str :- tural failures relating to changing stress conditions.

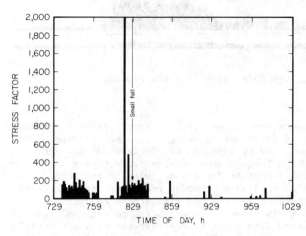

Figure 4. Precursor to small roof fall.

In the process of monitoring underground coal mine entries for roof falls, another type of stress-related failure was detected. In a development section where entries were being advanced, the equipment was set up for roof fall monitoring. The sensor was placed about 200 ft outby the active mining face (two crosscuts from active mining). The stress factor did respond to the active mining at the face from 9:45 to 10:30 am. (fig. 5). There was some re-adjustment of stresses during the nonmining periods, reflected in changes in the stress factor that were not commonly seen in other data sets. Normally there are few or no event counts during nonmining periods. The fact that there were stress factor values is indicative that stress concentrations were building up in the area. As active mining progressed, there was an anomalous stress factor peak at 11:33 am. Four minutes later there was a face "push," which covered the front of the mining machine with loose coal released from the face. No activity of this nature had ever experienced in this section prior to this occurrence.

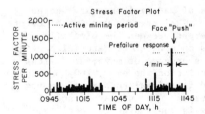

Figure 5. Face push data.

These are but a few examples of data collected that support the conclusion that the detection and monitoring of high-frequency rock noise generated from changing stress conditions can be used to monitor the structural stability of underground mining operations.

An extension of this technology was provided through a cooperative study with the U.S. Geological Survey. In the Talus Room of the Lehman Cave National Monument, Baker, NV, two falls of material from the roof had been noted, as well as movement along one of the arches contained in the room. The Talus Room had been closed to the public because of concern as to its structural stability. The Bureau of Mines was requested to provide assistance in determining the structural stability of the room.

711

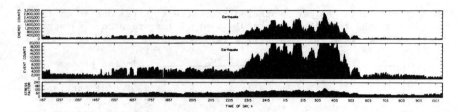

Figure 6. Lehman Cave, structural stability monitoring.

The Talus Room is a large underground opening resulting from erosion
of material by underground water moving along planes of weakness. The
resulting opening is about 400 ft long, 40 to 100 ft wide, and a maximum of 100 ft high. A high-frequency microseismic monitoring system
was installed to detect and monitor for any activity in the room. The
system, as previously discussed, has provided precursors to structural
failures and has been shown to monitor changing stress conditions in
mines. If the Talus Room was dynamic and adjusting to regional geologic processes, there should be a structural response with a change in
event count and stress factor data. Two single-channel units were installed for 3 weeks in various parts of the Talus Room to monitor any
changes with time. The single most significant data set was obtained
on March 17, 1984. The sensor was placed on a solid block of material
at the base on one arch in the north end of the Talus Room. This site
was monitored for 24 h beginning at 11:57 am. During the ensuing hours
(fig. 6), there was a dramatic increase in the event and energy data
starting at 10:45 pm. There was no significant increase in the stress
factor levels. Something had occurred during that time frame, but the
adjustment was normal with no change in the structural stability of the
area. The Geological Survey obtained earthquake records for the region
from a network of seismographs near the Nevada Test Site, 120 miles
away. An earthquake in the local area had occurred at 10:06 pm. The
conclusion drawn from the available data is that the arch in the Talus
Room had adjusted to the local earthquake.
The arch is made up of many large blocks of material that are "keyed"
together in a Vosoir Arch configuration. The large change in the event
count data resulted from frictional movement between the blocks in
close proximity to the sensor, which was on a block of material contiguous to the structure. There were no convergence or movement devices
present in this area to confirm this conclusion; however, 100 kHz signals can be transmitted up to 60 ft, and frictional rubbing of competent material would produce these conditions. The primary conclusion
that can be drawn is that the Talus Room is responding to local tectonic activity and is dynamic in these responses. This experiment is
the first use of the equipment and technique in a nonmining environment
to monitor structural stability of an underground opening. The results
were positive and could lead to future applications.

5 CONCLUSIONS

The high-frequency microseismic monitoring equipment developed through
Bureau of Mines contract and in-house research efforts has shown the
potential to monitor changes in structural loading, provide precursors

712

to stress-related failures, and be useful as a tool to assess the structural stability of underground openings. This technique will not locate where a failure will occur in the present configuration and has a limitation in that the sensor must be located on a solid block of material that is contiguous to the source structure. A loose block of material cannot respond to changing stress conditions in the remaining structure and will not provide meaningful information. However, when the equipment is not responding where load conditions are known to be changing, then that itself is evidence that this piece of material is not connected to the structure and may be loose. This is an important piece of information in the monitoring of an opening.

This technique has provided precursors to roof falls (large and small), face pushes, coal outbursts, massive floor heave, pillar spalling, and rockbursts. This is a new and innovative methodology that shows considerable promise. However, sufficient data have not been collected to totally insure the reliability of the detected precursors. Future research efforts should provide this necessary information.

REFERENCES

Steblay, B. J. 1979. Progress in the Development of a Microseismic Roof Fall Warning System. Proceedings Tenth Annual Institute on Coal Mining Health and Safety Research, p. 177-192.
Fisher, C. 1980. Microseismic Roof Fall Warning System Development. Final Report Contract H0272009, Integrated Sciences, Inc.
Ohnaka, M. 1983. Acoustic Emission During Creep of Brittle Rock. International Journal of Rock Mechanics and Mining Sciences, XX:3: 121-134.
Vance, J. 1983. Application of Microseismic Techniques in Potash Mines. Potash '83, Saskatoon, Saskatchewan.

Determining peak stress history using acoustic emissions

D.J.HOLCOMB
Geomechanics Division, Sandia National Laboratories, Albuquerque, New Mexico, USA
R.J.MARTIN, III
Applied Research Associates, South Royalton, Vermont, USA

1 BACKGROUND

As part of the test program at the Nevada Test Site, there is a need for determining the peak stress induced by explosions in tuff. Standard techniques make use of various gages grouted into the tuff prior to the test. There are difficulties in interpreting the output of these gages and there is always the chance that the gage will not survive long enough to allow a stress determination to be made. As an alternative, we have been testing a passive technique for determining peak stress as a function of distance from a test. Using core samples retrieved from the vicinity of an explosion, we have tested for the existence of a threshold stress for the onset of acoustic emissions, the Kaiser effect (Kaiser 1950). From laboratory results it is known that for many rock types, the previously applied peak stress can be detected by restressing a sample while monitoring acoustic emissions (Kurita and Fujii 1979), (Haimson and Kim), (Holcomb 1983). An abrupt onset for acoustic emission activity typically occurs at a stress state close to the previous peak. The point of this work was to determine if the Kaiser effect occurred in tuff and, if so, whether it could be used to determine the peak stresses induced by an explosion. A similar approach (Kanagawa et al. 1976) has been used to determine in situ stress in tuff due to tectonic processes. Our work shows that explosion-induced stresses can be detected by the Kaiser effect method, but that proper allowance must be made for the effects of saturation and yielding of the tuff.

2 SAMPLES AND TEST PROCEDURES

Four samples of tuff cored from the vicinity of a test conducted at the Nevada Test Site were tested under triaxial conditions, either at constant confining pressure or under uniaxial strain conditions. Samples were right circular cylinders, jacketed with shrink fit tubing. Instrumentation consisted of a pair of LVDTs mounted parallel to the sample axis for measuring axial strain, an LVDT ring gage (Holcomb and McNamee 1984) for transverse strain and one or two PZT-5 piezoelectric transducers for detecting acoustic emissions (AE). Testing was done in a servo-controlled load frame using a pressure vessel with a working pressure of 200 MPa. Output from the piezoelectric transducers was amplified by 60 db before being input to a discriminator. To reduce the incidence of false counts due to electronic noise, the received signals were required to meet three conditions before being accepted as AE events. First, a threshold of about 30 millivolts had to be exceeded. Second, this threshold had to be exceeded more than 10 times. Third, the frequency had to be above 50 kHz. After these criteria were met, a single count was generated and the detector turned off for 1 millisecond to allow the transducer to ring down. A counter kept track of the total number of events and a multichannel analyzer (MCA) was used as multichannel counter to keep subtotals at five second intervals. In

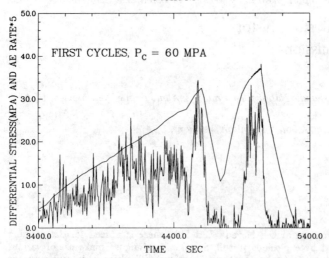

Figure 1. First two cycles of differential stress (smooth line) applied to the dry control sample **07MR42**, showing increasing AE rate (number of events per second times 5, jagged line) during the first cycle. During the second cycle, little AE was observed until the previous peak differential stress was nearly regained.

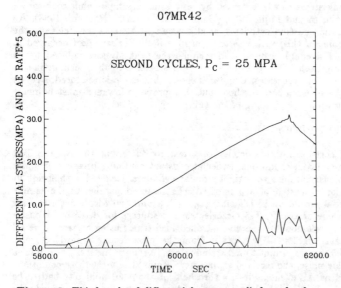

Figure 2. Third cycle of differential stress applied to the dry control sample **07MR42**. Figure 1 shows the previous test history of this sample at a confining pressure of 60 MPa. After lowering the confining pressure to 25 MPa, this cycle was done to investigate the effect of changing pressure on the differential stress at which a previously established Kaiser peak was observed. As Figure 1 shows, the previous peak was about 38 MPa at a pressure of 60 MPa. At 25 MPa, the Kaiser peak is observed at 26 MPa.

effect, the MCA served to take the derivative of the total AE count with respect to time, using a five second average.

3 RESULTS

Sample **07MR42**, a control sample from a relatively unstressed area, was tested "dry". Under the initial hydrostatic loading to 67 MPa, acoustic emission activity was high, with almost 11,000 events recorded. The AE rate was quite constant during pressurization, but activity decreased immediately after depressurization began and AE rates remained close to zero while the confining pressure (P_C) was lowered to 33 MPa and then increased to 60 MPa. Differential stress ($\sigma_D = \sigma_{11} - P_C$) was applied, starting at $P_C = 60$ MPa. During the first of three load cycles, the differential stress was increased to 32 MPa. AE rates increased as soon as shear stress was applied and continued to increase up to the peak stress (Figure 1). A pause in loading at $\sigma_D = 28$ MPa caused the dip in AE rate. Unloading and then reloading produced the characteristic Kaiser effect; a rapid decrease in AE rate during unloading until the rate was down to the background rate, where it remained until reloading reached nearly the previous peak stress. Then, the rate increased abruptly at about 31.5 MPa, compared to the initial peak stress of 32 MPa (Figure 1). Loading was continued to a peak differential stress of 37 MPa. A further demonstration of the Kaiser effect and its dependence on all of the principal stresses is given by the rest of the test. P_C was lowered from 60 MPa to 25 MPa before the next load cycle. Reloading resulted in a fairly sharp increase in AE rate at about $\sigma_D = 26$ MPa (Figure 2).

Sample **07MR4C**, cored from an area that had been significantly stressed by the explosion, was tested dry under triaxial conditions. First, the sample was subjected to hydrostatic pressure up to 150 MPa, followed by depressurization to 78 MPa. Compared to the control sample (**07MR42**), the total number of AE events at $P_C = 67$ MPa for **07MRC** was only 1/3 as great. A maximum in the AE rate was observed at around 100 MPa, coinciding with the beginning of a stiffening in the stress-strain response. Only a few AE events were observed during depressurization to 78 MPa.

Differential stress was applied starting at $P_C = 78$ MPa. Two cycles were done to a peak stress $\sigma_D = 72$ MPa. During the first cycle, yielding was observed above 25 MPa. AE activity was markedly reduced compared to the control sample. For the control (**07MR42**), application of the peak differential stress of 38 MPa caused more than 3000 events. For the prestressed sample **07MR4C**, application of 72 MPa induced only about 400 events. A plot of σ_D and AE rate as a function of time shows no clear onset of AE as stress increases. However, this is not really the proper plot. Since the Kaiser effect is a function of stress, we are really interested in the number of events per increment of stress, not per unit time. For the control sample, σ_D increased approximately linearly with time. Thus the number of events per unit time and the number of events per unit stress are proportional. Since $d(Total\ AE)/dT$ is available automatically from the MCA, it is usually the quantity plotted. However, for sample **07MR4C** yielding caused the rate of increase of σ_D with time to vary, forcing the use of $d(Total\ AE)/d\sigma_D$. When the stress derivative, computed as the secant between successive points, is plotted as a function of time and overlaid with a plot of σ_D as a function of time, it is clear that there was indeed a detectable onset of AE (See Figure 3). The onset is not as sharp as the Kaiser peak shown in Figure 1, but it is definitely above 45 MPa and below 58 MPa. Extrapolating the later trends back, the upper limit seems closer to the true onset of increasing AE rate. To complete the test, confining pressure was lowered to 38 MPa and a third load cycle done to check the effect of changing confining pressure. A Kaiser peak was found at a differential stress of 60 MPa.

The two tests just described show that the Kaiser effect is observed in the tuff of interest and that there was a threshold stress detectable in the sample **07MR4C**. However, the test conditions were not representative of the *in situ* conditions. Duplicating *in situ* conditions may be important in correctly determining the stress history. *In situ*, the tuff would normally be saturated and would be loaded along a uniaxial strain path by the explosion. To duplicate these conditions, two samples were saturated using the standard

717

07MR4C

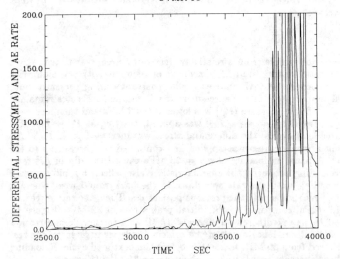

Figure 3. First cycle of differential stress applied to **07MR4C**. The AE rate (jagged line) is computed as number of events per MPa to take into account the yielding of the sample. A threshold for the onset of AE can be picked at about 3400 seconds. There is activity earlier, but extrapolating the later AE rates back, indicates that the onset is at about 3400 seconds, which corresponds to a differential stress of 58 MPa.

25AP41

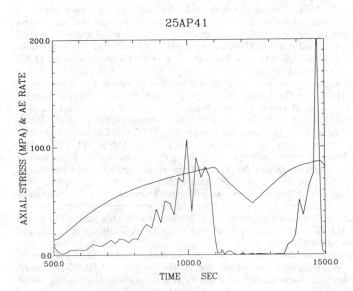

Figure 4. Enlarged view of the first two cycles for sample **25AP41** with the axial stress (smooth line) and AE rate (number of events per MPa) plotted versus time. No threshold stress for the onset of AE is evident in the first cycle. A clear Kaiser peak, induced by the first cycle is evident at T= 1350 seconds.

vacuum technique and then tested under uniaxial strain conditions. Sample **25AP41** was a control sample, while sample **26AP42** was cored from a point near the explosion.

The control sample was loaded hydrostatically to 14 MPa and then differential stress was applied while the transverse strain was held constant by the application of pressure. The sample compacted rather linearly up to about 30 MPa and then showed signs of yielding when loading was continued to a peak stress of $(\sigma_D, P_C) = (45\ MPa, 36\ MPa)$. Acoustic emission activity increased from the start of the loading cycle, with no indication of a threshold stress (Figure 4). Unloading and reloading under uniaxial strain conditions produced a Kaiser peak at $(\sigma_D, P_C) = (43 MPa, 34 MPa)$ which is slightly below the original peak stress. Figure 4 shows the AE rate as the derivative with respect to axial stress. Since both σ_D and P_C were changing, the stress derivative was taken with respect to the axial stress, which contains both.

The final test (**26AP42**) was on a saturated sample that had been near the test. An initial pressure of 5 MPa was applied to the sample, followed by one loading cycle under uniaxial strain conditions. Figure 5 shows that there were three distinct stages in the deformation. Initially, the sample compressed linearly up to about $\sigma_D = 35$ MPa. Then an apparent yield stress was reached, although there is no indication of a change in material properties in a plot of confining pressure versus axial strain. After 6% axial shortening a second "yield" point was reached at $\sigma_D = 58$ MPa. At that point the pressure required to maintain uniaxial strain began to increase rapidly. The test was terminated when the pressure neared the 200 MPa rating of the pressure vessel. Acoustic emission activity was observed to be steady at about 2–3 counts per second until the second "yield" point was reached. Then the time derivative rate increased, coinciding with the increased rate of pressurization. When the derivative of number of AE events with respect to axial stress was plotted, the rate was found to be more or less constant with no pronounced peaks or thresholds (Figure 6). In fact, the rate tended to decrease after the initial loading.

4 DISCUSSION

A primary purpose of this work was to determine if tuff from the test area exhibited the Kaiser effect. A secondary purpose, assuming that the Kaiser effect was observed, was to apply the technique to samples that had been prestressed by the actual test. Because of the small number of prestressed samples that were available and the developmental nature of the work it seemed unlikely that tests on the prestressed samples would be conclusive. In the two tests on control samples, we found that the Kaiser effect is observed in the tuff, whether dry or saturated, and under standard triaxial or uniaxial strain conditions. After an initial loading cycle to establish a stress history, a subsequent load cycle under the same conditions produced a clear Kaiser peak in acoustic emission rate(see Figures 1,2, and 4). To an accuracy of a few MPa, the Kaiser peak indicated the previous peak stress.

Finding a Kaiser peak along one stress path is usually not sufficient to uniquely establish the previous stress state. It is known that the entire stress tensor can have an effect on the onset of acoustic emissions, not just the traction along the loading axis (Holcomb 1983). This is exactly the same as the fact that the ultimate strength of rock under triaxial conditions is a function of the confining pressure. Untangling the interaction between the principal stresses is a major difficulty in the use of the Kaiser effect technique to determine the *in situ* stress. As a first step in determining the interaction, tests were done where the confining pressure was changed after the initial load cycles. An example is the history of test **07MR42**, which was a control sample done dry under triaxial conditions. The initial stress cycling was done at a confining pressure of 60 MPa, and continued to a differential stress of 38 MPa, which was an arbitrarily selected value. After removing the differential stress, confining pressure was lowered to 25 MPa, with the expectation that this would lower the differential stress required to produce AE. During the second set of cycles, at $P_C = 25$ MPa, acoustic emissions were observed to begin at a differential stress of about 26 MPa. Thus lowering P_C by 35 MPa, lowered

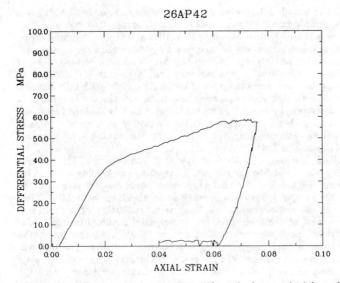

Figure 5. Differential stress versus axial strain for a uniaxial strain test conducted on a wet sample **26AP42**, that had been near the test. Yielding is evident above 35 MPa and differential stress could not be increased above 58 MPa.

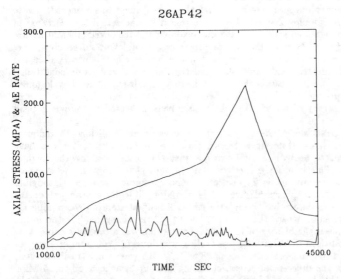

Figure 6. Axial stress and AE rate for sample **26AP42**. AE rate is in terms of number of events per MPa of axial stress, to take into account changes in stress rates which were necessitated by the sample yielding. There is no indication of a threshold stress for the production of AE.

the differential stress required to produce AE from 38 to 26 MPa. If this is considered to be similar to the effect of changing the confining pressure on ultimate strength, then the two points can be used to determine a line that is analogous to a Coulomb failure criterion. Using the Coulomb criterion in the form

$$\sigma_1 - \sigma_3 = (\sigma_1 + \sigma_3)\sin\phi + 2S_0\cos\phi,$$

the angle of internal friction ϕ as determined by the onset of AE is about 8 degrees in this case. For the prestressed sample (07MR4C) the angle of internal friction was only about 6 degrees. A low value for ϕ is expected for very porous (>40%) tuffs (Olsson and Jones 1980).

A small dependence of AE onset on confining pressure implies that only the previous peak shear traction component along the present loading axis will strongly affect the onset of AE activity. Thus, in this case, the stress history could indeed be determined by loading cores along various axes and neglecting the interaction between the stresses.

Two samples (07MR4C and 26AP42) were tested that had been prestressed by the explosion. Test 07MR4C was conducted on a room dry sample under triaxial conditions, while test 26AP42 was done on a saturated sample under uniaxial strain conditions. Test conditions for the second sample (saturated and uniaxial strain) were chosen in an attempt to mimic the *in situ* conditions, in particular the hydrostatic component of the stress field.

As Figure 3 shows, there was a threshold stress for the onset of AE between 45 and 58 MPa. No indication of the pressure *in situ* is possible from our data. However, as discussed earlier, this tuff seems to have only a weak interdependence between AE onset and confining pressure for a given peak differential stress. Thus it is predicted that the peak differential stress experienced at the origin of this core was indeed between 45 and 58 MPa. From the back extrapolation of the AE rate at higher stresses, the upper bound seems more probable. Note that the peak differential stress did not necessarily occur at the same time as the peak radial stress. In general, for an explosion, the tangential stresses are released more rapidly than the radial stress, resulting in a peak in differential stress that occurs after the peak radial stress.

One area where we lack understanding is how to determine the hydrostatic component of the stress history. In principle, it should be possible to apply hydrostatic stress to a previously stressed sample and observe a Kaiser peak at the previous hydrostatic stress. In fact, this can be shown to be the case for samples which are prestressed in the lab. Figure 4 shows that for a uniaxial strain path, where both the differential stress and confining pressure were changing, the Kaiser effect is observed. In contrast, the initial pressurization of the prestressed sample 07MR4C produced high acoustic emission activity, even though the sample had been exposed to at least the lithostatic pressure *in situ*. One possible explanation for the absence of an AE threshold attributable to the hydrostatic stress is that the *in situ* tuff is saturated, which greatly reduces the effective hydrostatic stress. When a sample of this tuff is then allowed to dry out before hydrostatic testing, the effective hydrostatic stress almost immediately exceeds the *in situ* effective hydrostatic stress and the result is AE activity beginning at essentially zero stress.

If the sample were resaturated and tested undrained, then it would be expected that the effective hydrostatic stress would remain close to zero during pressurization, producing few AE events. In an attempt to resaturate the samples, the standard vacuum saturation method was used on samples 25AP41 and 26AP42. The outcome was not what we had expected. Application of hydrostatic pressure still produced significant acoustic emission activity. One possible explanation for this result is that we were not successful in resaturating the sample, so that empty voids felt the full applied hydrostatic stress and collapsed. Further work is required to decide this point.

Because hydrostatic stress did induce AE, the uniaxial strain tests were unlikely to show a threshold stress attributable to the *in situ* stress. Any AE threshold due to changing differential stress would be obscured by the AE due to simultaneous changes in confining pressure. Unfortunately, this was not realized until after the tests were run. However, it is still possible to draw certain conclusions from the two tests on saturated samples.

First, as Figure 4 shows, for the preconditioning stress applied in the laboratory there is definitely a Kaiser effect for the stress path required to produce uniaxial strain. Since this path is probably representative of the stress path induced by the explosion, the observance of a Kaiser effect increases the chances that properly conducted tests would also observe a Kaiser effect due to the explosion-induced stress. Second, the test on the prestressed sample (26AP42), indicates that the sample had been stressed to yield. As Figure 6 shows, the acoustic emission activity, expressed in terms of number of events per stress increment, was rather constant and tended to decrease at higher stresses. This is in contrast to the behavior of the other three samples which showed a pattern of rising AE rate with increasing stress (See Figures 1,3, and 4). The absence of any sustained increase in AE rate at stresses up to yield can be explained by assuming that the sample had already been yielded. Thus the expected Kaiser peak has been essentially eliminated because the greatest possible differential stress had already been attained. This would indicate a differential stress at the origin of this sample of about 55-60 MPa, using the end point stress of this test as the yield stress.

5 SUMMARY

On the basis of four tests it is only possible to draw tentative conclusions. There does seem to be enough evidence of the existence and stress dependence of the Kaiser effect in the tuff to allow hope for the use of this technique in studying past stress states. In future tests the saturation state of the samples should be carefully controlled. Tests should be done on variously oriented subcores from a main core to determine the other components of the *in situ* stress tensor. If the components are indeed decoupled, as these few tests indicate, then a complete stress determination can be made this way. It would be interesting to use the same technique to try and determine *in situ* stresses in tuff.

6 REFERENCES

Haimson, B. C., and K. Kim, Acoustic Emission and Fatigue Mechanisms in Rock, Proc. of the First Conf. on Acoustic Emission/Microseismic Activity In Geologic Structures and Materials, Ed. H. R. Hardy and F. W. Leighton, Trans Tech Publications, Clausthal, Germany, 1977

Holcomb, D. J., Using Acoustic Emissions to Determine In-situ Stress: Problems and Promise Geomechanics–AMD-Vol. 57, Ed. S. Nemat-Nasser, Pub. The American Society of Mechanical Engineers, 1983.

Holcomb, D. J. and M. J. McNamee, Displacement Gage for the Rock Mechanics Laboratory Sandia National Laboratories Report, SAND84–0651, 1984.

Kaiser, J., An Investigation Into the Occurrence of Noises in Tensile Tests or a Study of Acoustic Phenomena in Tensile Tests, Ph. D Thesis, Tech. Hochsh. Munchen, Munich, Germany, (English translation available from Lawrence Radiation Laboratory, Livermore, CA., UCRL-Trans-1082(L), June, 1964), 1950

Kanagawa, T., M. Hayashi, and H. Nakasa, Estimation of Spatial Geo-stress Components in Rock Samples Using the Kaiser Effect, Rep. 375017, Cent. Res. Inst. of Electr. Power Ind., Abiko, Japan, 1976

Kurita K. and N. Fujii, Stress Memory of Crystalline Rock in Acoustic Emission, Geophys. Res. Lett., Vol. 6, 1979, pp. 9-12

Olsson, W. A. and A. K. Jones, Rock Mechanics Properties of Volcanic Tuffs From the Nevada Test Site Sandia National Laboratories Report SAND80-1453, 1980.

* This work performed at Sandia National Laboratories supported by the U. S. Department of Energy under contract number DE–AC04– 76DP00789

Directional acoustic emission activity in response to borehole deformation in rock masses

ROBERT J.WATTERS & AMIR M.SOLTANI
Geological Engineering Division, Mackay School of Mines, University of Nevada, Reno, USA

1 INTRODUCTION

The earliest investigations on acoustic emissions by Obert and Duvall (1942; 1957) from stressed rock, showed that a general correlation exists between emission rate and the stress level, and that is has significance in the design and performance of rock excavations. Many investigators have pursued this promising research area both in the laboratory and field.

One interesting direction research has taken, is in attempting to identify previously applied stress levels, by the acoustic emission response on reloading specimens to the previous stress levels and greater. Kaiser (1953) found that the acoustic emission level showed a significant increase, for many metals, when the previously applied stress level was exceeded. Investigators in rock attempting to prove the "Kaiser Effect," however, have had mixed successes (Goodman, 1963; Hayashi et al; 1979). In recent work on soils for determining the stress history (preconsolidation pressure), Koerner et al (1984) found a correlation of higher acoustic emissions when the stress level was above the preconsolidation pressure.

The present paper reports on the results of in-situ testing and deformation of rock utilizing a hydraulic borehole jack and monitoring the resulting acoustic emissions to see if a directional response existed. This concept had been first mentioned by Boyce (1981), Lord and Koerner (1983) and Watters (1984) as a possible technique for obtaining the locked-in tectonic stress field, assuming that the "Kaiser effect" holds for the rock being tested.

2 FIELD AREAS AND EXPERIMENTAL PROCEDURE

Two rock types, limestone and granite, were tested as well as concrete. A limestone in eastern Nevada, the Joana Limestone and a granite in western Utah in the House Range, were selected for in-situ testing. In addition, a one meter cube of concrete and a detached granite boulder, with approximate dimensions 1 X 2 X 2 meters, were also tested.

The two rock types differed not only in mineralogy but in the degree of fracturing. The limestone was moderately well jointed and bedded whereas the granite was massive with no joints close by. The NX core produced on drilling showed an R.Q.D. of about 60% for the limestone and 100% for the granite.

The test procedure was developed to record variations in acoustic emissions depending upon the orientation of the loading. It was recognised early in the investigation that as the actual near surface in-situ stress field was unknown both in orientation and magnitude, the acoustic emissions could not be correlated to absolute values. However, at this early research stage it was felt that this was not crucial if relative differences could be shown to exist. For this reason it was decided to test a detached, and isolated granite boulder for comparison purposes, which would be free from lateral constraint, and should therefore be free from a tectonic stress field. For similar reasons a concrete block was also tested.

Figure 1 contains details of the test set up. An NX vertical hole was drilled to a depth of between 1 - 1.25 meters and then four EX holes were drilled to a depth of 0.3 - 0.4 meters surrounding the NX hole at a distance of 4-5 NX hole diameters. In each EX hole an aluminum wave guide was grouted the full depth into the hole, and a 30 KHz transducer (sensor) attached. The signal was transmitted via a cable to a 60db preamplifier and then to a 4 channel micro-computer based acoustic emission system. Total gain of the system was 97.1 db. Real-time multiple displays including events, ring down counts, peak amplitude, and event duration for each transducer were obtained in the field or recorded on floppy discs for post processing. Power was supplied by a portable power generator. The borehole hydraulic jack consisted of two movable rigid bearing plates, which transmitted the hydraulic pressure. Two LVDT displacement transducers were mounted within the jack at each end of the movable plates. Hydraulic line pressure up to a maximum of 68-95 MPa can be developed via a hydraulic hand pump, with a undirectional force against the rock.

After drilling the NX and EX holes and installing wave guides and sensors, the jack was inserted into the NX hole. The jack was pressurized in 3.45, 6.9 or 13.8 MPa increments depending on the strength of the rock and degree of confinement. The loading plates were oriented to load the rock generally in a North-South or East-West orientation i.e. parallel and normal to the waveguides. The pressure was maintained for 3 to 5 minutes at each pressure increment, changes

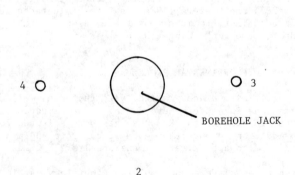

Figure 1. Typical test set up.

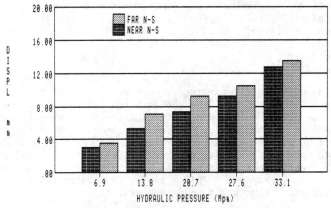

Figure 2. Borehole deformation (m.m.) vs. hydraulic pressure (MPa).

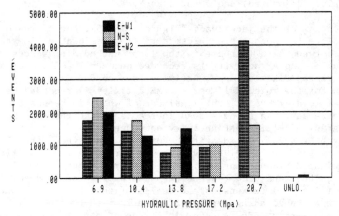

Figure 3. Events vs. hydraulic pressure for concrete (First loading East-West).

in borehole dimensions noted, and acoustic emission levels recorded. The pressure was then rapidly increased and the procedure repeated. In tests where the same borehole was used for both North-South and East-West testing, an attempt was taken to ensure that the first loading cycle did not exceed the elastic range for the rock, this was not always successful. Permanent deformation and failure of the borehole (tensile failure) occurred when detached boulders or concrete blocks were tested.

3.0 Results

A systematic approach was utilized in determining the directional use of acoustic emission (AE) data. Due to the lack of information on the AE response for this type of borehole loading, data were obtained from unconfined material, granite and concrete, and from confined (insitu) rock, massive granite and jointed limestone. The testing procedure was similar for each rock type tested. The behavior varied significantly due to the material properties and degree of confinement. A typical plot of borehole deformation with increasing jack pressure is contained in Figure 2.

3.1 Concrete

Concrete was utilized for testing to enable the testing procedure to be developed. Figure 3 contains the data for the three loading cycles, utilizing the borehole jack and monitoring system. The East-West and one North-South loading cycles were used to enable the AE response to directional loading to be observed. Figure 3 shows a bimodal distribution with very high activity recorded for the initial loading, thereafter dropping off at subsequent loadings, and then increasing dramatically until rupture. This activity is interpreted as first the matrix failing then the aggregate/matrix.

3.2 Massive (unjointed) and Jointed Rock.

On application of the jack load, (Figure 4 and 5), the AE response was immediate for both the unjointed granite and jointed limestone. However, between each increase in the load, marked differences are identifiable. No AE activity is recorded between loadings for the granite, in the elastic range, activity is recorded only during loading. For the jointed limestone, AE activity is recorded between individual loading cycles, the magnitude of which increases as the stress increases. When the stress increases beyond the elastic range for the granite, similar AE activity commences.

Mogi type behavior was identified for both rock types, though as reported by Boyce et al (1981) variations were observed. Difficulty was experienced classifying the rock behavior due to the small number of tests. The granite corresponding both to Mogi and Boyce's dense Type III (Figure 6) and unstable type II for the limestone. Due to the nature of the loading cycle differing from that of normal loading, i.e. a consistent steady increase in stress as opposed to an intermittant increase at 3 to 5 minute intervals, the AE response is not exactly comparable.

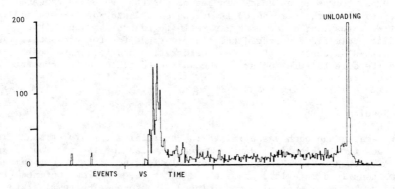

Figure 4.   Events vs. time for unjointed granite.

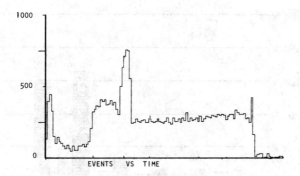

Figure 5.   Events vs. time for jointed limestone.

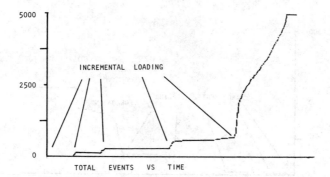

Figure 6.   Total events vs. time for granite boulder.

During one of the tests on the granite boulders, complete failure
was induced across the entire boulder diameter.   The fracture propagated normal to the loading direction, and intersected both North-
South wave guides.   Figure 7 contains the AE monitored during the
loading.   The borehole was first tested North-South, then the jack
was rotated through 90 degrees and tested East-West.   The greatest
number of events were recorded on the first loading cycle (North-
South), with the last loading of the cycle producing high events,
interpreted as fracture propagation.   The subsequent East-West loading,
apart from the initial AE response, consistently yielded lower events,
event at rupture.   This indicates that the failure plane propagated
through already highly fractured rock.

3.3 Confined and Unconfined Granite

The granite testing provided interesting information.   The loading
direction was changed to N 45 W and N 45 E for the in-situ testing,
and incremental loading changed to 13.8 MPa increments, due to the

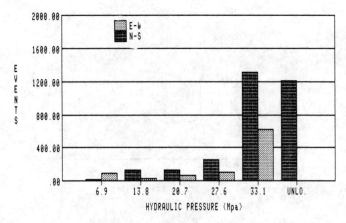

Figure 7. Events vs. hydraulic pressure for both North-South (first) and East-West loadings.

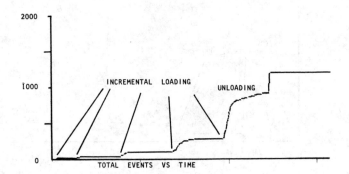

Figure 8. Total events vs time for N. 45 E. loading direction.

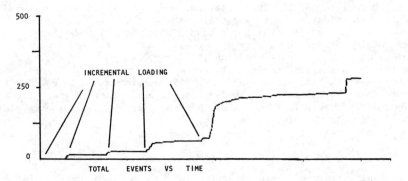

Figure 9. Total events vs. time for N. 45 W. loading direction.

728

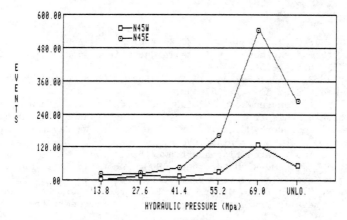

Figure 10.   Events vs. hydraulic pressurce response for both directions.

strength increase caused by confinement. Figures 8 and 9 contain the
response for the loading in the two directions. Marked differences
are obvious. Loading in the N 45 E direction has AE levels 3 to 4
times greater than the N 45 W direction. Both directions show fracture propagation between 55.2 - 69.0 MPa.
    Plotting only the AE information which occurs during the loading
increment, Figure 10, change in response occurs at the 41.4 MPa level
for the N 45 E direction, but at the 55.2 MPa level for the N 45 W
direction.   This type of response, together with the overall total response, Figures 8 and 9, suggests that the N 45 E direction is or has
experienced stress level(s) greater than the N 45 W direction.

4.0 Conclusions and Recommendations

In-situ Acoustic Emission response from rock loading by a borehole
jack shows Mogi and modified Mogi behavior. A directional behavior
suggesting different AE levels in response to a stress field was observed in the in-situ testing for granite, but not for the limestone.
The horizontal distance of the waveguides from the borehole should be
experimented with, to find an optimum distance for signal monitoring.
The author's found that placing a transducer on the jack was possible,
but due to electrical interference from the LVDT's large numbers of
erroneous AE's were recorded. However, lowering gain levels reduced
the number, though it may affect the response characteristics of the
sensor. Consequently, this type of sensor mounting was not chosen.
No account was taken of the petrographic character of the rock and it
is possible that different AE levels may be related in part to aniso-
trophy in the rock (Montoto et al, 1984). Further testing taking into
account mineralogical variations, known in-situ stress field, three
dimensional testing, and laboratory directional loading of rock blocks
is suggested.

REFERENCES

Boyce, G. M., W. M. McCabe & R. M. Koerner 1981. Acoustic Emission Signatures of Various Rock Types in Unconfined Compression. In ASTM Pub. 750, p. 142-154.

Goodman, R. E. 1963. Subaudible Noise During Compression of Rocks. Bull. Geol. Soc. Am., 74:487-490.

Hayashi, M. T. Kanaguawa, S. Hibino, M. Motozima, Y. Kitahara, 1979. Detection of Anisotroic Geo-stresses Trying by ACOUSTIC Emission, and Non-linear Rock Mechanics on Large Excavating Caverns. 4th Int. Conf. Roc k Mech. Switzerland, Vol 2.

Kaiser, J., 1953. Arch Eisenhuettenwesen 25:43.

Lord, A. E., Jr. and R. M. Koerner, 1983. Acoustic Emissions in Geologic Materials. Jour. Acoustic Emission, 2:3, p. 195-219.

Koerner, R. M., A. E. Lord, Jr. & W. L. Deutsch 1984. Determination of Pre Stress in Granular Soils Using AE. Jour. Geot. Engr., Vol 110, 3, p. 346-358.

Montoto, M., L. M. Suarez del Rio, A. W. Khair & H. R. Hardy, Jr. 1984. AE in Uniaxially Loaded Granitic Rocks in Relation to their Petrographic Character. Third Conf. on AE/MA in Geologic Structures and Materials, Oct. 5-7, 1981. Trans. Tech. Publications.

Obert, L. and W. Duvall 1942. Use of Subaudible Noises for the Prediction of Rock Burst, Part II. U.S. Bureau of Mines Report of Investigations, R.I. 3654.

-1956. Microseismic Method of Predicting Rock Failure in Underground Mining. U.S. Bureau of Mines Bulletin. 573.

Watters, R. J., 1984. Potential for Obtaining the In-Situ Rock Stress via Acoustic Emission Monitoring, Abstracts with Program, 27th Annual Meeting, Ass. Engr. Geol., Boston, p. 82.

Location of acoustic emissions during fracture of slightly anisotropic granite

C.H.DOWDING, L.SAMAMA & S.P.SHAH
Northwestern University, Evanston, Illinois, USA

J.F.LABUZ
University of Colorado, Denver, USA

INTRODUCTION AND ABSTRACT

Locations of energy release during controlled fracture propagation in two dimensional granite specimens were determined with acoutic emission (AE) techniques. A method was developed to account for a small directional anisotropy in wave propagation velocity. The location technique resulted in calculated locations near the microscopically (x100) visible fracture plane. The proximity of the AE events to the crack verified the usefulness of the technique to determine the location of the region of plastic deformation associated with fracture propagation - the fracture process zone. This paper presents the location techniques, before the description of the material tested and the event locations themselves.

EVENT LOCATION

Two Dimensional Analytical Solution

For one set of acoustic emission (AE) transducers, T_i and T_j shown in Figure 1, the possible AE event locations, the locus of points from which the compressive wave reaches the two transducers with a constant time interval Dt_{ij}. Assuming a homogeneous and isotropic wave velocity, v_p, the difference in distance from location E to the two transducers T_i and T_j is a constant and equal to $V * Dt_{ij}$ and is expressed as

$$v_p * Dt_{ij} = \sqrt{(x_E - x_i)^2 + (y_E - y_i)^2} - \sqrt{(x_E - x_j)^2 + (y_E - y_j)^2} \quad (1)$$

where x_E, y_E are the coordinates of the possible event location E and x_i, y_i are the coordinates of the AE sensor T_i.

The location along the locus, E, can be found from the solution of the system of two equations (1) corresponding to three transducers that form two different pairs of transducers. These two equations can be rearranged to find the two unknowns, x_E and y_E. The

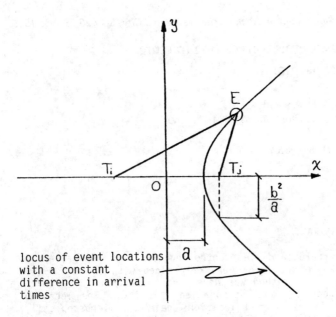

locus of event locations
with a constant
difference in arrival
times

Figure 1. Characteristics of the Hyperbola described by equation 1 where the arrival time differences at transducers T_i & T_j is constant.

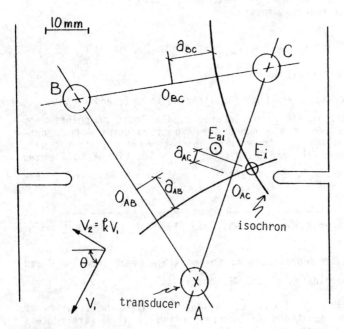

Figure 2. Isochron construction with three transducers by assuming an isotropic wave velocity, Vp.

arrangement of the three tansducers is shown in Figure 2.

Two Dimensional Graphical Solution

The locus of points shown in Figure 1 describes a hyperbola with the following characteristics:

foci: the two transducers T_i and T_j;

distance between origin and vertex: $a = V * Dt_{ij}$

eccentricity: $e = (x_{Ti} - x_{Tj})/2a$

Therefore, the equation of this hyperbola in the system of coordinates (x,y), x being the transfoci axis and y being the transucer bisector, is:

$$(x/a)^2 - (y/b)^2 = 1 \qquad\qquad (2)$$

where $b = a * \sqrt{e^2 - 1}$

As shown in Figure 2, for a geometry with 3 transducers, the event location E_i (i.e. the solution of two equations (1)) is the intersection of two branches of hyperbolae from two different pairs of transducers AB and AC. Alternately Cross et al. (1972) proposed an appolonian graphical construction of the hyperbolic isochron that did not require knowing the equation of the hyperbola. It leads to the same solution as the hyperbola technique.

Graphical Solution with Anisotropic P-wave Velocity

The two dimensional graphical solutions (Cross et al., 1972) obtained for a specimen with homogeneous and isotropic wave velocity can be extended to those with slightly anistropic wave velocity with a transformation of coordinates. Stevens (1936) first presented such a transformation to analyze groundwater flow in anisotropic and heterogeneous media. Similarly, these transformations can be applied to analyze wave propagation in an anisotropic specimen. Nevertheless, for very anisotropic materials the wave travel path is curved and the phase velocity, which is relatable to material properties, is not identical to the group velocity (Chang, 1984). Consequently, the hyperbola technique cannot be applied to very anisotropic specimens.

As illustrated in Figure 2, if the principal directions of anisotropy and the P-wave velocities, v_{p1} and v_{p2}, in these directions, the geometry can be transformed into that for a specimen with isotropic P-wave velocity, say $v_{p'1}$. If the angle between the principal directions of anisotropy and the axes of the coordinate system (x,y) is θ , the new coordinates are obtained from the old by the following transformations.

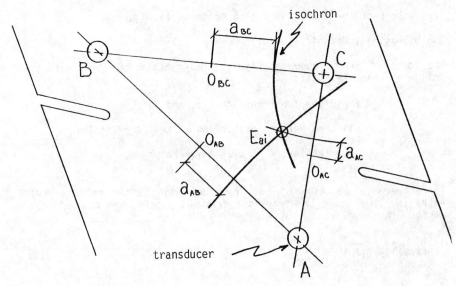

Figure 3. Transformation of Figure 2 to draw isochrons for locating AE events in slightly anisotropic materials.

The old coordinate system (x,y) is rotated an angle θ into the system of coordinates (x_1, y_1) parallel to the principal directions of anisotropy.

(x,y) is transformed into (x_1, y_1) so that

$$x_1 = x$$

$$y_1 = ky$$

where $k = V_p/V_{p2}$.

The system (x, y) is rotated an angle $-\theta-$ to get the new coordinate system (x_1, y_1), then:

$$
\begin{vmatrix} x_1 \\ y_1 \end{vmatrix}
=
\begin{vmatrix} \cos\theta \ \sin\theta \\ -\sin\theta \ \cos\theta \end{vmatrix}
\bullet
\begin{vmatrix} 1 \ 0 \\ 0 \ k \end{vmatrix}
\bullet
\begin{vmatrix} \cos\theta \ -\sin\theta \\ \sin\theta \ \cos\theta \end{vmatrix}
\bullet
\begin{vmatrix} x \\ y \end{vmatrix}
\tag{3}
$$

thus:

$$
\begin{vmatrix} x_1 \\ y_1 \end{vmatrix}
=
\begin{vmatrix} \cos^2\theta + k\sin^2\theta & \cos\theta\sin\theta\,(k-1) \\ \cos\theta\cdot\sin\theta\,(k-1) & k\cos^2\theta + \sin^2\theta \end{vmatrix}
\bullet
\begin{vmatrix} x \\ y \end{vmatrix}
\tag{4}
$$

As illustrated in Figure 3, hyperbolic isochrons (or appolonian circles) are drawn in the transformed configuration. The inverse transform of the intersection of two hyperbolas is the source location in the actual geometry of the slightly anisotropic specimen.

The two locations, isotropic E_i and slightly anistropic E_{ai}, are compared in Figure 2.

Inaccuracy from Heterogeneous Wave Velocity

The region around the crack is usually characterized by lower wave propagation velocities due to microcrack growth and structural rearrangements. Arrivals of waves traversing this zone around the crack will be delayed. Consequently, typical analyses will produce calculated locations more distant from the crack. Calculations of such an error in event location were made (Samama, 1985). They lead to an error of 2.2 mm for a 2.5 mm wide fracture process zone in which signals propagate at a velocity of 2/3 of the wave velocity in the rest of the specimen.

FRACTURE PROPAGATION

Material Tested

Fracture tests and simulated acoustic emission tests were conducted on specimens of Charcoal granite. The Charcoal granite, or Saint Cloud granodiorite, featured anisotropic wave velocities of 4100 and 4800 m/s, and 1 mm average grain size.

Two geometries were tested. The simplest was a double-edge-notched (DEN) specimen (Labuz et al., 1984), illustrated in Figure 4. A two-dimensional geometry was assumed since the thickness (6 mm) was small with respect to other dimensions (270 mm by 73 mm). The second was a double-cantilever-beam (DCB) specimen, (406 mm x 152 mm x 38 mm) shown in Figure 5, with a groove (6.35 mm deep, 25.4 mm wide) in the middle of each face to direct the crack down the midplane. A chevron notch (0.4 mm wide and 11.1 to 23.4 mm deep) was saw cut to initiate the crack.

Experimental Procedure

The fracture test with the DEN thin plate was conducted in a 89 kN (20 kip) MTS closed-loop testing machine. The crack mouth opening displacement, which was the feedback parameter, was measured with strain-gauge type extensometers. Further details are given by Labuz et al. (1984). The DCB specimen was fractured in a 550 kN (120 kip) MTS displacement-controlled closed-loop testing machine. A linear variable differential transformer (LVDT) measured the crack mouth opening displacement with a precision better than $\pm$ 0.01 mm (Labuz 1985). The optical crack was observed with a traveling optical microscope with x100 magnification. The precision on the optical crack location was 0.25 mm (1/100 in).

As indicated in Figure 2 for the DEN specimen, three sensors were placed on the same face of the rock. They were about 50 mm (2 in.) apart from each other and they were no closer than 12 mm (1/2 in.) from the edges. To allow more flexibility, six acoustic emission sensors were glued to the DCB Specimen (Figure 5). Four of them (forming a tetrahedric array) were connected to the digital oscillo-

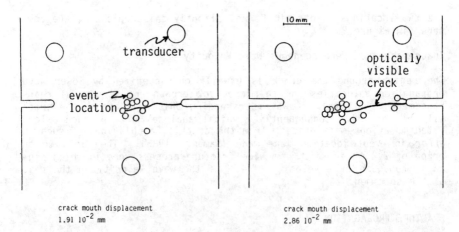

Figure 4. Location of Acoustic Emissions compared to the optically visible crack for a Double Edge Notched specimen at two different crack mouth displacements.

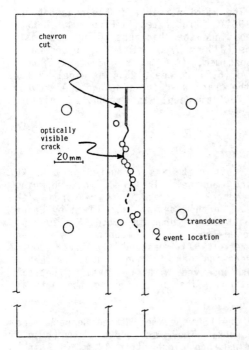

Figure 5. Location of Acoustic Emissions compared to the optically visible crack for a Double Cantilever Beam specimen during increasing crack mouth displacement.

scope at any one time. The oscilloscope digitized signals at a rate of 2,000,000 samples per second.

Acoustic emissions were recorded at different points of the loading history of the rocks. Most data were obtained while the crack mouth opening displacement was held constant and the load was decreasing because of stable crack propagation.

Agreement between Simulated AE and Calculated Event Location

In order to check the precision and accuracy of the calculated location of acoustic emissions (AE), simulated AE events were generated by failing a 0.5 mm pencil lead at the rock surface. This check was conducted before fracture tests. Acoustic emissions were able to be located within 3 mm for the DEN specimen and 6 mm for the DCB specimen.

Event Locations During Fracture

As shown in Figure 4 for the double-edge-notched (DEN) specimen and in Figure 5 for the double-cantilever-beam (DCB) specimen, most recorded acoustic emissions were located behind the microscopically visible crack tip.

Results from the DEN specimen indicate that the width of the zone, wherein most AE events were located was 3.5 mm on both sides of the crack plane. This width must be evaluated with respect to the 3 mm accuracy of event locations. The vast majority of acoustic emissions clustered in the region behind the optical crack tip. No AE event was recorded near the notch which did not initiate a crack. The AE location technique confirms that the non-cracked notch only underwent elastic deformation and that the DEN specimen behaved as a single-edge-notched (SEN) specimen (Labuz et al., 1984).

As in the case of the DEN specimen, most acoustic emissions in the DCB specimen were located in the region behind the optical crack tip. Furthermore, the cloud of events was located within about 5 mm of the crack plane, probably due to the poorer precision, viz. 6 mm, obtained with this geometry. When the displacement was held and the load was relaxing while the crack extended, a few recorded events were observed ahead of the crack, indicating the zone where the crack was growing. Nevertheless, the amount of AE activity all along the crack suggests that, as for the DEN specimen, more energy is released in the widening of the optically visible crack than in its growth near the tip.

SUMMARY

Double-edge-notched (DEN) and double-cantilever-beam (DCB) specimens of Charcoal granite were fractured in a closed-loop testing machine in a displacement controlled mode. The specimens were instrumented with acoustic emission (AE) transducers and a traveling optical microscope was used to measure the crack length. After the determination of the arrival times of the AE waves, recorded with a digital oscilloscope, events were located on the rock using a two-dimensional (2-D) graphical solution that accounted for a 15% wave propagation anisotropy. The position of AE events with respect to the crack showed that within the accuracy of the method, the events were located close enough to the crack to estimate the size and location of the fracture process zone.

ACKNOWLEDGEMENTS

This work is being supported by the National Science Foundation under grant CEB 8314442.

REFERENCES

Chang, H. S. (1984), "A Study of Acoustic Emission Source Location Generated in Stressed Rock Solved by a Least-Squares Iterative Technique," Master Thesis, Department of Civil Engineering, Northwestern University, Evanston, Illinois.

Cross, N. O., L. L. Loustin, and J. L. Thompson (1972), "Acoustic Emission Testing of Pressure Vessels for Petroleum Refineries and Chemical Plants," Acoustic Emission, Special Technical Publication, 505, American Society for Testing and Materials, 270-296

Labuz, J. F. (1985), "A Study of the Fracture Process Zone in Rock", Ph.D. Thesis, Department of Civil Engineering, Northwestern University, Evanston, Illinois.

Labuz, J. F., S. P. Shah, and C. H. Dowding (1984), "Experimental Analysis of Crack Propagation in Granite," International Journal of Rock Mechanics

Samama, L. P. (1985), "Detection and Analysis of Acoustic Emissions in Laboratory Granite Specimens, Master Thesis, Department of Civil Engineering, Northwestern University, Evanston, Illinois.

Stevens, O. (1936), "Discussion of Ground Water and Seepage," First International Congress of Soil Mechanics and Foundation Engineering, Cambridge, 3:165-166.

Propagation of acoustic waves through cracked rock

ROBERT W.ZIMMERMAN
Department of Mechanical Engineering, University of California, Berkeley, USA
MICHAEL S.KING
Earth Sciences Division, Lawrence Berkeley Laboratory, California, USA

1 INTRODUCTION

Most transport and mechanical properties of rocks, such as electrical resistivity, thermal conductivity, hydraulic permeability, compressibility, and the velocities and attenuation of acoustic waves, are strongly influenced by the presence of microcracks and fractures in the rock, and by the fluids contained in these cracks. The importance of microcracks and fractures, particularly at low confining stresses, has been demonstrated in laboratory experiments by, among others, Brace and Orange (1968) for electrical resistivity, Walsh and Decker (1966) for thermal conductivity, Walsh (1981) for hydraulic permeability, Simmons et al. (1974) for compressibility, Toksoz et al. (1976) and Feves et al. (1977) for elastic wave velocities, and Johnston and Toksoz (1980) for acoustic wave attenuation.

A knowledge of the presence and properties of microcracks in rocks, and their relationship to the mechanical and transport properties, therefore has considerable practical importance. For example, the exploration for and exploitation of mineral, hydrocarbon, and geothermal resources depend on the in situ measurement of many of the physical parameters previously mentioned. The underground isolation of hazardous wastes depends on the ability to select sites where the transport properties of the rock are favorable.

In a major advance in the ability to predict the transport properties of rock, Cheng and Toksoz (1979) devised a scheme to extract crack populations and pore aspect ratio distributions from seismic data. The resulting crack statistics were used by Seeburger and Nur (1984) as input to a network model for the permeability of some consolidated sandstones, with fairly encouraging results. Zimmerman (1984a) has recently refined the Cheng and Toksoz approach by incorporating the relationship between crack closure and bulk compressibility that follows from the reciprocal theorem of classical elasticity.

2 EFFECTIVE MODULI THEORIES

Most analytical theories of the effect of cracks on the elastic moduli of rocks are based on the idealization of these cracks as thin, "penny-shaped" oblate spheroids. The earliest attempt to quantify this effect was by Walsh (1965), who used a method based on the calculation of the

739

excess strain energy due to an isolated crack in an infinite medium under
uniaxial or hydrostatic loading. This method ignores stress-field interactions between neighboring cracks, and is therefore accurate only for
relatively low crack concentrations. An early attempt to account for
these interactions was the "self-consistent" theory of O'Connell and Budiansky (1974), in which a typical crack is assumed to be imbedded in an
equivalent homogeneous medium whose elastic moduli are those of the
cracked rock. This theory predicts a much more rapid decrease in moduli
(as a function of crack density) than does Walsh's "no-interaction" method, and actually predicts that the moduli will vanish at some finite
crack concentration. Kuster and Toksoz (1974) equated the sum of the
waves scattered off an assemblage of cracks to the wave which would be
scattered off a single "equivalent" homogeneous inclusion, and arrived
at expressions for the effective elastic moduli which lie between those
of Walsh and O'Connell-Budiansky, but which also vanish at a certain finite crack concentration.

Salganik (1973) developed a modification of the self-consistent method
in which the cracks are conceived to be placed in the rock one at a time,
and the strain energy of the (n+1)st crack calculated as if it were
placed in a homogeneous medium whose moduli are those of the body with n
cracks. For a material with spherical pores or inclusions, it has been
shown by Zimmerman (1984b) that the predictions which follow from this
approach are fairly accurate; furthermore, this method always predicts
finite moduli. Salganik's method leads to a pair of coupled ordinary
differential equations for the moduli as functions of crack density,
the solution to which has recently been obtained in closed form (Zimmerman 1984a). For all cases of geophysical interest (Poisson's ratio less
than about 0.40) the exact solution is within 2% of the following approximate solution derived by Bruner (1976):

(1) $E/E^0 = \exp(-16c/9)$,

(2) and $\nu/\nu^0 = \exp(-16c/10)$,

where E is Young's modulus, ν is Poisson's ratio, c is a crack density
parameter defined as the number of cracks per unit volume multiplied by
the mean value of the cube of the crack radius, and the superscript 0
denotes the properties of the uncracked rock.

A number of other theories have considered physical models of cracks
and fractures that are not ellipsoidal (Mavko and Nur 1978, Walsh and
Grosenbaugh 1979). However, these models have not lent themselves to
a calculation of the effective shear modulus G. Since both the compressional and shear wavespeeds depend on G, these theories are insufficient
for wave propagation problems.

3 VERIFICATION OF THEORY

Direct verification of equations 1 and 2 is probably not possible, due
to the difficulty in accurately measuring the crack density parameter c.
In order to provide a partial verification of the applicability of these
equations to cracked rock, we will show that they can be used to relate
changes in shear wave velocities (Vs) to changes in compressional wave
velocities (Vp). This is a non-trivial test, since in general Vp and Vs
are independent.

For the purposes of arriving at an unbiased set of data for this test,

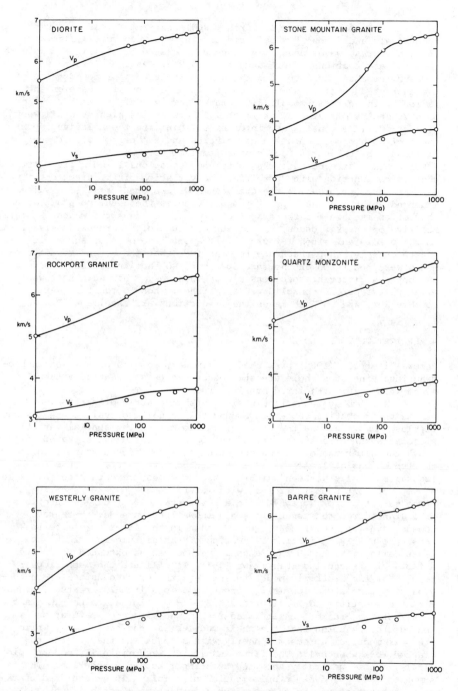

Figure 1. Use of equations 1 and 2 to predict changes in Vs from changes in Vp, for six unsaturated, low porosity crystalline rocks. Vp data from Birch (1960), Vs data from Simmons (1964).

we choose the measurements of Birch (1960) and Simmons (1964), which have been widely and frequently referred to in the geophysical literature. In these works, wavespeeds of various unsaturated crystalline rocks were measured as functions of pressure to 1000 MPa. As the pressure was increased, cracks closed up, and the wave velocities approached those of the uncracked rock; these measurements in effect provide data on the variation of the elastic moduli with crack density. Only rocks for which both Vp and Vs differed by at least 10% between the highest and lowest pressure will be considered, in order to minimize the relative importance of both experimental uncertainties and the effect of pressure on the moduli of the uncracked crystals themselves.

For the six sets of data thus obtained, equations 1 and 2 are first used in conjunction with Vp to find the variation of the crack density with pressure, from which the changes in Vs are predicted. The values measured at the highest pressures are used as the datum points, and no correction is made for the effect of pressure on density, which is small. For five of the six cases, the measured values of Vs are extremely close to the predicted values (Figure 1). The one case of poor agreement (Barre granite) is perhaps due to the fact that the Vp and Vs measurements were not taken on the same specimen, so that inhomogeneities existing between different specimens may be involved. This same test was applied to two porous consolidated sandstones, whose porosities were roughly 20%, and in both cases the predictions are excellent (Figure 2).

4 APPLICATION TO FIELD DATA

Rezowalli et al. (1984) presented preliminary results of a research program involving cross-hole acoustic measurements adjacent to a tunnel mined in a columnar-jointed basaltic rock mass. The objectives of the program were to evaluate the in situ dynamic elastic properties, and to assess their spatial variation around the tunnel; to evaluate the extent of blast damage around the opening; and to assess the spatial variation of jointing and fracturing around the opening. Although situated well above the water table, it was suspected that the rock mass surrounding the tunnel was at least partially saturated with water, because the horizontal boreholes between which the acoustic measurements were made were slowly but continuously filling with water.

The variations of Vp and Vs (in a horizontal direction) as functions of distance from the tunnel face are shown in Figure 3a. Both wavespeeds were much lower near the face than in the interior of the rock mass, presumably indicating a lowering of the elastic moduli due to blast damage. Although the Salganik method can be extended to include anisotropic fracturing (Nishizawa 1982), we will use the much simpler results of the isotropic model to estimate the crack density (c) and degree of water saturation (s). First, equations 1 and 2 are used, along with the identities $G=E/2(1+\nu)$ and $K=E/3(1-2\nu)$, to determine the elastic moduli of the cracked, unsaturated rock. The effect of saturation is included by assuming that the shear modulus is unaffected by s, while the bulk modulus increases linearly with s, equaling that of the uncracked rock when s=1. The first assumption was originally made by Biot (1941), and is generally accepted as being reasonably accurate. The assumption that the dynamic bulk modulus of a fully fluid-saturated cracked rock equals that of the uncracked rock is also well established, and has theoretical justification (O'Connell and Budiansky 1974). The linear dependence of K on saturation follows from the theoretical results of

742

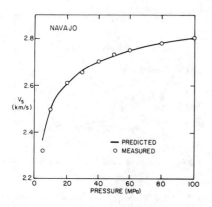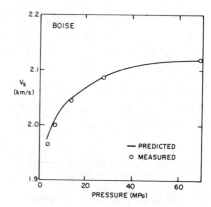

Figure 2. Use of equations 1 and 2 to predict changes in Vs from changes in Vp, for two unsaturated, porous consolidated sandstones. Data for Navajo sandstone from Johnston (1978), data for Boise from King (1966).

Vodak (1981), in the limit of low porosity. Mathematically, these assumptions can be expressed as

(3) $G(c,s) = G(c,0)$,

(4) and $K(c,s) = sK^0 + (1-s)K(c,0)$.

The wavespeeds are related to the moduli by the usual relations:

(5) $Vp^2 = (K + 4G/3)/\rho$,

(6) and $Vs^2 = G/\rho$,

where ρ is the density. Finally, since the porosities of the basalt are quite low (less than 2%), the density is taken to be constant, in which case it actually drops out of the calculations.

Use of equations 1-6, along with the Vp and Vs measurements, allows the straightforward determination of the crack density parameter c and the saturation s as functions of position (Figure 3b). As was expected, the amount of microcracking due to blast damage decreases rapidly with distance from the face. The rock mass is also seen to be partially saturated throughout, with a lower degree of saturation near the face, presumably due to evaporation. The saturation increases away from the face in an irregular manner, and does not level off to a constant value. This inhomogeneity is plausible if we assume that the apertures of the fractures are randomly distributed, since the ability of the fractures to drain into the borehole should vary with aperture.

5 SUMMARY AND CONCLUSIONS

By comparing the changes in Vp and Vs for various rock specimens, it has been shown that the predictions of the Salganik equations are consistent with the actual behavior of cracked rock. These equations have

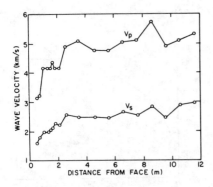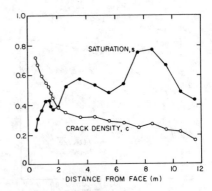

Figure 3. Acoustic wavespeeds in a basaltic rock mass adjacent to tunnel (a); saturations and crack densities derived from acoustic data (b).

then been used, along with some reasonable assumptions concerning the effects of fluid saturation, to determine the degrees of microcracking and saturation in a basaltic rock mass, starting from acoustic data. Although this analysis utilized the approximation of isotropy, which is certainly not true for basalt, this can be improved upon at the cost of only a slight increase in the computations required. Nevertheless, even this simplified treatment yields plausible results, and certainly provides more information than merely qualitative or subjective measures of rock quality.

REFERENCES

Biot, M.A. 1941. General theory of three-dimensional consolidation. J. Appl. Phys. 12:155-164.
Birch, F. 1960. The velocity of compressional waves in rocks to 10 kilobars, Part I. J. Geophys. Res. 65:1083-1102.
Brace, W.F. & A.S. Orange. 1968. Electrical resistivity changes in saturated rocks during fracture and frictional sliding. J. Geophys. Res. 73:1433-1445.
Bruner, W.M. 1976. Comment on "Seismic velocities in dry and saturated cracked solids" by Richard J. O'Connell and Bernard Budiansky. J. Geophys. Res. 81:2573-2576.
Cheng, C.H. & M.N. Toksoz. 1979. Inversion of seismic velocities for the pore aspect ratio spectrum of a rock. J. Geophys. Res. 84:7533-7543.
Feves, M., G. Simmons & R.W. Siegfried. 1977. Microcracks in crustal igneous rocks: physical properties. In Geophysical Monograph #20 (Earth's crust), p.95-117. Washington: American Geophysical Union.
Johnston, D.H. 1978. The attenuation of seismic waves in dry and saturated rocks. Ph.D. thesis, Massachusetts Institute of Technology, Cambridge, Massachusetts.
Johnston. D.H. & M.N. Toksoz. 1980. Ultrasonic P and S wave attenuation in dry and saturated rocks under pressure. J. Geophys. Res. 85:925-936.
King, M.S. 1966. Wave velocities in rocks as a function of changes in overburden pressure and pore fluid saturants. Geophysics 31:50-73.
Kuster, G.T. & M.N. Toksoz. 1974. Velocity and attenuation of seismic waves in two-phase media: Part I. Theoretical formulations. Geophysics 39:587-606.

Mavko, G.M. & A. Nur. 1978. The effect of nonelliptical cracks on the compressibility of rocks. J. Geophys. Res. 83:4459-4468.

Nishizawa, O. 1982. Seismic velocity anisotropy in a medium containing oriented cracks - transversely isotropic case. J. Phys. Earth 30:331-347.

O'Connell, R.J. & B. Budiansky. 1974. Seismic velocities in dry and saturated cracked solids. J. Geophys. Res. 79:5412-5425.

Rezowalli, J.J., M.S. King & L.R. Myer. 1984. Cross-hole acoustic surveying in basalt. Int. J. Rock Mech. Min. Sci. & Geomech. Abstr. 21:213-216.

Salganik, R.L. 1973. Mechanics of bodies with many cracks. Mechs. Solids 8(4):135-143.

Simmons, G. 1964. Velocity of shear waves in rocks to 10 kilobars, I. J. Geophys. Res. 69:1123-1130.

Simmons, G., R.W. Siegfried & M. Feves. 1974. Differential strain analysis: a new method for examing cracks in rocks. J. Geophys. Res. 79: 4383-4385.

Seeburger, D.A. & A. Nur. 1984. A pore space model for rock permeability and bulk modulus. J. Geophys. Res. 89:527-536.

Toksoz, M.N., C.H. Cheng & A. Timur. 1976. Velocities of seismic waves in porous rocks. Geophysics 41:621-645.

Vodak, F. 1981. Porous materials: The effect of a fluid on the elastic moduli and on the velocity of elastic waves. Acta Mech. 39:37-42.

Walsh, J.B. 1965. The effect of cracks on the compressibility of rock. J. Geophys. Res. 70:381-389.

Walsh, J.B. 1981. Effect of pore pressure and confining pressure on fracture permeability. Int. J. Rock Mech. Min. Sci. & Geomech. Abstr. 18:429-435.

Walsh, J.B. & E.R. Decker. 1966. Effect of pressure and saturating fluid on the thermal conductivity of compact rock. J. Geophys. Res. 71:3053-3061.

Walsh, J.B. & M.A. Grosenbaugh. 1979. A new model for analyzing the effect of fractures on compressibility. J. Geophys. Res. 84:3532-3536.

Zimmerman, R.W. 1984a. The effect of pore structure on the pore and bulk compressibilities of consolidated sandstones. Ph.D. thesis, University of California, Berkeley, California.

Zimmerman, R.W. 1984b. Elastic moduli of a solid with spherical pores: new self-consistent method. Int. J. Rock Mech. Min. Sci. & Geomech. Abstr. 21:339-343.

16. Field testing for nuclear waste

Chair: WILLIAM C.McCLAIN
         Roy F.Weston, Rockville, Maryland, USA
Cochair: WILLIAM F.UBBES
         Battelle Project Management Division, Columbus, Ohio, USA

Thermal-cycle testing of the G-Tunnel heated block[*]

ROGER M.ZIMMERMAN
*Sandia National Laboratories**, Albuquerque, New Mexico, USA*

MICHAEL L.WILSON, MARK P.BOARD & MICHAEL E.HALL
Science Applications International Corporation, Las Vegas, Nevada, USA

ROBERT L.SCHUCH
*Sandia National Laboratories**, Albuquerque, New Mexico, USA*

1 INTRODUCTION

Volcanic tuffs are being considered by the Department of Energy (DOE) as a medium for disposal of high-level radioactive wastes. The Nevada Nuclear Waste Storage Investigations (NNWSI) Project was established in 1977 to evaluate such disposal in geologic formations on or adjacent to the Nevada Test Site (NTS). Sandia National Laboratories (SNL), as one of the NNWSI project participants, is responsible for the rock mechanics program to support the design of underground portions of a radioactive-waste repository in tuff. A rock mechanics field testing program is underway in G-Tunnel in Rainier Mesa on the NTS, where tuffs similar to those at Yucca Mountain, the potential candidate site, are found; later experiments are planned as part of the exploratory shaft investigations in Yucca Mountain. Science Applications International Corporation (SAIC) has been under contract to SNL to prepare and install instrumentation and control systems and to aid in the evaluation of the heated-block rock mechanics experiment.

2 BACKGROUND

The objective of the heated-block experiment is to evaluate rock mass thermal, mechanical, thermomechanical, and hydrothermal responses on a relatively large scale under conditions where stress and temperature-boundary conditions can be controlled. The block was formed by cutting four 3-m-deep orthogonal slots around the periphery of a block of jointed-welded tuff 2 m square to form a large prism. Flatjacks were grouted around the block, as illustrated in Figure 1. Heaters were located in two opposite rows parallel to the flatjacks to provide nearly uni-directional heat fluxes.

Data collection covered three stages: slot cutting, ambient-temperature testing, and thermal-cycle testing. The slot-cutting stage involved measurements taken before and after the slot cutting and up to the time when the flatjacks were pressurized to a selected value

---

[*] This work was supported by the U.S. Department of Energy (DOE) under contract DE-AC04-DP00789.
[**] A U.S. Department of Energy Facility.

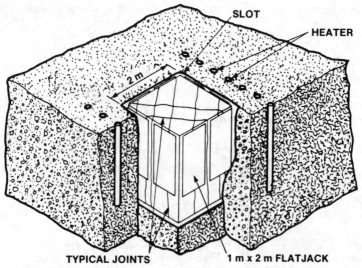

Figure 1   Perspective of Heated Block Experiment Setup

closely representing the in-situ state of normal stress. All subsequent ambient-temperature and thermal-cycle pressure changes were
made relative to this flatjack initialization pressure (FIP) of 3.1
MPa.

This paper provides thermal-expansion and hydrologic data results
for the thermal-cycle testing. Other data, such as modulus of
deformation and cross-hole ultrasonics measurements, were taken but
results are not included in this brief paper. The thermal-expansion
data are needed primarily for repository designs in order to evaluate the stability of repository drifts to be used for waste handling, emplacement, and retrieval. Hydrologic data and their relation to thermomechancial conditions are used in performance assess-
ments of the waste isolation system. Hydrologic data provided in
this testing consist of fracture permeability measurements and
determinations of pore-moisture content changes due to the heating.
In particular, effects of excavations, stress changes, and heat on
the permeability of the rock mass around the drifts are impacts
being evaluated in performance-assessment modeling, where these
field-scale data provide valuable inputs. Hydrologic data are used
as input to and the validation of models addressing coupled
thermal/mechanical/ hydrologic behavior.

3 INSTRUMENTATION

Figure 2 shows a cross section of the tuff block with pertinent
instrumentation, equipment, and physical features.

Deformation data for determining the thermal-expansion characteristics were obtained from four horizontal surface extensometers
(HSX) and two multiple-point borehole extensometers (MPBX). Both
types of measurements were monitored on a Hewlett Packard HP-9845-
based data acquisition system.

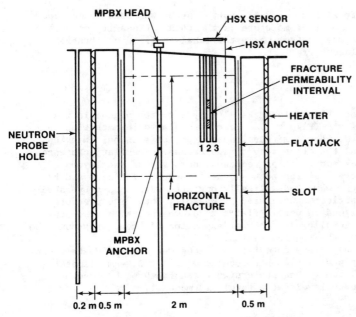

Figure 2   Schematic Illustrating Test and Measurement Details

The HSX system was a new development for this experiment and was used to measure the horizontal deformations across the block. Figure 2 shows typical placement of one of the units. The measurement system consisted of connected vertical anchor pairs that were bonded to the block beneath the top level of the flatjacks. For reasons discussed later, the anchors were removed, lengthened by 0.5 m, and bonded to the block in deeper holes after the second thermal cycle. Horizontal displacements were measured with Trans Tek Model 043-11 direct current-linear variable displacement transformers (DC-LVDT). Schaevitz, Model LSOC-30, tiltmeters were rigidly attached to platforms on the anchors at positions near the tops to monitor anchor rigid-body rotations.

Two vertical 4-anchor MPBX's were located on the block, with three of the four anchors located in the first 2 m. Typical anchor locations are illustrated for one MPBX in Figure 2. The bottom anchor was located 7.3 m from the collar in underlying nonwelded tuff. All anchors were grouted in place.

A single fracture was selected for permeability testing with a SAIC designed system (Zimmerman et al. 1984). Steady-state pressure injections were made with water, heated to block temperatures in the central hole 2, and flow rates into each of the two adjacent collector holes (Figure 2) were measured. The injection interval was 18 cm and injection pressures were less than 0.25 MPa.

The block, located approximately 600 m above the static water level, was partially saturated in the beginning. Moisture contents changed during heating and changes were monitored with 136 thermocouples used and a neutron probe. Eighty-three of the thermocouples were located within the block. Temperature measurements verified that the line heaters provided a nearly uni-directional heat flux to the block. A Troxler Model 2651 neutron probe was used to monitor changes in the amount of moisture in the rock. Linearity of neutron count with moisture content was established in field calibration tests using welded tuff.

4 EQUIPMENT

Sixteen stainless steel flatjacks, 1 m by 2 m were placed in the four vertical slots (Figure 1). Four were placed in each slot in two tandem pairs, thus 4 m^2 was loaded. One of each pair was the primary unit and the other served as a backup. The flatjacks were grouted in place and friction reducers, composed of two layers of Teflon film, were inserted between the innermost flatjacks and the block. Flatjacks were hydraulically operated with an air–operated pressure intensifier manufactured by Haskell, Inc. The pressure system was designed to permit flatjack volume reduction at a constant pressure to allow for thermal expansion of the rock around the flatjacks during the thermal cycles.

Fourteen immersion–style heaters 3 m long were used. Heaters consisted of hairpin-bend elements located within a 3.2–cm–diameter stainless steel tube. The heaters were manufactured by Accutherm, Inc. Heater power levels were regulated manually.

5 TEST CONDITIONS

The thermal–cycle testing consisted of three heating periods. The thermal cycles were designed so that the block could be evaluated at different pore–water content conditions that were evaluated with temperature measurements. The first cycle consisted of heating the block for 15 days with a power output of 700 W from each of the 14 heaters. The block–center temperature (at the midplane depth of 1 m) increased from a nominal 18°C to 48°C. At the block boundary, the average temperature increased to 78°C. After a 31–day cooldown, thermal cycle 2 was started. Thermal cycle 2 lasted for 21 days at the same power level. Temperatures increased from 32°C to 69°C at the center, and the boundary temperatures increased to 95°C. Thermal-cycle 3 was started about 4 months after the end of thermal cycle 2 and the average initial temperature was 21°C. After 46 days of heating at a power level of 800 W for each of the heaters, the center temperatures increased to more than 94°C (boiling temperatures). Corresponding boundary temperatures increased to 145°C.

6 RESULTS

Test results and discussions are separated into categories of thermal–expansion determination, fracture permeability measurements, and moisture–change monitoring.

6.1 Thermal Expansion

The Table summarizes the thermal–expansion test results for the three test cycles. Thermal-expansion coefficients were determined from measurements obtained with the HSXs and MPBXs. Effective

Summary of Effective Thermal Expansion Coefficients

Thermal Cycle	Normal Stress (MPa)	Sensor Type	Average ($10^{-6}\,°C^{-1}$)
1	10.6	HSX	3.5*
		MPBX	19.4*
2	8.1	HSX	5.0
		MPBX	8.7
3	5.6	HSX	5.3
		MPBX	6.2

*Values influenced by block fracture propagation

values were calculated from measurements with these instruments and thermocouples distributed throughout the block. Plane-stress elastic equations were used to make the calculations. It was assumed that all biaxial stresses were constant during the thermal cycles. Larger biaxial stresses were applied at lower temperature thermal cycles to minimize possible joint shear effects because of the one-dimensional heat flux across the block.

Variations in the thermal-expansion coefficients, particularly with respect to thermal cycle 1, require an explanation because of unexpected mechanical behavior that occurred during that cycle. At the end of thermal cycle 1, a sharp crack was heard as personnel were reducing the flatjack pressures to prepare for a modulus-of-deformation measurement. The results of the HSX measurements at that time were somewhat in variance with previous measurements taken during ambient temperature testing (Zimmerman et al. 1984). There was no evidence of added fracturing on the block surface and the decision was made to initiate the second thermal cycle. The thermal-expansion coefficients were closer together in that cycle, but subsequent HSX-based modulus of deformation measurements continued to vary. During this period of evaluation after thermal cycle 2, two new horizontal fractures were discovered in the block, one at a depth of approximately 0.3 m and the other near 2 m. Apparently, they had completed forming during thermal cycle 1. It was assessed that an upper slab had decoupled from the central part of the block and that this could influence HSX measurements. The HSX anchors were deepened by 0.5 m prior to thermal cycle 3 (see Figure 2) and the later modulus of deformation determinations returned to expected values.

The small value for the thermal-expansion coefficient, as determined with the HSX measurements in thermal cycle 1, is attributed to decoupling effects of the upper slab. The relatively large value based on the MPBX measurements is attributed partially to the decoupling and partially to the growth of the upper fracture during the first cycle. The fact that the values were more uniform during the second thermal cycle indicates that both displacement-measuring systems were measuring thermal-expansion behavior under constant stresses, as assumed. Data from the third cycle confirm this hypothesis.

The conclusion is that the values for the thermal-expansion coef-

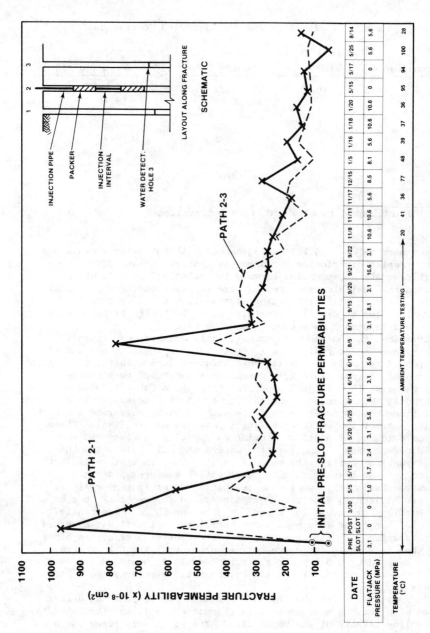

Figure 3 Fracture Permeabilities as a Function of Pressure and Temperature

754

ficient are better represented in the latter two cycles and reflect a reasonable range for field values: 5.0 to 8.7 x 10^{-6}°C^{-1}. The observed range represents measurement bounds and is not the result of a detailed error analysis, thus statistical variations are not shown. This range compares well with the laboratory range for intact tuff from the heated block. This range is reported as 6.4 $\pm$ 2.2 to 8.0 $\pm$ 0.6 x 10^{-6}°C^{-1} for 5-cm by 10-cm intact rock samples by Lappin and Nimick (in prep).

The observation that laboratory and field values for the thermal-expansion coefficient are essentially similar has a logical explanation. Two joint surfaces initially in contact should close only with an increase in normal stress, thus thermal expansion in the absence of stress increases should only affect the intact rock portion of a rock mass. Because of the conditions imposed by this testing, the thermal-expansion coefficient should be a result of intact rock behavior. Thus, repository designers could use laboratory values for their analyses.

This consideration has one caveat. It was assumed that the unstressed aperture is the smallest value possible before physical contact of the surfaces occurs. If for some geological reason the actual joint has an aperture a^1 greater than a (the unstressed aperture of contact), rock segments would close by the difference (a^1-a) before physical contact, and the field thermal-expansion coefficient would be smaller than the laboratory by an amount related to the (a^1-a) dimension for each joint. Thus in situ fracture mapping efforts may be required in heater experiments to support model validation efforts.

This discussion on thermal-expansion effects would be incomplete without an analysis of those effects on the block. The layout of the 3-m-long heaters relative to the block probably contributed to the development of the fracture at the 2-m depth. The development of the fracture at the 0.3 m depth was likely due to the uneven surface of the block and to the presence of a pumice-filled cavity, as explained in Zimmerman et al 1984, and is not judged to be a thermomechanical effect. Two-dimensional, plane-strain, finite-element calculations have shown that the difference in boundary and block centerline temperatures in thermal cycle 1 (30°C) could cause tensile stress increases on the order of 3 MPa on a horizontal plane near the bottom of the flatjacks, assuming there was no coupling of the vertical surface of the block to the opposite surface nearer the heaters. Even though friction reducers were used, it is probable that additional tensile stresses were induced because the flatjacks were at their maximum pressure for that cycle. Additional flatjack coupling stresses could increase the block tensile stresses to near the laboratory tensile failure value that ranged from 7.5 to 10.6 MPa. Indirect "Brazilian" tension tests on heated block core samples showed this. Thermally induced fracture potentials should be a factor in designing future heated-block experiments.

6.2 Fracture Permeability

Figure 3 presents the fracture permeability data as a function of time and flow path. Flatjack pressures and temperatures are shown to aid in the analyses. Permeability measurements were made at select times to record responses to the variable temperatures and pressures. The data were calculated using methods discussed by Hardin et al. 1981.

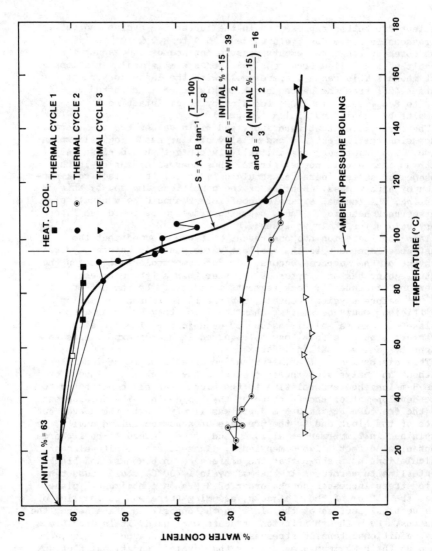

Figure 4 Neutron Probe Water Content Measurements vs Temperature of 1.0 m Depth

The data show that the permeabilities along the two flow paths
varied considerably at unloaded conditions. The data suggest that
the fracture did not open uniformly and that the 2-1 path opened
more than the 2-3 path. Once the FIP was applied, the permeability
changes were generally insensitive to stress changes, as reported by
Zimmerman et al. 1984, and the trend was for a slightly reduced
fracture permeabilities at higher temperatures. This is the same
trend observed for a granite block as reported by Hardin et al.
1981, and the reason given is that the fracture asperities are more
compatible at higher temperatures; hence, fracture permeabilities
were reduced. The fracture appeared to be close approaching its
initial pre-excavated value as the thermal cycling progressed.

The significance of the fracture permeability data is that the
permeabilities are only moderately sensitive to the coupled effects
of stress and temperature. The entire range of variation is within
one order of magnitude; this information can be used to estimate
sensitivities of fractured welded tuffs to hypothetical flow
scenarios in performance assessment studies.

6.3 Moisture Changes

Representative moisture content changes, as measured with a neutron
probe, are shown in Figure 4. Data shown were taken at a depth of
1 m at the location shown in Figure 2 and represent a cumulative
record of over eight months of measurements. Initial water contents
ranged from 55% near the surface to over 75% at a depth of 2 m.
Once the temperatures exceeded nominal boiling, 94°C, the moisture
content changes for all depths followed the trend of the data
shown. An empirical equation has been fit to the data for that
depth in Figure 4 to quantify the high rate of water loss near
100°C. The equation can be adjusted to account for the initial conditions. The lower water content limit of 15% appears to be a measurement restraint and further testing is planned to determine if
this is an actual limit.

7 CONCLUSIONS

The measurements in the G-Tunnel heated block showed
   (1) The thermal-expansion coefficient for constant stress temper-
        ature increases had a range of 5.0 to 8.7 x 10^{-6}°C^{-1}, and
        values compared well with a laboratory range of 6.4 to 8.0 x
        10^{-6}°C^{-1}.
   (2) Single-fracture permeabilities were relatively insensitive to
        stress and slightly sensitive to temperature increases under
        representative in situ conditions. Excavation effects showed
        the most influences. The measurements ranged from 49 to
        956 x 10^{-8} cm^2.
   (3) Moisture contents varied from 55-75% saturation before heat-
        ing to 15% after heating as measured with a neutron probe.
        There was a pronounced temperature dependence above 90°C.

8 REFERENCES

Zimmerman, R. M., Board, M. P., Hardin, E. H., and Voegele, M. D.
   1984, "Ambient Temperature Testing of the G-Tunnel Heated Block,"

Proceedings 25th U. S. Symposium on Rock Mechanics, Evanston, Ill.

Hardin, E. H., Barton, N., Lingle, D., Board, M. P., and Voegele, M. D., 1981, "A Heated Flatjack Test Series to Measure the Thermo-mechanical and Transport Properties of In Situ Rock Masses (Heated-Block Test)," TR81-88, Terra Tek Report for Office of Nuclear Waste Isolation, Contract E 512-04700, Salt Lake City, Utah.

Lappin, A. R. and Nimick, F. B. In prep. "Thermal Properties of the Grouse Canyon Member of the Belted Range Tuff and of Tunnel Bed 5, G-Tunnel, Nevada Test Site," SAND82-2203, Sandia National Labora-tories, Albuquerque, New Mexico.

9 ACKNOWLEDGEMENTS

The authors are indebted to others for their many contributions to this effort. At SNL contributions by C. A. Denney, J. E. Van Meter and J. J. Bradshaw are gratefully acknowledged. D. Mason from EG&G provided invaluable assistance with the data acquisition and proces-sing.

Analysis of a loading test on a large basalt block

ROGER D.HART & PETER A.CUNDALL
Itasca Consulting Group Inc., Minneapolis, Minnesota, USA
MICHAEL L.CRAMER
Basalt Waste Isolation Project, Rockwell Hanford Operations, Richland, Washington, USA

1 ABSTRACT

A comprehensive analysis program has been applied to the evaluation of data generated during triaxial loading of a large-scale block of jointed basalt. The intent of this program was to develop a logical approach for evaluating both elastic and inelastic behavior observed during the test. A statistically-based technique for data analysis was developed to quantify the elastic behavior, and the two-dimensional Universal Distinct Element Code (UDEC) was used to investigate how rock joint characteristics affect the observed response. Through this approach explanations are postulated for the distinctive features of the deformational response evident from the block test results.

An important conclusion of the analysis is that a complex deformation mechanism may be attributed to the hexagonal shape of the columnar basalt. Consequently, this investigation is considered to form a basis for development of a three-dimensional mathematical characterization of the basalt rock mass behavior which incorporates the anisotropic and inelastic influence of the joint structure on the rock mass properties.

2 INTRODUCTION

The large-scale block test conducted at the Hanford site in southeastern Washington is designed to characterize the rock mass behavior of closely jointed basalt. The test was performed by the Basalt Waste Isolation Project, as part of the geomechanics characterization of a proposed nuclear waste repository site.

The deformational behavior of the closely-jointed basalt is recognized as an important design parameter which may influence several design components such as the stability of shafts, determination of optimum room shapes, and design of tunnel support requirements. The high joint frequency produces deformation behavior of the rock mass which is significantly different from that of the intact material. The large-scale block test provides a means for investigating the influence of the frequency, orientation and deformability of the joints.

The test was located at the Near-Surface Test Facility in the Pomona basalt flow at a depth of 50 meters. The rock at the test site is distinguished by undulating, well-developed hexagonal basalt columns which have almost vertical inclination and are approximately

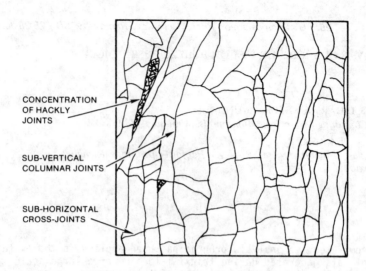

CONCENTRATION
OF HACKLY
JOINTS

SUB-VERTICAL
COLUMNAR JOINTS

SUB-HORIZONTAL
CROSS-JOINTS

Fig. 1 Mapped Jointing Pattern

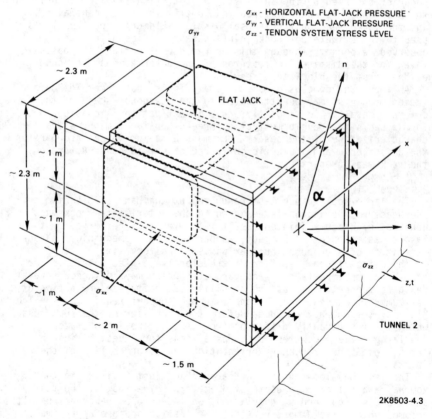

σ_{xx} - HORIZONTAL FLAT-JACK PRESSURE
σ_{yy} - VERTICAL FLAT-JACK PRESSURE
σ_{zz} - TENDON SYSTEM STRESS LEVEL

FIGURE 2. GENERAL LAYOUT OF BLOCK TEST

2K8503-4.3

760

20 cm in diameter. A set of subhorizontal joints subdivides the columnar joints and occasionally extends through two or more columns. A complete description of the actual joint structure within the test block can only be surmised from limited surface joint mapping and boring logs. A representation of the jointing patterns exposed at the test site is shown in Fig. 1.

The block test loading series consists of 26 ambient temperature loading/unloading cycles. The test geometry and construction is described by Cramer and Black (1983), and the layout of the test is shown in Fig. 2. A load/unload cycle involves the application of an equal, constant load in two directions while cycling the load in the third direction. This is repeated for all three loading directions at several confining stress levels. Deformations are monitored in the block by use of extensometers and an electro-optical displacement measuring device developed specifically for this project. An example stress-strain plot from a load cycle test is shown in Fig. 3.

A significant amount of inelastic behavior is observed during the loading cycle. This behavior occurs even though the applied loads are low (not exceeding 12.5 MPa) and the resulting strains in the block are very small (on the order of 10^{-4}). Five features of the deformational response are evident from the results:

- anisotropy in modulus values measured in the three orthogonal directions of loading;
- linearity in the deformational response during loading;
- an increase in deformation modulus with confining stress;
- a high degree of hysteresis in the loading/unloading cycles which is not significantly reduced upon recycling; and
- a significantly stiffer response in the rear portion of the block compared to the front, measured in the axial (z-) direction during horizontal (x-) direction loading only.

3 BASIS OF ANALYSIS

The basis for this analysis is the assumption that the nature of the observed deformational response of the block test can be explained in terms of the characteristics of the joint structure in the basalt rock mass. A preliminary assessment of the block test data lead to the following assumptions concerning the effect of the joint structure:

(1) The pattern of jointing and the anisotropy in deformational response indicate transversely isotropic behavior of the rock mass, with the axis of anisotropy parallel to the axis of the basalt columns.

(2) The low level of applied loading and the high degree of hysteresis in the stress-strain data suggest that the deformational response can be described in terms of an elastic component, due to elastic deformation of the intact rock and elastic movement along joints, and an inelastic component, due only to inelastic movement (slip and separation) along joints.

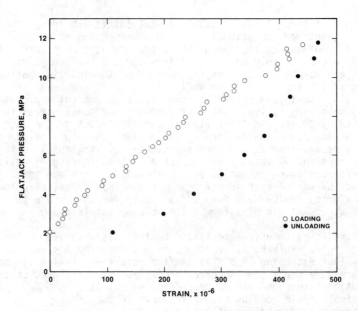

Fig. 3   Block Test Results for Load Cycling in the Horizontal
Direction (Vertical and Axial Direction Loads = 5 MPa)

The experimental data demonstrate a strongly-hysteretic stress-
strain response which is markedly similar to that produced by a simple conceptual model of a rock specimen containing a single crack,
first reported by Brady et al (1984). In this model, the stress-
strain curve is idealized by three components: a loading segment
and two unloading segments. The response of the model features
loading with elastic deformation and slip, initial loading without
slip, and final unloading, again with elastic deformation and
slip. Two important insights are gained from this simple analysis:
   (1) The load/unload cycle is accompanied by hysteresis.
   (2) Only in the initial stage of unloading is it possi-
        ble to observe the true elastic behavior of the
        rock specimen and suppress the inelastic effect of
        the crack.
In the block test analysis, therefore, useful information on the
equivalent elastic properties of the rock mass is recovered by a
selective analysis of the data set generated during initial unloading of the block. Inelastic response related to the joint inelastic
behavior can then be evaluated separately. The composite effect of
both the elastic and inelastic behavior is assumed to produce the
type of response observed in the test.
   This rationale provides the basis for the formulation of a program to evaluate the data and give some understanding of the effect
of the basalt joint structure. In the first phase, a statistical
data analysis technique is used to derive transversely isotropic
elastic parameters which best-fit the elastic component. This analysis also allows correlation of the best-fit solution to the dip
angle of the subvertical basalt columns so that some confidence can

762

be attached to the estimated values. In the second phase, the
Universal Distinct Element Code (UDEC) is used to evaluate the
influence of the joint structure. Results from both phases of the
analysis, in conjunction with laboratory properties of intact basalt
and basalt joints, are used to assess the deformational response of
the block test.

4 ASSESSMENT OF THE BLOCK TEST RESPONSE TO A LOAD CYCLE
4.1 Elastic behavior
    The analysis of the elastic response of the block test leads to
two findings. First, a set of transversely isotropic elastic parameters which are physically realistic can be derived from the
initial unloading data. Second, realistic estimates can be made for
elastic stiffness values of the joints based on the derived elastic
parameters and the average measured joint spacings in the block.
    The Singular Value Decomposition (SVD) Method [see Forsythe,
Malcolm and Moler (1977)] was used to derive the elastic parameters
from the known stresses and strains. The SVD Method is particularly
suitable for ill-conditioned problems typically encountered in
least-squares regression analysis. The stresses and strains were
produced from the best-fit slopes to the initial unloading portion
of statistically-acceptable data sets (coefficient of determination
>0.36 (Richards, 1970)). Confidence in the solution was then based
on this correlation requirement and the redundancy in the measurements.
    The direction normal to the plane of isotropy was anticipated to
coincide with the dip angle of the subvertical columnar jointing,
establishing the composite effect of this joint set. The dip angle
direction is represented by the n-axis and the plane of isotropy by
the s, t plane in Fig. 2. The angle of dip is denoted as α in this
figure. The five elastic constants describing transverse isotropy
are defined with reference to these axes.
    Equations relating stresses and strains for a transversely iso-
tropic material are given by Lekhnitskii (1981, pp. 37-38). The
orientation of the measurement legs in the test block provided sufficient independent measurements to permit the determination of only
four of the five elastic constants. Therefore, the approximate formula given by Lekhnitskii (1981, p. 60), relating shear modulus to
modulus of elasticity parallel and normal to the plane of isotropy,
was used to reduce the number of unknowns from five to four. Using
transformation techniques, measured strains and applied loads were
rotated in terms of α to the n, s and t axes. The regression analysis was then performed to derive estimates for the five elastic
constants at a prescribed dip angle.
    The analysis was applied for a range of dip angles, and the
elastic constants which best fit the composite of the statistically-
acceptable unloading slopes were found to correspond to dip angles
between approximately 60° and 80°. These angles are slightly lower
than the average dip angle of 85° measured at the test site.
Table 1 summarizes the best-fit elastic constants calculated for dip
angles of 60° and 80°. Both sets of elastic constants satisfy
"positive definite" criteria (Pickering, 1970) for physically-
realistic parameters. The moduli are also lower than the labora-
tory-measured intact modulus of basalt (approximately 87 GPa).

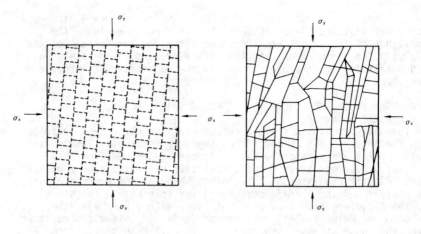

FIGURE 4. PATTERN 1 -
ORTHOGONAL
JOINT SETS

FIGURE 5. PATTERN 2 -
MODEL OF
MAPPED JOINTS

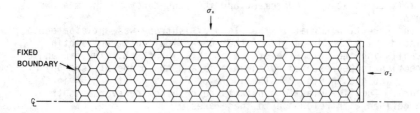

FIGURE 6. PATTERN 3 - HEXAGONAL PATTERN, ORIENTATION A

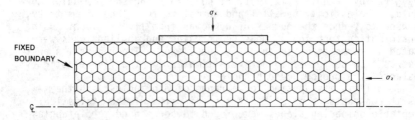

FIGURE 7. PATTERN 4 - HEXAGONAL PATTERN, ORIENTATION B

2K8503-4.1

Table 1. Best-Fit Transversely Isotropic Elastic Constants

Dip Angle	E_n	E	G_{sn}	ν_{sn}	ν_{st}
60°	52.6	41.9	20.4	0.16	0.34
80°	42.7	35.1	15.3	0.29	0.20

Estimations for joint stiffness properties were derived by making use of the equations for continuum characterization of jointed rock given by Singh (1973). These equations relate transversely isotropic elastic rock mass properties to orthogonal joint sets with staggered cross joints. The average joint spacings were assumed to be 20 cm for both the subvertical and subhorizontal joint sets. The estimated normal and shear joint stiffnesses are given in Table 2. Measured joint stiffnesses from laboratory tests are presently being evaluated for comparison to the estimated values.

4.2 Inelastic behavior

The basalt block did not respond in a simple way to the applied loading and unloading tests: it exhibited hysteresis, non-uniform strain distribution and stress-dependent stiffness. Because these effects were suspected to be associated with joints rather than intact material, a series of numerical tests on jointed samples was planned. However, the effects noted above are not necessarily reproduced simply by including the usual elastic-plastic joints, particularly at low strain levels, when most joints may remain below their slip threshold. There appears to be at least three ways in which joints can introduce non-uniformity and hysteresis:

(1) The orientation and position of joints is such that local stress concentrations are sufficient to allow slip during loading.

(2) Individual joints exhibit continuous yielding and hysteretic behavior at all stress levels.

(3) In-situ stress concentrations existed in the block before cutting. Although these concentrations vanish when the block is detached from the host rock, they may reappear when it is reloaded because of a consequent lack-of-fit.

Only the first item, and to some extent the second, was examined. Furthermore, the analyses were performed in two dimensions, whereas three-dimensional effects undoubtably exist. The precise locations of all discontinuities in the block are unknown, but the general nature of the jointing pattern is known. For the numerical simulations, jointing patterns were generated that correspond to two sections through the block. Four of these patterns are reproduced in Figs. 4-7.

All numerical tests were performed with UDEC (Cundall, 1980; Cundall and Hart, 1983). UDEC can simulate the behavior of discontinuous rock subjected to varying mechanical loading and allows

Table 2. Estimated Joint Stiffness Values

Joint Stiffness (GPa/m)	Subhorizontal		Subvertical	
	60°	80°	60°	80°
Normal	531.9	350.7	395.9	289.8
Shear	438.8	238.6	438.8	238.6

relevant joint characteristics to be specified directly. Owing to the incomplete nature of the simulation, exact correspondence of physical and numerical results are not expected; rather, we are trying to find a hypothesis for behavior that is consistent with observation.

Joint stiffness properties used in the simulations are shown in Table 2 for a dip angle of 60°. Values assumed for joint friction

765

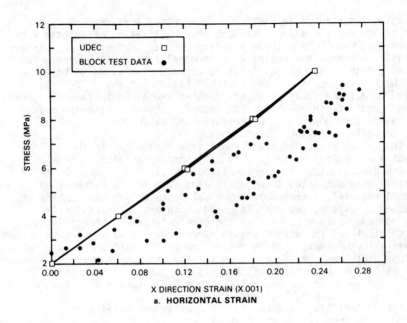

a. **HORIZONTAL STRAIN**

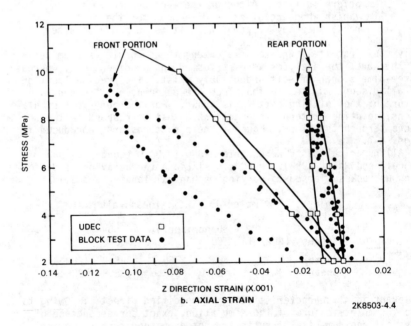

b. **AXIAL STRAIN**

2K8503-4.4

FIGURE 8. LOAD CYCLE IN X-DIRECTION OF PATTERN 3 MODEL
(WITH COMPARISON TO BLOCK TEST DATA)

angle (47°) and intact rock elastic modulus and Poisson's ratio
(89 GPA and 0.26, respectively) were based upon reported laboratory
values.
　The mechanical loading is simulated by directionally-applied
stresses at the model boundary. For each load cycle, the stress in
one direction was held constant at either 2.5 MPa or 5 MPa, while
the stress in the other direction was increased in 2 MPa increments
from 2 MPa to 10 MPa and then decreased back to 2 MPa.
　In all the results from tests on patterns 1 and 2, for the given
value of friction, very little or no slip or opening was observed,
and hence no hysteresis. Only by repeating the tests with an unrea-
sonably low value of friction was hysteresis induced. It appears
that the field observations cannot be explained by mechanisms
occurring in the plane corresponding to patterns 1 and 2.
　In contrast, the tests on patterns 3 and 4 induced slip and opening and significant hysteresis, normal to the direction of the
cycled load (Fig. 8). Furthermore, the responses at the front and
rear measuring stations were markedly different, and in the same
sense as observed in the field. Although some details differ, the
general behavior in the simulation resembles that of the field
test. Fig. 9 demonstrates that the deformation occurs through a
mechanism involving coherent rotations of hexagonal blocks. This
mechanism appears to be largely responsible for the anomalous
behavior in the block test.
　Some limited tests were done with a constitutive model for joints
that allows continuous yielding: as expected, hysteresis was
increased both parallel and normal to the cycled load.

5 Characterization of basalt
　The major contribution of this study to the understanding of
basalt deformational behavior is the realization that an adequate
mechanical description of the basalt rock mass must take account of
the mechanisms associated with rotation and slip of the basalt
columns. Also, it appears that non-linearity and non-uniformity can
occur at very low strain levels, even though the assumed joint law
is very simple. With a more realistic law, and perhaps by including

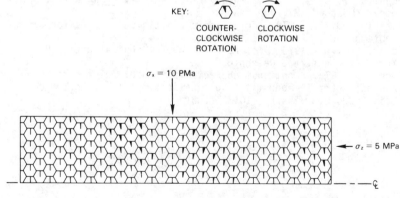

KEY:　　COUNTER-　　CLOCKWISE
　　　　CLOCKWISE　ROTATION
　　　　ROTATION

$\sigma_x = 10$ PMa

$\sigma_z = 5$ MPa

FIGURE 9. HEXAGON ROTATIONS FOR PATTERN 3 (THICKEST
　　　　　WEDGE IS MAXIMUM ROTATION)

2K8503-4.2

initial locked-in stresses, it is believed that the correspondence with observation will be further improved.

In order to arrive at a full three dimensional model for basalt rock mass, future work should include numerical tests performed on representative samples of the blocky material. A similar approach is taken by Cundall and Strack (1983) in describing granular material. The resulting continuum model can then be used in a 3-D finite difference or finite element code to simulate the boundary value problems associated with mining, tunneling and long-term stability of repositories. The use of a 3-D jointed block program to model a full repository may be uneconomic, and unnecessary if a good constitutive model for the rock mass is developed.

6 References

Brady, B. H. G., M. L. Cramer, and R. D. Hart. 1984. Preliminary analysis of a loading test on a large basalt rock. RHO-BW-SH-432 P. Rockwell Hanford operations, Richland, Washington. Technical note submitted for publ., Int. J. Rock Mech. Min. Sci. & Geomech. Abstr.

Cramer, M. L., and M. T. Black. 1983. The design and construction of a block test in closely jointed rock. In Proc. 24th U.S. Symp. Rock Mech.

Cundall, P. A. 1980. UDEC - A generalized distinct element program for modelling jointed rock," U.S. Army Contract DAJA37-79-C-0548, European Research Off.

Cundall, P. A., and O. D. L. Strack. 1983. Modeling of microscopic mechanisms in granular material. In Materials: new models and constitutive relations. Amsterdam: Elsevier Scientific Publications, B.V.

Cundall, P. A., and R. D. Hart. 1983. Development of generalized 2-D and 3-D distinct element programs for modeling jointed rock," Contract DACA 39-82-C-0015, U.S. Army Engineering Corps WES, Vicksburg, Miss.

Forsythe, G. E., M. A. Malcolm, and C. B. Moler. 1977. Computer methods for mathematical computations. Englewood Cliffs, N.J.: Prentice-Hall, Inc.

Lekhnitskii, S. G. 1981. Theory of elasticity of an anisotropic body. Moscow: Mir Publishers.

Pickering, D. J. 1970. Anisotropic elastic parameters for soil. Geotechnique. 20(3):271-176.

Richards, J. W. 1970. Interpretation of technical data. New York: Van Nostrand-Reinhold.

Singh, B. 1973. Continuum characterization of jointed rock masses: part 1 - constitutive equations. Int. J. Rock Mech. Min. Sci. & Geomech. Abstr. 10:311-335.

The use of field data to evaluate and improve drift response models for the Waste Isolation Pilot Plant (WIPP)*

HAROLD S.MORGAN, CHARLES M.STONE & RAYMOND D.KRIEG
Applied Mechanics Division I, Sandia National Laboratories, Albuquerque, New Mexico, USA

INTRODUCTION

The Waste Isolation Pilot Plant (WIPP) is currently being excavated near Carlsbad, New Mexico by the U. S. Department of Energy as a research and development facility to demonstrate the safe disposal of defense generated radioactive waste in bedded salt. Structural response data collected from underground rooms and drifts at the WIPP will ultimately be used to evaluate and improve computational models for predicting time dependent room deformations caused by salt creep. An initial evaluation, based on a comparison of computed and measured room closures for one of the early WIPP excavations known as the South Drift. has already been completed (Morgan et al 1985). Some of the highlights of that evaluation are presented in this paper. First the finite element model used to compute the response of the South Drift is described Then closure measurements from the South Drift are presented, and comparisons with the calculations are made. Attempts to resolve the resulting discrepancies are summarized next, and finally some directions for future work are offered.

COMPUTATIONAL MODEL

Structural modeling for WIPP has been an evolutionary process which began long before field data became available for comparison. The models will continue to be refined throughout the project's lifetime with the ultimate goal being to develop a modeling capability founded on sound mechanics principles and transferable to other salt repositories. At the time of the South Drift comparison, information from several sources formed the basis for the models. Results from laboratory tests on core samples provided material properties; core analyses provided the stratigraphy, design and excavation plans provided geometrical configurations, and computational parametric studies provided assurance that proper boundary and initial conditions had been chosen. Data from each of these sources were not obtained independently but rather as part of an integrated research and development program. That is, knowledge of the stratigraphy impacted both material testing and room location; material testing helped determine room geometry, room geometry helped determine stress levels for material testing; and so forth. The

*This work was supported by the U. S. Department of Energy under contract number DE-AC04-76DP00789

concepts of a reference stratigraphy and reference material properties
were adopted so that a consistent set of parameters could be used by all
project participants involved in modeling (Krieg 1984). The reference
stratigraphy and properties have been updated periodically as new and
better information has become available. The structural model presented
here represented the state of the art when the South Drift was analyzed.

The South Drift, as shown in Figure 1, extends southward from the
exploratory shaft for a distance of 1.12 km (3664 ft) to the southern
extreme of the site. It was excavated in December 1982 through January
1983, and no other mining activity occurred in the area until the summer
of 1984. The main purpose for mining the South Drift was to examine the
geologic formation from one end of the site to the other. The drift's
value as a source of data for model evaluations was also recognized as
indicated by the instrumentation that was provided. Technology
experiments in the northern portion of the WIPP site, as shown in
Figure 1, were designed to provide most of the data for comparisons to
predictions (Matalucci et al 1983). However, the South Drift with its
two-dimensionality and isolation from other excavations provided the
first opportunity to compare WIPP models to field data.

The two dimensional plane strain model used to analyze the South Drift
is shown in Figure 2. The drift is 7.62 m (25 ft) wide by 2.44 m (8 ft)
high with the floor located 653.42 m (2144 ft) beneath the surface. Only
half of the drift is shown in Figure 2 as the left boundary represents a
symmetry plane along which horizontal displacements are zero. Horizontal

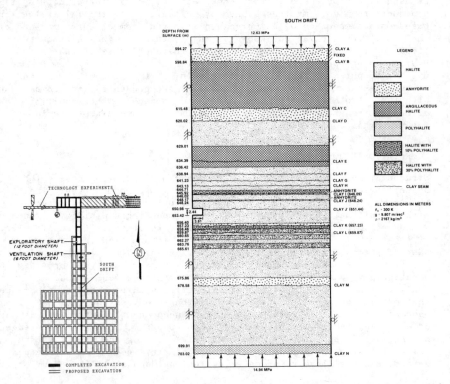

Figure 1. Plan
view of the WIPP.

Figure 2. Two-dimensional plane strain model
of the South Drift.

displacements are also zero along the right boundary which was chosen to be 50 m away. The results of a parametric study on boundary effects indicated that this distance between boundaries was adequate for modeling a single isolated room. Vertical displacements are constrained to be zero along the right boundary at the uppermost anhydrite location so that the boundary value problem is properly defined with unique rigid body motions in the vertical direction. Overburden pressures of 12.63 MPa (1832 psi) and 14.94 MPa (2167 psi) are applied to the top and bottom boundaries, respectively, which are approximately 50 m above and below the drift. A density of 2167 kg/m^3 was assumed for all rock layers in computing these tractions. This density was also used to compute gravitational body forces for each finite element location and to compute the initial stress state which is hydrostatic and varies linearly with depth. The reference stratigraphy at the time of the South Drift calculations consisted of layers of halite, argillaceous halite, halite with 10% polyhalite, halite with 30% polyhalite, anhydrite, polyhalite, and clay as shown in Figure 2. All layers containing halite were modeled as materials which undergo elastic bulk strains and a combination of elastic and secondary creep deviatoric (shear) strains. Primary creep was not included. Components of the total deviatoric strain rate $\dot{\varepsilon}_{ij}$ are expressed in terms of the deviatoric stress rate components $\dot{s}_{ij}$, the deviatoric stresses s_{ij}, and the magnitude of the deviatoric stresses $|s_{ij}|$ as

$$\dot{\varepsilon}_{ij} = \dot{s}_{ij}/(2G) + (\sqrt{1.5})^{n+1} D \exp[-Q/(RT)]s_{ij}|s_{ij}|^{n-1} \qquad (1)$$

where G is the elastic shear modulus, T is the absolute temperature (300 K for this problem), Q is the activation energy of 12 kcal/mole, R is the universal gas constant of 1.987 cal/mole-K, and D and n are material constants. The two terms on the right side of Eq.(1) represent the elastic and secondary creep strain rates, respectively. Details of this constitutive model are given elsewhere (Krieg 1984). The anhydrite layers and the polyhalite layer at the bottom of the configuration in Figure 2 were modeled as elastic materials which do not creep. Material properties for all layers are given in Table 1. Clay seams in the stratigraphy are extremely thin and have low shear strengths. Nevertheless, they are important structurally because they represent interfaces along which adjoining rock layers can slip with respect to each other. Thus, clay layers I, J, J', K, and L in Figure 2 were modeled computationally as slide lines along which frictional slip could occur. The other clay layers were found to have little effect on South Drift response and were neglected. A coefficient of friction of 0.4 was used for all slide lines. SANCHO, a finite element code developed for WIPP, (Stone et al 1984) was used to compute the South Drift response.

Table 1. Material properties used in the South Drift analysis.

Material	Bulk Modulus (GPa)	Shear Modulus (GPa)	Secondary Creep Parameters D (Pa$^{-4.9}$ - sec^{-1})	n
Halite	20.7	12.4	5.79E-36	4.9
Argillaceous halite	20.7	12.4	1.16E-35	4.9
Halite with 10% polyhalite	22.2	12.9	5.21E-36	4.9
Halite with 30% polyhalite	26.1	14.0	4.05E-36	4.9
Anhydrite	83.4	27.8	–	–
Polyhalite	65.8	20.3	–	–

Horizontal (rib-to-rib) and vertical (floor-to-ceiling) closures were measured at more than 10 different stations along the length of the South Drift. However, for each closure station, a time period ranging from two to as many as 26 days had usually elapsed between the end of excavation and the initial closure measurement. The exception was station S1246 where a measurement was made on the day of excavation. As a result, significant early time closures were not measured except at S1246. Failure to account for these early closures can lead to erroneous conclusions when data and calculations are compared. Figures 3 and 4 are used to show the consequences of not providing for them. Horizontal closures from various stations in the South Drift are plotted in Figure 3 as functions of the time from the initial measurement. Data are often presented in this manner with no provisions for missed early time

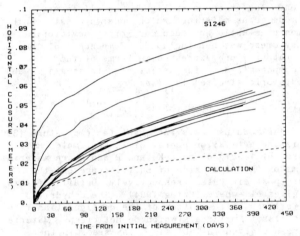

Figure 3. South Drift closure versus time from initial measurement.

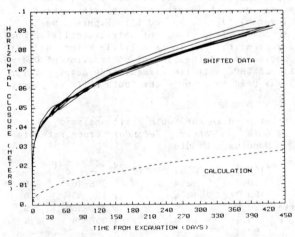

Figure 4. South Drift closure versus time from excavation.

772

closures. The largest closures in Figure 3 are obviously associated
with station S1246 where almost no data were missed. Significantly
smaller closures are observed for the other stations where various
amounts of the early time data are missing. If the data in Figure 3 were
analyzed without knowledge of the missing early time measurements, one
could easily conclude that closure varied considerably along the length
of the South Drift and could thus infer that a two-dimensional plane
strain model was inappropriate. At the same time, however, the closure
computed with the two-dimensional model, shown by the dashed line in
Figure 3, matches most of the data reasonably well at early times and is
off by less than a factor of two at later times. Entirely different
conclusions are drawn when the data are presented as shown in Figure 4.
In this figure, closure is plotted in terms of days from excavation, and
the early time data from station S1246 is used to estimate the closure
missing from the other histories and to shift them upward. When
presented in this manner, closure measurements are extremely uniform
along the length of the drift but are substantially larger (almost four
times) than the computed closures. Rate of horizontal closure data,
which do not require provisions for missed early time measurements, also
show uniformity along the drift and are about three times larger than
computed rates. Comparisons of measured and computed vertical closure
rates show a similar discrepancy. Thus, the conclusions drawn from
Figure 4 rather than those for Figure 3 appear to be the proper
interpretation of the data. Unfortunately, closure data cannot always
be presented as shown in Figure 4 because early time measurements from
at least one closure station are required. As a case in point, vertical
closure data for the South Drift are not presented here because no early
measurements were made at any closure station.

The comparison of computed and measured closures in Figure 4, although
somewhat disturbing, initiates another stage in the model development
process, namely that of determining the reason (or reasons) for the
discrepancy between the measured and computed behavior. This stage is
not simple because the model for the South Drift is extremely complex
with many parameters as possible sources of error. In the next step of
the analysis, most of these sources were examined individually through
model parameter variations. Due to the nonlinearity of the closure
curves in Figure 4, some of the variations produced better agreement
with the data at the early times and worse agreement at the later times
or vice versa. Thus, before judgments could be made on any parameter
change, the question of what constituted good agreement with the data
also had to be addressed.

This question was difficult to answer until the data were presented in
a third manner with the closure histories plotted on logarithmic scales
as shown in Figure 5. In this figure, the log closure versus log time
curves for both the data and the calculation are almost linear with
slopes of approximately 0.3 and 0.4, respectively. This observation has
several important implications. One is that closure may be a function
of time raised to a power defined by the slope. Other investigators
(Fernandez and Hendron 1984) have made similar observations about
borehole closure data for salt from other sites. However, they
concluded, presumably without performing the appropriate calculation,
that the use of a purely secondary creep model was not valid for
borehole or drift calculations because the resulting log closure – log
time curve would have a slope of 1.0 since strain is linear with time in
secondary creep. The computed closure curve in Figure 5 clearly shows
that the WIPP reference constitutive model with only secondary creep
produces a logarithmic closure history with a slope of much less than

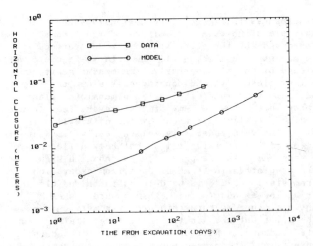

Figure 5. Closure histories plotted on logarithmic scales.

one. The reason for this is that drift and borehole problems do not
involve pure creep but a combination of creep and creep relaxation where
the stress state is always changing. The linearity of the logarithmic
closure histories in Figure 5 also provides an easy means of
extrapolating data into the future. Extrapolation from the logarithmic
histories is must less uncertain than extrapolation from the nonlinear
histories in Figure 4 for which many different final slope estimates can
be made. For example, extrapolation suggests that the computed and
measured closure curves in Figure 5 will intersect at approximately
ninety years. This prediction is almost impossible to make from Figure
4. Finally, the log-log closure histories in Figure 5 suggest that the
appropriate parameter changes for the South Drift model are those which
raise the vertical position of the computed history and reduce its slope
to that of the data. This observation became our criterion for
evaluating parameter variations.

MODEL VARIATIONS

Over thirty calculations have been performed in investigating the
discrepancy between computed and measured closures. Usually only one
parameter in the South Drift model was varied per calculation.
Variations to the boundary conditions, the initial stress state, and the
properties of all materials in the stratigraphy were considered.
Physical justification for a specific parameter change was to be
deferred until parameters producing the appropriate changes in the
closure history had been identified. Discussion of each model variation
is impossible in a paper of this length so the details are provided
elsewhere (Morgan 1985). Instead only a few of the changes which help
to illustrate the conclusions of the study are presented.

Logarithmic plots of closure histories obtained (1) by changing the
clay seam coefficient of friction from 0.4 to 0.0, (2) by reducing the
strength and hence stiffness of the anhydrite layers, and (3) by
using a borehole configuration rather than a drift configuration are

774

shown in Figure 6 along with the history computed with the baseline model and the South Drift data. These changes are related in that only non-salt parameters are involved. The corresponding closure curves in Figure 6 differ only in their vertical position on the plot. That is, they all have the same slope. This seems to imply that model changes not associated with the salt properties cannot totally account for the discrepancy between the data and baseline model.

The results of a few of the variations to the salt properties are shown in Figure 7. The new curves in this figure are associated with (1) a reduction in the shear modulus, (2) a reduction in the shear modulus plus the addition of primary creep to the creep law, (3) an increase in the constant D in the secondary creep law (Eq. 1), and (4) a two mechanism secondary creep law in which the power law exponent is switched from 4.9 to 1.0 when the stresses become extremely low. Each of these salt property change produces a change in the slope of the

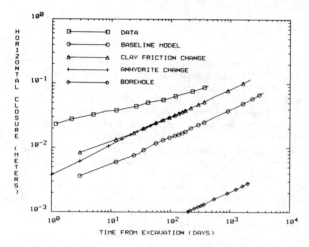

Figure 6. Closures associated with non-salt parameter changes.

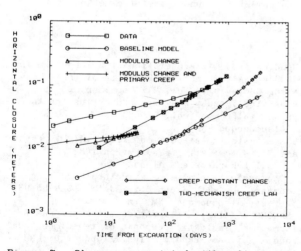

Figure 7. Closures associated with salt property variations.

775

corresponding logarithmic closure history as well as a shift in its
vertical position. The shear modulus reduction and the combination of
the shear modulus reduction with the addition of primary creep both
produce closure histories with slopes closer to the slope of the data.
However, the effects of primary creep soon die out. Changing the
secondary creep constant D and the use of the two mechanism model
increase the slope and thus do not improve agreement with the data. This
is an important observation because a change to the secondary creep
constant is often advocated as the quickest and easiest way to obtain
agreement with data. Another important observation is that none of the
changes shown in Figure 7 results in good agreement with the data. In
fact, even when the most promising salt property variations are combined
with the most promising non-salt parameter variations, the computed and
measured closures are still significantly different. This seems to
imply that some important phenomenon or phenomena, yet to be identified,
are missing from the model.

CONCLUDING REMARKS

The results presented in this paper indicate that a significant
unresolved discrepancy exists between computed and measured closures for
the South Drift. However, the results also indicate that a great deal
has been learned about WIPP computational models and about the
characteristics of the discrepancy. This knowledge will guide future
investigations which will involve an even larger data base provided by
the WIPP in situ experiments. Some modeling issues which still need to
be addressed include other elastic property variations, microcracking of
the salt, and alternate forms of the creep law. Any future
investigation must proceed in accordance with the ultimate goal of the
WIPP modeling program which is to to develop a modeling capability that
is transferable from one salt site to another without a priori knowledge
of room response at the new site. Attaining this goal requires models
based on sound physics. Obviously, parameters could be introduced into
the model to fit a computed closure to South Drift data. However,
unless such curve fitting parameters can be explained physically, they
fail to meet the WIPP requirement of sound scientific methodology.

REFERENCES

Fernandez, G. and A.J. Hendron 1984. Interpretation of a long-term in
    situ borehole test in a deep salt formation. Bulletin of the
    Association of Engineering Geologists. Vol. 21, No. 1, p. 23-38.
Krieg, R.D. 1984. Reference stratigraphy and rock properties for the
    Waste Isolation Pilot Plant (WIPP) project. SAND83-1908. Sandia
    National Laboratories, Albuquerque, NM.
Matalucci, R.V. et al 1982. Waste Isolation Pilot Plant (WIPP) research
    and development program: in situ testing plan, March 1982.
    SAND81-2628. Sandia National Laboratories, Albuquerque, NM.
Morgan, H.S. et al 1985. An evaluation of WIPP structural modeling
    capabilities based on comparisons with South Drift data. SAND85-0323.
    Sandia National Laboratories, Albuquerque, NM, in draft.
Stone, C.M. et al 1985. SANCHO - A finite element computer program for
    quasistatic, large deformation, inelastic response of two-dimensional
    solids. SAND84-2618. Sandia National Laboratories, Albuquerque, NM.

In-situ load-deformation characterization
of the CSM/OCRD jointed test block

A.M.RICHARDSON, W.HUSTRULID & S.BROWN
Colorado School of Mines, Golden, USA
W.UBBES
Battelle Project Management Division, Columbus, Ohio, USA

1 INTRODUCTION

An extensive ambient-temperature test series has recently been completed on a block of Precambrian Gneiss at the Colorado School of Mines
(CSM) Experimental Mine in Idaho Springs, Colorado. Block tests came
into existence out of a desire to test a relatively large volume of
rock and thereby minimize the scaling problems encountered when laboratory test results are used to obtain modeling parameters for full-size
structures. A typical block test involves isolation of a large, approximately two-meter cube of rock by cutting slots on four sides and inser-
ting flatjacks for loading. Much interest has recently centered around
block tests as a promising method for in-situ characterization of rock-
masses for licensing future commercial nuclear-waste repositories in
crystalline rock. To date only a few block tests have been conducted
(Pratt et al, 1977, Hardin et al, 1981, Cramer et al, 1983, and Zimmerman et al, 1984).
   The CSM/OCRD test block is a two-meter cube cut by three prominent
continuous vertical fractures which effectively divide it into four
individual subblocks with scattered small-scale discontinuities (Figure
1). An east-west foliation is also evident in the block, comprised of
interlayered chloritized biotite schist and coarser-grained quartzofeld-
spathic gneiss. The boundary conditions are provided by a free upper
surface, four sides in contact with grouted flatjacks, and a bottom
attached to the main rock mass. No horizontal fracturing has been
detected. The block was originally excavated by Terra-tek, Inc.,
(Hardin et al, 1981) and was subjected to ambient and elevated-tempera-
ture testing (Hustrulid and Ubbes, 1983). The present testing is an
extension of this earlier work and uses a completely redesigned instrumentation system in an attempt to answer some fundamental questions
about block behavior.

2 DISPLACEMENT INSTRUMENTATION

For the current test a unique instrumentation system was developed to
measure displacements in the interior of the block, avoiding a suspected decoupled zone at the block's surface. The system, shown schematically in Figure 2, was developed with the following features:
   o all measurements referenced to a rigid frame, giving absolute
      displacements,

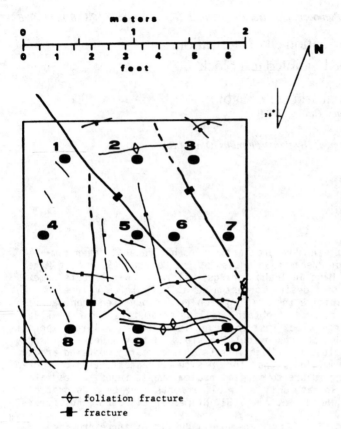

foliation fracture
fracture

Figure 1. Surface fracture expressions of the test block,
CSM/OCRD experimental room (Sour,1985).

- o   interior (subsurface) measurements with multiple-horizon
      capabilities, and
- o   electronic monitoring with non-contacting sensors.

Referenced or absolute displacements have important advantages over the
more common relative measurements. They enable study of relative
displacements between any pair of measurements points without the
necessity of long rods spanning every distance to be measured. More
importantly, they enable kinematic studies of subblock behavior under
various applied load conditions. Comparisons with computer modeling
displacements are convenient because direct comparisons can be made
between measured and modeled displacements if nodal points are selected
at measurement locations. Discontinuous deformation analysis using the
method of Shi and Goodman (1984), which involves a least-squares fit of
displacement data to a mathematical model to separate subblock translation, rotation, and strain components, requires absolute measurements.
Thus, with a given array of displacement locations, absolute measurements will provide much more information about block behavior than will
relative measurements.

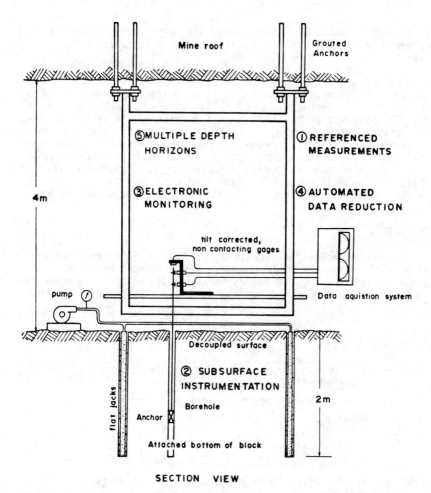

Figure 2. Schematic of the block and instrumentation system.

Interior (subsurface) measurements are important if unusual boundary effects are to be avoided. The block surface is vertically uncon-strained and may be partially decoupled from the applied stress field due to the difficulty of achieving total block side coverage using flatjacks. Stiffnesses measured at the block surface may be much higher than actual rock-mass stiffness due to this effect.

Electronic monitoring with non-contacting sensors was selected to provide rapid measurement scans at each stress level without the neces-sity for personnel in the immediate block area. Inductive sensors (proximity transducers) were chosen to avoid instrument contact with the anchor rod assembly. Proximity transducers operate on the principle of impedance variation caused by eddy currents induced in a conductive metal target. They have been extensively used for many years in preci-sion gaging applications. Their primary disadvantage involves a some-what limited range, which is determined by sensor coil diameter. Lar-ger sensors require a larger target, which should be at least three

times the coil diameter. However, over the range of displacements
encountered in the present test series, suitable transducers were
available.

The resulting system is based on 50 inductive proximity transducers,
mounted on a rigid reference frame anchored to the mine roof. The
transducers are used in ten groups of five to track the movement of ten
expansion anchors located in EX boreholes at various depths in the
block. The movement of the anchors is transmitted, via aluminum rods,
to the surface, where an array of five transducers provides an absolute, three-component displacement measurement which is corrected for
rod tilting. Five transducers are necessary at each location to correct for tilt about the horizontal reference axes: two sensors vertically
separated by one foot are used in each horizontal direction (x and y),
and a single vertical transducer monitors vertical anchor movements.

3 TEST MATRIX

Table 1 shows the ambient-temperature test matrix. Before-and-after
equal biaxial tests were conducted to evaluate changes in block
behavior resulting from intervening shear tests. All testing was done
at ambient temperatures with a nominal applied stress range from 0 to
5.17 MPa.

Table 1. Test matrix

	Loading Configuration	Measurement Horizon		
1.	Equal Biaxial (I)	U	M	L
2.	N-S Uniaxial	U	M	L
3.	E-W Uniaxial	U	M	L
4.	Equal Biaxial (II)	U	M	L

Note: U = Upper horizon (0.46 m (18") below block surface)
      M = Midplane
      L = Lower horizon (0.46 m (18") above block bottom)

4 DISPLACEMENT RESULTS

Figure 3 shows an uncorrected displacement result for a typical channel
and shows the same result corrected for anchor rod tilting. Over 600
such plots were collected in the course of the test series. The magnitude of the displacement curves can be greatly affected by tilt; some
results even showed a complete direction reversal with this correction.
Apparent hysteresis in the displacement data in Figure 3 was reduced by
the tilt correction. The importance of the tilt correction is further
demonstrated by Figure 4, which compares an uncorrected displacement
vector plot for an equal biaxial upper-horizon test cycle with a corrected version of the same plot. Although the system used in the present
study was unusually sensitive to tilt because of the long rods used, the
possibility of errors due to tilt should be considered in design of any
displacement system. Figure 5 shows N-S and E-W uniaxial results.

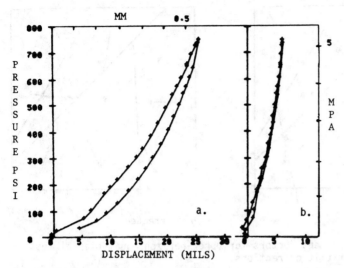

Figure 3. Typical uncorrected (a) and corrected (b) load-versus-displacement plots.

5 DEFORMATION MODULUS

Average deformation modulus was computed from four measurement points, each located near the center of one of the four vertical block edges. One pair of E-W and one pair of N-S readings were used for these averages, obtained for three complete upper-horizon equal-biaxial test cycles. Values taken near the block edges are stiffer than those taken in the center, probably due to frictional interactions with the flat jacks, and were not felt to be as representative of rock mass modulus.

Table 2. Deformation Modulus, Upper-Horizon Equal-Biaxial Test

Measurement Direction	Boreholes (Figure 1)	Modulus	Number of Observations
N-S	2-9	10.69 GPa	3
E-W	4-7	12.96 GPa	3
	Average	11.83 GPa	6

Very little variation was noted in displacements for repeated cycles of the block. Any hysterisis originally present may have been lost during repeated cycling of the block prior to this test series.

6 EFFECT OF MEASUREMENT DEPTH

The N-S pair of channels used above to calculate modulus were also used to demonstrate the change in block stiffness with depth. At the upper horizon, the first equal-biaxial test yielded a N-S displacement of 0.71 mm (0.028 in.) between boreholes 2 and 9 across a distance of 1.48 m (4.87 ft.). At the middle horizon, the same loading produced 0.36 mm (0.014 in.), and at the lower horizon, only 0.15 mm (0.006 in.). This

781

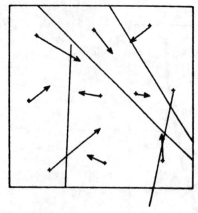 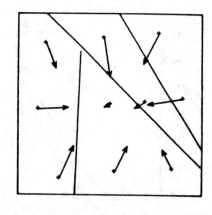

a. Uncorrected   b. Corrected

Figure 4. Displacement vectors for upper-horizon equal-biaxial test.
Note influence of tilt corrections.

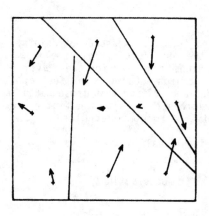 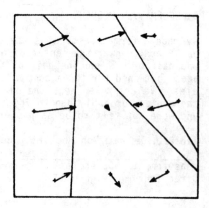

a. N-S Uniaxial   b. E-W Uniaxial

Figure 5. Displacement vectors for upper-horizon uniaxial tests.

is believed to result from the attached bottom as well as from increasing rock competency with depth.

7 SCALE EFFECTS

It is interesting to compare the effects of scale and type of test on
the measured modulus of the rock at the CSM/OCRD test facility. A
number of tests of different types have been conducted at the site,
both in-situ tests and lab tests on rock samples taken from boreholes.

Table 3. Deformation modulus from vicinity of CSM/OCRD test block by different methods

Test Type	Sample or Test Site	Volume (cubic cm)	E (GPa)
1.Block Testing (Upper Horizon) Eq. Biaxial	T.B.*	8×10^6	11.83
2.Block Testing (Hardin, 1981) (Boundary-Crack-Monitoring Surface) Eq. Biaxial	T.B.	8×10^6	13.86 - 50.2
3.Block Testing (Hardin, 1981) (Surface extensometers)	T.B.	8×10^6	36.8 - 140
4.Dilatometer Testing (Brown, 1985)	T.B.**	9.22×10^3	20.3
5.Biaxial Testing, (El Rabaa, 1981) (Overcores)	Rm.	3.47×10^3	60.9
6.Dilatometer Testing (El Rabaa, 1981)	Rm.	9.22×10^3	31.3
7.Lab Testing, (El Rabaa, 1981) (NX Cores)	Rm.	1.85×10^2	61.4
8.Lab Testing, (Amadei, 1985) (NX Cores)	Rm.	1.85×10^2	63.0

*T.B.=Test Block   **Rm.=CSM/OCRD test room

The results of these tests have been tabulated together with loaded volume in Table 3. Dilatometer tests do not have a clearly defined loaded volume. However, it has been suggested (Heuze, 1980) that this volume can be defined as the volume bounded by a "bulb of pressure" at two percent of the stress applied to the interior of the hole, as calculated by elastic thick-walled cylinder equations.

It is evident that modulus values obtained from the block test yield significantly lower modulus values than those obtained from any smaller-scale tests. It should be noted that boundary conditions and test configuration also have an influence on results. There are differences in stress distributions and mean stress levels throughout the test volumes.

Values for modulus from previous tests on the same block (Hardin, et. al., 1981) are somewhat higher than CSM values. The following factors may have contributed to this result: (1) Earlier values were obtained using surface instrumentation; CSM results vere derived from subsurface measurements, (2) the block had accumulated substantial deformational history since earlier testing.

8 EXPERIMENTAL PROBLEMS

The proximeters used were operated past their linear range to deal with unanticipated tilt maginitudes. A fourth-order polynomial was used to fit calibration data. Range extension causes a decrease in instrument stability, which becomes a problem when pairs of proximeters are compared to compute tilting of a long rod. Errors thus induced necessitated repeating some of the lower horizon tests with very strict calibration procedures. Higher-quality signal condition systems with larger-diameter sensors would alleviate this problem, along with more vertical separation between pairs of proximeters. Also, the long slender rods necessitated by the small EX holes were sensitive to air currents - a potential problem in ventilated areas.

9 CONCLUSIONS

In conclusion, it is evident from these tests that boundary effects influence the behavior of a block test. Careful planning of block test layout should incorporate referenced interior measurements. More work is also needed on methods of defining the critical volume for sizing future block tests.

DISCLAIMER   The views expressed are those of the authors and do not necessarily represent those of OCRD or of the Department of Energy.

REFERENCES

Amadei, B. 1985, Personal Communication.
Brown, S.M. 1985, Personal communication.
Cramer, M.L., J.P. Cunningham, K. Kim 1983, Rock mass deformational properties from a large scale block test, Proc. 24th Symp. Rock Mech., p.267-269.
El Rabaa, A. 1981, Measurements and modelling of rock mass response to underground excavation, M.S. Thesis, Colorado School of Mines (T-2470).
Hardin, E., N. Barton, D. Lingle, M. Board, M. Voegele 1981, A heated flatjack test series to measure the thermomechanical and transport properties of in-situ rock masses, TR-81-88, Terra-tek, prepared for the Office of Nuclear Waste Isolation, Battelle Memorial Institute, Columbus, Ohio.
Heuze, G. 1980, Scale effects in the determination of rock mass strength and deformability, Rock Mechanics, 12:167-192
Hustrulid, W. and W. Ubbes 1983, Results and conclusions from rock mechanics/hydrology investigations: CSM/ONWI test site, Geological Disposal of Radioactive Waste: In-situ Experiments in Granite, Proc. NEA Workshop Stockholm, Sweden (Oct. 25-27, 1982), OECD, p.57-75.
Pratt, H.R., H.S. Swolfs, W.F. Brace, A.D. Black and J.W. Hardin 1977, Elastic and transport properties of an in-situ jointed granite, Int. Journal Rock Mech. Min. Sci., 14:35-45.
Shi, G., and R.E. Goodman 1984, Discontinuous deformation analysis, Proc. 25th Symp. Rock Mech., p.269-277.
Sour, L. 1985, Personal communication.
Zimmerman,R.M. and M.P. Board 1984, Ambient temperature testing of the G-tunnel heated block, Proc. 25th Symp. Rock Mech., p. 281-295.

Mechanical response of jointed granite during shaft sinking at the Canadian Underground Research Laboratory*

T.CHAN, P.A.LANG & P.M.THOMPSON
Atomic Energy of Canada Ltd, Whiteshell Nuclear Research Establishment, Pinawa, Canada

1 INTRODUCTION

As part of the geoscience research within the Canadian Nuclear Fuel Waste Management Program, Atomic Energy of Canada Limited (AECL) is constructing an underground research laboratory (URL) in a previously undisturbed portion of a granitic intrusive, the Lac du Bonnet batholith, approximately 100 km northeast of Winnipeg, Manitoba (Davison and Simmons 1983). The overall geotechnical objectives of the URL are to assess and improve our ability to interpret and predict the geological, geophysical, geochemical, geomechanical and hydrogeological conditions of large bodies of plutonic rock, as well as to assess the accuracy of mathematical models used to predict the near-field mechanical and hydrogeological responses of the rock mass to excavation and thermal loading. Construction will be completed in 1986 July. Large-scale testing will commence soon afterwards and will last until the facility is decommissioned in the year 2000.

A rectangular access shaft, 255 m deep x 2.8 m x 4.9 m, was sunk during the period 1984 May to 1985 March. Rock displacements and stress changes were monitored as the excavation face (bottom) of the shaft advanced. The major objectives of this monitoring were

    (a) to evaluate and improve the ability of numerical models in predicting the mechanical response of the rock mass,

    (b) to back-calculate the rock-mass deformation modulus as a function of depth,

    (c) to assess the influence of natural fractures on the mechanical response of the granitic rock mass, and

    (d) to evaluate the quality of the geomechanical instrumentation, to determine instrumentation needs for future field experiments.

Analysis of the data from this monitoring will aid the design and modelling of further experiments in the URL.

In this paper, the rock displacements measured by an array of extensometers at 15 m below ground surface are presented and compared with predictions by a three-dimensional elastic continuum finite-element model. The nature of the deformational response of the granitic rock mass is discussed in the light of this data analysis and the distribution of natural fractures intersected by the instrumentation holes.

*Issued as AECL-8690

2 SITE DESCRIPTION

2.1 Geology

The URL site is situated within the boundaries of the Lac du Bonnet granite batholith, which is considered to be representative of many of the granitic intrusives formed in the Precambrian Shield of Canada. Surface and borehole geological, geophysical and hydrogeological site characterization studies from 1979 to 1983 by researchers from AECL and Energy, Mines and Resources Canada (Brown et al. 1983) have produced the following general picture of the site geology.

The batholith consists of several granitic phases. At the location of the access shaft, the upper lithologic unit is a moderately fractured, pink porphyritic granite with biotite-rich, biotite-poor, gneissic-foliated and zenolith-rich zones. Below approximately 220 m depth, there is a grey hornblende-biotite granite phase that grades into quartz monzonite. Fracture mapping indicated that the grey granite is much less fractured than the pink granite.

At the URL site, there are three major extensive low-intermediate dipping, hydraulically conductive fracture zones in the upper 500 m of the batholith. These dip about 25° southeast.

Apart from these fracture zones, the rock mass is of very good quality. There is one main near-vertical joint set that trends about 020°. The spacing is zonal. The spacing of the zones and the spacing of the joints within the zones vary with location. From surface to 30 m depth, the zones are spaced about 10 m apart, and are 1 to 3 m wide. The spacing of the megascopic joints within the zones is about 0.2 to 0.5 m. There is a horizontal joint set that extends down to about 15 m depth. The joint spacing is about 1 m near surface, and increases to about 3 m at 15 m depth. In addition to the two joint sets mentioned, a number of other minor joint sets are present locally. In the upper 30 m of shaft, there is a second near-vertical joint set that trends about 110°. This set is much less prominent than the first near-vertical set.

2.2 In situ stress

Prior to shaft sinking, the in situ stress was determined by hydraulic fracturing to a depth of 310 m (GeoTech 1982). Successful hydraulic fracturing was achieved at eight depths. The fracture trace on the impression packer was vertical in five of the measurement zones, and steeply inclined (sub-vertical) in the remaining three. Orientation of maximum horizontal stress ($\sigma_{H\ max}$) ranged between 042° and 158°, with a mean value of 067°. This was taken into consideration in the shaft design so that the long (4.9 m) side of the shaft is parallel to this mean orientation. The hydraulic fracturing test at 12.5 m depth, which is the most relevant to this paper, gave $\sigma_{H\ max} = 7.75$ MPa and $\sigma_{H\ min} = 4.66$ MPa, and an orientation of 060° for $\sigma_{H\ max}$.

Photoelastic strain-relief measurements on surface outcrops gave a maximum principal stress direction of 020°. Subsequent overcoring stress measurements in near-vertical drill holes at various depths from the shaft bottom, using the USBM method (two-dimensional stress determination), gave a $\sigma_{H\ max}$ orientation of 020° at 185 m depth and 030° at 218 m depth. These orientations are approximately parallel to the major vertical joint set. More detailed overcoring stress measurements will be conducted during the geotechnical characterization phase beginning in summer 1985.

3 ROCK RESPONSE MONITORING DURING SHAFT SINKING

The shaft, which has recently been completed, is 255 m deep with an upper shaft station at the 130 m depth and a lower shaft station and main testing area in horizontal development at the 240 m depth. During shaft sinking, four instrument arrays, at depths of 15 m, 62 m, 185 m and 218 m, were used to monitor excavation-induced displacements, excavation-induced stress changes and rock temperatures. These depths were chosen on the basis of borehole geological information.
    Figure 1 illustrates schematically the instrument array at 15 m depth in the shaft. Each array consists of
    (a) four to six 15-m long, sonic-probe, five-anchor borehole extensometers installed in horizontal boreholes, 0.2 - 0.5 m above the shaft floor, to monitor rock displacements,
    (b) six CSIRO, hollow, inclusion triaxial strain cells to monitor stress changes, and
    (c) six convergence pins to monitor shaft convergence as excavation progresses.
Thermistors were provided to measure temperatures to be used in correcting for thermal variation in instrument readings. Detailed layout of the measurement points was arrived at by a compromise between practical considerations (such as excavation schedule and local structural features) and the recommendations of the numerical

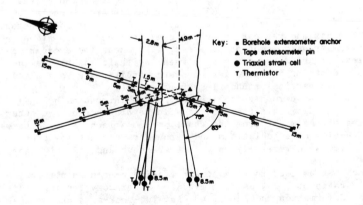

URL SHAFT CONVERGENCE ARRAY (275m ELEV.)

Figure 1.   Instrumentation array at 15 m depth (275 m elevation) to monitor the rock response to shaft sinking. All dimensions in metres.

787

modeller, based on preliminary elastic continuum boundary-element and finite-element analyses.

4 NUMERICAL MODELLING

4.1 Scoping calculations

In the design phase, scoping calculations were carried out using a two-dimensional boundary-element model and plane-strain and axisymmetric finite-element models. The following are some important results that influenced the layout of instrumentation:

(a) Displacement varies inversely with distance from the shaft axis so that at a point 15 m behind the wall the excavation-induced displacement is about 10 to 15% of the displacement at the wall. At 25 m behind the wall, the displacement is 5% of that at the wall.

(b) It is important to install the extensometers as close to the floor of the shaft as possible because measurable displacements are very sensitive to the height of the extensometer above the shaft floor. For example, displacements measured by an extensometer 0.2 m above the shaft floor would be 50% more than corresponding measurements by an extensometer 0.5 m above the shaft floor.

(c) Stress concentration or reduction is significant only within about one shaft diameter of the excavation boundary. For example, 8 m below the shaft floor, the stress is expected to be within 1% of the in situ stress.

4.2 Three-dimensional finite-element model

Prior to commencement of shaft sinking, the displacements and stress changes expected at all instrumented points in the rock were calculated. These three-dimensional linear elastic continuum analyses were performed using the MARC code (MARC Analysis Research Corporation 1983). The finite-element mesh consisted of 1700 eight-noded hexahedronal elements and was carefully designed to concentrate elements around high-stress concentration areas, i.e., near the excavation boundaries. Figure 2 shows the mesh when the shaft has been excavated to a depth of 62 m. Roller boundary conditions were applied to the bottom and vertical boundaries of the model.

To estimate the errors that might have been introduced by the finite-element discretization and the finite distance of the outer boundaries of the model from the shaft, a comparison was made between the finite-element calculations and a boundary-element solution. Discrepancies were generally only a few percent and did not exceed 20% anywhere.

The rock was assumed to be a linear elastic continuum with a Poisson's ratio of 0.26, as determined by laboratory testing, and a rock-mass deformation modulus of 40 GPa. Two rock-mass classification systems, i.e., the NGI (Barton et al. 1974) and the CSIR (Bieniawski 1976) schemes, were employed to estimate the rock-mass deformation modulus. It should be borne in mind that the site-specific values assigned to some of the parameters in these classification systems are highly subjective. The value of 40 GPa input to the model was a

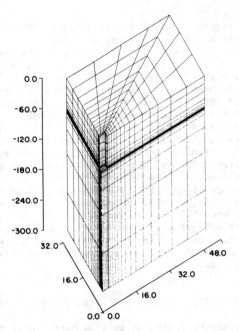

Figure 2.   Perspective view of the finite-element mesh showing the shaft excavated to 62 m depth.

general consensus among the authors of this paper and various rock mechanics experts who visited the URL.

Three cases were analyzed. In Case 1 (Base Case), the rock mass was assumed homogeneous with a deformation modulus E_o = 40 GPa. Case 2 included a 0.5-m thick excavation-damaged zone (EDZ) with a reduced modulus varying linearly from $E = 0.7E_o$ at the excavation perimeter to $E = E_o$ 0.5 m or more behind the perimeter. Case 3 was similar to Case 2 except that $E = 0.4E_o$ at the excavation perimeter. Numerical comparison indicated that calculated displacements in Cases 2 and 3 were, respectively, 10% and 16% higher than those in Case 1.

The value for the thickness of the EDZ was based on the observation that no new cracks were visible to the naked eye beyond 0.5 m in the rock cores recovered from the horizontal drill holes. Only a minor reduction in deformation modulus was considered because no definite variations of rock properties with distance from the shaft wall had been detected by in situ testing using a variety of techniques, including cross-hole ultrasonic velocities, air permeability tests and borehole dilatometer measurements.

In situ stress values input to this model were

(a) from ground surface to 86.5 m depth – a maximum horizontal principal stress of 10.6 MPa parallel to the long wall of the shaft and a minimum horizontal principal stress of 6 MPa,

(b) below 86.5 m – both horizontal principal stresses increasing linearly with depth with values given by the best-fit straight lines to the measurements (Baumgartner, private communication), and

(c) a vertical stress based on the lithostatic pressure of the overlying rock with a specific gravity of 2.65.

The values of the horizontal in situ stress at shallow depths input to the model were slightly higher than those determined by hydraulic fracturing. These higher values were chosen because a preliminary analysis of displacement data in a pilot instrumentation array at 8 m depth indicated an unrealistically low rock-mass deformation modulus (about 10 GPa) if the in situ stresses from hydraulic fracturing wereused in the model. It was recognized that at 8 m below ground surface there were complications, such as thermal expansion of the rock due to seasonal temperature variations, that may explain the higher measured displacements. Nevertheless, the differences between the stress values used in the model and the hydraulic fracturing data were within the range of uncertainty in this method of stress measurement (Haimson 1981), in view of the nonaxial, hydraulically induced fracture at the 12.5-m zone. The assumed linear variation for the in situ stress at depths greater than 86.5 m is debatable. This, however, was not an important factor since the calculated displacements and stresses around the 15 m depth were insensitive to in situ stresses below 86.5 m.

5 COMPARISON OF MEASURED DISPLACEMENTS WITH THE FINITE-ELEMENT MODEL

Of the six extensometers installed at 15 m depth, only three (two in the west wall and one in the south wall) were found to be working properly. Figure 3 illustrates a comparison between calculated and

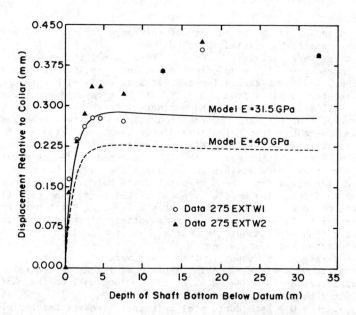

Figure 3. Measured and calculated relative horizontal rock displacements between points 15 m and 0.17 m (collar) behind the west wall as a function of the depth of the shaft bottom below the datum line.

measured displacements as a function of shaft bottom advance below
the "datum line" (the depth of the shaft bottom at the time the extensometers were installed). The recorded field data were relative
displacements between Anchor No.1, which was 15 m behind the shaft
wall, and the collar of the extensometer hole for the two extensometers in the west wall, designated 275EXTW1 and 275EXTW2. The dashed
curve represents the relative displacements predicted by the original
model, referred to as Case 1 in Subsection 4.2. Clearly, the model
underpredicts the displacements. This indicates that the in situ
rock-mass deformation modulus E is lower than 40 GPa. The solid curve
corresponds to the "calibrated" model using E = 31.5 GPa, the value
obtained by linear regression, as explained below. A distinct feature
in the displacement data is that the general trend agrees very well
with the calibrated model until the shaft bottom advances by more
than 7.5 m below the datum line. At that point, the measured displacement gradually increases to a second plateau. This second plateau may be attributed to thermal expansion of the rock as the warmer
air in the shaft increased the rock temperature. A rough estimate
shows that a temperature rise of a few degrees in the rock can lead
to the observed time-dependent displacement. The validity of this
hypothesis will be tested in the future by detailed thermomechanical
calculations.

Figure 4 is scatter plot of measured and calculated displacements
relative to the collar for all five anchors of the two extensometers, 275EXTW1 and 275EXTW2. The ordinate for each point is the
relative displacement for a particular anchor at a given time while
the abscissa is the corresponding displacement predicted by the model
using $E = E_o = 40 GPa$. Only data pertaining to shaft advance to a

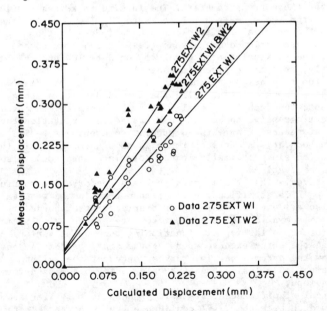

Figure 4.   Scatter plot (with regression lines) between measured and
calculated displacements for all anchors on the two extensometers in
the west wall.

depth of 7.5 m below the datum line have been included. Linear regression analyses were carried out for the following four cases:
(1) using only 275EXTW1 data,
(2) using only 275EXTW2 data,
(3) using the combined set of data from both W1 and W2, and
(4) using data from the four functioning anchors of 275EXTS2.
The regression parameters are summarized in Table 1.

Table 1. Linear regression parameters for cross-correlation between measured and calculated displacements.

Data	a(mm)	b	S_E(mm)	r	E(GPa)
275EXTW1	0.02262	1.071	0.0242	0.958	37.3
275EXTW2	0.02970	1.459	0.0313	0.961	27.4
275EXTW1 & W2	0.02767	1.269	0.0422	0.912	31.5
275EXTS2	0.003145	2.158	0.0465	0.961	18.5

Key: a = intercept, b = slope, S_E = standard error of estimate, r = cross-correlation coefficient, E = back-calculated rock-mass modulus.

The high values of the cross-correlation coefficient suggest that, to a good approximation, the rock mass at 15 m depth is linear elastic. This is also evident from the small values for a and S_E, which are comparable to the extensometer resolution ($\pm$ 0.025 mm). If the rock mass were highly nonlinear or anelastic, large values would be expected for these two parameters. The in situ rock-mass modulus was calculated from the formula $E = E_o/b$ where E_o (40 GPa) was the value input into the original finite-element model. For the two models including an excavation-damaged zone (Cases 2 and 3 in Subsection 4.2), the back-calculated E values would be 10% and 16% higher, respectively, than those given in Table 1.

In an attempt to delineate the extent of the EDZ, the deformation modulus was back-calculated, using the method described above, from displacements for each individual anchor. The results indicated that there is a progressive reduction in E around the excavation boundary. This zone of reduced E appears to persist to about 3 m behind the excavation boundary. At present there is some uncertainty in this interpretation since thermally-induced displacements could also explain the observations.

Table 1 reveals that the in situ rock-mass deformation modulus in the south wall is significantly lower than that in the west wall. This is also evident from the higher displacements recorded by 275EXTS2, as shown in Figure 5. Plotted here are the displacements relative to the collar for all functioning anchors at various positions along the three extensometers as the shaft bottom advanced to 7.5 m below the datum line. The curves represent the calibrated finite-element model using the back-calculated rock-mass deformation modulus as input.

Statistical significance tests using Student's t (Miller and Freund 1965) showed that at the 99.9% confidence level the three sets of displacement data are from different populations. Therefore, it is very unlikely that the differences were caused by random variations. The lower deformation modulus in the south direction may indicate an

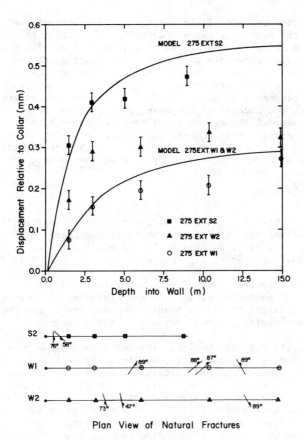

Plan View of Natural Fractures

Figure 5. Top: relative displacement as a function of depth into
the wall. Continuous lines are calibrated models. Bottom: plan view
of natural fractures along extensometer holes.

anisotropic rock mass or the influence of natural fractures. As
illustrated in the lower part of Figure 5, two fractures cross the S2
hole between the collar and the shallowest anchor (at 1.5 m) where
most of the rock deformation occurred. No satisfactory explanation
has yet been found for the discrepancy between the displacements
recorded by W1 and W2. Possible reasons are localized heterogeneities, local geometrical irregularities in the shaft wall, and shaft
bottom or nonuniform response of the two extensometers under field
conditions.

6 CONCLUSIONS

Rock deformations at 15 m depth in response to shaft excavation at
the URL have been compared to a three-dimensional finite-element
model. The following observations and preliminary conclusions
emerge:

793

1. Excavation-induced displacements in the relatively unfractured portion of the rock mass agree reasonably well with a linear elastic model with deformation modulus ranging from 18.5 to 37.3 GPa.

2. On a scale comparable to the fracture spacing, the rock mass is heterogeneous and some of the natural fractures may need to be modelled as discrete fractures.

3. Minor temperature changes lead to displacements comparable in magnitude to the mechanical response. Both air and rock temperatures should be recorded throughout these types of experiments.

4. More accurate extensometers (Kovari et al. 1979) with closely spaced anchors are essential for future geomechanical experiments at the URL, to elucidate the nature of rock movements across fractures.

REFERENCES

Barton, N., R.Lien & J.Lunde 1974. Engineering classification of rock masses for the design of tunnel support. Rock Mech. 6:189-236.
Bieniawski, Z.T. 1976. Rock mass classifications in rock engineering. Proc. symp. exploration for rock engineering 1:p.97-106. Rotterdam: Balkema.
Brown, A., C.C.Davison, P.Kurfurst, D.Peters & G.R.Simmons 1983. The influence of geotechnical data on the design of the underground research laboratory at Lac du Bonnet, Canada. Proc. int. conf. on underground mining, Lisbon, Portugal, 1983 September 3:p.141-154.
Davison, C.C. & G.R.Simmons 1983. The research program at the Canadian underground research laboratory. Proc. NEA workshop on geological disposal of radioactive waste and in situ experiments in granite. Stockholm, Sweden, 1982, October 25-27: p.197-219.
Geotech Inc. 1982. In situ stress determination by hydraulic fracturing in well bore URL-6. Report to Atomic Energy of Canada Limited.
Haimson, B.C. 1981. Confirmation of hydrofracturing results through comparisons with other stress measurements. Proc. 22nd U.S. Symp. Rock. Mech. :p.379-385. Cambridge: MIT.
Kovari, K., Ch.Amstad & J.Köppel 1979. New developments in the instrumentation of underground openings. Proc. 4th rapid excav. and tunneling conf., Atlanta, U.S.A.
MARC Analysis Research Corporation 1983. MARC general purpose finite element program user information manual.
Miller, I. & J.E.Freund 1965. Probability and statistics for engineers. Englewood Cliffs: Prentice-Hall.

17. Heat and fluid flow

Chair: H.D.OUTMANS
        Union Oil Company of California, Brea, USA
Cochair: M.S.KING
        Lawrence Berkeley Laboratory, California, USA

Measurement methods for thermal transport properties of rocks

T.ASHWORTH & DAVID R.SMITH
Physics Department, South Dakota School of Mines & Technology, Rapid City, USA
E.ASHWORTH
Mining Engineering Department, South Dakota School of Mines & Technology,
Rapid City, USA

1 INTRODUCTION

Measurement of the thermal properties of geologic materials (particularly
thermal conductivity, specific heat, and diffusivity) is becoming
increasingly important for applications such as nuclear waste disposal in
deep repositories (Sweet and McCreight 1983), underground energy storage,
construction in or on permafrost, geothermal energy utilization, and deep
mine ventilation. Unfortunately the accurate measurement of thermal
properties of materials of low thermal conductivity, even under ambient
conditions, is not trivial to perform (Tye 1984, Morgan and West 1980,
Pratt 1969); measurements under conditions of very high temperature
and/or pressure, or measurements on specimens containing significant
amounts of moisture, are particularly difficult to perform. It is hoped
that eventually the thermal properties of a given specimen of, say, rock
can be estimated analytically based on the composition of the material
and the thermophysical properties of its components. Currently
considerable effort is being applied to the treatment of geological
materials as composites. In some situations good estimates can now be
obtained. But significant progress is required before this type of
modeling can be applied with confidence to materials having complex
structures. Thus, at least for quite a while, we must resort to
measurement.

All measurements of thermal conductivity are based upon the energy
conservation equation coupled with the definition of thermal conductivity
embodied in Fourier's Law. Monitored thermal energy is injected into a
material, or the heat influx from the surroundings is monitored, and the
resulting temperature distribution determined. Usually one attempts to
impose a simple symmetry on the experiment to aid in the interpretation
of the heat flow.

In the ideal case of unidirectional heat flow Fourier's Law reduces to
the simple form $dQ/dt = -kA(dT/dx)$, where dQ/dt is the time rate of flow
of heat into the specimen, A is the cross-sectional area through which
the heat flows and which is normal to the direction of flow, dT/dx is the
temperature gradient along the direction of heat flow, and k is the
thermal conductivity coefficient which may be, and usually is, a function
of temperature as well as of the physical properties of the material
constituting the specimen. In the case of composite fibrous or granular
materials the thermal conductivity coefficient may be a function of
position and/or direction, or it may demonstrate its tensor nature with

797

properties related to the principal crystallographic axes of the
material(s) comprising the specimen. Most measurement systems attempt to
produce the condition of unidirectional heat flow or alternatively
attempt to set up nearly ideal radial heat flow.

In this paper we review the advantages and disadvantages of some of the
more common methods available for measurement of thermal conductivity and
diffusivity of geological materials, particularly hard rock, and mention
some current projects which aim to simplify and verify procedures.

2 THE GUARDED HOT PLATE METHOD.

Measurement of thermal conductivity by the guarded hot plate method is
currently considered to be the most reliable method of measurement and is
the standard method recognized by the ASTM for homogeneous materials
(ASTM C177-76 1983). It has been used at temperatures as low as -180 C
and as high as 600 C. At higher temperatures both the specimens themselves and the electrical insulators used with the temperature-sensing
elements become ionic conductors which can introduce serious errors in
the measurement of temperature and heater power.

This method has been used for measurements of relatively high precision
and to establish standard reference materials (Siu 1980, Smith, Hust, and
Van Poolen 1981). Advantages of this method are that:
  a. The measurement apparatus is simple in principle.
  b. The measurements take place under steady-state equilibrium with no
     transient effects to be corrected for.
  c. The effects of edge heat losses are greatly reduced by thermal
     guarding of the monitored main heater by a surrounding, separately
     controlled guard heater.
  d. The measurement conditions agree closely with the conditions
     assumed by the theoretical definition of thermal conductivity
     (Fourier's Law).
  e. It is an absolute method.
The disadvantages of this method are that:
  a. In addition to the control circuits required in the actual
     measurement under steady-state conditions, additional control
     circuitry of high sensitivity is needed to hold the temperature of
     the guard region very close to that of the measured region.
  b. The apparatus is expensive to build or buy because of the precision
     of construction and sensitivity of control systems that are
     required.
  c. Steady-state equilibrium takes a time measured in hours to be
     achieved.
  d. Although this apparatus can be used with only a single specimen
     this variation has not won formal acceptance by standards
     organizations; the standard method requires two matched specimens,
     and the value of thermal conductivity obtained is an average over
     the properties of two specimens rather than a measurement of the
     property of a single specimen.
  e. Large specimens must be obtained with diameters of at least 150 mm
     (6 in); the 200 mm (8 in) diameter is the standard size used. This
     size requirement is often very inconvenient for measurement of
     geological specimens. Furthermore the specimens must be free of
     cracks and other mechanical defects and any inhomogeneities must be
     of a size of the order of less than millimeters.

f. It is not a routine method of measurement; it must be carried out under the direction of a skilled and scientifically knowledgeable operator.

3 COMPARATIVE METHODS

Comparative methods are being used presently with considerable success, both in the United States and in Europe. With these methods the heat flow through the sample essentially is obtained from knowledge of the temperature gradient across a standard reference material (SRM) placed at either side of the sample. Both the specimen and the SRM are fabricated into right cylindrical prisms, usually of 12 to 25 mm (0.5 to 1.0 in) diameter and of about the same height, or about 100 mm (4.0 in) diameter and 12 mm (0.5 in) thick. Although this configuration involves quasi-linear heat flow, it is very popular because it is difficult to fabricate other geometries. Heat losses which give rise to the non-linearity of the heat flow can be kept small by providing some form of thermal shield, and the extent of the heat losses can be determined by comparison of the temperature difference across the SRM's. Preparation of specimens for this configuration is relatively straightforward, using standard techniques to core, slice, and polish the specimen. However, if uncertainties due to thermal contact resistance are to be avoided, it is necessary to groove the sample and insert a fine thermocouple. Although a greater number of temperature differences must be measured at one time, this method has the advantage of providing an estimation of the radial heat losses.

In principle comparative methods can be used up to quite high temperatures (approaching 1000 C), but care must be taken that the thermocouples used are suitable for work at the highest temperatures employed. Above about 500 C it is also a requirement that both the specimen and SRM are opaque to infrared radiation; otherwise large, inobvious errors may result. In this high temperature regime problems of ionic conduction can invalidate thermal conductivity measurements, as is also true with the guarded plate method. Sweet, Moss and Sisson (1985) recently have analysed the heat flow in a comparative apparatus.

Morgan and West (1980) used the cut-bar comparative method for work on the U. S. Bureau of Mines Standard Rock Suite, with Pyroceram 9606 disks as the SRM. In a similar apparatus, Singer and Tye (1979) used two Pyrex 7740 disks for work up to 350 C on coals and cokes; two Pyroceram 9606 disks were used for measurements at higher temperatures.

4 RADIAL METHODS

Radial heat-flow methods generally require more machining to prepare the sample and are thermally more complex. Systems can be subdivided into those employing central heaters of significant dimensions and those using a very fine, one-dimensional source of heat. Those of the former group are best used under steady state conditions so that the heat capacity of the heater does not enter into the measurement; sensors placed at different radial positions are needed to determine the temperature gradient generated. Systems of this type are capable of excellent precision, but as with the guarded hot plate system, require precise control of temperature to eliminate loss of heat out the ends of the specimens. An excellent review of these methods has been given by McElroy and Moore (1969).

Good examples of radial heat flow systems are those developed at Oak Ridge National Laboratory (Godfrey, Fulkerson, Kollie, Moore, and McElroy 1964), T.P.R.C., Purdue University (Navarro and DeWitt 1974), and more recently and specifically for measurements on rocks, at Lawrence Livermore National Laboratory (Durham and Abey 1983; Durham, Boro, and Beiriger 1985). The latter system demonstrates the advantages of this geometry which facilitates measurement at elevated temperatures under hydrostatic pressure; measurements have been made up to 200 C on Climax Stock Quartz to 50 MPa. and Permian Basin Salt to 31 MPa.

When the heat source is practically one-dimensional and has a negligible heat capacity, the system can be operated in a number of different modes. Additional temperature sensors can be installed to determine the temperature gradient for steady state measurements as before. It can also be used in two non-steady-state modes using only the temperature of the wire itself, determined from its electrical resistance or by use of a very fine thermocouple, to give the properties of the surrounding material. Heat can be applied to the wire continuously, causing a corresponding continuous rise in the temperature of the sample, or a short heating pulse may be applied. In the latter case particularly it is important that the configuration of the experiment (e.g. the dimensions of the wire, the rate of heating, and the duration of the heating pulse) be appropriate to the thermal properties of the sample material, since in the evaluation of the data the "linear response region" must be used. This requirement is due to approximations used to make the data reduction tractable.

It should also be pointed out that, in the hands of an operator who is knowledgeable about the analysis of transient radial heat-flow and the errors that can arise from non-ideal conditions, the transient line source method is accurate and versatile. Some of the best examples are the work on materials under pressure at the University of Umea, Sweden, (Andersson and Backstrom 1976), and the work on ceramic materials being done in both England and Germany (Davis 1984, Emmerich and Peters 1984, Jeschke 1978). Specifically, the hot-wire method used according to the specifications of DIN 51046 is a German standard method for refractories up to 1600 C. Under these specifications the method has been found safe for materials with conductivity up to 2 W/m-K, and may be used for materials with conductivity up to 6 W/m-K if certain precautions are observed. Other details of the method, its use and standardization are given in Jeschke's paper.

The thermal conductivity system developed and marketed by TerraTek Inc. is of the hot-wire, radial heat flow type; this instrument apparently has had a significant amount of use for measurements on rocks, but unfortunately reports of the performance of the instrument and data obtained are hard to find in the open literature. In addition, a variety of this hot-wire method is being used in the important developments of measurements at ultra-high pressures and high temperatures (Schloessin and Beck 1983).

5 UNGUARDED METHODS

Guarded systems are designed to constrain the heat flow to be close to that of an ideal configuration. Additional components (such as heaters and temperature sensors) and control systems are incorporated into the apparatus to achieve this. Corrections for non-ideal behavior are then small and are often neglected. In unguarded systems the design philosophy is one of simplicity, both for the apparatus itself and usually for the preparation of the sample. Additionally the approach to system errors can be simplified. Rather than take elaborate steps to reduce stray heat conduction, the boundary conditions can be more clearly defined due to the greater simplicity of the system components, and the corrections can then be estimated to a greater certainty. Numerical techniques such as finite-element analysis can be usefully employed for this task.

Significant work on systems of this type has been performed at Oak Ridge National Laboratory (Graves, Yarbrough, and McElroy 1985), the National Physical Laboratory, Teddington, England (Salmon and Williams 1984), and South Dakota School of Mines & Technology (Ashworth and Ashworth 1980; Ashworth, Alexander, and Ashworth 1983; Ashworth and Ashworth 1985). Simple unguarded apparatuses are versatile in application. Quasi-linear flow and quasi-radial flow systems have been successfully used for measurements under pressure, at high temperature, for powders, for complex highly anisotropic samples, and even for samples containing moisture. For example, a simple unguarded stack comprising a 100 mm. diameter plate sandwiched between equi-diameter specimen disks with thermometer plates at either side, has been used in a uniaxial tester to obtain the room temperature value of thermal conductivity of several rocks (in the conductivity range 2 to 5 W/m-K) and Nylon (conductivity 0.36 W/m-K) up to pressures of 17 MPa (2500 psi) in our laboratory. In another apparatus conductivity measurements can be made in the temperature range -60 to +100 C, and this range is being extended up to 250 C. In principle the ranges that can be covered by guarded and unguarded apparatus are the same, but unguarded systems by virtue of their simplicity do provide easier application than equivalent guarded systems in may cases. In addition, once set up, unguarded systems may be used successfully by relatively unskilled operators provided that skilled supervision is available. Many of the systems used in the comparative mode and the heat-flux meter methods are in fact unguarded systems.

6 OTHER METHODS

Besides the radial transient line source method discussed in section 4, two additional transient methods are gaining popularity. They are the flash heating method and the Angstrom or wave method. Good examples of these methods are described by Bittle and Taylor (1984) by and Vandersande and Pohl (1980) respectively. Data obtained for thermal properties of rocks by the laser flash method have been reported by Hanley, DeWitt and Taylor (1977).

In flash methods one monitors the thermal response of the back-side of a specimen disk to a pulse of thermal energy on its front side. The thermal diffusivity of the material is related to the time between the application of the energy pulse and the peaking of the back-side temperature; the amount by which the temperature changes is not needed so that this method has the significant advantage of not requiring precise thermometry; specific heat values obtained by other methods are used to convert the data to thermal conductivity values. The method is fast and requires relatively small samples. However, for reliable measurements the parameters of the specimen and the apparatus must be appropriate to the range of the thermal properies being measured. Corrections for sample inhomogeneities must be considered carefully.

In the Angstrom method the attenuation and phase retardation of periodic (usually sinusoidal) heat pulses are determined as they propagate along a rod. This method produces thermal diffusivity data; knowledge of specific heat values is required to allow conversion of the data obtained to conductivity values. The main advantages of the method are that it eliminates the effect of heat losses, and it is relatively simple and adaptive. Care has to be taken, however, with the details of the attachment and thermal tempering of the temperature sensing thermocouples and with other experimental details.

In addition to the two transient methods discussed above, steady-state heat-flux meter methods provide another relatively simple, and effective, measurement alternative (Acton 1978). Most of the work performed on rocks by this technique has utilized apparatus designed and fabricated by Dynatech (Coumou and Tye 1981; Kopietz and Neumann 1985) which conforms to ASTM C518. The method uses steady-state conditions so the rate of data acquisition is controlled by the specimen equilibrium time as all other steady-state methods, and the heat-flux meter must be calibrated by use of a SRM as a specimen. However, the method is simple and well suited to use with geological materials. Kopietz and Neumann present a good comparison of heat-flux meter data with data obtained using the comparative method and the flash-laser method; they conclude that data accurate to better than 10% can be obtained if care is taken in the evaluation of thermal contact resistance.

7 STANDARD REFERENCE MATERIALS

Work on standard reference materials is very active. For several years a committee of the CODATA Task Group has been considering materials for evaluation as SRMs. These have been mainly materials having fairly high thermal conductivity such as Armco iron, stainless steel, and tungsten. However materials with conductivity in the range 0.5 to 5.0 W/m-K, the range found in geological materials, have also been considered and are presently receiving some emphasis.

Preliminary findings of an interlaboratory study on Pyroceram 9606 and Pyrex 7740 were reported at the recent 9ETPC. Although this study was not a full round-robin, this work aimed at providing a reference material for nuclear waste isolation projects. Professor F. Cabannes (C.N.R.S., Orleans, France), who is a member of the CODATA committee, is directing a round-robin program of measurements of a sintered mineral. By powdering the material and then recombining it by sintering at high temperature, an artificial material which is highly homogeneous and isotropic is obtained. Besides making measurements on some of the above materials, workers at the National Physical Laboratories have found some plastics, such as Lucite, and some metal alloys to be useful reference materials. The range of thermal conductivity covered by materials proposed as SRM's are summarized in figure 1 showing the relationship to the conductivity of common and important geological materials and other technical materials; data in this figure are taken from Bogaard (1985), Clark (1966), Morgan and West (1980), Skvarla, Vandersande and Pohl (1981), Sweet and McCreight (1983), Touloukian, Powell, Ho and Klemens (1970), and from papers by the authors.

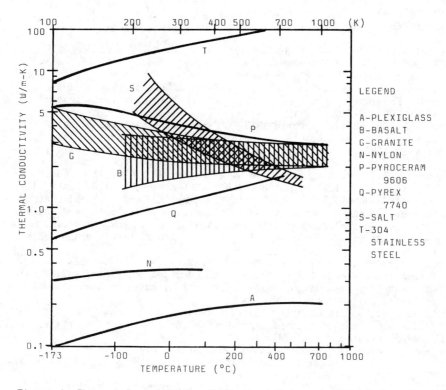

Figure 1. Thermal Conductivity of Standard Reference Materials and
Selected Geological Materials.

8 GENERAL CONSIDERATIONS

In choosing a method for the measurement of thermal conductivity or
thermal diffusivity there are many factors which should be considered.
These include the range in which the conductivity of the material lies,
the available facilities and skill levels of personnel involved in
preparation of specimens, the required accuracy, the required speed of
measurement, and special considerations such as the need to measure
specimens subjected to high pressure. Each method discussed has its own
set of advantages and disadvantages, and each method is best suited to a
limited set of conditions. Attention should be given to the specimen
preparation, particularly whether grooving and thermocouple placement is
necessary to eliminate the effects of thermal contact resistance in the
measurement stack, or whether there is a greater uncertainty in the
thermocouple placement. These factors will depend on the particular
apparatus and method chosen, and on the skill of the operator. In all
cases it is recommended that a SRM be used to evaluate the performance of
a system and to provide a direct comparison to other apparatuses. It was
the conclusion of the workshop on geological materials conducted at the
9th European Thermophysical Properties Conference (9ETPC) that further
studies on the methods of measurement were still required.

REFERENCES:

Acton, R.U. 1978. Thermal Conductivity of S. E. New Mexico Rocksalt and
Anhydrite, in V.V. Mirkovich (ed.), Thermal Conductivity 15, p263-76.
New York and London: Plenum Press.

Andersson, P., and G. Backstrom 1976. Thermal Conductivity of Solids
under Pressure by the Transient Hot Wire Method, Rev. Sci. Instrum.,
47/2: 205-209.

Ashworth, E., and T. Ashworth 1980. A Simple Apparatus for Thermal
Conductivity Measurements on Rocks Under Applied Stress, in K.E.
Gray(ed.), 20th U.S. Symposium on Rock Mechanics (Austin, Texas), p27-
33.

Ashworth, T., T.M. Alexander, and E. Ashworth 1983. Thermal Conductivity
of Carbonate Gneiss Under Applied Uniaxial Stress, in J.G. Hust (ed.),
Thermal Conductivity 17, p737-744. New York and London: Plenum Press.

Ashworth, E., and T. Ashworth 1985. Finite Element Analysis of Unguarded
Hot-Plate Thermal Conductivity Apparatuses, in T. Ashworth & D.R. Smith
(eds.), Thermal Conductivity 18, p599-609. New York and London: Plenum
Press.

ASTM C-177 1983. Standard Test Method for Steady-State Thermal
Transmission Properties by Means of the Guarded Hot Plate, Annual Book
of Standards, vol. 04.06: Thermal Insulation, Environmental Acoustics,
pp 21-54. Philadelphia:ASTM.

Bittle, R.R., and R.E. Taylor 1984. Step-Heating Technique for Thermal
Diffusivity Measurements of Large-Grained Heterogeneous Materials,
J. Amer. Ceramic Soc., 67/3: 186-90.

Bogaard, R.H. 1985. Thermal Conductivity of Selected Stainless Steels, in
T. Ashworth & D.R. Smith (eds.), Thermal Conductivity 18, p175-185. New
York and London: Plenum Press.

Clark, S.P. Jr. 1966. Thermal Conductivity, Handbook of Physical
Constants, New York: The Geological Society of America.

Coumou, K.G., and R.P. Tye 1981. A Laboratory Instrument for Rapid
Determination of Thermal Conductivities in the Range 0.4 to 5 W/m-K,
High Temperatures-High Pressures 13:695.

Davis, R.W. 1984. The Hot-Wire Method for the Determination of the
Thermal Conductivity of Ceramic Fibres, presented at the 9th European
Conference on Thermophysical Properties, Manchester, England.

Durham, W. B., and A. E. Abey 1983. Thermal Conductivity and Diffusivity
of Climax Stock Quartz Monzonite at High Pressure and Temperature, in
J.G. Hust (ed.), Thermal Conductivity 17, p459-68, New York and London:
Plenum Press.

Durham, W. B., C. O. Boro, and J. M. Beiriger 1985. Thermal Conductivity
of Permian Basin Bedded Salt at Elevated Pressure, in T. Ashworth &
D.R. Smith (eds.), Thermal Conductivity 18, p687-698. New York and
London: Plenum Press.

Emmerich, W. D., and E. Peters 1984. The Determination of Thermal
Conductivity Using the Hot Wire Method in the Temperature Range from
Room Temperature up to 1400 C, presented at the 9th European Conference
on Thermophysical Properties, Manchester, England.

Godfrey, T.G., W. Fulkerson, T.G. Kollie, J.P. Moore, and D.L. McElroy
1964. Thermal Conductivity of Uranium Dioxide and Armco Iron by an
Improved Radial Heat Flow Technique, ORNL-3556.

Graves, R.S., D.W. Yarbrough, and D.L. McElroy 1985. Apparent Thermal
Conductivity Measurements by an Unguarded Technique, in T. Ashworth &
D.R. Smith (eds.), Thermal Conductivity 18, p339-355. New York and
London: Plenum Press.

Hanley, E.J., D.P. DeWitt, and R.E. Taylor 1977. The Thermal Transport
   Properties at Normal and Elevated Temperatures of Eight Representative
   Rocks, Proc. Symp. Thermophys. Prop. 7, 386-91.
Jeschke, P. 1978. Thermal Conductivity of Refractories: Working with the
   Hot-Wire Method, in R.P. Tye (ed.) Thermal Transmission Measurements
   of Insulation (ASTM STP 660), p172-185. Philadelphia: ASTM.
Kopietz, J., and W. Neumann 1985. Thermal Conductivity and Thermal
   Diffusivity Measurements of Salt Rocks by Different Methods, in
   T. Ashworth & D.R. Smith (eds.), Thermal Conductivity 18, p661-672. New
   York and London: Plenum Press.
McElroy, D.L., and J.P. Moore 1969. Radial Heat Flow Methods for the
   Measurement of the Thermal Conductivity of Solids, in R.P. Tye (ed.)
   Thermal Conductivity, Vol. 1, p185-239, London and New York: Academic
   Press.
Morgan, M.T., and G.A. West 1980. Thermal Conductivity of the Rocks in
   the Bureau of Mines Standard Rock Suite, ORNL/TM-7052.
Navarro, R. A., and D. P. DeWitt 1974. Line Heat Source Method and Its
   Suitability for Measuring Thermal Conductivity of Rocks, Thermophysical
   Properties Research Center, Purdue University, Report 26, (May 1974).
Pratt, A. W. 1969. Heat Transmission in Low Conductivity Materials, in
   R.P. Tye (ed.), Thermal Conductivity, Vol. 1, p301-405. London and New
   York: Academic Press.
Salmon, D.R., and I. Williams 1984. Investigation of Edge-Heat-Losses in
   Three Standard Guarded and Unguarded Hot-Plates, presented at the 9th
   European Conference on Thermophysical Properties, Manchester, England.
Schloessin, H.H., and A.E. Beck 1983. High Pressure Thermal Measurements
   in a Solid Medium Cube, private communication.
Singer, J.M., and R.P. Tye 1979. Thermal, Mechanical, and Physical
   Properties of Selected Bituminous Coals and Cokes, U. S. Bureau of
   Mines Report of Investigation 8364.
Siu, M.C. 1980. Fibrous Glass Board as a Standard Reference Material for
   Thermal Resistance Measurements Systems, Thermal Insulation Performance
   (ASTM STP 718), p343-360. Philadelphia:ASTM.
Skvarla, M.J., J.W. Vandersande, M.L. Linvill, and R.O. Pohl 1981.
   Thermal Conductivity of Selected Repository Materials, in J.G. Moore
   (ed.) Scientific Basis for Nuclear Waste Management, p43-50. New York
   and London: Plenum Press.
Smith, D.R., J.G. Hust and L.J. Van Poolen 1981. Measurement of Effective
   Thermal Conductivity of Glass Fiberboard Standard Reference Material,
   Cryogenics, 21/7: 408-410.
Sweet, J.N. and J.E. McCreight 1983. Thermal Conductivity of Rocksalt
   and Other Geologic Materials from the Suite of the Proposed Waste
   Isolation Pilot Plant, in D.C. Larson (ed.), Thermal Conductivity 16,
   p61-78. New York and London: Plenum Press.
Sweet, J.N., M. Moss, and C.E. Sisson 1985. The Use of Numerical Heat
   Transfer Techniques to Analyze Thermal Comparitor Conductivity
   Measurements, in T. Ashworth & D.R. Smith (eds.), Thermal Conductivity
   18, p43-59. New York and London: Plenum Press.
Touloukian, Y.S., R.W. Powell, C.Y. Ho, and P.G. Klemens 1970.
   Thermophysical Properties of Matter, Vol. 2, Thermal Conductivity:
   Nonmetallic Solids, New York - Washington: IFI/Plenum.
Tye, R.P. 1984. A Review of Factors Influencing Thermal Conductivity
   Measurements on Composites, presented at the 9th European Conference on
   Thermophysical Properties, Manchester, England.
Vandersande, J. W., and R. O. Pohl 1980. Simple Apparatus for the
   Measurement of Thermal Diffusivity between 80-500K using the Modified
   Angstrom Method, Rev. Sci. Instrum., vol. 51/12, p1694-99.

Preliminary evaluation of alterant geophysical tomography in welded tuff

A.L.RAMIREZ & W.D.DAILY
Lawrence Livermore National Laboratory, California, USA

ABSTRACT

The ability of alterant geophysical tomography to delineate flow paths in a welded tuff rock mass has been preliminarily evaluated based on the results of a field experiment. Electromagnetic measurements were made before, during and after a water-based, dye tracer flowed through the rock mass. Alterant geophysical tomographs were generated and compared with independent evidence -- borescope logs, neutron logs and dyed rock samples. Anomalies present in the tomograph match the location and orientation of fractures mapped with a borescope. The location of tracer-stained fractures coincides with the location of some image anomalies; other geophysical anomalies exist where tracer-stained fractures were not observed, perhaps due to poor core recovery. Additional drilling to locate stained flow paths and other experiments are planned so that the applicability of the technique can be further evaluated.

1 INTRODUCTION

The Nevada Nuclear Waste Storage Investigations (NNWSI) Project is studying the suitability of the tuffaceous rocks at Yucca Mountain, Nevada Test Site, for the construction of a high-level nuclear waste repository. Lawrence Livermore National Laboratory (LLNL), Livermore, California, has been given the tasks of evaluating the waste package environment and designing and verifying the performance of waste packages for the NNWSI Project.

Various in-situ tests will be conducted within the Topopah Springs member of the Paintbrush Tuff at Yucca Mountain to investigate its behavior in the vicinity of simulated waste packages. The planned tests will simulate the waste package by emplacement of heaters within the rock mass. Rock behavior will be monitored during the heating and cooling phases and with water percolating through the rock mass.

A possible hydrologic scenario that could develop around a heater is shown schematically in Figure 1. The heater will dehydrate the partially saturated rock near the emplacement borehole. The water vapor formed will travel thru the matrix until it intersects a fracture and then moves along the fracture. The water vapor

807

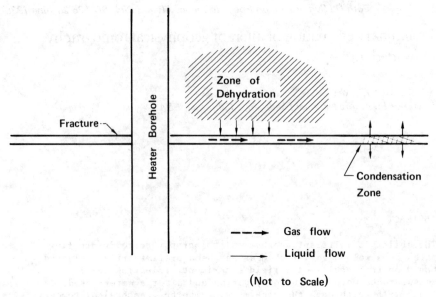

Figure 1. Schematic diagram of a possible hydrologic scenario around a heater in partially saturated, welded tuff.

condenses where the temperatures are sufficiently cool. Part of this water may move into the matrix due to capillary action while the remainder may flow along the fracture. When the heater is turned off, the dehydrated region is expected to slowly resaturate.

The hydrologic behavior of the near field waste package environment will be studied with various measurement techniques (Yow, 1985). This paper discusses the preliminary results of an experiment in which one of the candidate measurement techniques, alterant geophysical tomography, (Ramirez and Lytle, 1984) was evaluated. In this particular experiment, our objective was to evaluate the capacity of alterant tomography to distinguish between water within a fracture and the much larger volume of water trapped in the surrounding welded tuff. Additional work is required to investigate the method's effectiveness in resolving the remaining components of hydrologic behavior shown in Figure 1.

2   DESCRIPTION OF EXPERIMENTS

For this study, we used measurements of very high frequency (VHF) electromagnetic waves having a frequency of 300 MHz. The region between the boreholes was divided into many cells and an attenuation rate is calculated for each cell from line integral equations which can be written for each ray path. This set of equations can be solved iteratively using various reconstruction algorithms (Lager and Lytle, 1977). The quantity of interest in this study is the attenuation rate (defined as the inverse of the distance along which the signal is attenuated by a factor of 1/e).

Rock mass electromagnetic attenuation rate is a sensitive function of (among other things) water content of the rock (Poley, et al., 1978; Daily and Ramirez, 1984). Typically, the larger the water content, the larger the attenuation rate. In Figure 1, water condensing in the fracture will change the attenuation rate. In this experiment, we used a water tracer to change the attenuation rate of the fractures accepting the tracer.

Water trapped in the rock matrix needs to be distinguished from water filling a fracture. We used a technique known as alterant geophysical tomography where measurements are made before and after a water tracer is added to the rock. The image formed by subtracting values of corresponding cells of the "before" and "after" tomographs is the alterant tomograph. Rock influenced by the tracer is represented in the alterant image by the changes in attenuation rate. Thus, alterant tomograph might be useful to define changes in fracture saturation by distinguishing between water within fractures and invariable anomalies such as those caused by water trapped in the matrix.

The experiment was conducted in an ash flow tuff formation of the Grouse Canyon member of the Belted Range Tuff. This formation is readily accessible and is lithologically similar to that of the proposed repository horizon, the Topopah Spring tuff, at Yucca Mountain. The Grouse Canyon tuff is in the unsaturated zone but has a degree of saturation greater than 85 percent. Porosity ranges from 13 to 25 percent (Johnstone and Wolfsberg, 1980). Measurements were made between three parallel coplanar boreholes drilled 90 centimeters apart into the rib of the extensometer drift in the G-tunnel complex at the Nevada Test Site. Figure 2 shows the borehole layout relative to the drift. Boreholes 2, 3 and 4 serve as measurement holes. Borehole 1 is drilled 2 degrees below horizontal to provide a reservoir from which water could infiltrate the rock. All boreholes are six meters long. This scale is similar to that planned for the waste package tests to be conducted in Yucca Mountain. Previous fracture mapping near this region of G tunnel indicates that most fractures are roughly vertical with two predominant sets striking approximately N40-60°W and N20-40°E. The azimuth of our measurement boreholes is N15°W.

Tomographs were made between holes 2 and 3 (referred as the upper measurement region) and between holes 3 and 4 (lower measurement region). The tomographs image the region along the holes between three and six meter depth (measured laterally). All depth distances were measured from a reference line just outside the hole collars. Initial measurements between boreholes 2 and 3 and between 3 and 4 were made prior to the start of tracer flow. Inversions of these measurements provide the baseline attenuation factor geotomographs of the rock and are designated as "before" measurements. Then borehole 1 was filled first with a solution of water and methylene chloride dye which stains the rock dark blue on contact. Several days later a second solution consisting of salted water and dye solution was added. Coring the rock mass was planned as the last part of the experiment to locate blue fractures and corroborate the tomographic data. Measurements were taken for the next two calendar weeks after adding water to borehole 1, alternating each day between the upper and lower measurement regions.

Additional geophysical information on the rock mass was collected in an effort to verify our inferences from the tomographic data. Neutron surveys were made to obtain overall rock mass saturation in

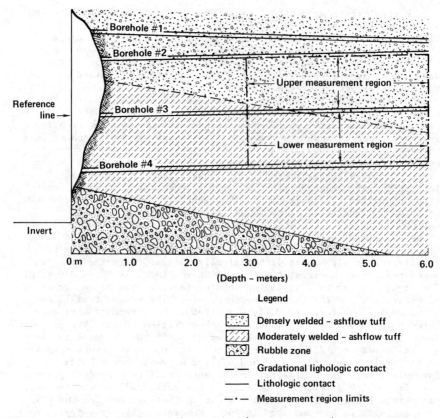

Figure 2. Borehole layout and tomographic plane relative to local geology (geology extrapolated from map by Langkopf and Eshom (1982) pp. 15-16).

an attempt to locate those fractures which accepted water. These surveys were made in holes 2, 3, and 4 before the water was added to the formation and again after the geotomographic data was taken when water had been infiltrating the formation for more than two weeks. In addition, boreholes were cored in the plane of measurement to locate fractures stained by the blue dye and thus identify the location of those fractures which conducted water. Two holes were cored between each of the three tomographic measurement holes after the tomographic data was collected. Also, a borescope was used to log fractures in holes 2, 3, and 4, and the four post-experiment core holes.

3 RESULTS AND DISCUSSION

Figure 3 presents alterant tomographs showing the changes in attenuation factors caused by salt water tracers along the upper measurement region. Unsalted tracers were also used; however portions of these data sets are inaccurate and are not shown. All

images shown in this paper consists of an array of 7.5 cm square
cells 40 rows long and 12 columns high. The gray scale represents
the changes in attenuation factor with the dark grey tones corresponding to large changes. The images from both the upper and lower
measurement regions, represent a combined region 180 cm high and
300 cm long.

Figure 3 shows the evolution of the image anomalies as the tracer
penetrated farther into the rock mass. As expected, the anomalies
in the top (early) tomograph show smaller changes in attenuation
actor than the anomalies in the bottom (later) tomograph. The two
vertical anomalies centered at depths of 3.4 m and 3.9 m could be
fracture flow paths. This interpretation is consistent with geologic
data (Langkopf and Eshom, 1982) that most of the fractures in this
unit are vertical. A diagonal anomaly beginning at a depth of 4.0 m
in borehole 3 is present in both cases. This anomaly suggests flow
paths other than vertical in the rock mass and appears to grow with
time.

An important element controlling the reliability of the alterant
tomographs shown in Fig. 3 is data noise. The relatively small
changes shown by the images are obtained by subtracting two data sets
consisting of relatively large numbers. Thus, slight errors in large
numbers could account for some of the changes. We have estimated

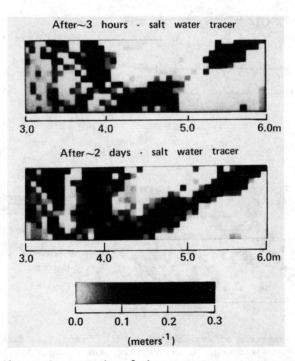

Figure 3. Alterant tomographs of the upper measurement region showing how the image anomalies changed as the tracer penetrated the rock
mass.

possible errors present in the data by comparing two data sets (subsequently used for tomographs) taken 16 hours apart while the rock
mass properties remained constant. The differences between corresponding measurements were used as the error estimates. We then used
computer simulations to investigate how these errors propagate in the
alterant tomographs. In this manner, we have discarded anomalies
which could have been associated with measurement error.

These "noise-free" (at a 99% confidence level) results are shown
in Figure 4b. The tomographs of the upper measurement region and the
upper half of Figure 4b in Figure 3 can be compared to evaluate the
significance of random measurement noise. There are differences
between these two tomographs. However, the major anomalies observed
in Figure 3 can also be recognized in the upper half of Figure 4b.
Thus, we suggest that the major anomalies in the tomograph are caused
by factors other than data noise.

The alterant tomograph (Figure 4b) is compared with fractures
mapped with a borescope (Figure 4a) along boreholes 2, 3, and 4.
Both fracture locations and the apparent dip of the fracture along
the plane of measurement are shown (orientation data reliable to

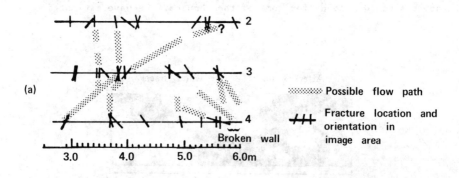

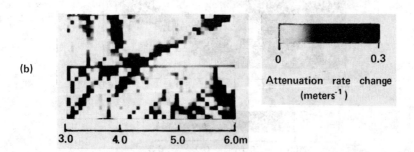

Figure 4. Comparison of available fracture orientation data (a) and
the final alterant tomograph (b) in which any changes likely to be
associated with random measurement errors (99% confidence level) have
been set to 0.0 m^{-1}. Combining the borescope mapped fractures and
the tomograph, possible flow paths have been postulated in (a).

approximately ± 20°). The orientation of a few fractures in
boreholes 2, 3, and 4 could not be determined and are not shown.

We have combined the fracture location and orientation data with
the tomographic data to construct the model of possible flow paths
in Fig. 4a. Several observations can be made based on Figure 4.
Some of the postulated flow paths are discontinuous; i.e., flow is
not fully contained in the tomographic plane. The postulated flow
paths of the tracer are all associated with fractures (i.e., there
is no evidence requiring matrix flow), but not all fractures serve
as flow paths. Positive indications of the technique's effectiveness
can be recognized in Figure 4. These are: a) the lineal trends
expected of fracture flow which are defined by the larger anomalies
and b) the general agreement between the larger image anomalies in
Fig. 4 and the orientation of some of the borescope-mapped fractures.

A substantial degree of uncertainty is associated with the possible
flow paths shown in Figure 4. The uncertainty is caused by the lack
of dyed core samples to match most image anomalies and the fact that
borescope data is insufficient to establish which fractures conduct
water. Post experiment coreholes were drilled between boreholes 2,
3, and 4 to locate stained fractures within the measurement plane.
This can be observed in Figure 5 where the location of recovered dyed
core is compared with an alterant image. Fractures mapped along
boreholes 2, 3, 4 and along the post-experiment boreholes are also
shown (orientation data for the fractures within the post-experiment
boreholes is unavailable; therefore orientation data are not
included). Figure 5 shows the range of depths along which the
recovered dyed core could have been located. This range of depths
is determined by the length of unrecovered core for each corresponding drill run. Figure 5 shows that the location ranges of 3 dyed
pieces match the location of 3 image anomalies and that the remaining
image anomalies occur along regions where no dyed samples were recovered. Figure 5 also shows that most image anomalies occur where
fractures were detected with the borescope.

The lack of dyed core to match several image anomalies may mean
that: a) no tracer flow occurred where image anomalies are present,
or b) the drilling process destroyed the evidence. At present, we
favor the latter explanation for the following reasons. All of the
recovered core was broken into small pieces and some of the core was
destroyed by the drilling. Many of the core faces are polished and
rounded suggesting grinding; dye could have been destroyed because
it only coated fracture surfaces and did not penetrate the matrix of
the rock. Furthermore, it is unlikely that the match observed in
Figure 4 between image anomalies and fracture location and
orientation is accidental. Additional drilling using different
equipment is planned to minimize core damage and obtain additional
data to continue the evaluation of these results.

5   SUMMARY AND CONCLUSIONS

In-situ electromagnetic measurements have been performed to evaluate
the applicability of alterant geophysical tomography to delineate
flow paths in fractured welded tuff. In-situ measurements of
electromagnetic attenuation factor at 300 MHz have been made before,
during, and after a water based dye tracer flowed through the rock
mass. From these data, alterant geotomographs were constructed and

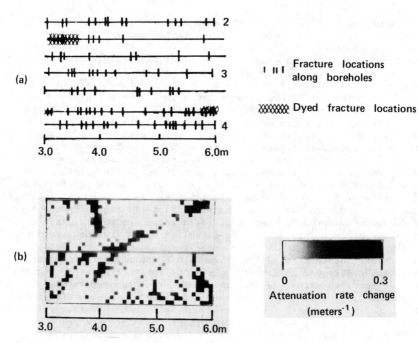

Figure 5. Comparison of an alterant tomograph, fracture location data, and the locations of recovered dyed fractures.

tracer flow paths were postulated. The following tentative conclusions can be reached based on evidence available at present.

1. There is indirect evidence suggesting that the tomograph anomalies represent fracture flow. The principal anomalies observed in the alterant tomographs coincide in orientation and location with fractures mapped by borescope surveys. Generally, mapped fractures can be matched with image anomalies which define lineal trends. The image anomalies changed and, in one case enlarged as tracer flow progressed. Analyses of measurement noise in the alterant images have shown that the major image anomalies observed are caused by factors other than noise.

2. Parts of 3 image anomalies coincide with the location of dyed core, but the remaining anomalies exist where no dyed core was recovered. Either the unverified anomalies are erroneous, or the drilling process destroyed the dyed fracture faces. Additional investigations, including coring, are planned to evaluate these possibilities.

3. The borescope logs yielded valuable fracture data which could be correlated with the tomographic data. However, from the borescope data alone, it was difficult to measure fracture orientation accurately and interpolate fractures between boreholes spaced only 30 cm apart, and it was impossible to tell which fractures would conduct water. Nevertheless, the value of correlating borescope and tomographic data suggests that the two techniques be used together in any attempt to map water flow in a rock mass.

814

6. ACKNOWLEDGMENTS

The authors are grateful to L. Ballou, R. J. Lytle, F. Heuze, E. F. Laine and J. Yow of Lawrence Livermore National Laboratory for helpful advice. This experiment was made possible by the generous cooperation of R. Zimmerman and R. Schuck from Sandia National Laboratory. This work was funded by the U.S. Department of Energy - Nevada Nuclear Waste Storage Investigations. Work performed under the auspices of the U.S. Department of Energy by the Lawrence Livermore National Laboratory under contract number W-7405-ENG-48.

7. REFERENCES

Daily, W.D. & A. L. Ramirez 1984. In-situ porosity distribution using geophysical tomography. Geophysical Research Letters. 11: 614-616.

Johnstone, K. J. & K. Wolfsberg 1980. Evaluation of tuff as a medium for nuclear waste repository: interim status report on the properties of tuff. Sandia National Laboratory, SAND 80-1464, Albuquerque, New Mexico.

Lager, D. L. & R. J. Lytle 1977. Determining a subsurface electromagnetic profile from high-frequency measurements by applying reconstruction technique algorithms. Radio Science, 12: 249-260.

Langkopf, B. S. & E. Eshom 1982. Site exploration for rock mechanics field tests in the Grouse Canyon Member, Belted Range Tuff, U12g tunnel complex, Nevada Test Site. Sandia National Laboratory, SAND 81-1897, Albuquerque, New Mexico.

Poley, J. Ph., J. J. Nooteboom & P. J. deWaal 1978. Use of VHF dielectric measurements for borehole formation analysis. Log Analyst, May-June. 8-30.

Ramirez, A. L. & R. J. Lytle 1984. Investigation of fracture flow paths using alterant geophysical tomography. Lawrence Livermore National Laboratory, UCRL-91621, paper submitted to the International Journal of Rock Mechanics and Mining Sciences.

Yow, J.L. Waste package environment conceptual test plan for exploratory shaft at Yucca Mountain. Lawrence Livermore National Laboratory, UCID in preparation.

Thermal convection through a system of rigid idealized fissures

GAURAV RAJEN & F.A.KULACKI
University of Delaware, Newark, USA

1 INTRODUCTION

Convection heat transfer in fissured media is a transport process of great relevance in the design and licensing of underground nuclear waste repositories, and in several other fields such as geothermal energy extraction and petroleum engineering. Canisters containing either spent fuel rod bundles or high level immobilized waste may be buried in tight, fluid-bearing crystalline rock which is (characteristically) fissured, or else has the possibility of becoming fissured owing to thermal stresses created by decay heat generation. The drilling and excavation required for emplacement of the waste package also will create fissures in the near-field environment of both the canister and the repository. Should the fissures propagate and become liquid saturated some time after the point of safe retrieval of the waste package, the possibility of transport of radionuclides to the ground water and surface environment becomes an issue. In this case, buoyancy enhanced convective transport of heat and species in the fissure system needs to be investigated.

Hydrothermal flow in fissured reservoirs has often been modelled as convective flow in saturated uniform porous media. Excellent reviews of the literature on convective heat transfer in porous media can be found in the works of Cheng (1978), Prasad (1983), and Combarnous and Bories (1973), among others. Another approach has been to measure orientations and spacings of fissures, assume a model of aperture distributions and thus derive a permeability tensor for the rock mass (Montazer & Hustrulid 1983, Witherspoon, Cook, & Gale 1981). The fissured rock is then modelled as an anisotropic porous medium. However, an equivalent permeability tensor can be easily determined only for simple geometric models of fissured media (Snow 1965). In general, statistical analyses are required, and there remains a degree of arbitrariness in assigning a distribution of aperture form and size to the fissures. Another problem is that the effective permeability depends on inter-connected fissures, and not on disconnected "dead-end" fissures, voids, etc. (Norton & Knapp 1977). Therefore, highly detailed mappings of the fissure systems around an excavated repository are required, but these cannot be easily obtained (Brace 1979). The level of detail required in mapping the fissure geometry is also open to question. Laboratory and numerical studies of geometrically simple fissure systems could resolve some of these problems.

The literature on thermal convection in fissured media is sparse but is growing rapidly, as the topic is of great current interest.

817

Interest in geothermal energy extraction led to several analytical studies being performed quite a few years ago on the temperature of water flowing through a set of infinite equally spaced fissures, a distance 'ℓ' apart. The analyses were for a prescribed flow rate of water, i.e., forced convection. Bodvarsson (1969) presented results for the temperature of water flowing through a single fissure, i.e., $\ell = \infty$. Romm (1972) solved the problem of finite ℓ. Gringarten, Witherspoon, and Ohnishi (1975) presented dimensionless values of ℓ ranging from 0.5 to infinity. Their results provide a suitable reference to test the validity of numerical codes which model convection through a discrete set of fissures.

Analytical investigation of thermal convection in porous media containing fissures has been quite limited. McKibbin and O'Sullivan (1980) have solved the problem of the onset of convection in a porous medium consisting of two and three layers of differing permeability. Masuoka, Katsuhara, Nakazono, and Isozaki (1978) presented results for the onset of convection, and flow patterns in a porous layer containing two layers of different media. Heat transfer results for slightly supercritical convection in layered porous media were presented by McKibbin and O'Sullivan (1981) in an extension of their earlier work. McKibbin and Tyvand (1982, 1983, 1984) in a series of papers studied multilayered porous media composed of alternating layers of different permeability. In the most recent of these publications, they consider the case of one of the layers being very thin and of high permeability--the "crack" limit. Calculated stream line patterns indicate that the flow in the thin layers is almost totally along the cracks, and local or small-scale convection is absent. The more relevant problem in the present context includes vertical as well as horizontal cracks, and treats a wider range of Rayleigh numbers than is possible by analytical techniques alone. The use of numerical methods is, therefore, unavoidable.

Surveys by Pinder (1979) and Wang, Tsang, and Sterbentz (1980) give accounts of the state of the art of modelling coupled hydrothermal flow in underground reservoirs. In a recent paper, Noorishad, Tsang, and Witherspoon (1984) describe a numerical code (ROCMAS) which has been used to solve for the thermal, fluid, and stress fields in the environment of an embedded heater. In the problem domain, they have included one large deformable horizontal fissure. They also provide a review of recent progress in the analysis of coupled fluid-solid-thermal processes.

The ROCMAS code (Noorishad & Ayatollahi 1980) uses linear finite elements to model the flow in the fissures. Other computer codes which exist, e.g., CCC (Bodvarsson & Lippman 1980), GWTHERM (Runchal, Trager & Segal 1979), SHAFT79 (Pruess & Schroeder 1980), etc., need a large number of nodes with a non-uniform irregular distribution to model a fissured porous system. If the fissures are considered as deformable, a fissure aperture-effective stress formula, and a fissure permeability-aperture formula are required. As the number of fissures in the problem domain becomes large, it becomes impossible to discretely model each fissure. The concept of a "fissure-phase," analogous to a porous medium, becomes useful. This approach, commonly known as the "double-porosity" model, assumes that there is a sufficiently large number of fissures in the domain, such that the problem becomes one of overlapping continua, i.e., a network of fissures through which the fluid moves overlaps a network composed of primary pores in the porous medium.

The double-porosity concept introduced initially by Barenblatt, Zheltov, and Kochina (1960), to study flow through fissured rock, is now used not only for fissured rock, but also reservoirs containing layers of high permeability in a low permeability matrix. A review of current knowledge of reservoirs exhibiting double porosity behavior is available in the recent paper by Gringarten (1984).

A finite element Galerkin method for the solution of isothermal flow in a double porosity medium has been developed by Duguid (1973), Duguid and Lee (1973, 1977), and Duguid and Abel (1974). They assumed non-Darcy flow in the fissures, and explicitly modelled the transient fluid transfer between the fissure phase and the porous medium.

O'Neill (1978) has carried out what appears to be the first comprehensive study of both heat and fluid transport in a fissured porous medium. A single pressure head variable was used to evaluate pore and fissure velocities, and two distinct temperature variables, one to represent the temperature of the fluid in the fissures, and another to represent the temperature in the porous medium (pore fluid and solid phase). Heat transfer between the fissure fluid and the porous medium was modelled with a heat transfer coefficient comprising two parts. One of these arises out of heat conduction, and the other out of the mixing and exchange of fluid between the fissures and the porous matrix. The heat transfer coefficient used by O'Neill was based on analytical considerations and an order of magnitude analysis. How closely the theoretical arguments approximate reality needs to be determined by careful laboratory and field experiments.

The focus of O'Neill's study was the effect of a pumped recharge to a geothermal reservoir under exploitation, and therefore buoyancy terms were neglected. His work, thus, needs to be extended to buoyancy dominated flows.

Basic to the double porosity approach is the assumption that in a small representative elementary volume (REV) of the fissured porous medium, there exist a large number of fissures such that locally averaged properties of the pore and fissure system can be used to formulate macroscopic transport equations. The underlying assumption of a suitable REV is discussed in some detail by O'Neill: "Obviously, media exist which violate this condition, for example, porous rock intersected by a large tectonic fault, widely separated from other faults." For the case of a nuclear waste repository, the relevant fissures range from grain to repository size, and are site specific (Brace 1979). The definition of a suitable REV, therefore, is not easily accomplished.

Two major problems remain in the characterization of thermal convection in a fissured media. These are,

1. What constitutes a sufficient number of fissures so that discrete fissures need not be individually modelled?

2. Should the sufficiently fissured system be modelled as an anisotropic porous medium, with a permeability derived from fissure aperture, orientation, etc., or should the double-porosity approach be used?

This paper presents results of a numerical study of geometrically simple fissure systems. Results have been obtained for the problem of steady thermal convection in an impermeable layer riven with fluid-saturated horizontal and vertical fissures, as shown in Fig. 1. The problem domain is a two-dimensional square region with impervious boundaries, and has a constant temperature line heat source along part or all of the lower boundary. The upper boundary is maintained at a constant sink temperature, and the remaining boundary surfaces are adiabatic. Results of a finite element solution to this problem which is essentially one of convection in the fissures and conduction in the matrix, have been obtained. Non-dimensional temperature and stream-line contours have been obtained for several Rayleigh numbers, and fissure geometries. Local Nusselt numbers for the heat source have also been obtained for each of the cases. The results presented are for the case of eleven horizontal and eleven vertical fissured paths of constant width and periodicity. The width to periodicity ratio of the fissures is varied in the cases considered.

2 FORMULATION AND SOLUTION

Isothermal steady-state flow through a system of rigid idealized fissures has been analyzed by Wilson and Witherspoon (1974), who used linear one-dimensional finite elements to represent the fissures. Their results compared very favorably with experimental data. Basically, their analysis assumed that the flow within the fissures is uniform (i.e. plug flows), and there is no pressure loss at the intersections of the fissure system. A similar approach is used here to model the buoyancy induced convective flow within the fissures.

Laminar creeping flow is assumed to hold within a fissure, and that the fluid is in local thermal equilibrium with the surrounding matrix. This means that every point in the domain has associated with it a unique temperature, the temperature across a fissure being constant. The assumption of laminar creeping flow means that Darcy's equation is valid as the equation of fluid transport. The Boussinesq approximation is made use of, and the fluid and thermal transport equations are coupled only through the changes in the density of the fluid.

2.1 Fissure System

In indicial notation, the equations of continuity, motion, and thermal transport for the fissures can be written as, (Hickox & Gartling 1981)

$$\partial v_i / \partial x_i = 0 \tag{1}$$

$$v_i = - K_f/\mu \, [\frac{\partial p'}{\partial x_i} - \rho_o g\beta(T-T_o) \frac{\partial y}{\partial x_i}] \tag{2}$$

$$\frac{\partial}{\partial x_i} \, [k_f \frac{\partial T}{\partial x_i}] = \rho_o c v_i \frac{\partial T}{\partial x_i} \tag{3}$$

In equation (2), the possibility of the fissures being filled with granular materials is accounted for, and thus, a volume averaged equation is used with an effective permeability K_f. The density, specific heat, and thermal conductivity are for the fluid saturated fissure material.

For computational convenience, and ease of graphical representation of the derived fissure fluid velocities, a representative stream function is defined for the fissured domain. This stream function is to be understood as giving the velocities at every nodal point in the computational domain (the nodal points being situated at the intersections of the fissures) and not being continuous through the impermeable matrix.

Using dimensionless variables, and the stream function form, one obtains,

$$\frac{\partial^2 \psi}{\partial x^2} \frac{\partial^2 \psi}{\partial y^2} = R_a \frac{\partial \theta}{\partial x} \tag{4}$$

$$\frac{\partial \psi}{\partial x} \frac{\partial \theta}{\partial y} - \frac{\partial \psi}{\partial y} \frac{\partial \theta}{\partial x} = \frac{\partial^2 \theta}{\partial x^2} + \frac{\partial^2 \theta}{\partial x^2} \tag{5}$$

820

where R_a is the Rayleigh number based on the fissure permeability and properties, and the height of the domain. In the present work, the height of the domain is taken equal to the width D., i.e., a domain aspect ratio of unity. The dimensionless stream function is defined as,

$$v_x = \frac{\partial \psi}{\partial y} \left(\frac{L}{\alpha_f}\right) \tag{6a}$$

$$v_y = \frac{\partial \psi}{\partial x} \left(\frac{L}{\alpha_f}\right) \tag{6b}$$

2.2 Matrix System

As indicated previously, the matrix is assumed impermeable, and Equations (1) to (3) for the matrix reduce to the heat conduction equation, which in dimensionless form is,

$$\frac{\partial}{\partial x} \left(k_m \frac{\partial \theta}{\partial x}\right) + \frac{\partial}{\partial y} \left(k_m \frac{\partial \theta}{\partial y}\right) = 0 \tag{7}$$

In the ensuing analysis, to restrict the number of different variables which affect the problem, it is assumed that the fissure thermal conductivity is the same as the matrix conductivity. The fissures are assumed to be of constant width, b, and the length from the center-line of one fissure intersection to another, ℓ, is also assumed constant. In the cases considered, the width b_h of the horizontal fissures may be different from the width b_v of the vertical fissures.

Letting S_a, S_q, and S_c denote the adiabatic, heated and cooled portions of the boundary, respectively, the relevant fluid and thermal boundary conditions may be written as,

$$\psi = 0 \qquad \text{on } S_a, S_q, S_c \tag{8}$$

$$\frac{\partial \theta}{\partial x_i} n_i = 0 \qquad \text{on } S_a \tag{9}$$

$$\theta = 1 \qquad \text{on } S_q \tag{10}$$

$$\theta = 0 \qquad \text{on } S_c \tag{11}$$

The mathematical problem posed by equations (4), (5), and (7) with the boundary conditions (8), (9), (10) and (11), has been solved using a finite element method. Linear triangle elements are used to model the heat conduction. One-dimensional line elements are used for the convection. The finite element formulations for the heat conduction linear triangle element and the convection line element are standard and will not be repeated here (Zienciwicz 1984).

The grid used in the computations consisted of 121 grid points with 200 triangular elements and 220 linear elements. Combarnous (1970) used a uniform grid of 10 x 10 nodes to solve a very similar problem, i.e., a porous layer heated from below, and obtained good correlation with experimental results. By making the fissures cover the complete domain, the present program could also be used to solve for the case of a uniform porous media. Results thus obtained were found to be essentially identical to those of Combarnous.

A Picard iteration scheme was used to solve the coupled set of equations obtained by application of the finite element method, with the convergence limit set at 10^{-3}. A check on total energy conservation was carried out and was found to be well satisfied (to well within 1 percent for the fully heated bottom surface and within 3 percent for the partially heated bottom surface).

3 RESULTS

All the cases considered are for eleven horizontal and eleven vertical fissured paths with fissures lying along the bounding surfaces. The parameters which are varied are as follows:

The ratio of the length of the heated surface, d, to the width of the cavity D is varied. It is either 1.0 (fully heated bottom surface) or 0.5 (half heated bottom surface).

The horizontal fissure width, b_h, and the vertical fissure width, b_v, are varied. Four cases are considered: (a) $b_h/\ell = 0.1$, $b_v/\ell = 0.1$; (b) $b_h/\ell = 0.25$, $b_v/\ell = 0.25$; (c) $b_h/\ell = 0.25$, $b_v/\ell = 0.1$; and (d) $b_h/\ell = 0.1$, $b_v/\ell = 0.25$.

The Rayleigh number is varied and takes on values from 200~1000, which represents large Rayleigh numbers for fissured media where permeability is in the order of $10^{-8}m^2$.

Figure 2 shows streamline and temperature isotherms for the case d/D = 1.0, $b_h/\ell = 0.1$, $b_v/\ell = 0.1$, and Rayleigh number = 200. The solution is that of conduction, showing that circulation has not yet been initiated. Figure 3 shows the effect of increased Rayleigh number (equal to 500) for the same fissure geometry. A clockwise circulatory flow has been set up, and the temperature isotherms are correspondingly distorted. Hot fluid rises along the left vertical wall, and cold fluid descends along the right vertical wall.

There is yet no temperature inversion in the core, which is characteristic of very strongly circulating cavity flows. In Figure (4), in which results are displayed for the same geometric configuration at a Rayleigh number of 1000, such a temperature inversion is evident in the core regions. Figure 5 illustrates the increase in heat transfer from the bottom surface, for the above three cases, with increasing Rayleigh number. As the Rayleigh number is increased from 500 to 1000, there is no appreciable change in the heat transfer from the region of ascending hot fluid. However, the heat transfer is appreciably increased in the region of descending cold fluid by an increase in Rayleigh number. For the fissured domain under consideration, it is easy to determine an effective permeability which corresponds to an equivalent porous medium. With no anisotropy in fissure widths, i.e., both horizontal and vertical fissures having a width 'b', it is possible to show that the results obtained for the fissured domain at a Rayleigh number R_a, can be related to results obtained for a porous domain at an equivalent Rayleigh number R_a^*, defined as,

$$R_a^* = \frac{b}{\ell} \cdot R_a \qquad (12)$$

For the results of Figure (3) therefore, the equivalent Rayleigh number is 50. This corresponds to a Rayleigh number of slightly supercritical flow, and an analytical estimate of the average vertical heat flux measured by an average Nusselt number is possible. Table 1 compares computed average Nusselt numbers with analytical estimates obtained from formulas provided in McKibbin and Tyvand (1984). For the anisotropic case, the equivalent Rayleigh number is defined as

822

Table 1. Computed and theoretical Nusselt numbers for d/D = 1.0, R_a = 500, and different fissure widths.

b_h/ℓ	b_v/ℓ	N_u computed	N_u theoretical
0.1	0.1	1.45	1.53
0.25	0.1	1.89	2.80
0.1	C.25	2.19	2.80

$$R_a^* = \frac{b_v}{\ell} R_a \tag{13}$$

For the isotropic case, it appears that a domain containing eleven vertical and eleven horizontal fissures can be treated, with little loss in accuracy, as an equivalent porous domain. However, anisotropy in the fissures does not translate as well into an anisotropic porous domain.

Figure 6 shows the effect of increasing fissure width on the convection. In this case, we have d/D = 1.0, b_h/ℓ = 0.25, b_v/ℓ = 0.25, Rayleigh number = 500. As compared to Figure 3, which is the corresponding case of Rayleigh number = 500, b_h/ℓ = 0.1, b_v/ℓ = 0.1, the increased convection is evident in the higher values of the stream-function, and the greatly distorted isotherms.

Figure 7 presents results for the case d/D = 1.0, b_h/ℓ = 0.25, b_v/ℓ = 0.1, Rayleigh number = 500. An interesting effect of the anisotropy in the horizontal and vertical fissures, one not entirely expected, is the increased heat transfer in the region of upwardly moving fluid.

This effect is even more prominent for the case of a localized heat source d/D = 0.5, and is discussed later.

Figure 8 presents results for the case of d/D = 1.0, b_h/ℓ = 0.1, b_v/ℓ = 0.25, Rayleigh number = 500. In this case, heat transfer in the region of upwardly moving fluid is decreased, but in the regions where cold fluid comes down it is greatly increased.

Figure 9 graphs the local Nusselt number at a Rayleigh number of 500, and d/D = 1.0, for various values of b_h/ℓ and b_v/ℓ.

As noted earlier, the effect of anisotropy in horizontal and vertical fissure widths is markedly different in the regions of upward moving hot fluid and downward moving cold fluid. Several conflicting mechanisms appear to be operative in the case of anisotropy, and detailed parametric studies are needed to be able to isolate them. It appears that over a hot surface, increased vertical permeability is needed in the regions of descending fluid to enhance the heat transfer, whereas in the regions of ascending fluid, increased horizontal permeability is what enhances the heat transfer.

Figures 10, 11, 12, 13 illustrate streamlines and temperature isotherms for the case of d/D = 0.5, Rayleigh number = 500, and b_h/ℓ, and b_v/ℓ corresponding to the pairs (0.1, 0.1), (0.25, 0.25), (0.25, 0.1), and (0.1, 0.25). The localized heat source creates a plume-like flow over itself, and this is exemplified in the shapes of the isotherms. The effect of anisotropy is even more striking for the localized heat source, as compared to the fully heated bottom surface. The heat transfer would be expected to be greatest for the case of widest horizontal and vertical fissures, and lowest for the case of the narrowest horizontal and vertical fissures. However, as is shown in Figure 14, the lowest heat transfer is when the vertical fissures are wider than the horizontal fissures. In this case, the vertical effective permeability is greater than the horizontal effective permeability. This result is qualitatively in

823

keeping with the analytical results obtained by Kvernwold and Tyvand (1979) for anisotropic porous media. Their results for a homogeneous porous medium show that a greater vertical permeability and a lower horizontal permeability will increase the critical Rayleigh number, and thus may decrease the heat transfer obtained at supercritical convection.

Correspondingly, for a greater horizontal permeability than vertical permeability, the analytical results of Kvernwold and Tyvand (1979) predict a possible enhancement of the rate of heat transfer. As shown in Figure 14, the greatest heat transfer is for the case of $b_h/\ell = 0.25$, and $b_v/\ell = 0.1$; and this, again, is in qualitative agreement with the analytical results. Of course, the net enhancement of heat transfer is not simply a function of anisotropy. However, it appears that for a nuclear waste repository, which probably will be operating in the regime of slightly supercritical convection, anisotropy in the spread and width of horizontal and vertical fissures could significantly increase or decrease heat transfer rates from the repository.

4 CONCLUSIONS

This paper presents a limited study of thermal convection through a system of rigid, idealized fissures. The results obtained are based on the simplifying assumptions of rigid fissures with uniform width and periodicity, and an impermeable matrix. Although highly idealized, the model is able to characterize the effects of varying fissure geometry and periodicity on convection in a fissured domain. Anisotropy in the horizontal and vertical fissures could significantly alter the heat transfer rate from the repository, as well as mitigate or enhance the spread of accidentally released radionuclides.

5 NOMENCLATURE

b	width of fissure, m
c	specific heat, J/kg-K
d	horizontal extent of heated surface, m
D	horizontal extent of domain, m
g	gravitational acceleration, m/s^2
h	heat transfer coefficient W/m^2K
k	thermal conductivity, W/m-K
K	permeability, m^2
ℓ	fissure spacing, or periodicity, m
L	vertical extent of domain, m
N_u	Nusselt number, hL/k
p'	total pressure, $p + \rho_o gy$, P_a
p	pressure, P_a
R_a	Rayleigh number, $g\beta k_f L(T_1-T_o)/\alpha_f \nu$
R_a^*	equivalent Rayleigh number, $(b/\ell)R_a$
S_a	adiabatic boundary, m
S_c	coded boundary, m
S_q	heated boundary, m
T	temperature, K
T_1	temperature of heated portion of lower boundary, K

T$_o$ temperature of upper boundary, K
v$_i$ velocity component in the fissure, m/s
x   horizontal Cartesian co-ordinate, m
X   dimensionless horizontal co-ordinate, x/L
y   vertical Cartesian co-ordinate, m
Y   dimensionless vertical co-ordinate, y/L

α thermal diffusivity, m^2/s
β isobaric coefficient of thermal expansion
θ dimensionless temperature, $(T-T_o)/(T_1-T_o)$
ν kinematic viscosity, m^2/s
ρ density, kg/m^3
ψ dimensionless stream function, Eq. (6)

Subscripts

f   fissure value
h   horizontal fissure value
i   Cartesian index, i = 1,2
m   matrix value
o   reference value
v   vertical fissure value

REFERENCES

Barenblatt, G.E., Zheltov, I.P., and Kochina, I.N. 1960. Basic concepts
  in the theory of homogeneous liquids in fissured rocks. J. of Appl.
  Math. and Mech. 24: 1286-1303.
Bodvarsson, G. 1969. On the temperature of water flowing through frac-
  tures. J. of Geophysical Res. 74: 1987-1992.
Bodvarsson, G., and Lippmann, J.M. 1980. Numerical model CCC. In Proceed-
  ings, Workshop on numerical modelling of thermophysical flow in frac-
  tured rock masses, Lawrence Berkeley Laboratory, Report LBL-11566.
Brace, W. 1979. Laboratory Measurement Workshop. In Proceedings, ONWI
  Workshop on thermomechanical modelling for a hardrock waste repository,
  Laurence Livermore Laboratory, Technical Report UCAR-10043.
Cheng, P. 1978. Heat transfer in geothermal systems. In J.P.Hartnett and
  T.Irvine (eds.), Advances in heat transfer. New York: Academic Press.
Combarnous, M. and Bories, S.A. 1973. Natural convection in a sloping
  porous layer. J. of Fluid Mech. 57: 63-79.
Combarnous, M. 1970. Convection naturelle et convection mixte dans ure
  couche poreuse horizontale. Revue Generale Theoretique 108: 1355-1375.
  (In French).
Duguid, J.O. 1973. Flow in fractured porous media. Ph.D.Thesis, Princeton
  University.
Duguid, J.O. and Abel, J.F. 1974. Finite element Galerkin method for
  analysis of flow in fractured porous media. In J.T.Oden, O.C.Zienciwicz,
  R.H.Gallagher and C.Taylor (eds.), Finite element methods in flow prob-
  lems. Huntsville: University of Alabama Press.
Duguid, J.O. and Lee, P.C.Y. 1973. Flow in fractured porous media. Dept.
  of Civil and Geological Engg. Research Report 73-WR-1, Princeton Univ.
Dugid, J.O. and Lee, P.C.Y. 1977. Flow in fractured porous media. Water
  Resources Res. 13: 558-566.
Gringarten, A.C. 1984. Interpretation of tests in fissured and multi-
  layered reservoirs with double porosity behaviour: theory and practice.
  J. of Pet. Tech., April issue: 547-564.

Gringarten, A.C., Witherspoon, P.A. and Ohnishi, Y. 1975. Theory of heat extraction from fractured hot dry rock. J. of Geophysical Res. 80: 1120-1124.

Hickox, C.E. and Gartling, D.K. 1981. A numerical study of natural convection in a horizontal porous layer subjected to an end-to-end temperature difference. ASME J. of Heat Transfer. 103: 797-802.

Kvernwold, O. and Tyvand, P.A. 1979. Non-linear thermal convection in anisotropic porous media. J. Fluid Mech. 90: 609-624.

Masuoka, T., Katsahura, T., Nakazono, Y. and Isozaki, S. 1978. Onset of convection and flow patterns in a porous layer of two different media. Heat Transfer - Japanese Research. 7: 39-52.

McKibbin, R. and O'Sullivan, M.J. 1981. Heat transfer in a layered porous medium heated from below. J. Fluid Mech. 111: 141-173.

McKibbin, R. and Tyvand, P.A. 1982. Anisotropic modelling of thermal convection in multilayered porous media. J. Fluid Mech. 118: 315-339.

McKibbin, R. and Tyvand, P.A. 1983. Thermal convection in a porous medium composed of alternating thick and thin layers. Int. J. Heat and Mass Transfer. 26: 761-780.

McKibbin, R. and Tyvand, P.A. 1984. Thermal convection in a porous medium with horizontal cracks. Int. J. Heat and Mass Transfer. 27: 1007-1023.

Montazer, P.M. and Hustrulid, W.A. 1983. An investigation of fracture permeability around an underground opening in metamorphic rocks. Technical Report, OCRD, Battelle Memorial Institute, BMI/OCRD-4(s).

Noorishad, J. and Ayatollahi, M.S. 1980. Program, ROCMAS - introduction and user's guide. Lawrence Berkeley Laboratory. Report LBL-12987.

Noorishad, J., Tsang, C.F. and Witherspoon, P.A. 1984. Coupled thermal-hydraulic-mechanical phenomena in saturated porous rocks: numerical approach. J. of Geophysical Res. 89: 10356-10373.

Norton, D. and Knapp, R. 1977. Transport phenomena in hydrothermal systems - the nature of porosity. Am. J. of Science. 277: 913-936.

O'Neill, K. 1978. The transient three-dimensional transport of liquid and heat in fractured porous media. Ph.D. Thesis. Princeton University.

Pinder, G.F. 1979. State-of-the-art review of geothermal reservoir modelling. Lawrence Berkeley Laboratory, Technical Report LBL-9093.

Prasad, V. 1983. Natural convection in porous media - an experimental and numerical study of vertical annular and rectangular enclosures. Ph.D.Thesis. University of Delaware.

Pruess, K. and Schroeder, R.C. 1980. SHAFT79 User's Manual. Lawrence Berkeley Laboratory, Report LBL-10861.

Romm, E.S. 1972. On one case of heat transfer in fractured rock. Problemy Razrabotki Mestorozhdeny Polznykh Iskopaenykh Severa, Leningrad Mining Institute. (In Russian).

Runchal, A., Traeger, J. and Segal, G. 1979. Program EP21 (GWTHERM) - two-dimensional fluid flow, heat and mass transport in porous media. Advanced Technology Group. Dames and Moore, Technical Note, TN-LA-34.

Snow, D.T. 1965. A parallel plate model of fractured permeable media. Ph.D.Thesis. University of California at Berkeley.

Wang, J.S.Y., Sterbentz, R. and Tsang, C.F. 1980. The state-of-the-art of numerical modelling of thermohydrologic flow in fractured rock masses. Lawrence Berkeley Laboratory, Technical Report LBL-10524.

Wilson, C.R. and Witherspoon, P.A. 1974. Steady-state flow in rigid networks of fractures. Water Resources Res. 10: 328-336.

Witherspoon, P.A., Cook, N.G.W. and Gale, J.E. 1981. Geologic storage of radioactive waste, field studies in Sweden. Science 211: 894-900.

Zienciwicz, O.C. 1984. The finite element method, Third Edition. London: McGraw Hill.

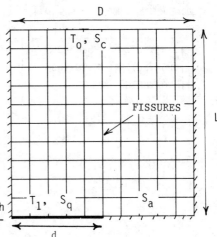

Figure 1 : Computational Domain with 11 x 11 fissures, and localized iso-thermal heat source along bottom.

$\psi = 0$ $\theta = 0$

Figure 2: Streamlines (a) and Isotherms (b) for $R_a = 200$, $d/D = 1.0$, $b_h/\ell = 0.1$, $b_v/\ell = 0.1$

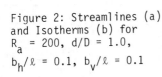

(a) $\Delta\psi = 0.02$ (b) $\Delta\theta = 0.1$

Figure 3: Streamlines (a) and Isotherms (b) for $R_a = 500$, $d/D = 1.0$, $b_h/\ell = 0.1$, $b_v/\ell = 0.1$

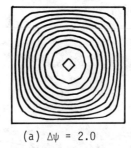
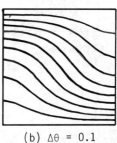

(a) $\Delta\psi = 2.0$ (b) $\Delta\theta = 0.1$

Figure 4: Streamlines (a) and Isotherms (b) for $R_a = 1000$, $d/D = 1.0$, $b_h/\ell = 0.1$, $b_v/\ell = 0.1$

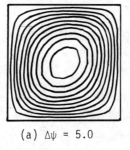

(a) $\Delta\psi = 5.0$ (b) $\Delta\theta = 0.1$

LOCAL NUSSELT NUMBER ALONG HEATED SURFACE

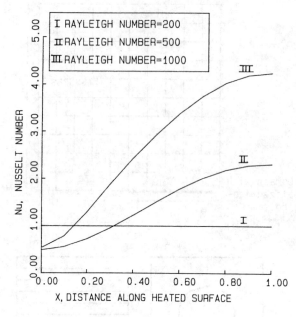

Figure 5: Local Nusselt numbers along heated surface for various Rayleigh numbers with $d/D = 1.0$, $b_h/\ell = 0.1$ $b_v/\ell = 0.1$

LOCAL NUSSELT NUMBERS ALONG HEATED SURFACE

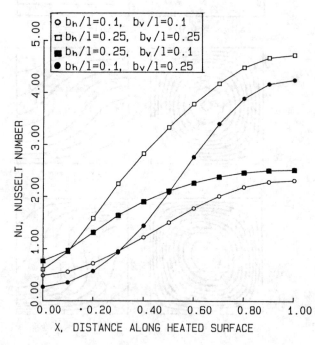

Figure 9: Local Nusselt numbers along heated surface for various fissure widths, with $R_a = 500$, $d/D = 1.0$

Figure 6: Streamlines (a) and Isotherms (b) for R_a = 500, d/D = 1.0, b_h/ℓ = 0.25, b_v/ℓ = 0.25

(a) $\Delta\psi$ = 5.0   (b) $\Delta\theta$ = 0.1

Figure 7: Streamlines (a) and Isotherms (b) for R_a = 500, d/D = 1.0, b_h/ℓ = 0.25, b_v/ℓ = 0.1

(a) $\Delta\psi$ = 5.0   (b) $\Delta\theta$ = 0.1

Figure 8: Streamlines (a) and Isotherms (b) for R_a = 500, d/D = 1.0, b_h/ℓ = 0.1, b_v/ℓ = 0.25

(a) $\Delta\psi$ = 5.0   (b) $\Delta\theta$ =0.1

Figure 10: Streamlines (a) and Isotherms (b) for R_a = 500, d/D = 0.5, b_h/ℓ = 0.1, b_v/ℓ = 0.1

(a) $\Delta\psi$ = 2.0   (b) $\Delta\theta$ = 0.1

Figure 11: Streamlines (a) and Isotherms (b) for R_a = 500, d/D = 0.5, b_h/ℓ = 0.25, b_v/ℓ = 0.25

(a) $\Delta\psi$ = 5.0   (b) $\Delta\theta$ = 0.1

829

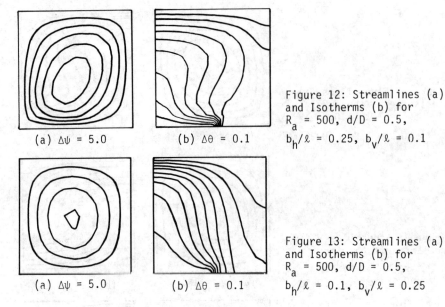

Figure 12: Streamlines (a) and Isotherms (b) for $R_a = 500$, $d/D = 0.5$, $b_h/\ell = 0.25$, $b_v/\ell = 0.1$

(a) $\Delta\psi = 5.0$ (b) $\Delta\theta = 0.1$

Figure 13: Streamlines (a) and Isotherms (b) for $R_a = 500$, $d/D = 0.5$, $b_h/\ell = 0.1$, $b_v/\ell = 0.25$

(a) $\Delta\psi = 5.0$ (b) $\Delta\theta = 0.1$

LOCAL NUSSELT NUMBERS ALONG HEATED SURFACE

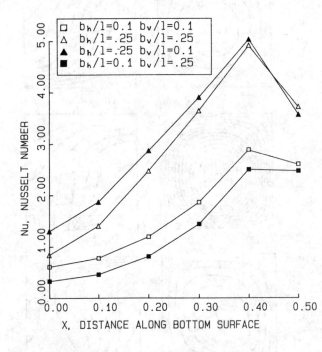

Figure 14: Local Nusselt numbers along heated surface for various fissure widths with $R_a = 500$, $d/D = 0.5$

ACKNOWLEDGEMENT
The authors appreciate the support of this work by the U.S. Nuclear Regulatory Commission under contract NRC-04-84-126.

Effect of stress on permeability of coal

SATYA HARPALANI
University of Arizona, Tucson, USA
Formerly at University of California, Berkeley, USA

MALCOLM J.McPHERSON
University of California, Berkeley, USA

1 INTRODUCTION

Over the past 30 years, emissions of methane into coal mines have increased significantly. This has occurred because of greater comminution of the coal by mechanized procedures, higher productivity, faster moving faces and a trend towards deeper workings (McPherson and Hood, 1981). In order to plan the ventilation requirements of a mine, it is important to have an estimate of the rate at which methane is emitted from source beds and migrates through the strata towards the workings.

Numerous computer models have been devised to simulate the release and migration of methane in strata surrounding mine workings, and to assist in the design of methane drainage systems. Most of these models rely upon a knowledge of the permeabilities of the coal and the associated strata. In order to achieve satisfactory simulations of gas migration, it is necessary to have a knowledge of the permeability of coal and its variation with respect to position and, hence, the relationships that exist between permeability and triaxial stress.

This paper examines the influence of applied stress - axial and hydrostatic - on the permeability and volumetric strain of coal. The results obtained have been used to interpret, mathematically, the relationship between stress and permeability.

2 SPECIMEN PREPARATION

One of the most important factors that influences the accuracy of permeability measurements is specimen preparation. Many rocks can be cored easily, cut and machined to the required size, but not coals which are friable. Various methods have been tried in the past to give cylinders of coal (Harpalani, 1985) but chipping has been a problem with each one of them. Patching the core with some kind of glue or cement has, therefore, usually been necessary to give smooth surfaces giving rise to an error due to variations in the actual cross sectional area of the specimen. A new technique was, therefore, investigated for this study.

A brick cutting bandsaw was used to slab the coal lump along the desired planes to give roughly rectangular prisms which were then shaped to approximate cylinders on a horizontal belt grinder. Hard plastic tubing, about half an inch in length, was glued to either end of the specimen and these ends clamped in a lathe machine. The specimen was then machined to the required diameter using a compressed air grinder, with a silicon carbide wheel, giving an excellent cylindrical surface. Lastly, the core faces were ground on a surface grinder to generate parallel and perpendicular faces.

It has been a routine procedure in the past to commence permeability tests by evacuating the samples to "clean" the internal voidage of any water vapour and adsorbed gases that might interfere with the permeability measurement (Somerton, 1974). However, during this investigation, it was observed that evacuation of coal at normal temperatures caused partial clogging of the flow paths and a consequential reduction in permeability. Evidence suggested that this may be due to liquefaction or sublimation of volatile materials at very low pressures. A technique to evacuate coal at low temperatures (-150 deg C) was developed, which avoided, or minimized this fall in permeability (Harpalani, 1984).

3   EXPERIMENTAL APPARATUS

For this investigation, it was necessary to design an experimental rig that permitted simultaneous measurement of applied stress and gas flowrate through the specimen. The experimental equipment is shown diagramatically on Figure 1.

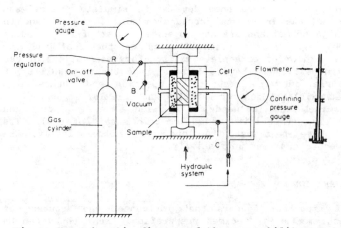

Figure 1. Schematic diagram of the permeability apparatus.

Independent control of the axial stress was maintained by mounting the cell in a stiff testing machine with fine load control, and of the radial stress by a hydraulic system exerting oil pressure on a 4 mm thick silicone rubber sheath around the coal. Gas was supplied via a regulator, with a pressure gauge to give the inlet pressure, to the top of the triaxial cell. Gas was led away from the lower end of the specimen to the soap bubble flow meter. After the first experiment, the equipment was modified to permit measurement of volumetric strain in addition to permeability.

832

When a cylindrical specimen is stressed axially, there is a reduction in its axial length, and an associated radial barreling (Poisson effect), causing an increase in the mean diameter of the specimen. For a determination of the change in bulk volume, it was necessary to monitor the variation in both axial and radial dimensions.

Two LVDT's (linear voltage differential transducers) were fitted on the sides of the cell to give the change in axial length of the specimen. An average of the two signals cancels out any effects arising from non-uniform strain on the two sides. To measure the change of volume in the radial direction, a small oil reservoir was fitted between the hydraulic pump and the cell body. It was possible to change the volume of this reservoir by a hand micrometer screw. Any radial dilation or contraction of the specimen caused a reaction on the pressure gauges that indicated confining stress. This could be return-ed to a desired value by changing the volume of oil in the oil cham-ber. Volume of oil taken from, or added to, the oil chamber, there-fore, gave the change in volume of the specimen in the radial direction.

4   PROCEDURE FOR TRIAXIAL PERMEABILITY TESTS

Two sets of permeability tests were conducted. The first involved variations in axial load while maintaining radial stress constant. The second utilized variations in hydrostatic stress. Mean gas pressure was held constant for every experiment.

The specimen to be tested was inserted into the cell. Two steel perforated discs were fitted to the flat ends of the specimen in order to apply the gas uniformly. Platens were then inserted into the ends of the cell. The upper one was connected to the gas cylinder and the lower one to the bubble meter. The entire cell assembly was placed in the center of the testing machine.

Using the fine control of the machine a small axial load was applied to the specimen. The specimen was then subjected to a confining pressure sufficient to seal the membrane against the solid surfaces. The regulator of the gas cylinder was adjusted to give a gas pressure of about 275 kPa (40 psi). Both confining and axial stresses were then increased simultaneously until their desired levels for that particular experiment were reached.

For the first set of experiments, commencing from an initial hydrostatic stress, the axial stress was increased in increments, flow rates being measured while the stress was kept constant at each stage. After the maximum stress had been reached, it was then decreased in steps, taking flow measurements at regular intervals until the initial low hydrostatic stress level was re-attained. The experiment was then stopped, leaving the specimen in the cell. Depending on the experiment, the procedure was repeated 2 or 3 times. The confining radial stress was kept constant for the entire experiment.

The procedure for the second set of experiments, to study the effect of hydrostatic stress, was similar except that as the axial stress was increased, the confining stress was raised simultaneously to remain equal to, and in phase with, the axial stress. Care was taken to ensure that the increase (or decrease) of confining and axial stresses was gradual and simultaneous. This prevented the specimen from being subjected to unduly high shear or tensile stress at any time.

5   EFFECT OF VARYING AXIAL STRESS

This section gives the results for experiments carried out at constant confining stress and gas pressure while the axial stress was varied. The axial stress was first increased from 3.07 to 13.16 MPa in increments of about 2 MPa. Three cycles were repeated with about 20 hours between each cycle.

The upper curve in Figure 2 shows the change in permeability with respect to axial stress level for one experiment. As had been noticed earlier (Gawuga, 1979), stressing caused a reduction in flowrate, this reduction being higher at the initial increase in stress. On destressing, the path followed by the permeability was lower, indicating that a part of the strain, during stressing, was irreversible. The experiment was stopped and the specimen left under a lightly stressed condition (300 psi) for 19 hours. When the experiment was started the next day, the flowrate was found to be much lower than that measured at the end of the first run under identical stress and pressure conditions. The cycle was repeated a second time. The second curve in Figure 2 shows the variation in permeability with change in axial stress.

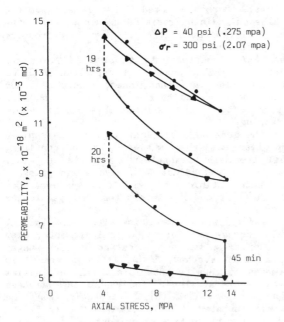

Figure 2. Variation of permeability with change in axial stress.

After a period of 19 hours, a third cycle was started, following a similar procedure. However, at the end of the increasing stress part of the cycle, the specimen was left in its stressed condition (1400 psi) for 45 minutes. This revealed significant information regarding the effect that stress level has on coal permeability. On restarting the experiment, the flowrate was far below its last value. Also, when the stress was gradually released, the flowrate indicated a lower degree of recovery for the entire destressing part of the cycle. The experiment was discontinued the next day due to very small flowrates.

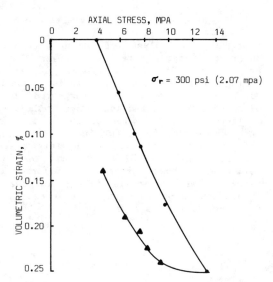

Figure 3. Variation of
volumetric strain with
change in axial stress.

This indicated clearly that high stress levels maintained for a
relatively short time are capable of reducing the permeability of coal
very significantly.

Before proceeding with the planned sequence of experiments, it was
felt by the authors that an explanation for this variation of
permeability should be sought. The equipment was, therefore, modified,
as explained in the third section, to enable measurement of volumetric
strain along with permeability.

Figure 3 shows the variation of volumetric strain with respect to
applied axial stress. Evidently, there is a decrease in volume of the
coal specimen when it is loaded axially, indicating that closure of
pores takes place during stressing. When the stress is released, only
a fraction of the pores reopen, causing an overall reduction in the
specimen volume. Some of the decrease in pore volume was, therefore,
elastic (recoverable) pore deformation and the rest was creep closure.
This appears to be a good explanation for the hysteresis observed in
the permeability-stress graphs. It also indicates that the overall
pore closure could be primarily responsible for the reduction in
permeability at the end of a cycle.

6   EFFECT OF VARYING HYDROSTATIC STRESS

Three samples were prepared for these tests: fresh cut coal obtained
from the working face of a mine; a sample taken from a face that had
been standing for several months; a sample from a surface borehole
core, all from the same mine. All tests in this series were conducted
at constant inlet gas pressures in the range of 0.276 to 0.55 MPa (40
to 80 psi). The hydrostatic stress was varied from 2.07 to 6.2 MPa
(300 to 900 psi) in increments of 100 psi. Two cycles of loading and
unloading were imposed upon each sample, during which permeability and
volumetric strain were measured.

835

6.1 Variation of permeability with hydrostatic stress

A preliminary analysis of the data revealed a picture similar to that obtained in earlier tests. However, there was much less evidence of hysteresis during a loading and unloading cycle than had been obtained during the earlier deviatoric (non-hydrostatic) stress tests. Furthermore, the results suggested a linear relationship between hydrostatic stress and logarithm of the permeability.

Figure 4 shows a plot of ln (k) against hydrostatic stres, σ, for the sample from fresh cut face. Following the first cycle of loading and unloading, the sample was left overnight in the triaxial cell, stressed hydrostatically at about 2MPa (300 psi). The second cycle commenced 18 hours after the completion of the first. Despite there being little hysteresis during any one cycle, the effect of creep (reduction in permeability under constant stress conditions) during the overnight period is apparent.

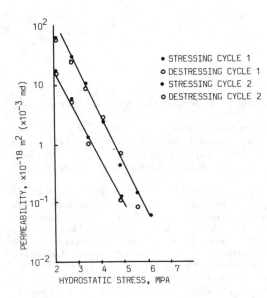

Figure 4. Variation of permeability with change in hydrostatic stress conditions (cycles 1 and 2 for fresh coal).

These results were analyzed by a regression analysis to determine the best fit to an equation of the form

$$k = Ae^{B\sigma}$$

where, σ is measured in MPa and k in m^2 while A and B are constants. The value of A is indicative of the theoretical permeability of the coal at zero stress. The value of B indicates the rate at which the logarithm of permeability will change with respect to hydrostatic stress.

The result for samples taken from the borehole core and standing face (old coal) were similar to that for fresh coal, with different values of A and B. Figure 5 shows lines representing the first load/unload cycle for all three samples and Table 1 gives the values of A and B for all of these.

836

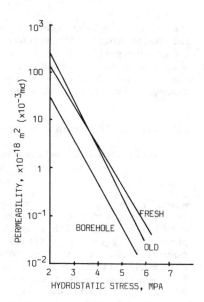

Figure 5. Variation of permeability with change in hydrostatic stress conditions. First cycle for all three coal samples.

Table 1 Constants A (m^2) and B (1/MPa)

	A		B	
	1st Cycle	2nd Cycle	1st Cycle	2nd Cycle
	(multiply values by 10^{-15})			
Borehole core	1.7044	0.4880 (28.6%)	-2.061	-1.8458 (90%)
Fresh-cut sample	6.2748	0.5339 (8.5%)	-1.9114	-1.7337 (91%)
8 month old sample	23.1540	14.4690 (62.5%*)	-2.2743	-2.2051 (97%*)

Figures in parentheses indicate percentage of 1st cycle values.
*Higher values as a result of 2nd cycle following immediately after first.

The results shown in Table 1 (1st cycle) show that the fresh cut sample from the mine has a significantly higher permeability at low stress levels (A) than the borehole core, indicating a greater degree of pre-stressing and microfracturing of the mine sample. The corresponding values of A for the 2nd cycle are much closer, revealing the effect of microfracture closure during maintained hydrostatic loading.

The values of A for the older mine sample are significantly higher than for the fresh-cut sample. This could have been caused by an increased degree of pre-stressing during mining or may suggest a time dependent relaxation during the period of location on the stress free front of a standing face.

The values of B indicate a fairly consistent rate of change of ln(k) with respect to hydrostatic stress. In all cases, B is a little lower for the second cycle. This shows that at the lower permeabilities of the second cycles there is more resistance to reduction in k with increasing hydrostatic stress.

One interpretation of these results is that the stress history of a coal sample has a marked effect on its "relaxed-state" permeability but has much less influence on the rate of decrease of permeability during subsequent hydrostatic loading.

6.2 Volumetric Strain

Volumetric strain is defined as

$$\Delta V/V \ X \ 100\%$$

where V is the initial volume of the sample and ΔV the change in volume from a datum at stress of 2.06MPa (300 psi). The variation of volumetric strain with respect to axial stress for the fresh sample is shown in Figure 6. Similar results were obtained for the other samples. The results show that in all cases there was a small residual volumetric strain remaining at the end of each load/unload cycle, but this was never more than 0.4 percent. Over the range considered, the volumetric strain was linear with respect to hydrostatic stress indicating the elastic properties of coal when stressed hydrostatically.

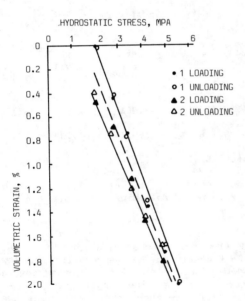

Figure 6. Variation of volumetric strain of fresh coal with change in hydrostatic stress.

Table 8.2 Volumetric Compressibility of Coal Samples

	Volumetric Compressibility percent/MPA
Fresh sample from mine	0.528
Borehole coal sample	0.451
Aged sample from mine	0.563

The volumetric compressibilities gained from these results are shown in Table 2. The lower compressibility exhibited by the borehole sample may again be indicative of the different stress history of the specimen.

7 CONCLUSIONS

From the experimental work described in this paper, the following conclusions can be drawn:

1. The variation of coal permeability with respect to applied axial stress indicates that coal exhibits visco-elastic properties. During loading, the stress at high points of contact between coal macerols may exceed the failure level. A time dependent crushing would then occur at these points leading to a non-recoverable component of the permeability-stress hysteresis.

2. Variation of volumetric strain with respect to axial stress appears to provide a good explanation for the variation in permeability. It also supports the hypothesis mentioned in the previous paragraph.

3. In the log-linear relationship established between permeability and hydrostatic stress, the constant A may be used to suggest the stress history of the sample - the degree to which it has been subjected to dynamic loading and unloading due to tectonic movements or mining. The constant B indicates the degree of compaction during consecutive cycles.

4. The irrecoverable effects on permeability and volumetric strain due to deviator stress are greatly reduced when the specimen is stressed hydrostatically. Furthermore, the volumetric compressibility of the coal samples may offer further evidence relating to the stress history of a sample.

ACKNOWLEDGEMENTS

This work was performed by the authors at the Mine Ventilation Laboratory of the University of California, Berkeley, as a part of a more general project to study the gas flow characteristics of coal. The project was conducted under contract to the U.S. Steel Corporation and funded by the Gas Research Institute. The authors wish to thank these organizations for their support.

REFERENCES

McPherson, M.J. and M. Hood 1981. Ventilation planning for underground coal mines. Annual report, U.S. Department of Energy. Contract W-7405-ENG-48.
Harpalani, S. 1985. Gas flow through stressed coal. Ph.D. thesis. University of California, Berkeley: 26-27.
Somerton, W. H., I. M. Soylemezoglu and R. Dudley 1974. Effect of stress on permeability of coal. Final report, U.S. Bureau of Mines Contract H0122027.
Harpalani, S. and M. J. McPherson 1984. The effect of gas evacuation on coal permeability. Intl. Jour. Rock Mech. Min. Sci. Vol. XXI, No. 3: 161-164.
Gawuga, J. 1979. Flow of gas through stressed carboniferous strata. Ph.D. thesis. University of Nottingham, U.K.

Permeability property effect on saturated-unsaturated seepage flow analysis in rock

HIDENOBU YOSHIDA & TAKASHI MATSUMOTO
Information Processing Center, Kajima Corporation, Tokyo, Japan

KENJI AOKI
Kajima Institute of Construction Technology, Tokyo, Japan

YUZO OHNISHI
Department of Transportation Engineering, Kyoto University, Japan

1. INTRODUCTION

When designing underground openings for electric power stations and/or underground storage stations of crude oil, it is necessary to estimate the change of seepage surface and discharge flow into caverns. In order to accomplish the above mentioned object, the finite element analysis of saturated-unsaturated seepage flow developed by Neuman (1973) and Akai, Ohnishi (1977) is often applied to the practical design.

In this analysis, we have to get the permeability property data in unsaturated zone. However, it is difficult to obtain them from laboratory tests. Especially in rock materials, few reliable unsaturated permeability data can be obtained. Therefore permeability data in saturated zone or those refered of similar previous studies are often used instead of conducting the exact laboratory tests.

On the other hand, from the computational point of view, numerical solution sometimes diverges because of the intensive nonlinearity of unsaturated permeability properties.

In this paper, some numerical studies are carried out to investigate the permeability property effects. Numerical results are compared with the observations obtained from a certain underground oil storage station in Japan. The followings are clarified to get stable and accurate numerical solutions. ; (1) The relationship between unsaturated permeability coefficient and volumetric moisture content should be revised when the suction pressure is very high. (2) When computing the unsteady seepage flow, the initial water level should be decided by taking account of rainfall influx.

2. FINITE ELEMENT ANALYSIS OF SATURATED-UNSATURATED SEEPAGE FLOW

2.1 Governing equation

By Neuman (1973) and Akai, Ohnishi (1977), the governing equation of saturated-unsaturated flow is described as :

$$div\, K(\psi)\,(\psi + z) = (C(\psi) + \beta Ss)\frac{\partial \psi}{\partial t} \qquad (2-1)$$

where,
$$\beta = 0 \text{ ; unsaturated zone}$$
$$1 \text{ ; saturated zone,}$$

K(ψ)=permeability coefficient, ψ=pressure head (capillary potential in unsaturated zone), z = gravitational potential, C (ψ) = the specific moisture capacity (defined as dθ / dψ), Ss = the specific storage.

In this procedure it is not necessary to modify the finite element mesh according to the ground water surface movement. The ground water surface is located by finding points where the pressure head equals to zero and the surface of seepage is handled by a special iterative method.

The finite element formulation of this equation may be accomplished easily by the Galerkin method. And finite difference techniques, that is time-centered scheme or backward difference scheme, are adopted.

2.2 Material properties

Material properties in this analysis are as follows.
1. Permeability coefficient Ks in saturated zone.
2. In unsaturated zone, functional relationship between relative conductivity Kr and the volumetric moisture content θ, where Kr = Kus / Ks, Kus = permeability coefficient in unsaturated zone (Fig. 2-1).
3. In unsaturated zone, functional relationship between pressure head ψ and θ (Fig. 2-1). The function C(ψ) is obtained as the slope of the curve.
4. Specific storage Ss and porosity n of constitutive material.
5. Distribution of initial pressure head in the entire flow domain.

In above mentioned properties, 2.and 3. are difficult to obtain experimentally. Some measurement methods are proposed by Kono and Nishigaki (1981) but few reliable data of rock materials can be obtained easily.

Therefore permeability data in saturated zone or those of similar previous studies are often used instead of exact ones.

Anyway, as material properties K(ψ) and C(ψ) are dependent on pressure head ψ, the governing equations have material nonlinearity. Therfore, iterative procedure would be necessitated to get numerical solutions.

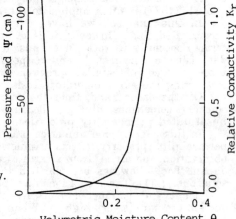

Fig.2-1 Permeability property in unsaturated zone

3. NUMERICAL EXAMPLES

Numerical studies are carried out modelling a certain underground storage station of crude oil.

3.1 Underground storage system

In underground rock caverns, liquid petroleum and petroleum gas are stored by means of natural or artificial underground water pressure. When the underground storage system often used in European countries is applied to the cracky rock mass in Japan, it seems to be most important to study the behavior of underground water around the rock caverns in advance.

3.2 Observations

The movement of water level, pore water pressure and discharge flow are observed at a certain underground storage cavern in Japan.

Twenty points of water level and fifty-three points of pore water pressure were measured every twelve hours. Discharge flow into caverns is measured at four points a day.

3.3 Finite element mesh

Fig. 3-1 shows the finite element mesh used in this study. Upper part is a weathered rock and lower part is an intact rock. A storage cavern and an artificially water supplying tunnel are A and B in Fig. 3-1. C means working tunnel.

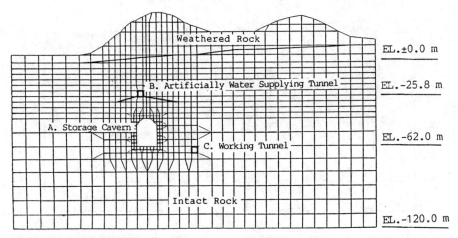

Fig. 3-1 Finite element mesh for seepage analysis

3.4 Computational conditions and material properties

In this paper three numerical examples are carried out (see Table 3-1).

Case-1 and Case-2 are steady flow analyses. Computational conditions and material properties in Case-1 and Case-2 are as follows.

1. Surface boundary : Rainfall influx is considered from the ground surface. The rainfall data are presumed by long term hydrologic ones.

2. Bottom boundary : Bottom boundary at EL. -120m are assumed to be impervious.

3. Lateral boundary : Assumed as hydrostatic pressure.

4. Artificially water supplying tunnel : Pressure head is fixed to be 25.8 m, that is, the supplying water level is kept at EL. ± 0 m.

5. Working tunnel : Pressure head is fixed to be zero. (Atmospheric air pressure)

6. Storage cavern : same as 5.

7. Permeability coefficient in unsaturated zone : The functional relationships between relative conductivity Kr and the volumetric moisture

Table 3-1 Numerical study cases

	Steady Usteady	Relative Conductivity Kr	Ss (1/m)	Rainfall Influx (mm/day)
Case-1	Steady	Kr $\geqq$ 0.0	10-6	0.7
Case-2	Steady	Kr $\geqq$ 0.2	10-6	0.7
Case-3	Unsteady	Kr $\geqq$ 0.2	10-6	Variant*

* Rainfall influx varies every month(mean value is 0.635).

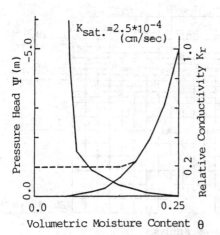

Fig. 3-2 (a) Permeability property in unsaturated zone (weathered rock)

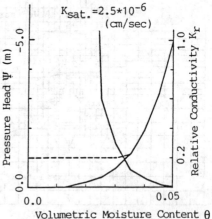

Fig. 3-2 (b) Permeability property in unsaturated zone (intact rock)

content θ are obtained as Fig. 3-2 (a) in weathered rock and (b) in intact rock respectively.

As can be seen from these figures, the value of relative conductivity Kr changes from 0.0 to 1.0 according to the negative pressure head ψ. When negative pressure head has large value, permeability coefficient in unsaturated zone becomes very small. The matrix to be solved, therefore, may become ill-conditioned. These material data bring the intensive nonlinearity and also tend to make the numerical solution diverged.

In order to prevent these phenomena, the relationships Kr-θ are modified to be Kr $\geqq$ 0.2 shown as dotted lines in Fig. 3-2 (a), (b).

In this paper, two kinds of Kr-θ curves, that is, Kr $\geqq$ 0.2 (modified) and Kr $\geqq$ 0.0 (not modified) are used.

Case-3 is an unsteady flow analysis. Computational conditions and material properties in Case-3 are as follows.

1. Initial condition : Initial water level is determined by solving the

steady flow analysis (Case-2) which considers rainfall influx.

2. Surface boudary : Considered rainfall from the ground surface changes according to the meteorological data.

3. Bottom and lateral boundary : same as Case-1 and Case-2.

4. Artificially water supplying tunnel : Pressure head moves according to the measured water level in this tunnel.

5. Working tunnel : same as 3.

6. Storage cavern : same as Case-1 and Case-2.

7. Period of computation : One year from the time when the artificially water supplying equipment is out of operation.

8. Permeability coefficient in unsaturated zone : The relationships between Kr and θ are modified to be $Kr \geqq 0.2$ same as Case-2.

4. COMPARISON BETWEEN NUMERICAL AND OBSERVED RESULT

4.1 Steady flow analyses (Fig. 4-1, 4-2)

1. Ground water level : In Case-1, the free water surface of numerical result neither has the smooth configuration nor agrees with that of observed one. The difference between numerical and observed one amounts 5-15 m. On the other hand, the result of Case-2 agrees with observed one very well.

2. Pore water pressure : Case-2 has better agreement with observed one than Case-1. However the numerical pore water pressure between the storage cavern and the working tunnel has fairy higher value than observed (see Fig. 4-3). One of the reason of this difference may be that the permeability becomes higher due to the decrease of stress by excavation. And the other reason is that the analysis is not three-dimensional but two-dimensional one.

3. Discharge flow into caverns : Table 4-1 shows the good agreement between numerical and observed result. The modification of Kr-θ curve brings little difference in discharge flow into caverns.

Table 4-1 Comparison about discharge flow into caverns

	Case-1	Case-2	Observed
Discharge (m³/day)	38.0	37.0	37.0

4.2 Unsteady flow analysis (Fig. 4-4)

Fig. 4-4 shows the result of unsteady flow analysis after 63 days.

The computed ground water level shows good agreement with observation and the difference between the two is only about 1-2 m.

The computed and observed pore water pressure agree rather well at the hatched part in Fig. 4-3 but at the dotted part the observed pressure is about 20% of numerical one.

About the discharge flow into caverns, computed one shows higher value than observed but the feature of variation with time resembles each other.

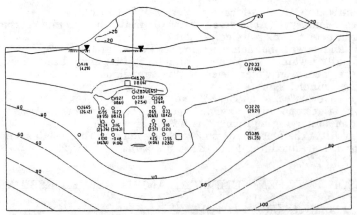

Fig. 4-1 Numerical result (Case-1)

▼ Observed water level
○ Observed pressure head

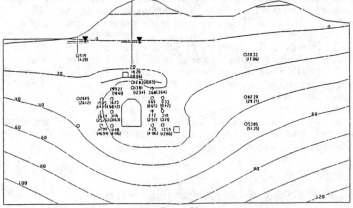

Fig. 4-2 Numerical result (Case-2)

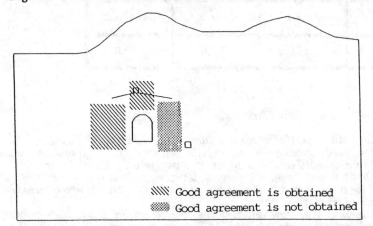

Good agreement is obtained
Good agreement is not obtained

Fig. 4-3 Comparison between numerical and observed result

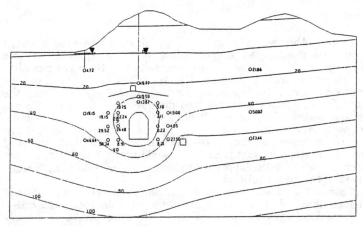

Fig. 4-4 Numerical result (Case-3)

4.3 Suggestions for the saturated-unsaturated seepage flow analysis

1. Permeability property data : It is difficult to get the permeability property data especially in rock material. Furthermore from the numerical point of view, solution sometimes diverges in the iterative procedure. In this paper it has been confirmed that better convergency in iterative procedure and better agreement between computed and observed result can be obtained by means of modifying the relationship of Kr - θ. The modification brings little difference about the discharge flow into caverns. From the technological point of view, modified permeability data should be used when analysing the seepage flow.

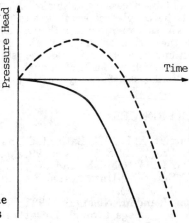

Fig. 4-5 Behavior of pressure head at the begining stage in unsteady flow analysis

2. The initial condition for unsteady flow analysis :Before the unsteady seepage flow analysis considering rainfall influx is conducted, the steady flow analysis should be carried out to determine the initial water level and pore water pressure. If the horizontal ground water surface for the uneven configuration is assumed, pressure head is apt to rise at the begining stage (see the dotted line in Fig. 4-5) and also often to make the solution diverged.

847

5. CONCLUSION

In order to estimate the behavior of seepage flow, the finite element analysis of saturated-unsaturated seepage flow is often applied. In this analysis following problems come out concerning the permeability property data in unsaturated zone ; (1) It is difficult to get the permeability property precisely, especially for rock materials. (2) From the numerical point of view, solution sometimes diverges due to the intensive nonlinearity of the permeability property data.

In this paper, taking the case of a certain underground storage station of crude oil in Japan, computed results are compared with observed ones and numerical studies about the permeability property data are carried out in order to suggest the appropriate procedure of inputting them.

Conclusion is obtained as follows.

1. Good agreement between computed and observed result is obtained and it is confirmed that this analysis is available even in rock materials.

2. From the technological point of view, it is appropriate to modify the permeability property data in case of having intensive nonlinearity. Thus, divergence of iterative procedure may be prevented.

3. Before the unsteady flow analysis considering rainfall influx is conducted, the steady flow analysis should be carried out to determine the initial water level and pore water pressure. If the horizontal ground water surface for the uneven configuration is assumed, pressure head is apt to rise at the begining stage and also often to make the solution diverged.

4. When the support of rock mass adjacent to the cavern is removed by excavation, the primary state of stress is changed. Thus the permeability would become higher. Moreover, rock joint may be opened. In order to estimate the seepage flow precisely even in these cases, it would be necessary to make the permeability coeffient higher or to carry out the coupled stress-flow analysis.

5. In two-dimensional analysis, the direction of the ground water flow at the primary state would not always coincide with the analytical section. Therefore, it can be stated that the pore water pressure, free water surface and discharge flow due to cavern excavation can be evaluated satisfactorily only by three-dimensional analysis.

REFERENCES

Neuman, S. P. 1973, Saturated-Unsaturated Seepage by Finite Element, Proc., ASCE HY, Vol. 99, No. 12, P.2233-2250.

Akai K., Y. Ohnishi and M. Nishigaki 1977, Finite Element Analysis of Saturated-Unsaturated Seepage in Soil, Proc. of JSCE, No.264 (in Japanese).

Kono I. and M. Nishigaki 1981 , An Experimental Study on Characteristics of Seepage through Unsaturated Sandy Soil, Proc. of JSCE, No. 307 (in Japanese).

18. In situ testing results and interpretations

Chair: PRISCILLA P.NELSON
          University of Texas, Austin, USA
Cochair: JOHN E.O'ROURKE
          Woodward-Clyde Consultants, San Francisco, California, USA

Observations of borehole deformation modulus values before and after extensive heating of a granitic rock mass

W.C.PATRICK, J.L.YOW, Jr. & M.C.AXELROD
Lawrence Livermore National Laboratory, California, USA

1 ABSTRACT

An extensive campaign of in situ deformation modulus measurements was recently completed using a standard NX borehole jack. These results were obtained in a granite intrusive where spent nuclear-fuel assemblies and electrical heaters had raised the rock temperatures 10°C to 40°C above ambient. We present an analysis of temperature effects based on 41 preheat and 63 post-heat measurements in three boreholes. Using analysis of covariance statistical techniques, we found that the deformation modulus is affected by heat, loading direction, and position within the borehole. The analysis also uncovered a significant interaction between the effects of heating and loading direction.

We used 123 measurements from the same boreholes to evaluate the "Draft Standard Guide for Estimating the In Situ Modulus of Rock Masses Using the NX-Borehole Jack" which was recently proposed by Heuze. In particular, we examined the criterion for screening measurements in those cases where contact between the jack platen and the borehole wall was incomplete. We found that the proposed screen appears to operate randomly on the data and is therefore ineffective.

2 INTRODUCTION

A test of deep geologic storage of commercial spent nuclear fuel assemblies was recently completed at the Spent Fuel Test-Climax (SFT-C). The SFT-C was conducted to demonstrate the technical feasibility of deep geologic storage and to evaluate the acceptability of granites as a medium for permanent disposal of nuclear wastes (Ramspott, et al., 1979).

Rock deformability characteristics were used in calculating displacements and stress changes that occurred as a result of excavating and heating the facility. Young's modulus values of intact cores range from about 50 to 70 GPa (Pratt et al., 1979).

The impetus for the present study was the need to determine what changes in large-scale deformability characteristics occurred as a result of elevating the temperature of the facility 10 to 40°C above the ambient. The heating caused thermal expansion of the rock which acted to change the stresses as much 40%, as discussed below. The spacial variability in deformability was also examined in detail. In addition, the study resulted in a data set which is large enough to support a statistical evaluation of the recently proposed "Standard Guide for Estimating the In Situ Modulus of Rock Masses Using the NX-Borehole Jack" (Heuze, 1984).

3 SITE DESCRIPTION

The basic geometry of the SFT-C facility is three parallel drifts which are connected at their ends (Fig. 1). The center drift is 6.1 m high x 4.6 m wide x 65 m long and has 17 storage boreholes in the floor that held 11 spent nuclear fuel assemblies and 6 electrical heaters during the three-year heated phase of the test. Parallel heater drifts measuring 3.4 m square are located on either side of the center drift. Each of these heater drifts had 10 electrical heaters located in the floor during the three-year heated phase of the test. Within the repository-model cell, this combination of heat and radiation sources simulated the thermal effects of a panel of a full-scale repository, raising rock temperatures to 85°C near the storage boreholes in the center drift and to well over 300°C near the electrical heaters in the two side drifts (Patrick et al., 1984).

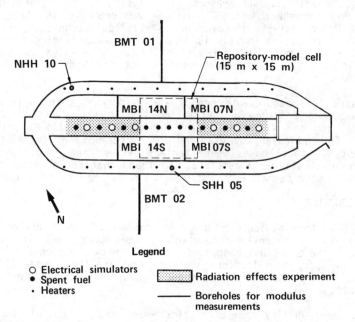

Figure 1. Plan view of Spent Fuel Test-Climax facility showing location of thermal sources, principal experiments, and boreholes.

The SFT-C is located 420 m below ground surface in the quartz monzonite unit of the Climax stock. The medium-grained ground mass contains scattered alkali feldspar crystals up to 150 mm long. The test level is about 150 m above the regional water table and is unsaturated but not dry.

Wilder and Yow (1984) report four dominant joint sets which account for about 93% of all joints mapped. They are oriented N44°W/20°NE, N24°W/vertical, N59°W/vertical, and N48°E/80°SE. The rock mass is moderately jointed with frequencies ranging from 0.90 to 2.2 joints/m. In addition to these systematic joint sets, there are several shears and faults present in the test area.

4 MEASUREMENT TECHNIQUE

We measured rock deformability in nine boreholes located throughout the SFT-C facility (Fig. 1) using a Slope Indicator Co. Model 52101 hardrock borehole jack and associated equipment. Although the "Draft Standard Guide" (Heuze, 1984) had not yet been proposed at the time of these measurements, our procedures were nearly identical to those recommended (Patrick, Yow, and Axelrod, 1984). The equipment was calibrated by the manufacturer or by LLNL, as appropriate. The depth and angular position of the borehole jack platens were established by means of scribe marks on the BX-size drill casing that was used to insert the jack into the borehole. Depths are accurate to one centimetre and angular position to about five degrees.

The borehole diameter at each test location was determined from the average of the two LVDT readings at a nominal seating pressure of 0.3 to 0.8 MPa. In general, we found that the MBI-series boreholes were undersized by as much as 1.52 mm because they were drilled with surface-set diamond bits and were not reamed. On the other hand, the BMT-, NHH-, and SHH-series boreholes were drilled with diamond impregnated bits and, therefore, were oversized as much as 1.52 mm.

5 DATA REDUCTION TECHNIQUES

The fundamental method of analysis was that suggested by Heuze (1984). The calculated deformation modulus E_c (psi) is

$$E_c = 0.86 \cdot 0.93 \cdot D \cdot \frac{\Delta Q_h}{\Delta D} \cdot T^* \qquad (1)$$

where D is the borehole diameter (3.0 in.), ΔD is the change in borehole diameter (inches) produced by a change in line pressure ΔQ_h (psi), and T^* is a function of Poisson's ratio and the half contact angle between the jack platen and the rock. Based on previous studies, we determined Poisson's ratio to be 0.246 and used a T^* value of 1.438 from Heuze and Amadei (1984).

Values of $\Delta Q_h/\Delta D$ were obtained graphically as the slopes of the linear portion of plots of jack gauge pressure versus the average of the two LVDT readings. For most tests, the low-pressure end of each curve was nonlinear but became linear at pressures of 20.7 MPa (6000 psi) or less. It is interesting that linear relationships were observed even where boreholes deviated substantially from the 76 mm (3.0 in.) ideal diameter.

To expedite the correction for longitudinal bending of the jack (Heuze and Salem, 1976, Meyer and McVey, 1974), we fitted an equation to the curve of "true" modulus E_t versus calculated modulus E_c which Heuze presented (1984). For a Poisson's ratio of 0.25, the equation is

$$E_t = 0.030320 + 0.979484E_c - 2.042103 \times 10^{-8}E_c^2 + 1.792758 \times 10^{-13} E_c^3$$

$$(2)$$

We considered screening the data according to the full platen seating criterion proposed by Heuze (1984). However, the proposed screen (as discussed below) fails to eliminate many implausibly high values which are obvious statistical outliers. Instead, we calculated all modulus values using the linear portion of the pressure versus displacement curves and deleted modulus values calculated to be greater than 85 GPa, the maximum modulus value obtained in testing 143-mm diameter cores of intact rock. Since these cores possessed no open fractures, which in situ reduce the deformation modulus, the laboratory modulus represents a physical upper bound. This physical argument is supported by a statistical analysis of the modulus distributions which shows that values greater than 100 GPa are part of a long tail of outliers.

We found the following factors to be influential: position within the borehole, location within the facility, loading direction, and heat. The appropriate variable to describe the position within the borehole is the distance of the measurement from the center of the borehole, a quantitative variable. The other factors are all qualitative, therefore an analysis of covariance model is convenient (Searle, 1971). If all the variables were quantitative, we would use regression analysis. Each of the qualitative factors has only two levels: north or south pillar, vertical or horizontal loading, and preheat or post-heat, respectively. Significant interactions between heat and loading direction and between heat and pillar location were detected. The following linear statistical model applies to the data from MBIO7N, MBIO7S, and MBI14S.

$$E_i = \mu + \beta d_i + \sum_{j=1}^{10} X_{ij}\, \gamma_j + \varepsilon_i \qquad (3)$$

Where E_i = deformation modulus (GPa), d_i = distance of the measurement from the borehole center, and the X_{ij} are factor variables. When the jth factor is present $X_{ij} = 1$, when absent $X_{ij} = 0$. The model parameters are μ, β_i, and γ_i, and the ε_i represent residual errors. The parameterization of the model is not unique, but all parameterizations will give the same results. The model parameters cannot be estimated separately, as is the case for regression. Instead only certain meaningful linear combinations are estimated, using the numerical technique of the singular value decomposition. The three factors at two levels require six terms, the two sets of interactions require four additional terms and the constant and slope coefficient add two more for a total of 12 terms.

6 RESULTS AND CONCLUSIONS

6.1 An Evaluation of the Screening Criterion

Heuze (1984) proposed a method for rejecting data when the jack platen is determined to be incompletely seated against the wall of the borehole. We evaluated this proposed screen using data from MBIO7N, MBIO7S, and MBI14S. The screen removes 67 of the 123 measurements in these boreholes, but fails to eliminate modulus values as high as 446 GPa, which are physically implausible. Only four of the 19 measurements greater than the physically realistic cut-off of 85 GPa are rejected by the screen. Moreover, the inclusion of these extreme values would distort the parameter estimates for the model given by Eq. 3.

We can investigate the behavior of the screen for the 104 measurements below the 85 GPa cut-off by enlarging the model given in Eq. 3 to include a "screening" effect. The screen is another qualitative factor with two levels, thus two terms are added to the model. Using the F test on the model estimates, we could detect no screening effect. This suggests that the intercepts for screened and unscreened data are identical. As an additional diagnostic, we plotted quantiles of the model residuals associated with screened points versus the residuals associated with unscreened points (Fig. 2). The points exhibit good conformity to a straight line with unity slope, indicating equality of distributions (no increase in variance).

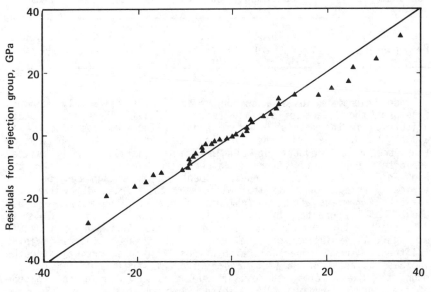

Figure 2. Quantile-Quantile plot comparing distributions of model residuals of data accepted (abscissa) and rejected (ordinate) by the screen. Conformity to a straight line with unity slope implies that the distributions are identical.

The proposed screen appears to randomly reject 63 of the 104 values below 85 GPa, and fails to reject values that are unrealistically high. We conclude that this proposed method is ineffective as a screen.

6.2 Data Analysis

To examine the affect of heating on the rock mass deformability, we analyzed 41 pre-heat and 63 post-heat modulus values. Table 1 lists the "intercept" terms for the various data subsets which were analyzed with the 12-term linear model described in Section 5. These intercepts represent the mean modulus values at the pillar center. The overall slope of the 104 data is -7.00 GPa/m. The physical interpretation of these coefficients is straightforward. For example, the predicted values of post-heating modulus under horizontal loading in the north pillar is 52.87 GPa at the pillar center and it decreases 7.00 GPa for each metre from the center in either direction. The data and associated line for this typical example are shown in Fig. 3.

Table 1. Intercept coefficients calculated using a 12-term general linear model for deformation modulus(GPa).

Time of Measurement	North Pillar		South Pillar	
	Vertical Loading	Horizontal Loading	Vertical Loading	Horizontal Loading
Pre-heating	46.54	57.23	26.26	36.96
Post-heating	62.71	52.87	54.63	44.80

Since this model uses a common slope, it is relatively easy to interpret the effect of various factors. First, there is a strong anisotropy in the modulus. Before heating, the rock mass modulus is about 10.7 GPa less in the vertical loading direction, indicating that the more frequent low angle joints (infilled with pyrite, sericite, and quartz) tend to affect the modulus more than the high-angle joints (which appear "open" at free surfaces but are typically clean or infilled with calcite). Second, while the anisotropy remains after the episode of heating, the modulus is now about 9.8 GPa greater in the vertical loading direction. This is consistent with a hypothesis that the stresses increase as a result of thermal expansion of the rock, and thereby increase joint stiffness. Thermomechanical calculations show that vertical stresses increase by about 5 MPa (40%) and horizontal stresses decrease by as much as 2 MPa (20%) in the pillar center as a result of the episode of heating (Butkovich, 1981). Third, note in this context that the modulus for vertical loading increased by 16.2 to 28.4 GPa while the modulus for horizontal loading in one case decreased by 4.4 GPa and in the other increased by only 7.8 GPa. This is compatible, in concept, with our understanding of the influence of stress changes on individual joints (Goodman, 1980, and Yow, 1985).

These data provide strong field evidence that extensive heating of a rock mass to moderate temperatures may induce significant changes in the deformability of the rock mass as a result of changes in the stress regime. Depending on the extent of heating and the geometry of the underground facility, deformability may increase or decrease.

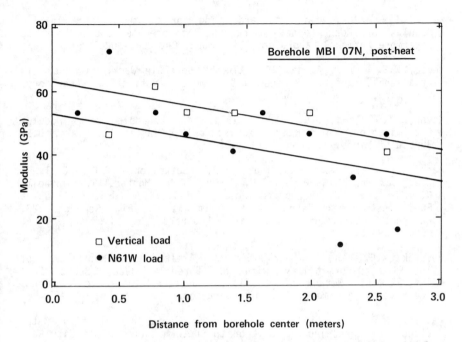

Figure 3. Typical example of relationship between borehole modulus value and distance from pillar center. The slope and intercepts of the lines were developed from a 12-term general linear model.

7 ACKNOWLEDGMENTS

The SFT-C is conducted under the technical direction of the Lawrence Livermore National Laboratory as part of the Nevada Nuclear Waste Storage Investigations. Funding for the project is provided through the U.S. Department of Energy.

Work performed under the auspices of the U.S. Department of Energy by the Lawrence Livermore National Laboratory under contract number W-7405-ENG-48.

8 REFERENCES

Butkovich, T.R. 1981. As-Built Mechanical and Thermomechanical Calculations of a Spent-Fuel Test in Climax Stock Granite, Lawrence Livermore National Laboratory, Livermore, CA, UCRL-53198.

Goodman, R.E. 1980. Introduction to Rock Mechanics, John Wiley, New York, NY.

Heuze, F.E. and A. Salem 1976. Plate Bearing and Borehole Jack Tests in Rock - A Finite Element Analysis, Proc. 17th U.S. Symposium on Rock Mechanics, Snowbird, Utah, pp. 488-1 to 488-6.

Heuze, F.E. 1984. Draft Standard Guide for Estimating the In-Situ Modulus of Rock Masses Using the NX-Borehole Jack, Lawrence Livermore National Laboratory, Livermore, CA, UCRL-90281.

Heuze, F.E. and B. Amadei 1984. The NX-Borehole Jack: A Lesson in Trial-and-Errors, Lawrence Livermore National Laboratory, Livermore, CA, UCRL-90282.

Meyer, T.O. and J.R. McVey 1974. NX Borehole Jack Modulus Determinations in Homogeneous, Isotropic, Elastic Materials, U.S. Bureau of Mines, RI 7855.

Patrick, W.C., L.B. Ballou, T.R. Butkovich, R.C. Carlson, W.B. Durham, G.L. Hage, E.L. Majer, D.N. Montan, R.A. Nyholm, N.L. Rector, F.J. Ryerson, H. Weiss, and J.L. Yow, Jr., 1984. Spent Fuel Test-Climax Technical Measurements Interim Report FY83, Lawrence Livermore National Laboratory, Livermore, CA, UCRL-53294-83.

Patrick, W.C., J.L. Yow, Jr., and M.C. Axelrod 1984. Measurement of In Situ Deformability with NX Borehole Jack, Spent Fuel Test-Climax, Nevada Test Site, Lawrence Livermore National Laboratory, Livermore, CA, in preparation.

Patrick, W.C., M.C. Axelrod, J.L. Yow, Jr. 1985. An Evaluation of the Effects of Screening Criteria on the Determination of In Situ Rock Modulus with the NX-Borehole Jack, Lawrence Livermore National Laboratory, Livermore, CA, in preparation.

Pratt, H., R. Lingle and T. Schrauf 1979. Laboratory Measured Material Properties of Quartz Monzonite, Climax Stock, Nevada Test Site, Terra Tek, Inc. Contractor Report, Lawrence Livermore National Laboratory, Livermore, CA, UCRL-15073.

Ramspott, L.D., L.B. Ballou, R.C. Carlson, D.N. Montan, T.R. Butkovich, J.E. Duncan, W.C. Patrick, D.G. Wilder, W.G. Brough, and M.C. Mayr 1979. Technical Concept for a Test of Geologic Storage of Spent Fuel in the Climax Granite, Nevada Test Site, Lawrence Livermore National Laboratory, Livermore, CA, UCRL-52796.

Searle, S.R. 1971. Linear Models, John Wiley, New York, NY

Wilder, D.G. and J.L. Yow, Jr. 1984. Structural Geology Report, SFT-C, Lawrence Livermore National Laboratory, Livermore, CA UCRL-53381.

Yow, J. L., Jr., 1985. Field Investigation of Keyblock Stability, Lawrence Livermore National Laboratory, Livermore, CA, in preparation.

The influence of rock mass fracturing on the measurement of deformability by borehole expansion tests

BERNARD AMADEI
Department of Civil Engineering, University of Colorado, Boulder, USA

1 INTRODUCTION

Scale effect is a major problem in rock mechanics (Heuze, 1980). Laboratory tests on small samples are usually found inadequate to measure the deformability of rock masses. This has led to the development of several static and dynamic field testing methods over the last twenty years. As far as the static methods are concerned, loads are applied on selected rock surfaces in boreholes, underground galleries or at the surface of rock outcrops and the resulting deformations are measured. They include plate bearing tests, flat jack tests, pressure chambers and borehole expansion tests. A review of these tests can be found in Goodman (1980). The present paper focuses on the analysis of borehole expansion tests.

A number of testing devices are available which can be inserted into a borehole to apply a load and measure the direct response of the walls of the borehole. These devices either (1) supply a uniform internal pressure in the borehole (borehole dilatometers), or, (2) supply a unidirectional pressure to a portion of the circumference of the borehole by forcing apart circular plates (borehole jacks). The results of tests conducted with these devices are often presented in terms of curves of applied pressure vs. diametral deformation. The latter is measured either in the direction of loading (borehole jack) or at one or several locations around the circumference of the hole (borehole dilatometers). A discussion on the advantages and disadvantages of boreholes dilatometers and jacks can be found in Goodman et al (1970).

A common practice in analyzing the measurements of diametral deformation in borehole expansion tests is to model the rock mass as a linearly elastic, isotropic and homogeneous continuum with Young's modulus E and Poisson's ration ν as deformability properties. A value for the Poisson's ratio is assumed and the constant E is determined from measured values of applied pressure and borehole deformations through equations borrowed from the theory of linear elasticity for isotropic media; e.g.

$$\frac{U_d}{D} = q \cdot \frac{(1 + \nu)}{E} \tag{1}$$

859

for the dilatometer test, and,

$$\frac{U_d}{D} = q \cdot \frac{K(\nu, \beta_c)}{E} \qquad (2)$$

for the NX borehole jack test (Goodman et al, 1970). In these equations, D is the diameter of the borehole, U_d is the diametral deformation, q is the pressure applied against the rock and $2\beta_c$ is an estimated value of the contact angle between the jack and the rock. The two previous equations are also used in terms of increments of diametral deformation, ΔU_d, and increments of applied load, Δq.

The analysis of test results described above is commonly followed in practice irrespective of the anisotropic, discontinuous and heterogeneous character of the rock mass of interest. The constant E is the true elastic Young's modulus of the rock mass if the latter actually behaves as a linearly elastic, homogeneous, isotropic continuum. Any departure from this "ideal" characteristics will make the coefficient E to become, instead, an apparent modulus of the rock mass in the direction of loading and/or measurement. This apparent modulus is sometimes called in the literature "modulus of deformation" or "field modulus". Its magnitude varies along the circumference of the hole. The main qualitative conclusion that can be drawn from such a variation is that the rock mass has directional deformability properties.

The purpose of this paper is to show that the directional character of the apparent modulus of an anisotropic rock mass, E_a, measured along the circumference of a borehole during expansion tests can be explained quantitatively by using closed-form solutions derived in a companion paper (Amadei). Then, analytical expressions for the modulus E_a are proposed for regularly jointed rock masses with one or several joint sets. The rock mass is replaced by an equivalent anisotropic, continuous medium. The modulus E_a is related to the apparent degree of rock mass fracturing in the direction of the borehole in which the expansion tests are conducted.

2 ANALYTICAL BACKGROUND

2.1 Geometry of the Problem and Assumptions

Consider the equilibrium of a rock mass that is modelled as an infinite, linearly elastic, anisotropic, continuous and homogeneous medium. The medium is bounded internally by a cylindrical surface of circular cross section of radius, a, that represents a borehole (Fig. 1).

Let x,y,z by a system of Cartesian coordinates attached to the hole with the z-axis parallel to the hole axis. Let, x',y',z' be another Cartesian coordinate system attached to apparent planes of anisotropy in the medium. For rocks these planes are defects of fabric elements in the form of bedding, stratification, layering, schistosity planes, foliation, fissuring, or jointing. The x'-axis is taken at right angle to the most dominant or to arbitrary planes of anisotropy in the medium. The orientation of the x,y,z and x',y',z' axes are defined with respect to a fixed, global coordinate system X,Y,Z.

The medium is assumed to be described as an orthotropic or a transversely isotropic material in the x',y',z' coordinate system with the following constitutive equations

$$
\begin{bmatrix}
\varepsilon_{x'} \\
\varepsilon_{y'} \\
\varepsilon_{z'} \\
\gamma_{y'z'} \\
\gamma_{x'z'} \\
\gamma_{x'y'}
\end{bmatrix}
=
\begin{bmatrix}
\dfrac{1}{E_1} & \dfrac{-\nu_{21}}{E_2} & \dfrac{-\nu_{31}}{E_3} & 0 & 0 & 0 \\
\dfrac{-\nu_{12}}{E_1} & \dfrac{1}{E_2} & \dfrac{-\nu_{32}}{E_3} & 0 & 0 & 0 \\
\dfrac{-\nu_{13}}{E_1} & \dfrac{-\nu_{23}}{E_2} & \dfrac{1}{E_3} & 0 & 0 & 0 \\
0 & 0 & 0 & \dfrac{1}{G_{23}} & 0 & 0 \\
0 & 0 & 0 & 0 & \dfrac{1}{G_{13}} & 0 \\
0 & 0 & 0 & 0 & 0 & \dfrac{1}{G_{12}}
\end{bmatrix}
\begin{bmatrix}
\sigma_{x'} \\
\sigma_{y'} \\
\sigma_{z'} \\
\tau_{y'z'} \\
\tau_{x'z'} \\
\tau_{x'y'}
\end{bmatrix}
\tag{3}
$$

For the orthotropic formulation, nine independent elastic constants are used to describe the deformability of the medium. E_1, E_2, E_3 are Young's moduli in the x',y',z' directions respectively. G_{12}, G_{13}, G_{23} are shear moduli in the x'y', x'z' and y'z' planes respectively. ν_{21}, ν_{31} and ν_{32} are the Poisson's coefficients. Poisson's ratio ν_{ij} determines the normal strain in the symmetry direction j when a stress is acting in the symmetry direction i. The ratios ν_{ij} and ν_{ji} are such that $\nu_{ij}/E_i = \nu_{ji}/E_j$. If the medium is now described as a transversely isotropic material in the plane y'z' of the x',y',z' coordinate system, eq. (3) still applies with the additional relations: $E_2 = E_3$; $G_{12} = G_{13}$; $\nu_{21} = \nu_{31}$. Five independent elastic constants are only needed to describe the deformability of the medium; e.g. E_1, E_2, G_{12}, ν_{21} and ν_{32}.

A general form of the constitutive equations for the medium in the x,y,z coordinate system can be written as follows

$$
(\varepsilon)_{xyz} = (A)(\sigma)_{xyz} \tag{4}
$$

where $(\varepsilon)_{xyz}$ and $(\sigma)_{xyz}$ are (6x1) matrix representations of the strain and stress tensors in the x,y,z coordinate system. (A) is a (6x6) compliance matrix whose components a_{ij} (i,j = 1-6) depend on the elastic constants defined in eq. (3) and the orientation of x,y,z with respect to x',y',z'.

The hole is loaded along its contour. X_n, Y_n, Z_n are the components in the x,y,z directions of the surface stress vector acting at any point along the contour of the hole. The positive directions of these components are in the negative x,y and z directions respectively. In addition, X_n, Y_n and Z_n are assumed not to vary along the z-axis and to be expressed as Fourier series in cos mθ and sin mθ where θ is an angle that assumes all values from zero to 2π. The resultants of X_n, Y_n, Z_n along the contour of the hole vanish. It is also assumed that under the influence of X_n, Y_n and

861

Z_n, the medium deforms under a condition of complete or generalized plane strain (Lekhnitskii, 1963). Finally, body forces are neglected.

General expressions for the components of stress, strain and displacement at any point in the medium, induced by the application of X_n, Y_n, Z_n can be found in Lekhnitskii (1963) and Amadei (1983). Closed-form solutions for the displacement components along the contour of the hole have also been proposed by Amadei for two special cases of Fourier distributions for X_n, Y_n, Z_n. They are associated with the uniform radial loading of a hole and the loading of a hole over two opposed arcs.

2.2 Uniform Radial Loading of a Hole (Fig. 2)

The loading of a hole with a uniform radial pressure q is equivalent to apply at any point located at any angle θ along the contour of the hole, a stress vector with components

$$X_n = -q \cos \theta; \qquad Y_n = -q \sin\theta; \qquad Z_n = 0 \qquad (5)$$

As shown by Amadei, if D = 2a is the diameter of the hole, the change in length of the hole diameter, U_d, at an angle θ from the x-axis can be expressed as follows

$$\frac{1}{q} \cdot \frac{U_d}{D} = A + B \cos 2\theta + C \sin 2\theta \qquad (6)$$

where A,B,C are three coefficients that depend on the elastic properties of the medium and the orientation of its planes of elastic symmetry with respect to the hole. Equation (6) implies that, as long as these three coefficients do not vanish, there are at most three independent changes in diameter in the hole when pressure q is applied. The vanishing character of the three coefficients depends on the isotropic or anisotropic properties of the medium and for an anisotropic medium, the orientation of its planes of elastic symmetry with respect to the x,y,z axes. It can be shown that if the medium is orthotropic in the x,y,z coordinate system or if it is transversely isotropic in planes xy, xz or yz, then coefficient C vanishes. If the medium is isotropic with Young's modulus E and Poisson's ratio ν, B and C vanish and A is equal to $(1+\nu)/E$. Equation (6) reduces to eq. (1). For the isotropic model, there is only one independent change in diameter in the hole.

2.3 Loading of a Hole over Two Opposed Arcs (Fig. 3)

The uniaxial loading of a hole with a constant surface force per unit area q acting in the y direction and being applied over two opposed sectors $2\beta_c$ wide, is equivalent to apply at any point located at an angle θ along the contour of the hole, a stress vector with components

$$X_n = Z_n = 0$$

$$Y_n = \sum_{m=1}^{N} (a_{my} \cos m\theta + b_{my} \sin m\theta) \qquad (7)$$

with

$$a_{my} = \frac{2q}{m\pi} \; [(-1)^m - 1] \; \cos m\frac{\pi}{2} \sin m\beta_c$$

$$b_{my} = \frac{2q}{m\pi} \; [(-1)^m - 1] \; \sin \frac{m\pi}{2} \sin m\beta_c \qquad (8)$$

As shown by Amadei, if $D = 2a$ is the diameter of the hole, the diametral deformation of the hole in the direction of load application (i.e. y axis), U_d, can be expressed as follows:

$$\frac{1}{q} \cdot \frac{U_d}{D} = \frac{180}{\beta_c \pi^2} A \qquad (9)$$

where A depends on the same parameters as coefficients A,B,C in eq. (6). For an isotropic medium, eq. (9) reduces to eq. (2) with

$$K(\nu, \beta_c) = \frac{720}{\beta_c \pi^2} \; (1 - \nu^2) \; \sum_{m=1}^{N} \frac{1}{m^3} \; (1 - (-1)^m) \; \sin^2 m\beta_c \qquad (10)$$

3 ANALYTICAL EXPRESSION FOR THE APPARENT MODULUS OF A ROCK MASS

The variational character of the apparent modulus of an anisotropic rock mass measured at different points along the circumference of a borehole during dilatometer or jack tests can be explained quantitatively by using the analytical solutions summarized in the previous section. In order to do so, lets rewrite eqs. (6) and (9) with the same form as eqs. (1) and (2) respectively. E is replaced by the apparent modulus E_a. For each diametral measurement in the dilatometer test, at an angle θ from the x-axis, we have

$$\frac{U_d}{D} = q \cdot \frac{(1 + \nu)}{E_a} \qquad (11)$$

with $\qquad E_a = (1 + \nu)/(A + B \cos 2\theta + C \sin 2\theta) \qquad (12)$

For the jack test with loading in the y direction, we have

$$\frac{U_d}{D} = q \cdot \frac{K(\nu, \beta_c)}{E_a} \qquad (13)$$

with $\qquad E_a = \frac{\beta_c \pi^2}{180} \frac{K(\nu, \beta_c)}{A} \qquad (14)$

In these equations, ν is the Poisson's ratio for the anisotropic rock mass when modelled as an isotropic material and $K(\nu, \beta_c)$ is defined in eq. (10).

Equations (12) and (14) provide analytical expressions for the apparent modulus of an anisotropic rock mass modelled as a linearly elastic continuum. The modulus depends on the anisotropic properties of the rock mass and the orientation of the planes of rock anisotropy with respect to the directions of measurement and/or loading in the borehole.

4 CONSTITUTIVE RELATION FOR A REGULARLY JOINTED ROCK MASS

Consider an anisotropic rock mass cut by three orthogonal joint sets 1, 2, 3 that are normal to the x',y' and z' axes, respectively. Each joint set i (i = 1,2,3) is characterized by its spacing S_i and its normal and shear stiffness k_{ni} and k_{si}. The intact rock in between the joints is assumed to be linearly elastic and isotropic with Young's modulus E and Poisson's ratio ν.

The regularly jointed rock mass is replaced by an equivalent orthotropic continuum in the x',y',z' coordinate system following the model proposed by Duncan and Goodman (1968). The joint stiffnesses are assumed to be constant. The constitutive relation of the equivalent medium in the x',y',z' coordinate system is given by eq. (3) with

$$\frac{1}{E_i} = \frac{1}{E} + \frac{1}{k_{ni}S_i}$$

$$\frac{1}{G_{ij}} = \frac{1}{G} + \frac{1}{k_{si}S_i} + \frac{1}{k_{sj}S_j}$$

(i,j = 1,2,3)   (15)

G is equal to $0.5E/(1+\nu)$ and all the non-zero off-diagonal terms in eq. (3) are equal to $-\nu/E$. The constitutive relation is also applicable when there is only one joint set. If the latter is taken normal to the x' direction, the spacings and stiffnesses of joint sets 2 and 3 can be set to infinity in eq. (15).

5 EXPRESSION FOR THE FRACTURE FREQUENCY FOR A REGULARLY JOINTED ROCK MASS

Consider a borehole expansion test conducted in a regularly jointed rock mass with three orthogonal joint sets. The constitutive equations of the rock mass are defined by eqs. (3) and (15). The orientation of the borehole with respect to the joint sets in the rock mass is also assumed to be known. For each diametral measurement conducted in the borehole, the apparent modulus defined in eqs. (12) and (14) can be calculated in terms of the rock mass properties. The apparent modulus can also be related to the apparent degree of fracturing or the fracture frequency measured along the axis of the borehole in which the expansion tests are conducted. The fracture frequency is defined as "the number of discontinuities encountered per unit length of a line in a particular direction through a rock mass". It varies with the orientation of the line with respect to the planes of weakness in the rock mass.

Let β_h and δ_h be two angles defining the orientation of the borehole and therefore the x,y,z-axes with respect to the fixed

864

coordinate system X,Y,Z. This is shown in Fig. 4a. The x-axis is taken in the XZ plane. Similarly, let β and ψ be two angles defining the orientation of the three orthogonal joint sets and therefore the x',y',z' - axes with respect to the XYZ coordinate system. This is shown in Fig. 4b. The z'-axis is taken in the XZ plane. As shown by Hudson and Priest (1983), the fracture frequency, λ_s along the z-axis of the borehole can be written as follows

$$\lambda_s = \sum_{i=1}^{3} \lambda_i \left| \cos \theta_i \right| \tag{16}$$

with $\lambda_i = 1/S_i$ and θ_i is the angle between the borehole axis z with unit vector $\vec{n_H}$ and the normal to the i-th joint set $\vec{n_i}$. The absolute value of $\cos \theta_i$ must be taken because λ_s is always positive. For the geometry shown in Fig. 4 we have

$$\cos \theta_1 = \cos \delta_h \cos \beta_h \sin \psi \cos \beta + \sin \delta_h \cos \psi +$$
$$\cos \delta_h \sin \beta_h \sin \psi \sin \beta$$

$$\cos \theta_2 = -\cos \delta_h \cos \beta_h \cos \psi \cos \beta + \sin \delta_h \sin \psi -$$
$$\cos \delta_h \sin \beta_h \cos \psi \sin \beta$$

$$\cos \theta_3 = -\cos \delta_h \cos \beta_h \sin \beta + \cos \delta_h \sin \beta_h \cos \beta \tag{17}$$

For a fixed orientation of the three orthogonal joint sets the fracture frequency λ_s varies with δ_h and β_h. The directions δ_{hm} and β_{hm} associated with a maximum discontinuity frequency can be found by substituting eq. (17) in eq. (16), partially differentiating eq. (16) with respect to δ_h and β_h, equating the results to zero and then solving simultaneously to obtain δ_{hm} and β_{hm}. Substituting these values for δ and β in eqs. (16) and (17), gives a value of maximum discontinuity frequency (Priest and Hudson, 1983).

6 CONCLUSIONS

An analytical model has been proposed in this paper to explain the variational character of the apparent modulus of an anisotropic rock mass measured at different points along the walls of a borehole during expansion tests. The modulus depends on the anisotropic properties of the rock mass and the orientation of the rock mass anisotropy with respect to the directions of borehole measurements and/or loading. The model is also applicable for a rock mass cut by several joint sets as long as the rock mass can be modelled as an equivalent linearly elastic continuum. For a regularly jointed rock mass, the apparent modulus depends on the joint set spacings and stiffnesses, the intact rock properties and four orientation angles defined in Fig. 4. These four angles can also be used to calculate the fracture frequency in the direction of the borehole in which the expansion tests are conducted.

The previous conclusions are illustrated in the following example with the geometry of Figs. 1 to 4. The rock mass has one joint set with strike line parallel to the Z-axis ($\beta = 0$) and dip angle ψ equal to 30 degrees. The joint stiffnesses k_n and k_s are equal to 10,000 and 5,000 MPa/m respectively. The intact rock has a Young's modulus equal to 40,000 MPa and a Poisson's ratio equal to 0.25. Two NX jack tests are conducted in a borehole with axis parallel to the Y-axis (δ_h = 90). In one test, the rock mass is loaded in the X direction (β_h = 0) and in the other test, it is loaded in the Z direction (β_h = 90). For both tests, the fracture frequency along the borehole, λ_s is equal to cos ψ/S. For each test, the value of the apparent modulus E_a, defined in eq. (14), was calculated for different values of the joint set spacing S assuming a contact angle β_c equal to 45 degrees. The variation of E_a with the fracture frequency has been plotted in Fig. 5 for the two tests. As the joint set spacing decreases, the fracture frequency increases and the apparent modulus E_a decreases. As the spacing goes to infinity, E_a approaches the isotropic solution; e.g. E_a = 40,000 MPa. In view of the two curves in Fig. 5, the rock mass shows a strong directional character in its response to loading.

7 LIST OF REFERENCES

Amadei, B. 1983. Rock Anisotropy and the Theory of Stress Measurements. Springer Verlag Lecture Notes in Engineering.
Amadei, B. Paper in preparation.
Duncan, J.M. and Goodman, R.E. 1968. Finite element analysis of slopes in jointed rocks. Contract report S-68-3, U.S. Army Corps of Engineers.
Goodman, R.E. 1980. Introduction to Rock Mechanics. Wiley.
Goodman, R.E., Van, T.K. and Heuze, F.E. 1970. Measurement of rock deformability in boreholes. Proc. 10th U.S. Symp. on Rock Mechanics, University of Texas at Austin, pp. 523-555, May (AIME).
Heuze, F.E. 1980. Scale effects in the determination of rock mass strength and deformability. Rock Mechanics, 12, pp. 167-192.
Lekhnitskii, S.G. 1963. Theory of Elasticity of an Anisotropic Elastic Body. Holden Day, San Francisco.
Hudson, J.A. and Priest S.D. 1983. Discontinuity frequency in rock masses. Int. J. Rock Mech. Min. Sci., Vol. 20, No. 2, pp. 73-89.

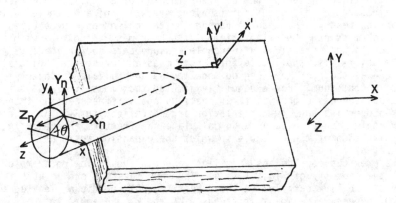

Figure 1. Geometry of the problem.

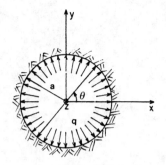

Figure 2. Radial loading of a hole.

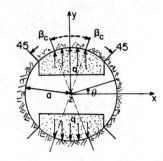

Figure 3. Loading of a hole over two opposed arcs.

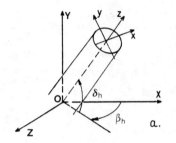

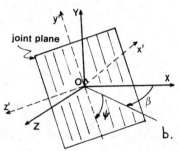

Figure 4. Orientation of the xyz and x'y'z' coordinate systems with respect to a global XYZ coordinate system.

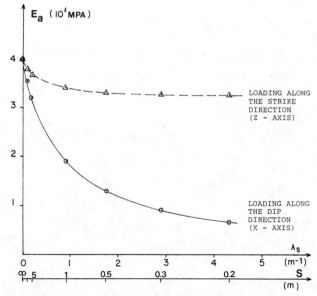

Figure 5. Variation of the apparent modulus E_a with the joint set spacing and fracture frequency.

867

In-situ determination of elastic coefficients of rock mass

PAN LI-ZHOU
Shanghai Institute of Applied Mathematics & Mechanics, People's Republic of China

ABSTRACT

Young's modulus E and Poisson's ratio ν are two important elastic coefficients in rock engineering practice, especially in the determination of in-situ stresses in a rock mass by the borehole deformation method. In measuring in-situ stress by this method, we cannot calculate the state of in-situ stress from the data obtained in the measurement, without the numerical values of these two coefficients just at the measuring point in the rock mass. As the properties of a rock mass are quite different from those of a rock sample, even if the sample is taken out of the same rock mass, the numerical results obtained from tests on rock samples in the laboratory cannot be used in engineering designs. We have to do in-situ tests to determine these two elastic coefficients E and ν. In the paper we give a method for this purpose. In the method we will use the same borehole, the same stress-relief groove and the same apparatus that are originally used for in-situ stress measurement. In fact, both of the two in-situ measurements, determining the state of stress in a rock mass and determining the elastic coefficients of the rock mass, can be done in the same time at the same site. As a result of this, the cost of the in-situ tests can be considerably reduced.

In general there are five different tests we can do. However, any two of them will be sufficient to determine the coefficients E and ν. For example, let us consider the following two tests. In the first test, we drill a circular hole of radius a in the rock mass to the depth where we want to know its elastic coefficients, pour a fluid into the borehole, pressurize the fluid to a pressure p_1, and then record with a probe the amount of the radial displacement u_1 of the borehole wall (Fig. 1). From the theory of elasticity, the relationship between u_1 and p_1 can be expressed as

$$\frac{u_1}{a} = \frac{1 + \nu}{E} p_1 \qquad (1)$$

In the second test, we cut an annular groove of radius b in the rock mass by overcoring concentrically around the borehole, pour a fluid both into the groove and the borehole, pressurize the fluid to a pressure p_2, and then record the amount of the radial displacement u_2 of the inner

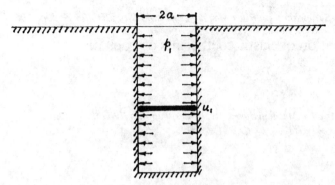

Figure 1: Diagram showing the variables used for a single borehole test.

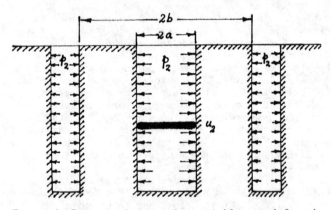

Figure 2: Diagram showing the variables used for the overcoring test.

wall of the tubelike rock core (Fig. 2). According to the theory of elasticity, u_2 is related to p_2 by the equation

$$\frac{u_2}{a} = -\frac{1 - \nu}{E}\, p_2 \tag{2}$$

From equations (1) and (2), it follows readily that

$$E = \frac{2a}{\dfrac{u_1}{u_2} - \dfrac{p_1}{p_2}}\, \frac{p_1}{u_2} \tag{3}$$

$$(3)$$

$$\nu = 1 + \frac{2}{\dfrac{u_1}{u_2} - \dfrac{p_1}{p_2}}\, \frac{p_1}{p_2}$$

870

The other three tests are described in detail in the paper. There are ten different ways in which we choose two out of the five tests. So we shall have ten numerical sets of E and ν. By using the usual technique in the theory of errors to treat these sets of values, we can get the best numerical values of E and ν.

To avoid the undesirable effect of the contact pressure between the probe and the wall on the required results, we had better use a strain gauge to measure the circumferential strain ε of the borehole wall, instead of using a probe to measure its radial displacement u. All the formulas are still valid except that the quantities u's have to be replaced respectively by a times ε's.

Some laboratory and field deformation modulus results and their application to a practical problem

D.P.RICHARDS
CRSS and M & E, Riyadh, Saudi Arabia
W.A.HUSTRULID
Colorado School of Mines, Golden, USA

1. INTRODUCTION

When any structure is built upon or in the earth, an important parameter related to the stability of the structure is the load-deformation response of the material beneath or around the structure. For a proper evaluation of this response, large-scale loading with appropriate deformation measurements is desirable. Ideally, the size of the loaded area would approximate that of the proposed structure. For most large construction projects such as dams and power plants, this test condition is unrealistic and alternative testing techniques must be employed.

The specific testing techniques appropriate for any given situation will vary, depending upon whether the proposed structure is to be founded in soil or in rock. This paper presents the results of a rather extensive program designed to evaluate the deformation characteristics of the foundation rock for a nuclear power plant founded in sedimentary rock in the northeastern part of the United States. It was the purpose of this study to evaluate the deformation properties of the rock encountered at the site with major emphasis on those rocks located within the influence zone of the planned reactor foundation mat which is approximately 200 feet (60 m) in diameter. For this study, both laboratory and field techniques were employed to determine the deformation properties of intact and in-situ rock.

The laboratory tests included 79 biaxial tests on 5 1/4-inch (133 mm) diameter, thick-wall cylinders in which Young's modulus was measured in three directions (in the plane of bedding for most cases); 16 uniaxial tests on NX (2-1/8 inch (54 mm)) diameter specimens loaded perpendicular to bedding; 5 uniaxial tests on NX specimens loaded parallel to bedding; 1 triaxial test on an NX specimen loaded perpendicular to bedding; and 22 triaxial tests on 1/2-inch (12.7 mm) diameter specimens loaded both in plane of bedding and at 30° to the plane of bedding.

Seismic surveys using refraction, uphole, and cross-hole techniques were employed. Both the refraction method of P-wave velocity measurement and the cross-hole method of S-wave measurement tend to indicate the response of the fastest, stiffest, most competent rock which they traverse. Using the results of these "fast" velocities (V_p = 16,000 fps (4880 m/s) and V_s = 14,000 fps (4270 m/s)), a dynamic Young's modulus of 5.4×10^6 psi was computed to serve as an upper bound value of the expected in-situ value of the rock mass.

TABLE 1. STATISTICAL YOUNG'S MODULUS SUMMARY

Rock Unit	Rock Type	Test Type	No. Tests	E Max (psix10^6)	E Min (psix10^6)	E Mean (psix10^6)	S.D. (psix10^6)	Orientation WRT Bedding
1	Sandstone	Uniaxial NX	3	5.0	4.2	4.6	0.4	⊥
		Biaxial	15	8.5	3.2	4.9	1.4	∥
		Borehole (Static)	13	2.7	0.1	1.0	0.7	∥
2	Sandstone/ Shale	Uniaxial NX	6	5.7	3.2	4.5	0.9	∥
		Biaxial	18	8.8	2.0	4.8	1.6	∥
		Borehole (Static)	11	1.7	0.1	0.6	0.4	∥
		Borehole (Dynamic)	14	4.5	3.6	3.9	0.5	⊥
3	Graywake	Uniaxial NX	3	5.7	5.1	5.3	0.3	⊥
		Uniaxial NX	5	2.4	1.8	2.1	0.2	∥
		Biaxial	14	6.3	4.1	5.4	0.8	∥
		Borehole (Static)	28	1.3	0.1	0.7	0.3	∥
		Borehole (Dynamic)	41	5.9	4.4	4.9	0.4	⊥
4	Shale	Uniaxial NX	4	4.2	3.1	3.4	0.6	⊥
		Triaxial 1/2"	4	6.7	4.6	5.6	1.2	∥
		Biaxial	26	4.7	2.1	3.5	0.5	∥
		Borehole (Static)	14	1.4	0.3	0.6	0.3	∥
		Borehole (Dynamic)	59	5.3	3.1	4.0	0.5	⊥
5	Shale	Biaxial	2	4.4	4.2	4.3	0.1	⊥
		Triaxial 1/2"	5	4.1	3.1	3.7	0.4	∥
		Borehole (Static)	4	0.3	0.2	0.3	0.05	∥
		Triaxial 1/2"	11	1.3	0.6	1.0	0.2	@ 30°
		Borehole (Dynamic)	12	5.3	2.7	3.9	0.9	⊥
6	Shale With Occ. SS	Biaxial	3	5.8	4.1	4.7	1.0	∥
All Zones		Uniaxial NX	16	5.7	3.1	4.4	0.9	⊥
		Uniaxial NX	5	2.4	1.8	2.1	0.2	∥
		Triaxial 1/2"	9	6.7	3.1	4.6	1.3	∥
		Biaxial	78	8.8	2.1	4.3	1.2	∥
		Borehole (Static)	70	2.7	0.1	0.7	0.5	∥
		Borehole (Dynamic)	126	5.9	2.7	4.2	0.7	⊥

In-situ measurements of Young's modulus sub-parallel to bedding were accomplished by the use of an Oyo borehole dilatometer in 12 boreholes to a maximum depth of 178 feet (54 m). The boreholes were selected to provide test locations spaced fairly uniformly across a known fault structure. The depths of individual tests were selected to provide data for the representative rock types encountered and a fair representation of rock quality (i.e., value of measured RQD) for each rock type.

2. OVERALL INTERPRETATION OF YOUNG'S MODULUS

Young's modulus data have been collected from uniaxial, triaxial, and biaxial laboratory tests and from in-situ borehole measurements. This extensive data base represents a wide range of values of Young's modulus. For design purposes, an engineering interpretation is necessary to define a representative single value or a narrow range of values for Young's modulus for each rock unit. For this purpose the rock mass has been divided into six distinct mechanical units in which the rock is expected to behave similarly. Each of these mechanical units is made up of one or more geologic stratigraphic units. In each of these units, all test data on Young's modulus has been statistically evaluated to provide a mean value of measured Young's modulus and an accompanying standard deviation. These data are summarized in Table 1 and shown graphically in Figures 1 and 2. These values which describe the intact rock properties then provide a reference datum from which adjustments can be made to develop Young's modulus values which would represent the properties of the rock mass.

At present, there is no generally accepted method by which to extrapolate the values obtained from intact (laboratory) samples of rock to those representative of the in-situ rock mass. The in-situ rock mass can exhibit two distinct types of behavior as discussed by Dodds (1974). The first type of behavior is commonly termed the in-situ modulus of deformation and represents the rock deformation characteristics between zero stress and a designated stress. The second type of behavior commonly known as the in-situ Young's (elastic) modulus represents the rock deformation characteristics under incremental stress changes. For this study, two distinct methods were applied to the in-situ borehole data and the laboratory data for estimating the in-situ deformation modulus.

The first method was an adaptation of the recommendations made by the Oyo Corporation (1975) for applying Elastmeter data. Oyo recommended increasing the Elastmeter modulii by an adjustment factor of 2.0 for the highest measured values, 1.5 for the mid-range values, and 1.0 for the lower values. After an appraisal of the total Elastmeter data base, it was felt that an adjustment value of 2.0 could not be used due to the increasing lack of resolution of the recorder data at the higher values; i.e., the pressure vs displacement curve becomes very steep and the possibility of making a reliable slope determination decreases. For the lower range test results, it was felt that the accuracy of measurement was equal to the mid-range measurements and, thus, the adjustment factors should be equal. In all tests, it was observed that the rubber packer tube exhibited a small amount of time-dependent deformation. This resulted in an apparent increase in the measured borehole

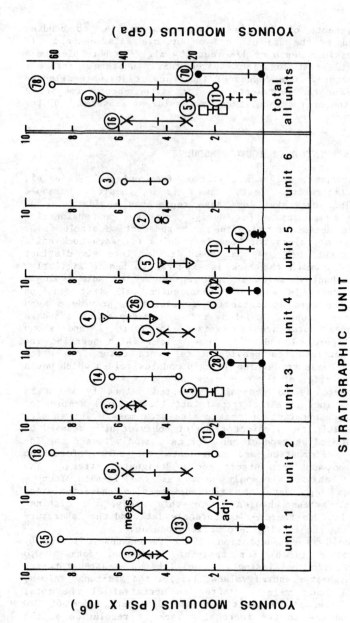

Figure 1. Summary of Young's Modulus Data by Stratigraphic Units

displacement and an associated flattening of the pressure-displacement curve. In view of the above thoughts and observations and engineering judgment, it was felt that an adjustment factor of 1.5 (as recommended by Oyo for the mid-range values) was reasonable for all Elastmeter data. This factor of 1.5 was then applied to both the mean and standard deviation of the in-situ borehole Young's modulus for each rock unit to provide upper and lower bounds of the in-situ rock mass deformation modulus.

The second method of estimating the in-situ deformation modulus for the rock mass was to use the mean value of the measure Young's modulus from the 15 biaxial tests conducted on the sandstone. This value, 4.9×10^6 psi (33.8 GPa) was selected as a reference datum since the sandstone is quite competent, massive and fairly uniform both with depth and with aerial extent over the site. This reference datum was then adjusted to represent an in-situ deformation modulus using experience, engineering judgment, and reported values of deformation modulus in the rock mechanics literature. Attempts were made to correlate deformation modulus with RQD as suggested by Deere (1967, 1969) and Coon (1970), and with fracture frequency as suggested by Hobbs (1974) and Fairhurst (1972). However, these reported tests were generally conducted at sites where RQD and fracture frequency were both carefully measured over short intervals in boreholes which had been drilled beneath areas to be loaded by large-scale plate jacking tests. The RQD or fracture frequency were then correlated to deformations measured during the jacking test. At the present site, no such large-scale tests have been conducted. The RQD of fresh core has been recorded for the entire length of the core run instead of over small intervals, and the rock types at this site are generally different from those reported in the literature. Therefore, the direct application of published results would be difficult and infact, inappropriate due to the differing site conditions. A review of the reported correlations in the literature, knowledge of the geologic conditions at this site, and engineering judgment were employed to arrive at lower and upper bound adjustment factors of 4.0 and 2.5. The intact laboratory Young's values are divided by these factors modulus to obtain an estimate of the in-situ deformation modulus.

Thus, the reference datum of 4.9×10^6 psi from biaxial tests on the sandstone was reduced by a factor of 4.0 and 2.5 to provide lower and upper bounds for the deformation modulus estimate for the in-situ rock mass. A second adjustment procedure was then required to arrive at reasonable values for the other rock types encountered. The relative magnitudes of modulus as determined by the Oyo Elastmeter in the other stratigraphic units was used for this purpose. Table 2 presents the various values of the deformation modulus determined by these two techniques for the different stratigraphic units.

As can be seen the mean values of deformation modulus agree quite well for the two methods of evaluation which provides a certain degree of confidence in the numbers determined. However, the upper and lower limits differ somewhat between the two methods. It is suggested that the upper and lower bounds as determined by method two be employed for the purposes of analysis, since it provides a narrower range for design. The large range produced by method one is thought due to the extreme variability in rock quality in the localized sections of borehole where the tests were conducted and not representative of longer sections.

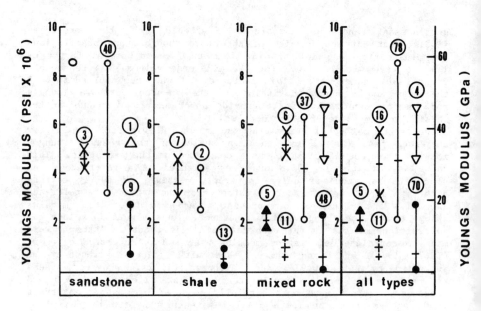

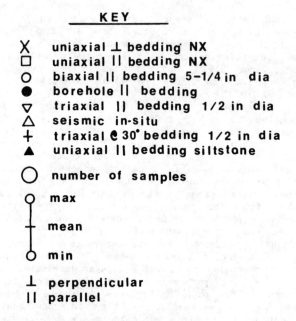

This applies to both Figures 1 and 2

KEY

✕	uniaxial ⊥ bedding NX
□	uniaxial ‖ bedding NX
○	biaxial ‖ bedding 5-1/4 in dia
●	borehole ‖ bedding
▽	triaxial ‖ bedding 1/2 in dia
△	seismic in-situ
+	triaxial ℂ 30° bedding 1/2 in dia
▲	uniaxial ‖ bedding siltstone
◯	number of samples
	max
+	mean
	min
⊥	perpendicular
‖	parallel

Figure 2. Summary of Young's Modulus Data by Rock Type

TABLE 2. DEFORMATION MODULUS SUMMARY

Rock Unit	Rock Type	No. of Oyo Tests	Elastmeter Measured E mean (psix10^6)	Elastmeter Measured Std. Dev. (psix10^6)	Adjusted Elastmeter Data			Correlation Method 2 Adjusted Biaxial Data		
					Upper Bound 1.5 times (E mean+S.D.) (psix10^6)	1.5 times E mean (psix10^6)	Lower Bound 1.5 times (E mean−S.D.) (psix10^6)	Upper Bound E lab x j (j = 0.4) (psix10^6)	E mean (psix10^6)	Lower Bound E lab x j (j = 0.25) (psix10^6)
1	Sandstone	13	1.04	0.74	2.67	1.56	0.45	1.96	1.60	1.23
2	Sandstone/ Shale	11	0.61	0.41	1.57	0.92	0.30	1.18	0.96	0.74
3	Graywacke	28	0.65	0.31	1.44	0.98	0.51	1.37	1.12	0.86
4	Shale	14	0.63	0.33	1.44	0.95	0.45	1.18	0.96	0.74
5	Shale	4	0.27	0.04	0.47	0.41	0.35	0.59	0.48	0.37

TABLE 3. SUMMARY OF IN-SITU MODULUS RECOMMENDATIONS

Stratigraphic Unit	Rock Type	Ed[1] psix10⁶ (mean value)	Ed: 2.5 psix10⁶	Eo[2] psix10⁶ (mean value)	Eo x 1.6 psix10⁶	Es[3] psix10⁶
1	Sandstone	--	--	1.60	2.56	2.56
2	Sandstone/ Shale	3.86	1.54	0.96	1.54	1.54
3	Graywacke	4.87	1.95	1.12	1.79	1.95
4	Shale	3.97	1.59	0.96	1.54	1.59
5	Shale	3.85[4]	1.54	0.48	0.77	1.00
6	Shale with occ. Sandstone	--	--	--	--	1.60[5]

[1]Ed = Dynamic In-Situ Young's Modulus

[2]Eo = Recommended In-Situ Modulus of Deformation

[3]Es = Best Estimate for In-Situ Static Young's Modulus

[4]This value not truly representative of entire zone since the measurements were restricted to the upper portion of the zone and were highly influenced by thin sandstone beds in the upper portion of the zone and did not reflect the fact the the majority of the zone is shale.

[5]Estimated from proportions of shale, graywacke and sandstone in the zone and accompanying weighted values of in-situ static Young's modulus for these rock types.

As discussed previously, the modulus of deformation values given in Table 2 are intended for evaluation of deformations due to the first-time loading of the rock mass. An in-situ Young's modulus is then necessary for evaluation of deformations due to incremental stress changes. For estimating the in-situ Young's modulus, two methods are again employed; one using recommended ratios of deformation modulus to Young's modulus by Zaruba (1976), and the other using borehole geophysical data (also based upon recommendations by Zaruba) obtained from a previous study at the site. Unfortunately, only one borehole had a length extending to the rock below the reactor excavation at the site and therefore the data are quite limited.

Zaruba recommended a ratio between the in-situ Young's modulus and in-situ modulus of deformation of 1.5 for competent rocks and up to 1.8 for jointed rock. The values of deformation modulus (Table 2) were multiplied by a factor of 1.6 for the various stratigraphic (mechanical) rock units at this site, to estimate the in-situ Young's modulus.

For each stratigraphic mechanical unit (as described previously), the maximum, minimum, and mean values of in-situ dynamic Young's modulus (from borehole geophysical logs) were calculated and are included in Table 1. Using the reduction factor range (as suggested by Zaruba) of 2 for competent rock to 6 for jointed rock, a reduction factor of 2.5 was selected to represent conditions at this site. Applying this correction to the mean values of in-situ dynamic Young's modulus, another estimate of the in-situ static Young's modulus was obtained.

Results of the above two methods of estimating in-situ static Young's modulus are shown in Table 3 together with the "best estimate".

3. CONCLUSIONS

The test program did provide data which could be used to estimate the in-situ modulus of deformation and in-situ Young's modulus. However, as noted, the introduction of a number of "factors" were required. This reduces the level of confidence in the final results and introduces some uncertainty in the engineering judgments based upon them. To increase the confidence level, it would be necessary to conduct a series of large scale jacking tests to properly confirm/evaluate the in-situ rock mass behavior. For critical structures, it seems that the increased confidence in the data would warrant the increased cost of field testing.

REFERENCES

Coon, F.F. and A.H. Merritt. 1970. Predicting In-Situ Modulus of Deformation Using Rock Quality Indices; in Determination of the In-Situ Modulus of Deformation of Rock; ASTM STP 477. American Soc. for Testing & Materials. pp. 154-173.
Deere, D.J.; A.J. Hendron; F.D. Patton; and E.J. Cording. 1967. Design of Surface and Near Surface Construction in Rock; in Failure & Breakage of Rock; Proc. 8th Symposium on Rock Mech. Minneapolis, Minn. pp. 237-303 New York: AIME.
Deere, D.U.; A.H. Merritt; and R.F. Coon. 1969. Engineering Classification of In-Situ Rock. Tech. Rpt No. AFWL-TR-67-144. Air

Force Weapons Laboratory. Kirtland Air Force Base, New Mexico.

Dodds, D.J. and W.L. Schroeder. 1974. Factors Bearing on the Interpretation of In-Situ Testing Results; in Proceedings 2nd RETC, Vol. 1, pp. 397-414. New York: AIME.

Fairhurst, C. 1972. Estimation of the Mechanical Properties of Rock Masses. ARPA-USBM Contract H0220011 Final Report. Minneapolis: Univ. of Minn.

Hobbs, N.B. 1974. Factors Affecting the Prediction of Settlement of Structures on Rock. Proc. Conf. on Settlement of Structures. Cambridge: British Geotechnical Soc. pp. 579-610.

Ohya, S.K. Ogura and M. Tsuji. 1975. The Instrument of New Type Dilatometer "Elastmeter" for Studying the Rock Mechanics. Oyo Technical Note TN-06. Oyo Corporation. Tokyo, Japan.

Zaruba, Q. and V. Mencl. 1976. Engineering Geology. New York: Elsevier Scientific Publishing Co.

A strategy for future laboratory rock mechanics programs

B.M.BUTCHER & A.K.JONES
Sandia National Laboratories, Albuquerque, New Mexico, USA

A strategy for future experimental rock mechanics laboratory programs at Sandia National Laboratories is described in this paper. This strategy is motivated by the need for long range planning of rock mechanics programs addressing the stability of complex underground structures, changes in in situ stress states during resource recovery and underground explosion technology. It is based on: (1) recent advances in underground structure stability analysis which make three-dimensional calculations feasible, and (2) new developments in load path control of laboratory stress-strain tests which permit duplication of stress and strain histories in critical parts of a structure, as determined by numerical analysis (Butcher and Hill 1984). The major constraint in the strategy is the assumption that there are no in situ joint features or sample size effects which might prevent simulation of in situ response in the laboratory.

Three-dimensional calculations represent a whole new dimension in design analysis. The problem of demonstrating that these numerical solutions are representative of actual in situ response, however, is very challenging. Execution of field tests are a traditional way of satisfying this objective, but difficulties are often encountered in verifying analytic results by this approach because of uncertainties in boundary conditions and complexity. Another aspect of assuring reasonable agreement is the appropriateness of the constitutive relations. Constitutive model development has generally proceeded independently of design analyses with material response predictions verified by observing material response along various, quite simple, load paths in the laboratory. Similar observations for soils have recently been expressed by Gudehus (1983). The objective of the strategy described in this paper is to provide both a supplemental approach to field testing and a method for evaluation of the accuracy of predictions for load paths which are more representative of excavation and operating conditions.

1 OBJECTIVE

1.1 Analysis phase

A critical stress-strain path for the structure is identified from the design calculation. This loading path might be for an element at the center of a drift roof, at corners, or perhaps at the midpoint of a

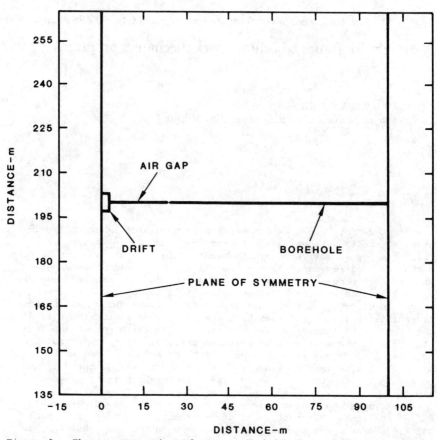

Figure 1. The cross section of an access drift in a preliminary configuration used to develop numerical procedures for predicting the consequences of various nuclear waste repository configurations.

drift wall where the numerical prediction indicates conditions approaching failure. For example, an abstraction of the cross section of an access drift of a preliminary configuration for predicting the consequences of various horizontal nuclear waste emplacement configurations is shown in Figure (1). A thin horizontal layer in the surrounding rock, which represents the location of the heat generating waste after emplacement, intersects the drift. A typical loading path for an element at the midpoint of the right wall of the drift is shown in Figure (2). The points in the figure represent the states of stress computed at various times. The maximum principal stress at this location was nearly constant and much larger than the intermediate and minimum principal stresses. Although this is a two-dimensional plane strain configuration, the stress field is three-dimensional and therefore beyond the capability of most present laboratory techniques. This limitation in capability illustrates an important advantage of the strategy: it provides direction for future development of laboratory facilities, in this case, development of three-dimensional simulation techniques.

884

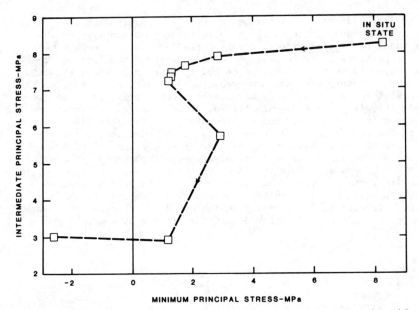

Figure 2. A typical load path for an element adjacent to the midpoint of the right wall of the drift shown in Figure 1. The maximum principal stress at this location was nearly constant and much larger than the intermediate and minimum principal stresses.

1.2 Experimental phase

Either the stress path, or the strain path is then duplicated in the laboratory, using a sample from the site. If a stress path is used for test control, then measurement of the strains produces a history which is representative of actual material response. This strain history is completely independent of any assumptions made for the calculation. If strain control is used, then a stress history is measured. An example of test control is the simulation of strain paths in partially saturated tuff, typical of underground explosive loading discussed later in the paper. This spherically symmetric problem can be simulated with present laboratory testing configurations. Similar load path investigations have also been reported by Bogart and Schatz (1983).

1.3 Interpretative Phase

Finally, the independent stress or strain history from the numerical prediction is compared with the laboratory data to determine the degree to which the computation reproduces real material response. This is the endpoint we are looking for, because the comparison permits quantitative assessment of the validity of the numerical prediction. Few investigations have completed this step in the past, but it is well within the grasp of current technology and is desirable as a routine procedure within the next ten years.

Several important consequences arise from comparison of the two histories. First, if close agreement is observed, greater confidence can certainly be placed in the prediction. This finding will help to dispel doubts about whether or not the constitutive relation is appropriate and if the analysis is being done correctly. On the other hand, beneficial effects occur if the lack of agreement between the two histories is quite pronounced because the comparison and the laboratory data provide direction on how to proceed further. Assuming that the laboratory simulation process posed no difficulties, reasons for lack of agreement could be because the constitutive relations used in this calculation are too simplified, or an important physical process has been overlooked. The experimental data from the laboratory test should be very helpful in resolving these questions, providing that there are no in situ joint features or sample size effects which preclude simulation of in situ response in the laboratory. The end result of the comparison is that a quantitative measure is provided of the merit of the analytic prediction, which can be used to conclude that the prediction is adequate for the purpose desired, or that improvement is warranted. An additional bonus from the strategy is that its experimental part also provides information about how to improve the prediction.

2 PROGRESS

2.1 Test equipment

Initial work on laboratory simulation is focused on load path control. Technology for duplicating prescribed stress or strain paths in a rock sample has progressed to the point where it can be considered a routine part of laboratory operation. Execution of tests proceeds as usual, with the exception that instead of setting control parameters, such as loading rate, on a load frame controller, the information describing the course of the test is entered directly into a computer. Since data acquisition in many laboratories is now computerized, using the computer for load control simply combines the two functions.

The test control to be described in this paper was accomplished with a single user MTS Systems Corporation Model 463 Data/Control Processor. This system, consisting of a Digital Equipment Corporation LSI 11/23 microcomputer, with other components and servocontrol units, is used to acquire data from various types of mechanical tests in our laboratory.

Current methods of test execution are accomplished by applying axial load to a sample with a hydraulic ram by controlling its stroke. Axial stress on the sample is measured with a load cell. Lateral pressurization of the sample is used to simulate the stress at various depths under the surface of the earth. Pressure is applied through a hydraulic fluid to the sample through a thin but impervious jacket, which prevents penetration of the fluid into the test material. Current testing is limited to axisymmetric states of stress because of the inability to independently vary the lateral principal stresses, although the 463 processor can be expanded to permit control of more than two test variables. Other test parameters are axial and transverse strains which correspond to the change in axial length of the sample and the diametrical change in length. Strain control of the test is thus feasible by controlling the load and pressure applied to the sample to produce a desired strain history. In a special case of strain control, described later in this paper, a constant state of strain is maintained as the control system monitors any length measurement

deviation from zero (or a preset value) and corrects the load path
accordingly. Strain control in our system differs little from stress
control, in contrast to the system described by Bogart and Schatz
(1983) which requires estimation of the next stress increment for a
given change in strain before execution of the next step of the test.

Execution of a test to determine the mechanical behavior of materials
with the MTS 463 processor is defined by a MTS conversational programming language, containing various MTS Systems Corporation enhancements of Digital Equipment Corporations MU Basic/RT11 language. The
MTS programming language permits the creation and control of analog
output to one or more servocontrol channels through hardware segment
generators that permit waveform definition by generating the intermediate steps between specified end levels. In addition, the language
is used to initiate and control data acquisition in a wide variety of
modes, monitoring the progress of the test to present to the user only
the data requested. Finally, graphical displays and hard copies of
the progress of the test can be generated to aid in its real time
interpretation. The latter feature is particularly essential in computer control applications because of the necessity of assuring that
the imposed load path is a reasonable reproduction of the prescribed
load path.

Programmed execution of a load path for a given material is achieved
by calling up various subroutines which permit waveform generation
using an internal function generator. This function generator performs essentially the same as an external function generator, the
diference being that the waveform is computer generated. Routines
exist that initiate or stop the control cycle, define the status of
the system, create waveforms and convert values in engineering units
to or from binary format. The degree of control during the test can
be adjusted by presetting the amplitudes of the feedback signal errors
that determine whether a direction in control is required, a process
which has been quite stable providing the error tolerances are not
too small. The most troublesome part of the test is at its beginning,
during manual application of slight preloads to get the test started.

2.2 Experimental results

Results from several relatively simple load paths will be used to
illustrate the types of load control currently feasible in our
laboratory. First, an example of loading a rock in compression at
constant mean stress will be shown to demonstrate load control. This
relatively simple path (Figure 3a) traditionally has been difficult
to generate in the laboratory because, during the constant mean stress
part of the stress path, the lateral stress on the sample must decrease
proportionally by half as much as the increase in axial stress. This
path is of interest in modeling porous rocks because it is a straightforward measurement of shear induced compaction. The sample is first
loaded hydrostatically to a predetermined mean stress level, point A
in Figure 3a, and then, during the constant mean stress portion of
the loading path from point A to point C in Figure 3b, its volume
continues to decrease. The sample in this test was a water saturated
sandstone taken at 329M depth from the Mounds Test Well, Mounds,
Oklahoma (Skinner Formation). The deviation from linearity of the
initial part of the constant mean stress portion of the curve, which
appears to recover at point B, may be an artifact of the lateral strain
gage measurement device. Additional testing is also necessary to

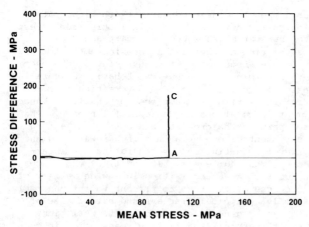

Figure 3a: Constant mean stress load path.

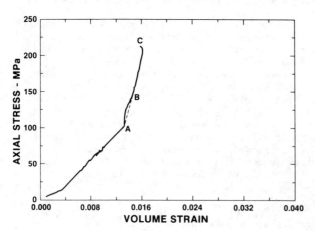

Figure 3b: Shear induced compaction

verify the slight indication of dilation just prior to failure, at point C. With load path control, the test path is very easy to achieve, however, and is expected to become a routine part of testing in connection with material models development.

The next two examples are a consequence of interest in containing the products of underground explosions. Our interest in this problem recently turned to the analysis of relatively small explosive containment tests using from 64 to 2000 lbs of conventional explosives. Spherical configurations were used in a relatively high porosity, nearly saturated tuff. A comprehensive series of numerical wave propagation studies were undertaken in connection with the field tests, from which the input for load path simulation was obtained. The conventional triaxial test configuration was then used to simulate this type of loading in the laboratory: the axial stress corresponds to stress in the radial, wave propagation direction and the confining pressure simulates the two principal hoop stresses. An assumption, however, is that the

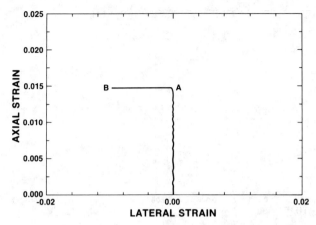

Figure 4a: Uniaxial strain lateral unloading strain path.

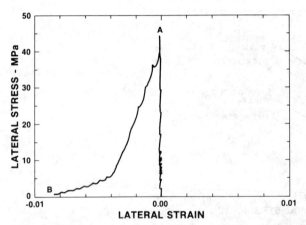

Figure 4b: Lateral stress strain unloading path.

deformation must be considered independent of time because the time
scale is much too fast to simulate in the laboratory.

While the exact strain path derived from the prediction could have
been used for input to the load path control, calculations suggest
that the results would differ little from the simplified path shown
in Figure 4a. In this path, the sample is first loaded in uniaxial
strain to point A (no change in lateral strain). The length of the
sample is then kept constant and the sample is unloaded by allowing·
it to relax laterally to obtain the results shown in Figure 4b. This
type of test is of interest because both the axial stress-strain and·
the lateral unloading paths are required as input for the material
model in the wave propagation analysis.

Another interesting feature of the uniaxial strain lateral unloading
test sequence is shown in Figure 5. Figure 5a is a stress time
prediction from the explosive containment calculation at the location
where the stress wave amplitude had decayed to 70 MPa. The

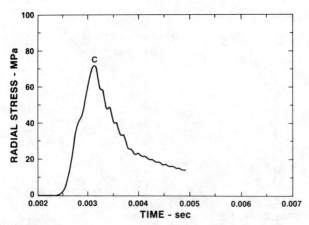

Figure 5a: Calculated stress wave profile from an underground explosion.

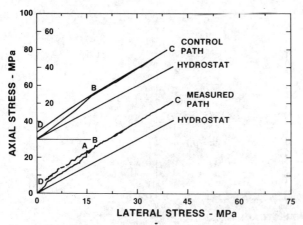

Figure 5b: Underground explosion history load path.

relationship between axial (radial) and lateral stresses predicted for this history, using classical plasticity, is particularly simple as shown in the upper part of Figure 5b. During the uniaxial strain part of the loading, the rock is predicted to load elastically to the failure (yield) surface, at point B, and then load along it to the point of maximum stress, at C. Lateral unloading (relief of hoop stress as the rock is displaced outward radially by the detonation products) is then predicted to proceed back down along the loading path to point D. The lower part of Figure 5b shows that the same path can be imposed on the rock when the exact stress history predicted by the wave analysis is applied to the sample. Inspection of the sample after the test revealed, however, that, unlike plastically deforming materials, tuff deformed as a frictional material under these conditions. The sample actually failed by the creation of major fractures across its diameter at an early state in the test (at point A). Although it was able to support the imposed load history, further displacement was by sliding of the fractured surfaces over each other. The mode of deformation of this sample was typical of others. The problem with the laboratory simulation is that we have attempted to re-produce the displacement boundary condition of wave propagation (no lateral strain) with a stress boundary condition (controlling the con-fining pressure to produce no lateral strain) using samples that are much too small in diameter. (The grain size was 0.2 to 0.1 times the sample diameter.) While actual deformation of the rock during wave propagation is still expected to be frictional, the displacement boundary condition will constrain crack sliding to a very localized scale. In contrast, our load control tests on this rock are prone to large scale sliding because of the heterogeneity of the rock, which promoted crack communication in the modest size samples (3.8 cm diameter). The lateral stress boundary condition does not inhibit instability. Tests at lower peak stresses in this series, using the strain control mode (Figure 4), were much more stable than the stress control mode. Other tests on a much finer grained sandstone have not shown evidence of instability, and therefore an increase in the dia-meter of the tuff samples may be sufficient to obtain more physically realistic results. The interesting conclusion of this work, however, is that this rock follows a path similar to that predicted for mate-rials that can deform plastically, even though its mode of deformation is completely different. Thus, these laboratory results give us some reassurance that low stress explosive containment calculations in the past are not in gross error because of use of the wrong material model. A number of interesting questions about scale effects of brittle de-formation leading to the onset of instability are also clearly illustrated, which need to be considered further.

3 CLOSURE

While progress in our laboratory is encouraging with regard to load path control of laboratory rock mechanics tests, the results clearly demonstrate how limited our capabilities are in this area: almost all testing continues to be axisymmetric in nature. Even tests duplicating the simplest stress states of interest to the analysts, plane strain, with three independent principal stresses, and plane stress, with two independently varying principal stresses, are beyond the reach of most laboratories. At the same time, studies of the relationship of micro-crack growth to brittle nature of rock deformation provide strong motivation for exploring path dependence. These observations have convinced us that in order to address some of these very complex questions we need to strive to achieve a true three-dimensional testing capability as soon as possible.

This work was performed at Sandia National Laboratories, supported by the U.S. Department of Energy (DOE) under Contract # DE-ACO4-76-DP00789.

REFERENCES

Bogart, J. A. and J. F. Schatz 1983. Specified strain path testing of geologic materials. Proceedings of the 24th U. S. Symposium on Rock Mechanics, (Texas A&M University and the Association of Engineering Geologists), pp. 473-477.

Butcher, B. M. and J. P. Hill 1984. A method for determining the dis-
tribution of triaxial states in underground structures. Sandia
National Laboratories Report, SAND83-2506.
Gudehus, G. 1983. Requirements on constitutive relations for soils.
Preprints of the William Prager Symposium on the Mechanics of
Geomaterials: Rocks, Concretes, Soils, September 11-15, 1983,
(Northwestern University), pp. 55-73, proceedings to be published.

19. Rock drilling and cutting

Chair: LEWIS V.WADE
US Bureau of Mines, Minneapolis, Minnesota, USA
Cochair: CARL H.SCHMUCK
Homestake Mining Company, Lead, South Dakota, USA

A review of waterjet excavation research

DAVID A.SUMMERS
University of Missouri-Rolla, USA

1 INTRODUCTION

On the northeast corner of the campus of the University of
Missouri-Rolla, a new monument has recently been erected. It is a
granite sculpture based on the concept of Stonehenge, an ancient British
megalith, but with certain modifications to recognize its American
location. This monument (Figure 1), stands some 5 meters high, and has
been carved, in its entirety, through use of high pressure waterjets. The
construction has been recognized, by the National Society of Professional
Engineers, as one of the ten Outstanding Engineering Achievements of
1984.

It is pertinent to begin this review with mention of this monument since
it indicates a major change in rock excavation technology. For five
thousand years, from a thousand years before the first Stonehenge was
constructed, rock has been cut and drilled with the mechanical impact of
a hard, often blunt, tool. The physical crushing and chipping of the
rock which occurs during impact consumes a considerable amount of
energy. This mechanical cutting has, in recent years, appeared to be
approaching an asymptote, as improvements in technique no longer give
dramatic advances in performance. Waterjet cutting, however, which has
been used to carve this new Stonehenge, is only in its infancy. The
technology is only just beginning to find commercial application in
industry for the cutting of such items as leather, cardboard, and food
products. And it is only within the last year or so that it has been
accepted for use in cutting rock.

It is pertinent to review the growing pains of this new industry and to
evaluate its current position as we move forward into its growth years.

2 THE DEVELOPMENT OF THE TECHNOLOGY

In the early 1970's, the National Science Foundation, in a very
far-reaching program organized, in large part by Dr. William Hakala, set
out to find novel techniques which might be of use for the excavation of

rock. A wide variety of different excavation systems were proposed in this program and funded through a primary evaluation of their conceptual use. Many different ideas were proposed ranging from the REAM gun (a device which fires concrete bullets at the rock surface) to the use of an electron beam device. Of the 25 different methods, however, which were discussed in a review meeting held at the 17th Rock Mechanics Symposium in Snow Bird, Utah (Brown 1976), only one has, to date, reached the point of commercial development and maintained and developed the progress that was in large part initiated as a result of the National Science Foundation's effort. That technology is the use of high pressure waterjets.

Since the time of that original review, the application of the water jets has also expanded, and they have successfully been combined both with mechanical picks for improved cutting, and abrasive materials have also been added to the waterjet system in order to improve cutting effectiveness. One illustration of the outgrowth of the program from the original NSF funding occurred in 1977 (Anon 1979). At that time, Georgia Institute of Technology, under subcontract from the Elberton Granite Association, and with NSF funding, examined potential novel techniques for use in the primary excavation of granite blocks in the quarry. Of the different methods evaluated in the original paper study, high pressure waterjets were considered to hold high potential, and since there was at that time (as perhaps there still is) some controversy as to the optimal cutting conditions, two different approaches were tested. Field demonstrations were arranged in an operating quarry in Elberton, Georgia to find whether high pressure (280 MPa) low volume flows, or lower pressure (100 MPa) higher volume flows (60 l/min.) would be most effective in cutting granite. As a result of that field test, the Granite Association funded development of a specialized waterjet cutting machine. Meanwhile, one of the companies supporting the original test program has carried out their own research in their quarries in South Dakota and, as a result, now manufacture and sell granite cutting equipment using the lower pressure higher flow rate system (Raether 1983). As an outgrowth of their granite cutting program, the company also developed the equipment so that high pressure waterjets could be used to drive the abutment tunnels for a large dam excavation in South America where material excavation rates on the order of 3 to 4 m^3/hr were achieved. These two items of progress illustrate the arrival of waterjet cutting in the commercial rock excavation area.

2. WATERJET ASSISTED CUTTING

Waterjets alone, however, have not been found to be the most productive method of generating large volumes of rock excavation under most circumstances. To explain why it is easiest to use an example. If a single high pressure waterjet is traversed across a rock surface (with the single known unique exception of coal), and then a second cut is placed adjacent to the first, the intervening material between the cuts will remain in place, even though the rib might be as thin as 6 mm. and the depth of the cut perhaps as deep as 5 cm. To remove the intervening rib of material with the waterjet, requires the full hydraulic power of the pumping unit even though the rib is weak enough to be easily broken by one's finger. Thus a combined waterjet and mechanical system has considerable advantage.

Additional advantages have been found for the combination, particularly where the waterjet is applied in the cutting zone of the mechanical tool. Three different benefits have been postulated for the improvement achieved, (Dubugnon 1981) specifically that the waterjets remove the crushed material underneath the cutting zone; that the waterjet enters, penetrates, and weakens the dilated material ahead of the cutting tool; and that the jet pressurizes and extends cracks made by the tool. Experimental results have shown that cutting forces may be reduced in some rocks by as much as 80 percent. This technique, known as waterjet assisted cutting, was initially developed in South Africa by Hood (Hood, 1976) to cool tungsten carbide bits when they were drawn across quartzite. It was shown that the depth of cut achievable, without stalling the machine, could be increased from 2 to 5 times when waterjets at a pressure of 70 MPa were directed to the corners of the drag bit.

On the basis of these reported results, the National Science Foundation funded a cooperative agreement between Colorado School of Mines, Flow Industries and the Robbins Company to develop a full-scale waterjet assisted tunnel boring machine test program. Equipment was constructed and tested at Skykomish in 1975 (Wang 1976). Although the combination was a prototype, a 30% improvement in tunnel boring machine performance was achieved in some tests indicating the promise of the technique. However, in what has become a familiar refrain to those working in the United States waterjet effort, this development occurred in the Federal Republic of Germany, being carried out with support from Federal German Republic and from the United States Department of Energy . Research is being carried out in cooperation with German commercial concerns at the Bergbau Forschung Research Laboratories in Essen-Kray, Germany (Schenk 1983). A modified German machine has been found to have penetration rates improved by approximately 50% when waterjets are added and commercial equipment has since been developed.

A more dramatic development has, however, been the addition of high pressure waterjets to the cutting picks of boom type tunneling machines. This work, which has mainly been carried out by the National Coal Board in the United Kingdom, was also partially funded by the United States Department of Energy (Anon 1982). Because of the need to counterbalance the thrust forces required to drive the cutting head into the rock face, while a 25 ton weight machine can cut through rock of approximately 100 MPa compressive strength, an 85 ton machine is required in order to cut through rock of approximately 115 MPa compressive strength. The idea for adding waterjets to these machines came from McNary (McNary 1976), who proposed use of the high pressure water to eliminate the dust generated in cutting. For this reason most of the water was directed to infuse the coal face ahead of the machine (which it did for approximately 5 om.), thereby dramatically reducing the amount of dust made. This basic rational for the use of the machine was also a large contributing factor to the development of the British work.

Preliminary experiments with waterjet assisted cutting were carried out on a sandstone face built in an underground limestone mine in Britain. Not only did the 70 MPa water allow the boom header to cut the sandstone

rock without sparks or dust generation, but it also permitted the cutters
to effectively and economically cut the 130 MPa limestone. The success
of the machine was, in fact, such that this 25 ton machine was able to
drive a full conveyer drift for the mine. The demonstration showed that a
25 ton waterjet assisted machine could out-perform an 85 ton machine
without waterjet assist, and has led to the strong commercial development
of this equipment. At present, two British manufacturers have products,
one of whom has already made considerable commercial sales of the new
equipment. At the same time, commercial concerns in Europe are also
developing similar machines. Again, a revolutionary technology
originally developed in the United States is commercially available only
from a European distributor.

Both Colorado School of Mines and the University of Missouri-Rolla
(El-Saie 1977) have demonstrated the benefits to be achieved if a slot is
cut around the profile of a tunnel, before removing the central core.
The free surface created unloads the core prior to fragmentation, and
allows the rock to be blown outward, reducing the amount of effort
required. The core is also decoupled from the surrounding rock so that
that cracks generated during the blast do not propagate into the tunnel
walls.   Prototype equipment will undergo quarry testing in Germany this
spring (1985) (Baumann 1981, and Summers 1985).

3. WATERJET COAL MINING

 In 1971, a paper was published in the United States in which the
potential advantages which would accrue if high pressure waterjets were
oscillated along the outer perimeter of a coal plow were considered
(Summers 1971). As a result the U. S. Bureau of Mines funded a program
from which surface trials of a cutting head design led to a prediction
that such a machine should be able to mine coal at 20 m/min. with a 1 m.
web depth, in a coal seam 1.5 to 2 m. high at existing machine
horsepower. Under similar operating conditions, such a machine, the
Anderton shearer-loader, is only able to achieve approximately 4 m/min.
While the American effort has been discontinued, two German equipment
manufacturers worked with support from both the Germany Federal and State
agencies to evaluate prototype equipment in surface and underground tests
and have proven, in the field, performance levels originally predicted
for the machine.   In fact, in underground tests, the GHH machine has
achieved advance rates of 24 m/min. (Schwarting 1981).

It thus appears that, with rare exception, the originating research
developed in the United States over the course of the past ten years in
this very promising new technology has not been allowed to come to full
potential in this country, but has only been brought to commercial
practice abroad. This is not true just for the intermediate pressure
range described to date. In the use of high volume, low pressure
waterjets, the technique was, in its modern form, originally developed in
the United States. This occurred in 1852 for the excavation of the gold
bearing ground near Sacramento, CA (Bowie 1885), but by 1976 was reduced
to only one lady carrying out a very low level of effort (Hillinger
1976). The technology had moved from the United States to Russia where
it was developed in the early part of the century for the mining of coal.
After passing through China, and Japan it is only, however, since the
technique reached Canada that it has reached its current level of high

performance. At Sparwood in British Columbia two men operate a high
pressure monitor which has consistently, over several years, averaged
some 3,000 tons of coal a shift (Grimley 1977), an output considerably
higher than that of the typical mining section in the United States. It
should, however, be recognized that the circumstances of that particular
output are somewhat rare and equivalent circumstances in the United
States would be limited, nevertheless, it is only now some 12 or 14 years
after that technique was introduced into Canada, that a mine in the
United States is being developed in Colorado to take advantage of that
technique (Arentz 1983).

4. CURRENT RESEARCH PROSPECTS

It is not, unfortunately, only in the area of implementation, that the
effort in the United States has declined. The scale of the US effort for
research in all areas of rock excavation, including high pressure
waterjet work, has fallen from the high point of the NSF and Bureau of
Mines funding of the 1970's. A recent inquiry to one of those agencies,
for example, concerning possible funding of a high pressure waterjet
proposal drew the response that this technology was considered no longer
novel and, therefore, could no longer be funded. And yet the technique
has consistently over the past ten years proven that it is capable of
achieving productivity gains in performance with improvement in safety
and health that will revolutionize the world of rock excavation. The
potential has been demonstrated for an order of magnitude increase in the
performance of equipment while, eliminating the problems of respirable
dust generation and the possibility of the ignition of explosive gas at
the cutting face (Anon 1982). This lesson has already been learned by
commercial concerns abroad. And yet at present, the research is receiving
little if any attention within the United States. It is pertinent to
discuss why.

Every two years, starting in 1972, the British Hydromechanics Research
Association has held international symposia on jet cutting (BHRA 1972 -
1984). These have now been supplemented by alternate year conferences in
the United States and meetings are now being held on a regular basis in
Japan and Europe with the first Chinese Symposium likely to be held in
1987. In the normal course of events, approximately 200 people will
attend each of the BHRA meetings. But by the 6th, only ten years after
the first, only five people were present who had also attended the first
meeting and only three of these were from the United States. There had
been therefore, very little continuity of research, or rather of
researchers, in this field over the last decade. The major reason for
this perhaps has been the relatively small size and short term funding
which has been available for the development of this research technology.
In general, very small amounts of funding have been made available with
the occasional rare exception from differing federal agencies for very
short periods of time. Very often, these contracts have been awarded to
contractors who have no great experience in the field of technology for
which they have received funding. Thus, the result of many of these
studies has been a superficial evaluation of the state-of-the-art of that
technology which has taken so great a time that very little meaningful
new work is achieved by the contracts which have been funded. Frequently
the work which has been carried out does not fully explore the work which
has preceded it and in some cases work has been repeated which has

previously been documented . This unfortunately, cannot be laid to the fault of the investigators since, until very recently, there has been no generally available broad coverage of the biography of the thousands of relevant papers which have now been written on this subject. Many of these, for the lack of a common home, have appeared in journals whose main emphasis is on something else.

Because of the relatively poor response which has been received from the investigators to the funding agencies, which have rarely been provided with the dramatic breakthroughs that were anticipated when the funding was originally provided, the research funding has been terminated and that particular research avenue discontinued. The unfortunate result is that technology with considerable promise has not been adequately followed through in this work and, in consequence, consistent long-term develop of research necessary for the achievement of realistic goals has not occurred.

There has been virtually no long-term funding of research at the applied level in this area. Similarly, basic research to evaluate the mechanisms whereby waterjets at differing pressures cut through materials and different properties has suffered the same crippling disadvantage. Four major theories to explain why waterjets cut rock have been proposed over the last ten years and three of these have been found to be wrong by subsequent research (Summers 1982). Unfortunately, due to a lack of a common source of information, the rebuttals for the erroneous theories have not received much attention nor has the possible viability of the one remaining theory been adequately discussed. Funding for theoretical research has been at an even lower level than the basic research carried out in the laboratory. And, in regard to the definition of the parameters which control waterjet performance, so that an optimization of the technology can be attempted, has been in relative terms non-existent. Over the last ten years it is extremely unlikely that as much as half a million dollars have been spent on the subject even though it has been demonstrated by those few programs that have carried through to experimentation that this technology will revolutionize the way in which rock is excavated with, as a direct result, a dramatic improvement in mine safety and in the cost of doing business.

The order of magnitude increase in performance of excavation equipment which is mandatory if American mining and civil contracting technology is to keep abreast with the world market in the next decade is available with this new technique, but it is at present being neglected by domestic concerns. The potential of the technology has, however, not been lost on the investigators and those who support research in Europe and the Far East. In the United States the only companies carrying out much research in the waterjet area are relatively small and, because of their size, the types of equipment that are being developed also is to a relatively small scale. The most successful today, perhaps, is a company in Colorado which has developed a combined waterjet mechanical drilling device (Zink 1983) . As with European experience, where the waterjet drill is used underground for drilling roofbolt holes, the very light weight machine combined with the low levels of noise achieved (approximately 85 db) and the speed and flexibility of the system have made it quite popular. Commercial acceptance of the tool, however, is likely to take some time. It is, however, encouraging to see a slightly larger concern recently field a fully mechanized waterjet roofbolter, for field evaluation both in the United States and South Africa (Griffiths 1984) for use in coal mines.

This review of the application of high pressure waterjets in mining and civil construction is somewhat pessimistic and is recognized as such, at least in the short term, but it has tried to be both honest and realistic. Despite the fact that high pressure waterjet cutting has been shown to be, either in certain circumstances alone, and more frequently in combination with mechanical tools, a system capable of providing an order of magnitude improvement in excavating machine performance with slightly lower equipment capital costs, operating costs, and environmental costs, it is at the present time a technology for which research in the United States has come to a virtual halt despite major investments being made in this technology by our commercial competitors abroad. There are no longer sufficient qualified investigators in the United States motivated to carry the research forward at the levels necessary in order for American industry to keep abreast of the technology let alone to achieve the dramatic improvements in performance for which it has proven capable. The knowledge base, uniquely developed in this country, is now rapidly being lost as experienced personnel retire or more often move on to other greener (pun intended) pastures. The net result of this is that the momentum for the development of this technology, uniquely developed initially in this country, has now been allowed to move abroad.

It is an unfortunate truth that it would appear that only when foreign equipment begins to be sold on a relatively large scale in the United States that it will be appreciated that a major and lasting change has occurred in the way in which rock is cut. At the time that that discovery is made, it is likely that there will be a radical and permanent change in the structure and components of the rock excavation equipment industry. Perhaps, on the same order as occurred for those people who at one time said that there was no viable replacement for the slide rule. For those who think that this will not occur, it is perhaps pertinent to close with the comment that the major component of the equipment used on the UMR campus to build the UMR Stonehenge from granite, using waterjets at a pressure of 100 MPa, in an operation which took approximately 1,000 cutting hours, was of German manufacture.

REFERENCES

Anon., "Waterjet Machine Tested in Elberton", Elberton Graniteer, Spring 1979.

Anon, Seminar on Water Jet Assisted Roadheaders for Rock Excavation, Pittsburg, Pennsylvania, May 1982, sponsored by U.S. Department of Energy.

Arentz, S.S., III, "Hydraulic Mining Studies of Storm King Mines", Proc. 2nd U.S. Water Jet Conf., University of Missouri-Rolla, May 1983, pp 243-254.

Baumann, L., "State of Applications on High Pressure Water Jet Assisted Road Profile Cutting Technology", Proc 1st U.S. Water Jet Symp., April 1981, Colorado School of Mines, pp V-3.1 to V-3.16.

Bowie, A.A., Jr., "A Practical Treatise on Hydraulic Mining in California", Van Nostrand-Reinhold, Princeton, New Jersey, 19885.

Brown, W. et al., "Rock Fragmentation - A Report of a Special Seminar", Utah Engineering Expt. Station, Salt Lake City, Utah, August 1976.

Dubugnon O., "An Experimental Study of Water Assisted Drag Bit Cutting of Rocks." Proc 1st U.S. Water Jet Symp., April 1981, Colorado School of Mines, pp II-4.1 to II-4.

El Saie, A.A., "Investigation of Rock Slotting by High Pressure Water Jet Assisted Jets for Use in Tunneling", Ph.D. Thesis, University of Missouri-Rolla, 1977.

Griffiths, W., "Hydrojet Drilling: It's Here Now." Conf. on Kentucky Coal - A Look at the Future, Lexington , Ky., NICOA, Oct. 1984.

Grimley, A.W.T., Annual Meeting, Can. Mining Inst., Ottawa, Canada 1977.

Hood, M., "A Study of Methods to Improve the Performance of Drag Bits Used to Cut Hard Rock", Chamber of Mines of South Africa Research Organization, Research Report No. 35/77, August, 1977.

McNary, O., et al., "Augmentation of Mining Machine with a High Pressure Jet", Proc. 3rd Int. Symp Jet Cutting Tech., BHRA Fluid Engineering, Chicago, Illinois, May 1976, pp D2-13 to D2-20.

Raether, R. J., Robison, R.G., and Summers, D.A., "Use of High Pressure Waterjets for Cutting Granite", Proc. 2nd U.S. Water Jet Conf., University of Missouri-Rolla, May 1983, pp 203-211.

Schenk, G.K., "Recent Developments in High Pressure Water Jet Assisted Cutting of Rock and Coal", Proc. 1983 RETC, Vol 2, pp 663-685, Chicago, Illinois, June 1983.

Schwarting, et al., "Development and Underground Testing of a Winning Method with High Pressure Jets", Gluckauf 23, 117, December 3, 1981, pp 642-644.

Summers, D. A., "WaterJet Coal Mining Related to the Mining Environment", Proc. Conf. on the Underground Mining Environment, University of Missouri-Rolla, October 1971, pp 183-194.

Summers, D.A. and McGroarty, S., "The Mechanisms and some Parameters Controlling, the Waterjet Cutting of Rock", Issues in Rock Mechanics, Proc. 23rd Symp. on Rock Mechanics, University of California-Berkeley, August 1982.

Summers, D.A. Personal observations and conversations during a visit to Germany, February 1985.

Wang, Fun-Den, Robbins, Richard and Olsen, John, "Water Jet Assisted Tunnel Boring", Excavation Engineering and Earth Mechanics Institute, Colorado School of Mines, Golden, Colorado, February, 1976.

Zink, E.A., et al., "Water Jet Uses in Sandstone Excavation", Proc. 1983 RETC, Vol. 2, pp 685-700,. Chicago, Illinois, June 1983.

Fig. 1 The UMR Stonehenge monument carved in its entirety by high pressure waterjets.

Mechanics of rock-bit interaction at elevated temperatures

MARIO G.KARFAKIS
Civil Engineering Department, University of Wyoming, Laramie, USA

ROBERT W.HEINS
Petroleum Engineering Department, Texas A & M University, College Station, USA

ABSTRACT

Using a micro-bit drill rig, a laboratory study was conducted to determine the effects of elevated temperatures on drilling penetration rates and how these penetration rates correlate with changes in the mechanical properties of rock due to heating.

Drilling tests were performed on Indiana Limestone with air as the drilling fluid. Response surface methodology was used in the design of the experiments.

From these tests, it was determined that rocks subjected to elevated temperatures are micro-fractured and drill more slowly than do intact rocks. Nevertheless, the magnitude of the temperature (at least in the range typically encountered in geothermal drilling, 177–316 °C) has no significant effect on drilling penetration rates.

Microcracks induced by differential thermal expansion of mineral grains in rocks subjected to elevated temperatures decrease drillability, as do macro-cracks already present and/or induced by temperature-gradient thermal stresses. Up to the point of inducing macro-cracks, the differential temperature between the flushing air and the rock mass enhances the penetration rate.

Change in the compressive wave velocity, Brazilian tensile strength, and uniaxial compression strength of the rock due to exposure to elevated temperature, showed no direct correlation with the change in penetration rates.

1 INTRODUCTION

Lower penetration rates encountered in geothermal drilling can be attributed in part to the elevated temperatures and/or to the effects of temperatures on rock properties. Changes in rock behavior, due to higher temperature exposure, inhibit the rock fragmentation processes that involve crushing or brittle fracture. In addition to these two adverse effects in geothermal drilling, high temperatures may also have a beneficial effect when air is used as the drilling fluid. The large temperature differential between the flushing air and the rock in the geothermal environment can aid fragmentation by thermally stressing the rock.

These effects of elevated temperatures in geothermal drilling are discussed in the following section under the headings of: -The Effects of Elevated Temperatures on Rocks -Rock Drillability at Elevated Temperatures -Effects of the Temperature Differential Between the Flushing Air and the Rock Masses.

1.1 The effects of elevated temperatures on rocks

Rocks in the earth's crust are subjected to a temperature gradient which varies from region to region. This exposure to heat will irreversibly alter the physical properties of the rocks. J. M. Ide,(1937) reported on how heat affects the elastic constants of rocks. Young's modulus and the rigidity modulus were permanently reduced to values determined by the highest temperatures with which the rock had been heated. Ide suggested that this might be explained by the development of micro-cracks in the rocks.

A number of experimental studies involving the uniform heating of rocks (Barbish & Gardner, 1969; Johnson et al., 1978; Freidman et al., 1979) have demonstrated that thermal cracking of rock results from the combined effects of uniform temperature changes and temperature gradients that induce thermoelastic stresses locally in excess of the fracture strength. These studies further have shown that the resulting micro-cracks, which were usually of grain-size dimensions or smaller, irreversibly altered certain physical properties of rock.

Micro-cracks develop preferentially along grain boundaries and secondarily as intergranular cracks. Micro-cracks are due to intergranular thermal stresses caused by differential thermal expansion or contraction of neighboring mineral grains (Richter & Simmons, 1974; Freidman and Johnson, 1978). In turn, the micro-cracks may significantly affect the development of macro-cracks induced by mechanical stresses or temperature-gradient thermal stresses. In addition to the structural damage that may occur due to differential thermal expansion of mineral constituents, a number of mineral alterations (including crystal inversion, loss of water of crystallization, and dissociation), may also contribute to changes in physical structures and properties of the rock.

In their studies on the effects of heat on the mechanical properties of rocks, a number of investigators (Bauer & Johnson, 1979) have demonstrated that these thermally induced micro-cracks decreased the elastic moduli, decreased the tensile and compressive strengths, and increased the porosity and permeability of the rock.

All these studies indicate that the physical properties of rocks subjected to elevated temperatures are altered through the formation of thermally induced microcracks.

1.2 Rock drillability at elevated temperatures

Drillability of any rock depends on the interaction of bit and rock. The bit tooth should be able to overcome the strength of the rock in order to indent it and form a chip. The easier the indentation and the quicker the chip is formed, the faster the bit penetration rate will be. Bit/rock interaction at elevated temperatures involves the mechanical behavior of a wide variety of fractured rocks at temperatures to 350 °C, a temperature typically encountered in geothermal drilling.

The mechanical properties of the rocks that directly influence bit/rock interaction are strength and ductility. The rock strength governs the ease with which the rock fails, and thus dictates the stress level required for the bit to fracture the rock. Ductility governs the failure mechanism for the formation of the chip.
The strength of the rock is drastically reduced with increased temperature. This decrease in strength is due to thermally induced micro-cracks. Consequently, rock drillability should actually increase with the increase in temperature. A brittle rock subjected to increasing temperatures will undergo changes in behavior from elastic-brittle to plastic-ductile. This ductility inhibits rock fragmentation processes that involve crushing or brittle fracture. The failure mechanisms that prevail in any given situation are dependent on rock behavior.
The failure mechanisms under the pressure and temperature regimes of geothermal drilling are: fracture, grain boundary slip, and intergranular gliding (Varnado, 1979). The quickest failure mechanism is fracture. If the chip is formed by fracture under the action of the bit tooth, higher penetration rates are obtained.
Rocks that become ductile at geothermal temperatures are invariably weak and are easily indented. They deform by grain boundary slip and intragranular gliding. Precursive microfracturing is extensive. Grain boundaries are broken and, to a large extent, frictional sliding contributes to the deformation. In certain rock such as limestones and dolomites, intragranular gliding becomes the major mechanism; when the chip is finally formed, it is by macroscopic shear fractures. Considering the greater deformation required for the formation of the chip, the drillability of rocks that are ductile at geothermal temperatures should decrease.
To date, much of the theoretical work relating to bit/rock interaction has been done for idealized conditions. In most cases, the rock has been assumed to be isotropic and homogeneous, and either perfectly elastic or perfectly plastic. This theoretical work has been based on experiments conducted on brittle and/or invariably ductile rocks. Some experiments have been conducted on brittle rocks whose behavior was altered by submitting them to confining pressures (Silkarskie & Cheatham, 1973). The results of these studies can also be applied to the bit/rock interaction at elevated temperatures, although to date no studies have considered the temperature factor.

1.3 Effect of the temperature differential between the rock mass and the flushing air

In laboratory and field drilling it has been shown that penetration rates are usually higher when air is circulated, rather than liquids. One of the possible reasons for these results may be the lower bottom hole temperatures.
Casual reference is often made in the literature to the fact that air expansion through the bit nozzle has a cooling effect on the bit. In field tests, temperature as low as 4° C have been observed on drill collars immediately above the bit when the temperature of the air being circulated was approximately 66° C upon entering the

drill pipe at the surface (Singh & Goodwin, 1965). From that it can be inferred that the temperature at or below the bit during drilling operations is significantly lower.

This cooling is due to the isentropical expansion of air through the nozzle. Portions of the hole bottom surface could be cooled by a high velocity, low temperature stream of air passing over it.The Joule-Thomson effect should also play a part in lowering the bottom hole temperature; that is, the temperature of the air that has expanded through the nozzle and lost its velocity should not quite reach the original temperature that it had before passing through the nozzle. The amount by which the temperature is lowered in this manner is only a few degrees, but if the expanded and cooled return air took heat from the incoming air (with the drill collars acting as a heat exchanger), then the temperature-reducing mechanism could progress toward even lower temperatures.

A cold blast of air suddenly coming into contact with virgin rock could quite rapidly stress the rock. The tendency of the rock to contract could either induce tensile stresses in the formation or reduce any compressive stresses already present. Since rocks are generally incapable of withstanding tension, fragmentation should be accelerated. This process would be further accentuated by the stress concentrations induced at the point of loading due to the bit teeth. The poor thermal conductivity of rocks would aid the breakage mechanism by ensuring that the temperature gradient across a thin layer of rock at the bottom of the hole remains steep (Finnie et al., 1979).

In geothermal drilling, the temperature differential between the flushing air and the rock mass would be substantially larger than in other drilling operations. Consequently, the effects discussed above would be enhanced and drillability would be increased.

2 EXPERIMENTAL WORK

The objectives of this investigation were as follows: a) to determine the effects of rock mass temperature on drilling penetration rates, b) to evaluate the effects of air-rock temperature differential on rock fragmentation, c) to determine whether the penetration rate is affected by the maximum temperature to which the rock has been subjected, and d) to understand how the penetration rate is affected by the change in mechanical properties of the rocks due to elevated temperatures.

2.1 The 2^4 factorial design

To meet these objectives, initial drilling experiments were carried out on Indiana limestone, with air as the drilling fluid, using a laboratory micro-bit drilling apparatus (Karfakis, 1983, 1985). The controllable variables were weight on bit, rotary speed, and rock temperature. Response surface methodology was used in the design of the experiments. Half of the rock specimens were slowly heated to appropriate maximum temperature; after soaking for two days, they were allowed to cool to room temperature in the oven. The remaining half were also heated in the same manner and maintained at design

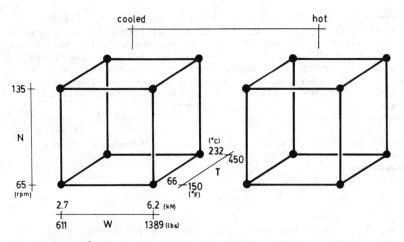

Figure 1. 2^4 Factorial design program—investigation of rock mass temperature effect.

temperatures until being drilled.   The specimens were tested at predetermined design variables and levels.   The arrangement of experimental points is shown in Figure 1.   The following section contains the analysis of the results of the experiments conducted.

Analysis and discussion of results

From these tests it was determined that penetration rates decrease as the temperature of the rock drilled increases.   This is contrary to what one would expect, since the temperatures tested were not high enough to produce ductile behavior in the Indiana limestone, and since any micro-cracks resulting from heating of the rock would enhance drillability.

These tests also show that hot rocks drill faster than do rocks heated and cooled to room temperature.   The temperature differential between the flushing air and the rock seems to have a beneficial effect on drillability, at least when low rotary speeds are used. This increase in drilling rate can be accounted for only by the temperature differential, since both groups of rocks were subjected to the same temperatures and consequently any structural damage should be the same.   Furthermore, the fact that the hot rocks drill faster than the cooled ones discredits ductility (in terms of softening of the rock) as a cause for reduced penetration rates at higher temperatures.

The decrease in penetration rate with temperature increase may be due to compaction by differential thermal expansion and/or to the compaction and firing of clays present in the Indiana limestone. Another cause for the reduction in drillability may be the change in fracture behavior of Indiana limestone with temperature.   Ductile failure in the form of excessive grain boundary sliding before breakage may take place as a result of the extensive micro-cracking.

The increase in penetration rate while drilling hot rocks, as compared to cool ones, may be due to the differential temperature between the flushing air and the rock. This would have a quenching effect on the rock, causing it to contract and inducing tensile stresses (or reducing any compressive stresses already present). Furthermore, this quenching would cause additional structural damage in the form of intergranular cracks, accelerating fragmentation and aiding the breakage action of the bit tooth.

Another result from these tests that may be of some interest is the fact that at high rotary speeds there is no practical difference in the penetration rate when drilling through cooled or hot rocks. In other words, thermal stressing is not a significant factor at high rotary speeds.

2.2 The 2 x 4 design

Additional tests were run to isolate the effects of temperature on penetration rates. These tests were conducted at constant rotary speed and constant bit weight (60 rpm and 2.7 kN respectively), in order to eliminate the relatively large effects of these variables on drilling rates.

The temperature range was extended to 316 °C. All the specimens were heated at appropriate temperatures. Half of them were cooled to room temperature before being drilled; the other half were drilled at the temperature to which they had been subjected. This experimental arrangement allowed assessment of the effect on the penetration rate of the structural damage caused by exposing the rock to elevated temperatures. Furthermore, the effect on penetration rate of the temperature differential between the flushing air and the rock mass can be determined.

Discussion of results

The plot of drilling penetration rates for rocks subjected to various temperatures is shown in Figure 2. The penetration rate for intact rocks is plotted in addition to the penetration rates for hot and cooled rocks.

It can be seen that rock which has been subjected to elevated temperatures and then cooled down drilled more slowly than did the intact rocks. The magnitude of the temperature they had been subjected to has practically no effect on the penetration rate. Considering that the rocks were at room temperature and that the magnitude of the temperature had no significant effect on the penetration rate, the decrease in drilling rate compared to that in the intact rocks cannot be explained by ductility in terms of softening due to elevated temperature. Rather, it can be explained by ductility caused by the presence of micro-cracks. Micro-cracks in rocks subjected to elevated temperatures are due to intergranular thermal stresses generated by differential thermal expansion or contraction of neighboring mineral grains. In micro-cracked rocks, there is extensive precursive microfracturing when the bit tooth impacts the rock; intragranular gliding is a major mechanism of deformation, and chips are formed by shear fracture. Considering the large deformation required for the formation of the chip, drillability would decrease.

From the plot in Figure 2 it can also be seen that rocks that are at elevated temperatures drill more slowly than do intact rocks. In

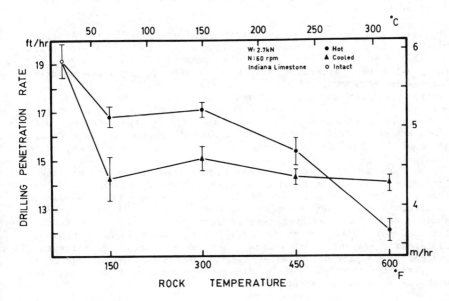

Figure 2. Effect of rock temperatures on drilling penetration rates.

this case, the penetration rates are dependent on the magnitude of the rock temperature. The penetration rate decreases as the rock temperature is increased. In spite of the fact that the penetration rates decrease with temperature, up to 232 °C the drillability is higher than in cooled rocks that have been subjected to similar temperatures. This increased drillability can be explained by the effect of the temperature differential between the flushing air and the rock mass. At 18-21 °C, the air exiting from the nozzles is at a substantially lower temperature than the rock. Under a cool blast of air the rock will tend to contract, inducing tensile stresses. Since rocks are weaker under tension, fragmentation will be accelerated. The poor thermal conductivity of rock would aid the breakage mechanism by ensuring a steep temperature gradient across a thin layer of rock. Above 232 °C the penetration rates decrease drastically. At 316 °C the penetration is even slower than in cooled rock that had been subjected to the same temperature. This decrease in penetration rate may be due to the formation of macro-cracks. Macro-cracks are induced by the temperature-gradient thermal stresses that exceed the fracture strength of the rock. The fractured rock would require large deformations before a chip could be formed, because of excessive frictional sliding along broken boundaries.

From the discussion above it seems that, for the temperature range currently encountered in geothermal drilling, the penetration rates are affected only by the fractured state of the rock. Furthermore, the differential temperature between the flushing air and the rock enhances the penetration rate up to the point where the temperature-gradient thermal stresses induce macro-cracks.

3 Correlation of penetration rates at elevated temperatures to rock properties

The correlation of penetration rates obtained from the 2 x 4 design with the change (due to heating) in some of the mechanical properties of the rocks was checked. The properties investigated were compressive wave velocity, Brazilian tensile strength, and uniaxial compressive strength.

Prior to drilling, the compressive wave velocity of each specimen was measured before and after subjected to elevated temperatures. Tests showed that the pulse velocity drastically decreased with temperature, indicating the formation of micro-cracks. This change in wave velocity showed no correlation with the penetration rates obtained.

From each sample that had been drilled, two specimens were taken for tests of Brazilian tensile strength. Tests showed that Brazilian tensile strength increased at 66 °C. This increase might be due to compaction and firing of clays present in the Indiana limestone. Above 149 °C the Brazilian tensile strength decreases—and more so for the hot rocks, where in addition to micro-cracks induced by differential expansion of grains, there were macro-cracks present, induced by temperature-gradient thermal stresses. This behavior of the Brazilian tensile strength with temperature showed no correlation with the penetration rates.

Four specimens were taken from each of the same drilled samples, for uniaxial compressive strength tests. Taking into consideration the scatter of the data, there is no significant change in the compressive strength of the rock and no correlation with the penetration rates.

From the mechanical properties investigated, the change in these properties due to elevated temperature exposure showed no direct correlation with the change in penetration rates obtained.

CONCLUSIONS

The laboratory micro-bit drilling apparatus, with the use of statistical experimental designs has been successfully used in an investigative study of the temperature factor in rotary drilling. Although the results obtained cannot be directly applied to field use, they give insight on how elevated rock temperatures affect drilling penetration rates. The following points summarize the conclusions of the investigation.

1. Rocks that have been subjected to elevated temperatures drill more slowly than do intact rocks. The magnitude of the temperature has no significant effect on drilling penetration rates. For the temperature range encountered in geothermal drilling the penetration rates are affected only by the fractured state of the rock.

2. The presence of micro-cracks induced by differential thermal expansion of mineral grains in rocks subjected to elevated temperatures decreases the penetration rates. Macro-cracks already

present and/or induced by temperature-gradient thermal stresses interfere with the drilling process.

3. The differential temperature between the flushing air and the rock mass enhances the penetration rate up to the point where the temperature-gradient thermal stresses induce macro-cracks.

4. The change in the compressive wave velocity, Brazilian tensile strength, and uniaxial compressive strength of the rock due to exposure to elevated temperature showed no correlation with the change in penetration rates.

This study is only a preliminary examination of the influence of elevated rock temperatures on drilling penetration rates. Further work on this problem should focus on including formation pressures while drilling at elevated temperatures, evaluating the effect of fracture intensity and geometry, and theoretical studies of bit-tooth and fractured rock interaction.

REFERENCES

Barbish, A. B. and Gardner, G. H. F. 1969. The effect of heat on some mechanical properties of igneous rocks, J. Soc. Petr. AIME, Vol. 9, pp. 395-402.
Bauer, S. and Johnson, B. 1979. Effect of slow uniform heating on the physical properties of westerly and charcoal granites, Proc. 20th U.S. Symp. on Rock Mech., pp. 7-18.
Finnie, I., Cooper, G. A. and Berlie, J. 1979. Fracture propagation in rock by transient cooling, Int. J. Rock Mech. Min. Sci & Geomech. Abstr., Vol. 16, pp. 11-21.
Friedman, M., Handin, J., Higgs, N. G. and Lantz, J. R. 1979. Strength and ductility of four dry igneous rocks at low pressures and temperatures to partial melting, Proc. 20th U.S. Symp. on Rock Mech., pp. 35-43.
Friedman, M. and Johnson, B. 1978. Thermal cracks inconfined Sioux quartzite, Proc. 19th U.S. Symp. on Rock Mech., Vol. 1, 423-430.
Ide, J. M. 1937. Velocity of sound in rocks and glasses as a function of temperature, J. of Geol., Vol. 45, No. 17, pp. 689-716.
Johnson, B., Gangi, A. F., and Handin, J. 1978. Thermal cracking of rock subjected to slow uniform temperature changes, Proc. 19th U.S. Symp. onRock Mech., Vol. 1, pp. 259-267.
Karfakis, Mario G. 1983. The temperature factor in rotary drilling of Indiana limestone, Ph.D. Thesis, University of Wisconsin.
Karfakis, Mario G. 1985. Micro-bit instrumentation bit bearing temperature measurements, Proc. 31st Int. Instrumentation Symp. ISA.
Richter, D. and Simmons, G. 1974. "Thermal expansion behavior of igneous rocks, Int. J. Rock Mech. & Min. Sci., Vol 11, pp. 403-411.
Sikarskie, D. L. and Cheatham, J. B., Jr. 1973. Penetration problems in rock mechanics, In Rock Mechanics Symposium, D. L. Sikarskie, Ed. AMD-Vol. 3, New York: ASME.
Singh, M. M. and Goodwin, R. J. 1965. Mechanism of drilling with air as the drilling fluid, SPE, AIME, Paper No. SPE 1052.
Varnado, S. G. 1979. Report of the Workshop on Advanced Geothermal Drilling and Completion Systems, SAND-79-1195.

20. Poster session B

A Monte Carlo method for studying thermal conductivity and thermal anisotropy in aggregates

LARRY J.VAN STONE
South Dakota School of Mines & Technology, Rapid City, USA

1 INTRODUCTION

Monte Carlo methods allow simulation of systems having uncontrolled parameters. Many rock units have quite variable compositions, and even those which are very uniform have very little regularity on a fine scale. Therefore, methods of estimating bulk properties derived using periodic or regularized geometries are not very successful. The Monte Carlo method described here allows the introduction of specific amounts of randomness in order to learn the scatter inherent in certain types of constrained-random systems.

This work is related to studies of thermal anisotropy in rocks being pursued at South Dakota School of Mines and Technology. Computer memory limitations and time constraints made the use of three-dimensional finite element modeling impractical, so the models used represent planar sections of blocks of fiber composites in a thermal conductivity apparatus. Thermal parameters of a material are assumed to be invariant.

The SI unit of thermal conductivity is W/m°K; many publications use the CGS unit cal/sec-cm°C. To convert: CGS·418.4 = SI and SI·0.00239 = CGS. Thermal conductivities of specific minerals mentioned were taken from Clark (1966) and Horai (1971). The symbol λ represents thermal conductivity.

2 DESCRIPTION OF THE METHOD

A computer program family was written to investigate the relationship between composition, orientation and thermal conductivity for various isotropic and anisotropic composites. The concept is similar to that of McCoy (1982), who used models having randomized geometries to study the usefulness of his bounding equations.

2.1 The basic grid and duplex extrapolation

A principal concern in designing the experiment was the exponential gradient of computer time used with respect to the size of a finite element model. It was desired to run hundreds of simulations, so the models had to be relatively small, yet too small a model has very poor accuracy. A simple experiment with various models of the same item, differing only in grid density, yielded a useful extrapolation for two models, in which the second has twice the grid density (four times as many elements) as the first. The finite element program calculates temperature T_1 for the node at location p in model 1, and T_2 for the congruent node in model 2. It was found that the error varies nearly as the $^3/_2$ power of grid spacing, so the extrapolated temperature:

$$T_p = \tfrac{1}{2}\cdot(\ 3\cdot T_2 - T_1\ ) \tag{1}$$

is much more accurate than either T_1 or T_2; it is roughly as accurate as T_6. However, the intermediate nodes of the second model cannot be used because no consistent extrapolation method for them has been found.

The grid shown in Figure 1 represents a slice of fibrous material in a thermal conductivity apparatus. Each square element represents one fiber in cross section, except in the upper and lower "plates", which simulate the heat sink and source in the apparatus.

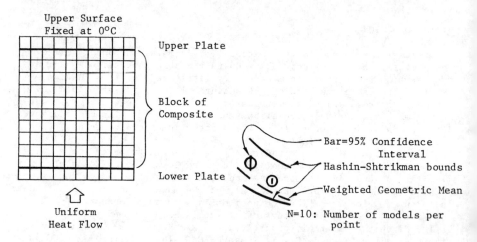

Upper Surface Fixed at 0°C

Upper Plate

Block of Composite

Lower Plate

Uniform Heat Flow

Bar=95% Confidence Interval

Hashin-Shtrikman bounds

Weighted Geometric Mean

N=10: Number of models per point

Figure 1. The basic grid used for the Monte Carlo models.

Legend for Figures 2 through 5.

2.2 The grid generating program

The first program, GRID2, prepares large numbers of models, each at single and double grid density. A group of models has the same bulk composition or, for single-material models, the same proportion of oriented elements. The locations of secondary elements are chosen randomly, and the orientations of the thermal axes of some or all elements may also be randomized. The randomizing function is seeded with the time of program initiation, ensuring a different pseudo-random sequence from run to run.

2.3 The thermal tensor

In anisotropic materials, thermal conductivity varies with direction as described by an ellipsoidal tensor derived by solving the thermal balance in a unit tetrahedron. The two-dimensional derivation, using a unit triangle, is described by Tsai and Hahn (1980, p.330). All

918

transformations in the derivation are orthogonal, so an equivalent derivation is coordinate transformation:

$$
|L\phi| \, |\lambda| \, |L\phi|^T = \begin{vmatrix} \cos\phi & -\sin\phi \\ \sin\phi & \cos\phi \end{vmatrix} \cdot \begin{vmatrix} \lambda_x & 0 \\ 0 & \lambda_y \end{vmatrix} \cdot \begin{vmatrix} \cos\phi & \sin\phi \\ -\sin\phi & \cos\phi \end{vmatrix}
$$

$$
= \begin{vmatrix} \lambda_x \cdot \cos^2\phi + \lambda_y \cdot \sin^2\phi & \cos\phi \cdot \sin\phi \cdot (\lambda_x - \lambda_y) \\ \cos\phi \cdot \sin\phi \cdot (\lambda_x - \lambda_y) & \lambda_x \cdot \sin^2\phi + \lambda_y \cdot \cos^2\phi \end{vmatrix} \quad (2)
$$

The formula presented by Birch and Clark (1940), apparently adopted uncritically in later geological literature, is only the first term of tensor (2).

2.4 Temperature and thermal conductivity calculations

Program HEAT by Wilson and Nickell (1966) was modified (Ashworth, 1983) using tensor (2) to transform the oriented anisotropic axes of each element to the global coordinates of the model. For this study, it was further modified to communicate with the other programs.

During one run of a group of models this program, renamed ANIHEAT, calculates temperatures at the nodes in each model, at both grid densities, prepared by GRID2, and passes them to THCON2, the conductivity computing program. THCON2 uses equation (1) to extrapolate temperatures at eleven nodes along each interface (the two heavy lines in Figure 1) and calculates the effective thermal conductivity of each model in the group. These results are stored for later analysis.

3 SUMMARY OF PRELIMINARY RESULTS

In all the models, λ_a of material 1 is 1.0, and the other conductivities (λ_{b1}, λ_{a2} and λ_{b2}) are equal to or less than 1.

3.1 For a single anisotropic material, partly or wholly randomly oriented

The first set of runs simulated single-material aggregates having a fixed proportion of from zero to ninety percent of the elements oriented either all parallel or all perpendicular to the heat flow, and the rest oriented randomly. These runs tested the assumption that the geometric mean (GM) of the axial conductivities accurately predicts the mean conductivity of a single-material aggregate having no preferred orientation, and that the weighted geometric mean (WGM) can be used directionally to combine the thermal conductivities of the oriented and non-oriented components. The GM is, for two axes and three axes:

$$
\lambda_{gm2} = \sqrt{\lambda_a \cdot \lambda_b} \quad (3a)
$$

$$
\lambda_{gm3} = \sqrt[3]{\lambda_a \cdot \lambda_b \cdot \lambda_c} \quad (3b)
$$

The general form of the WGM is:

$$\lambda_{wgm}^{\cdot} = \prod_{i} \lambda_{i}^{x_{i}} \tag{4}$$

in which x_i is the relative proportion of component i. In these runs, λ_1 was either λ_a (= 1.) or λ_b, and λ_2 was found using equation (3a).

Figure 2 summarizes the results. In Figures 2 through 5, the bars through the data points encompass the statistical ninety-five percent confidence interval for the mean; see the Legend for this and other notations.

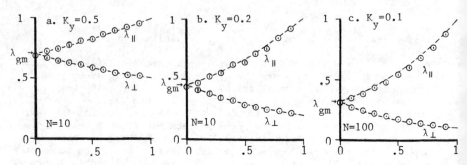

Figure 2. Comparison of the weighted geometric mean with Monte Carlo data for aggregates of anisotropic elements having various amounts of preferred orientation. Axes: Ordinate = relative preferred orientation; Abscissa = thermal conductivity (λ_x = 1.0).

3.2 For a mixture of two isotropic materials, and for a porous material

Six sets of runs simulated mixtures of two isotropic materials, and tested the usefulness of the WGM adn of the bounds of Hashin and Shtrikman (1962). Figure 3 summarizes the results. McCoy (1982) noted that the Hashin-Shtrikman bounds (HSBs) are second-order bounds, and are the most restrictive bounding equations we may use when only component proportions are known and no preferred orientation or layering exists. Horai (1971) advocates the average of the HSBs as the most likely value of combined conductivity.

Another set of runs was made in which the less-abundant material had a conductivity of 0.001, simulating compact (in two dimensions) pore spaces in one material. Figure 4 shows that the simple formula:

$$\lambda_{p} = \lambda \cdot (1 - 2 \cdot p) \tag{5a}$$

adequately corrects for porosity p in such cases. In the more usual cases of porosity composed mostly of cracks, Horai and Baldridge (1972, part II) empirically derived:

$$\lambda_{p} = \lambda \cdot (1 - 5.56 \cdot p) \tag{5b}$$

920

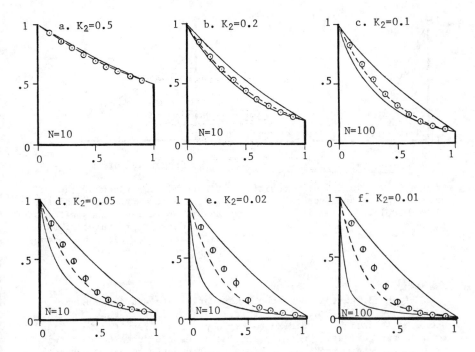

Figure 3. Comparison of the weighted geometric mean and the Hashin-Shtrikman bounds with Monte Carlo data for isotropic composites. Ordinate = proportion of material type 2.

3.3 For mixtures of two anisotropic materials

One set of runs simulated mixtures of two materials having anisotropic conductivities chosen to represent quartz ($\lambda_a = \lambda_b = 6.4$, $\lambda_c = 10.2$, $\lambda = 7.5$) and muscovite ($\lambda_a = 4.5$, $\lambda_b = 4.9$, $\lambda_c = 0.77$, $= 2.6$); the conductivities used in the model were normalized to λ_c of quartz. No simulations having preferred orientation were made; all elements were given random orientations. These tested the WGM and HSBs when used with mean conductivities calculated using the GM (equation 3a). Figure 5 summarizes the results.

4 DISCUSSION AND SUGGESTIONS

Although the models strictly apply to fiber composites, the results are here applied to rocks.

Figure 2 demonstrates that the GM estimates the effective thermal conductivity of a nonporous, nonoriented, single-material aggregate within two percent, and that the WGM estimates within three to five percent the directional conductivities when an oriented fabric exists.

Parts a, b and c of Figure 3 cover the range of relative thermal conductivity found in most rocks, and demonstrate that the WGM estimates the effective thermal conductivity of such aggregates within a few percent. Even in this range, the HSBs become rather widely separated (as much as ±35%) and their average is usually a poorer estimator than

921

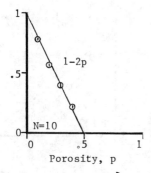

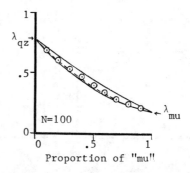

Figure 4. Simulation of porosity composed of equant "spaces" ($\lambda_2 = 0.001$).

Figure 5. Comparison of the weighted geometric mean and the Hashin-Shtrikman bounds with Monte Carlo data for mixtures of two anisotropic materials having no preferred orientation.

the WGM.

In Figure 3, part a, both the Monte Carlo data and the WGM fall slightly below the lower HSB. This indicates firstly that the tradeoffs accepted in designing this Monte Carlo procedure resulted in a bias of at most two percent. Secondly, it indicates that the WGM, while it is empirically useful and nearly bias-free, is not rigorously correct. Within its limitations, the WGM has the virtue that it is easily memo-rized and is computable either by slide rule or hand calculator. All bounding equations, including the HSBs, require a computer to evaluate.

Parts d, e and f of Figure 3 illustrate the dilemma of extreme cases. None of the predictive methods yields an adequate estimate throughout the range of compositions. In addition, the Monte Carlo data represent a specific set of geometrical constraints most likely to be found in crystalline rocks. Materials having extreme geometrical arrangements, such as foams, are not predictable by these methods, and bounds such as those of McCoy (1982) or Milton (1982), requiring higher-order geometric parameters, must be used.

For rocks in which one component has a much greater thermal conducti-vity than the others, such as pyrite in shale, we may establish rough guidelines:

1. When the lower-conductivity materials comprise more than seventy percent of the whole, use the lower HSB.
2. When the lower-conductivity materials comprise between forty and seventy percent, use the WGM.
3. When the lower-conductivity materials comprise less than forty percent, use porosity equation 5a for blocky textures, and equation 5b for stringy or foamy textures.

Figure 5 is very similar to Figure 3, part b, which illustrates a fun-damental point: in the abscence of directional fabric, we are justified in treating aggregates of anisotropic materials as though they were isotropic, and the nonoriented portion of a material having preferred orientation of some components can be treated as an isotropic material having a mean thermal conductivity found using the GM (equation 3b in three dimensions).

It would be interesting to pursue the modeling efforts with bigger programs on faster computers. However, it is more expedient to shift the focus to applying the bounding equations of McCoy (1982) or Milton (1982), and to studying a variety of foliated rocks.

Conventional petrographic analysis often includes a modal analysis by point counting. Fabric analysis, if any, is commonly an eye-estimate of preferred orientations and other geometrical characteristics, couched in conventional, general terms. The HSBs are second-order bounds, because their use assumes macroscopic isotropy and homogeneity. To use higher-order bounds, precise geometric parameters must be recorded in addition to the point count. Corson (1974) has done valuable preliminary work, but a technique needs to be developed which is less tedious than machining rock samples and measuring their thermal conductivities in a divided-bar or guarded-plate apparatus.

REFERENCES

Ashworth, E. 1983. Applications of finite element analysis to thermal conductivity measurements. M.S.Thesis. South Dakota School of Mines and Technology.
Birch, F. & H.Clark 1940. The thermal conductivity of rocks and its dependence upon temperature and composition, Part I. Am.J.Sci., 238(8):529-558. Part II. 238(9)613-635.
Clark, S.P. 1966. Thermal conductivity. In S.P.Clark (ed.), Handbook of physical constants, revised edition, sect. 21, p.459-482. Geol.Soc. America Memoir 97.
Corson, P.B. 1974. Correlation functions for predicting properties of heterogeneous materials. J.Appl.Phys. 45(7):3159-3182.
Hashin, Z. & S.Shtrikman 1962. A variational approach to the theory of effective magnetic permeability of multiphase materials. J.Appl.Phys. 33:3125-3131
Horai, K-I 1971. Thermal conductivity of rock-forming minerals. J.Geo-Phys.Res. 76(5):1278-1308.
Horai, K-I & S.Baldridge 1972. Thermal conductivity of nineteen igneous rocks. Phys.Earth Planet.Interiors 5:151-166.
McCoy, J.J. 1982.Bounds of the transverse effective conductivity of computer-generated fiber composites. J.Appl.Mech. 49(6):319-326.
Milton, G.W. 1982. Bounds on the elastic and transport properties of two-component composites. J.Mech.Phys.Solids 30(3):177-191.
Tsai, S.W. & H.T.Hahn 1980. Introduction to composite materials. Wesport, CT:Technomic.
Wilson, E.L. & R.E.Nickell 1966. Applications of the finite element method to heat conduction analysis. Nuclear Eng.and Design 4:276-286.

An experimental determination of mixed and forced convection heat transfer coefficients in a modeled nuclear waste repository

RODNEY L.OSBORNE & RICHARD N.CHRISTENSEN
Nuclear Engineering Program, The Ohio State University, Columbus, USA

Turbulent mixed and forced convection were investigated experimentally in a horizontal duct which modeled both thermally and hydraulically a nuclear waste repository. Reynolds numbers ranged from 6,000 to 180,000. The maximum Grashof number achieved was $1.5 * 10^9$.

The experimental apparatus consisted of a horizontal duct, 30.5 cm wide by 45.2 cm high (12 inches by 18 inches), and 4.42 m (14.5 feet) in length. The duct had 29 heater sections in the axial direction, each 15.2 cm (6 inches) long.

Heat flux profiles were imposed on the four walls of the duct by a network of resistance heater pads. The opposing sidewall heaters were connected by pairs in parallel, giving five independently controlled sets of heaters: floor, lower side, middle side, upper side, and ceiling. Since the power inputs to these five heater sets were controlled separately, a wide range of heat flux profiles could be investigated. A sketch of the heater pad arrangement is below.

Heat transfer parameters were determined by using thermocouples on the duct walls. A metering section with a flow nozzle was placed after the test section to determine flow rates.

Data were taken for the floor, lower side, middle side, upper side, and ceiling heaters for heat flux profiles which varied from constant circumferential heat flux to a hot floor case to a hot side case.

The data at a fully developed point were plotted as Nusselt numbers versus Reynolds numbers. The data above Re = 50,000 compared well with those of past workers, i.e., the slope was about 0.7, for all five wall locations. Below Re = 50,000, the data from the different wall locations and different heat flux profiles varied widely. The Nusselt numbers for the floor decreased with decreasing Reynolds numbers but were much higher than for the purely forced convection case. The floor Nusselt numbers approached a horizontal asymptote as the Reynolds number was lowered and generally began increasing as the Reynolds number dropped below 10,000. This indicates a strong natural convection

[Heaters 3 and 4 were connected in parallel, heaters 5 and 6 were connected in parallel, and heaters 7 and 8 were connected in parallel.]

component superimposed on the forced convection component. The lower side wall exhibited a similar phenomenon, although less pronounced. The middle and upper side wall Nusselt numbers were also above the purely forced convection line, but less so than the lower side and floor. The ceiling followed the forced convection line until approximately Re = 15,000, where the Nusselt numbers dropped below the forced convection line. This can be expected as the natural convection from the ceiling (a downward facing plane) is unaiding. These trends compare qualitatively with the trends of the data of Danko and Cifka (1984).

The results indicated that for Reynolds numbers below 50,000, heat transfer calculations based solely on forced convection correlations can underpredict the Nusselt number by as much as a factor of five. Doing so would drastically overestimate the need for cooling capacity in a nuclear waste repository.

Because heat transfer coefficients below Re = 50,000 are a function of heat flux and wall location, determination of temperature and heat flux profiles for a given heat loading was is an iterative process. This iterative process and the resultant temperature and heat flux profiles are described in the poster session.

REFERENCES

Danko, G., and I. Cifka 1984. Measurement of the convective heat transfer coefficient on naturally rough tunnel surfaces. Third international mine ventilation congress. M. J. Howes and M. J. Jones (eds.), The Institute of Mining and Metallurgy, pp. 375-380.

Theoretical background to the development of a computer code for the modeling of seam-like deposits

J.P.E.MORIS
Consulting Engineer, Waterloo, Belgium
K.I.ORAVECZ
New Mexico Institute of Mining & Technology, Socorro, USA

1 INTRODUCTION

In order to obtain the stress and displacement distributions around practical workings in mines, it is required to develop efficient computer codes that allow the modeling of extensive areas of excavations together with the non-linear behavior of the seam material and are able to take into account such features as backfilling and support. The theoretical background to such a computer code is outlined in this paper.

2 THEORETICAL BACKGROUND

2.1 The singular integral approach

One of the most efficient methods for the digital solution of the linear partial differential equations in elastostatics together with the appropriate boundary conditions consists in reformulating the problem in terms of singular integral equations. In two dimensional cases this is done by using Cauchy integrals, while in the case of three dimensions, potentials or integral representations of harmonic functions are utilized, in terms of which the elastic quantitites may be expressed. Single and double layer potentials play a fundamental role in this approach.

The integral must be taken over the boundary surfaces, where, in consequence, the singularities inherent in the layer potentials will be encountered. Integral equations are obtained when the relations holding between elastic quantities are given on the boundaries (i.e. boundary conditions).

It will be immediately apparent that the domain of integration is a two-dimensional space while the problem space is three-dimensional. This reduction in dimensionality is very important for the numerical solution of the integral equations.

The method of solution involves the quantization of the domain of integration, which is identical with the problem boundaries. Further, the integrals may be replaced by their finite sum approximations, thus yielding a finite set of linear equations. The order of this linear system is directly related to the adopted mesh-size of quantization. Because of the reduction in dimensionality, the number of terms in the equations can be limited to a reasonable value, thus allowing the digital solution of large-size configurations.

In this case the system matrix is not sparse, however, considerable simplifications may be obtained by lumping boundary elements together for the computation of remote influences. The justification of lumping is based on the observation that the kernel functions decay with distance. Lumping results in a reduced number of equations with consequent savings in the generation of the system matrix and reduced iteration time. An other advantage of the method is that the remote boundaries need not be explicitly modeled.

In stratified media the two-sided boundaries between adjacent homogeneous blocks (e.g. the seam and the surrounding rock) will be included in the integration domain. A vector potential will be applied to each side of the boundary surfaces. The boundary conditions require continuity across the boundary surfaces of both the displacement and stress vectors associated with each boundary elements. This will increase the order of the system matrix.

A special case of two adjacent media is formed by the rock/cavity interface, for which the boundary conditions require the vanishing of the stress vector acting on the boundary elements. This is achieved by applying a vector potential along the boundary surface inside the rock medium. Again, the order of the system matrix will be increased.

In order to satisfy the boundary conditions of the stress-free ground surface, the mirror-image approach was used. This approach eliminates these boundary conditions from the final linear system, at the expense of additional time needed for matrix element computation.

A complete solution of a problem in elastostatics requires two steps:

(i) Solution by iteration of the approximate linear system derived from the exact integral equations, that expresses the boundary conditions.

(ii) Computation by approximate integration of known quantities of the elastostatic solution at freely selected positions in the medium, referred to as 'benchmarks'.

Such a free choice is not possible with the finite element or finite difference methods, where solution must be obtained for the whole problem space. In the integral equation approach the elastostatic solution can be computed at any 'benchmark' by 'remote action' from the boundaries, once the solution of the final linear system has been obtained. The mechanism of this remote action is the same as the Newtonian theory of gravitation.

2.2 The 'slit model' for excavation in narrow deposits

Excavations created by underground mining in deposits of small width, such as seams, reefs, veins, lodes, etc., may be approximately likened to cracks or slits whose widths tend to zero when their effects on the surrounding rock are analyzed. They may be viewed also as surfaces of discontinuity in the medium. On these surfaces the displacement vector of elastic theory must have a singularity, as in the real excavation the displacement vector in the roof is different from that in the floor. A mathematical expression for such a vector is given by the double-layer vector potential, which exhibits exactly the required discontinuity across the layer.

In mining, the difference betwee the two displacement vectors is referred to as the 'closure-ride vector'. It may be convenient to use the expression 'slit model' for the concept of double-layer potentials, used in connection with narrow deposits. The purpose of the replacement of a real three-dimensional deposit by an ideal two-dimensional slit is to achieve a reduction in the dimensionality and a significant decrease in the order of system matrix.

An unwanted feature of the slit model arises when the width of the deposit is made to tend to zero. The passage to the limit generates singularities in the stress components, some of which become unbounded in the vicinity of solid excavation faces. Known analytical two-dimensional slit solutions display this singular behavior of the stress components. However, in digital slit solutions, using a finite quantization 'mesh', the appearance of singularities in the stress components can be prevented. This is due to the 'smoothing effect' of quantization. Mathematically, the singularities are weak, and integration of the unbounded stress components over part of the slit boundary produces bounded forces and bounded average stress components.

Another unwanted phenomenon arising in the passage to the limit is the disappearance of all free stope faces and the elimination of the associated boundary conditions from the problem. This situation can be avoided if the vector potential, which is applied to the stope faces before the passage to the limit, is preserved in the limit process. This modification leads to an improved slit model as the boundary conditions on the free excavation walls can be satisfied. The integration domain of the vector potential will be a strip, composed of all excavation faces of the configuration. The width of the strip will be finite and equal to the hight of the excavation walls. The number of equations of the final linear system will be increased by a discrete, one-dimensional set.

The improved slit model should give a more realistic picture of stress distribution, particularly in the vicinity of the excavation faces. Also, a more reliable result can be obtained when analyzing pillar layouts to obtain pillar loads.

In the case of homogeneous models, when the seam and rock materials have the same elastic properties the integration domain of the basic double-layer potential need to extend only to the mined area of the deposit. In the intact, unmined parts of the seam the closure-ride vector vanishes, thus they are excluded from the integration domain as their contribution would be zero. However, this does not imply 'incompressibility' of the seam material, as it has been assumed in the past.

The slit model can be extended to the analysis of narrow deposits of ore in rock, both materials having different elastic properties. In this, non-homogeneous case, the displacement discontinuity, used as a support for the double layer potential may take two different forms:

(i) In excavated parts, ore or rock, the displacement discontinuity coincides with the closure-ride vector, as measured in the rock.

(ii) In intact ore, the displacement discontinuity of the double-layer potential represents the difference of the displacement vectors at the two interfaces: rock/ore and ore/rock, the measurements being made in the rock.

Thus the integration domain of the double-layer potential extends over the area of the whole ore deposit, whether the ore is excavated or not. Thus, there are three regions, in each a different set of boundary conditions apply:

(i) In excavated parts, ore or rock, the stress vector acting on the roof or floor elements must vanish.

(ii) In intact ore or seam, at each of the two interfaces rock/ore and ore/rock, the displacement and stress vectors must be continuous

929

(i.e. remain unchanged) in crossing the interface. Moreover, in passing from the first interface to the second, the stress vector is assumed to remain unchanged. On the other hand, the displacement vector is assumed to vary linearly from one interface to the other. The actual width of the orebody or seam is used as a parameter in the computation. The result is a set of three linear relations expressing the components of the displacement difference vector in terms of the stress components, all quantitites referring to the rock medium. The ore or seam medium, on the other hand, is treated as a series of elastic dipoles (two distinct points, separated by an infinitely small distance). The elastic state in the roof differs from the elastic state of the floor within the orebody.

(iii) In intact rock no conditions are imposed.

2.3 Tabular deposits

So far the description of the proposed model and method of solution is applicable to narrow deposits of arbitrary shape, because the two-dimensional integration domain of the elastic potentials has been left undetermined. However, an important simplification can be realized in the case of tabular, plane deposits.

In the case of a single-plane seam or several parallel-plane seams the kernel functions of the elastic potentials have an important property of translation invariance. This reduces the number of discrete kernel values which must be computed and kept in storage. Morover, they have well-defined parities and symmetry properties that lead to important savings in computer running time.

In the case of two, non-parallel seams the interaction kernel functions keep translation invariance and symmetry properties only with respect to the direction of their intersection. However, self-action kernels, that are used to account for the action of the seam element on itself possesses full invariance and symmetry.

A special case of two-seam interaction is given by a shallow plane seam interacting with the plane ground surface. If both planes are parallel, all kernel functions have maximum translation invariance and symmetry.

For piece-wise plane seems or ground surfaces there are several planes interacting; two by two, and the problem becomes a multi-seam problem.

In the general multi-seam problem the only invariant and symmetric interactions left are the self-actions of the seams. In the exceptional case of all seam intersections being parallel to one single direction, there is a general translation invariance and symmetry with respect to this direction.

3 MATHEMATICAL FORMULATION

3.1 Symbols and notation

The following symbols and notation are adopted for this paper:

R, x, y, z, i, j, k	coordinate vector and components, unit vectors
p_n, p_x, p_y, p_z	stress vector on plane with normal n and components
u, u, v, w	displacement vector and rectangular components
s, s_x, s_y, s_z	convergence-ride vector and rectangular components
d, d_x, d_y, d_z	displacement difference vector and components

b	either s or d, or b = ps + (1 - p)d, where p is the mined portion of a composite mesh
$\underline{\underline{\tau}}$, $\underline{\underline{\varepsilon}}$, $\underline{\underline{1}}$	stress, strain and unit tensors (9 components)
grad, grad^T, div	tensor gradient and its transpose, divergence
Δ	Laplacian operator
F	force vector
ν, λ, G, E	Poisson's ratio, Lame's constants, elastic modulus
u^-, u^+	limit value of u on the negative or positive side of the slit
x_p, y_p, z_p	coordinates of slit plane P
$r = (x_p - x)\mathbf{i} + (y_p - y)\mathbf{j} + (z_p - z)\mathbf{k}$	vector between a point on the slit plane and a point in the medium
$Tr\underline{\underline{\varepsilon}}$	trace of tensor $\underline{\underline{\varepsilon}}$ ($Tr\underline{\underline{\varepsilon}} = \varepsilon_x + \varepsilon_y + \varepsilon_z$)
A, B, B_x, B_y, B_z	harmonic functions and rectangular components of B
u_0	a singular solution
a.c, a.$\underline{\underline{b}}$	scalar product of vectors a, c; tensor product of vector a and tensor $\underline{\underline{b}}$

3.2 Generalized Hook's Law in tensor notation

$$\underline{\underline{\tau}} = 2G\underline{\underline{\varepsilon}} + (Tr\underline{\underline{\varepsilon}})\underline{\underline{1}} \tag{1}$$

As $\quad \underline{\underline{\varepsilon}} = (\text{grad}\,u + \text{grad}^T u)/2 \quad$ and $Tr\underline{\underline{\varepsilon}} = \text{div}\,u$

Thus $\underline{\underline{\varepsilon}} = G(\text{grad}\,u + \text{grad}^T u)/2 + (\lambda\,\text{div}\,u\,)\underline{\underline{1}} \tag{2}$

3.3 The partial differential equation of elastostatics and solutions

$$\text{grad}\,\text{div}\,u + (1 - 2\nu)\Delta u + \frac{1}{\lambda + G} F = 0 \tag{3}$$

and the Papkovich-Neuber's solution for a general geometry

$$u = u_0 + A - \frac{1}{4(1 - \nu)} \text{grad}(R - A + h), \tag{4}$$

where h is a harmonic function ($\Delta h = 0$), and Salamon's solution for a plane seam, with the z axis perpendicular to the excavations

$$u = u_0 + 2(1 - 2\nu)\frac{\partial B}{\partial z} - (1 - 2\nu)\,\text{grad}\,B_z - z\,\text{grad}\,\text{div}\,B + (1 - 2\nu)(\text{div}\,B)\mathbf{k} \ . \tag{5}$$

For the plane slit model, let z = 0 be the equation of the slit plane P. Salamon's solution u, given in (5) is used with

$$B(x,y,z) = \frac{1}{8\pi(1 - \nu)} \iint_P (s(x_p, y_p) + d(x_p, y_p))\frac{1}{r}\,dx_p\,dy_p \tag{6}$$

where r is the absolute value of vector r.

Among the three spatial derivatives of B, $\partial B/\partial x$, $\partial B/\partial y$, $\partial B/\partial z$ the latter, $\partial B/\partial z$, has a singularity for z = 0. In fact

$$\lim_{z \to 0} \left(\frac{1}{2\pi} \iint_P \frac{\partial}{\partial z}(\frac{1}{r})\,dx_p dy_p\right) = \lim_{z \to 0} \left(-\frac{1}{2\pi} \iint_P \frac{z}{r^3}\,dx_p\,dy_p\right) = -\text{sign}\,z = \begin{cases} +1 \text{ if } z \to 0^- \\ -1 \text{ if } z \to 0^+ \end{cases}$$

Hence, if $\partial B^-/\partial z$ denotes the value of $\partial B/\partial z$ on one side of the plane and $\partial B^+/\partial z$ denotes its value on the other side, which is also the positive normal to the slit plane, then it follows that

$$\left. \begin{array}{l} 2(1 - \nu)\partial B^-/\partial z = s/2 \\ 2(1 - \nu)\partial B^+/\partial z = -s/2 \end{array} \right\} \quad \text{in the excavated region of the plane, and}$$

$$\left. \begin{array}{l} 2(1 - \nu)\partial B^-/\partial z = d/2 \\ 2(1 -)\partial B^+/\partial z = -d/2 \end{array} \right\} \quad \begin{array}{l} \text{in the intact region of the plane except} \\ \text{in rock.} \end{array}$$

931

If the same limit process is applied to the displacement vector **u**, then according to (5), it follows that

$$\left.\begin{array}{l} u^- = s/2 + u_0 \\ u^+ = -s/2 + u_0 \\ u^- - u^+ = s \end{array}\right\} \begin{array}{l} \text{in excavated} \\ \text{parts of P} \end{array} \quad \text{and} \quad \left.\begin{array}{l} u^- = d/2 + u_0 \\ u^+ = -d/2 + u_0 \\ u^- - u^+ = d \end{array}\right\} \begin{array}{l} \text{in intact parts} \\ \text{of P, except in} \\ \text{rock, where d=0} \end{array} \quad (7)$$

It can be shown that components σ_z, τ_{xz}, τ_{yz} of stress vector $p_z = k.\underline{\varepsilon}$ are of the same magnitude on each side of the plane slit elements, indicating continuity. However, components σ_x, σ_y, τ_{xy} are discontinuous across the slit. For these components

$$\left.\begin{array}{l} \sigma_x^- - \sigma_x^+ = E/(1-\nu^2)(\partial s_x/\partial x + \nu \partial s_y/\partial y) \\ \sigma_y^- - \sigma_y^+ = E/(1-\nu^2)(\partial s_y/\partial y + \nu \partial s_x/\partial x) \\ \tau_{xy}^- - \tau_{xy}^+ = E/(2(1+\nu))(-\partial s_x/\partial y + \partial s_y/\partial x) \end{array}\right\} \begin{array}{l} \text{in the} \\ \text{excavated} \\ \text{region} \end{array} \quad (8)$$

Similar relationships hold in the intact region, d_x and d_y replacing s_x and s_y.

3.4 Boundary conditions for the intact region

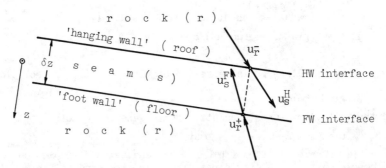

Figure 1. Boundary conditions for the intact region

For the HW interface: $\quad u_r^- = u_s^H \qquad$ For the FW interface: $\quad u_r^+ = u_s^F$
$$p_{zr}^- = p_{zs}^H \qquad\qquad\qquad\qquad\qquad p_{zr}^+ = p_{zs}^F \qquad (9)$$

Also $\quad p_{zr}^- = p_{zr}^+$, hence $\quad p_{zr}^- = p_{zs}^H = p_{zs}^F = p_{zr}^+ .$ $\qquad\qquad (10)$

For the seam a linear variation is assumed for u_s between the two interfaces, thus
$$u_s^F = u_s^H + (\partial u_s/\partial z)\delta z .$$

Taking $\qquad\qquad \partial u_s/\partial z \approx (\partial u_s^H/\partial z + \partial u_s^F/\partial z)/2$, and using
$$u_s^H - u_s^F = u_r^- - u_r^+ = d, \text{ yields the condition}$$

$$-d = (\delta z/z)(\partial u_s^H/\partial z + \partial u_s^F/\partial z) \qquad (11)$$

which in turn leads to the boundary conditions:

$$\left.\begin{array}{l} \dfrac{d_z}{\delta z} + \dfrac{1}{\lambda_s + 2G_s}\left((1+\dfrac{2\lambda_s \nu}{E})\sigma_z - \dfrac{\lambda_s(1-\nu)}{E}(\sigma_{xcont} + \sigma_{ycont})\right) = 0 \\[3mm] \dfrac{d_x}{\delta z} + \dfrac{\tau_{xz}}{G_s} - \dfrac{\partial w_{cont}}{\partial x} = 0 \quad \text{and} \quad \dfrac{d_y}{\delta z} + \dfrac{\tau_{yz}}{G_s} - \dfrac{\partial w_{cont}}{\partial y} = 0 \end{array}\right\} \quad (12)$$

932

In (12) subsripts r have been dropped, all elastic quantities refer to the rock medium, except λ_s, and G_s, which refer to the seam material. Subscript cont indicates the continuous part of the relevant quantitites.

3.5 Boundary conditions on excavation (stope) faces - improved slit model

The vector potential B applied on the excavation faces may be written

$$B = \int_{-\delta z/2}^{+\delta z/2} \int_C g\,(t_p, z_p)\,\frac{dt_p dz_p}{r} \quad, \text{ where} \tag{13}$$

δz extracted seam width (stoping width), locally constant

C   contour of the excavation faces in the slit plane

t_p curvilinear coordinate along C

$dt_p = (dx_p^2 + dy_p^2)^{\frac{1}{2}}$ on the real contour, C and

g   layer density.

At first, the real excavation face contour C will be replaced by piece-wise linear segments, parallel to the coordinate axes. In this case, the boundary conditions imposed on faces parallel to the x axis:

$$p_y = j.\underline{\underline{\tau}} = G(\partial u/\partial y + \text{grad}v) + (\lambda \text{div}u)j = 0$$

and on the faces parallel to the y axis: $\tag{14}$

$$p_x = i.\underline{\underline{\tau}} = G(\partial u/\partial x + \text{grad}u) + (\lambda \text{div}u)i = 0$$

In (14) u is the total displacement vector, resulting from the contributions of the seam, the excavation faces and the ground surface. The elastic parameters λ and G refer to the medium in which the face is cut.

3.6 The ground surface

If the ground surface is a horizontal plane a single vector potential will be applied to it:

$$B = \int_S \int \frac{1}{r}\,dx_S dy_S \quad, \text{ where}$$

x_S, y_S, z_S plane coordinates on S, with z_S = constant

$l(x_S, y_S)$ layer density.

In this case Salomon's displacement vector (5) is formed with B and the method of mirror image seams may be also employed.

For a general surface or for a piece-wise linear surface, S with a number of plane segments, it is more convenient to form a Papkovich-Neuber displacement vector. The expression is given in (4), with A expressed by a general surface integral:

$$A = \int_S l\,\frac{\partial}{\partial n}\left(\frac{1}{r}\right) dS \quad, \text{ where} \tag{15}$$

$\frac{\partial}{\partial n}$ is a derivative with respect to the normal of S.

The boundary condition is that the stress vector, p_n must vanish on S

$$n.\underline{\underline{\tau}} = G(\partial u/\partial n + \text{grad}\,u_n) + (\lambda\,\text{div}\,u\,)n = 0 \tag{16}$$

4 ADDITIONAL TOPICS

4.1 Remote effects

In the homogeneous model, in which the seam material has the same elastic coefficients as the rock material, the integration domain for the elastic potentials is restricted to the excavated parts of the deposit.

In the non-homogeneous model, in which the seam and rock materials have different elastic properties, the integration domain extends over the whole deposit. In the excavated parts the closure-ride vector s occurs as a factor of the integrand, in the intact parts it is the displacement difference vector d which occurs in the integrand. The magnitudes of the two vectors are quite different: s is considerably larger than d.

In order to limit the size of the problem, it is necessary to 'cut-off' the remote influences in the non-homogeneous model. The criterion for limiting the extent of the region to be modeled is based on the requirement that the effect of the 'cut-off' region on the excavated region is negligible, that is, smaller than the precision limit of the computations. Three different regions will be thus recognized:

(i)   Excavation region, within which all excavations are confined,
(ii)   'Cut-off' region, the region beyond the cut-off limit, and
(iii) Intermediate region, situated between the other two regions.

The effect produced by the cut-off region on the excation region is negligible, but not so for the intermediate region. An approximation, however, may be used for its evaluation. It consists of the extrapolation of d, as computed on the cut-off circumference, to the interior of the cut-off region.

Thus, essentially, the originally unbounded domain of integration in the plane of the seam is replaced by a bounded domain, which is made up of two sub-regions. One of them contains all the excavated parts of the seam, where the remote influences are negligible. The other sub-region is free of excavations, where the remote effects manifest themselves in the form of a finite contour integral.

As a first step towards the final solution, the boundary problem for the total region within the cut-off limit is solved, using somewhat coarse meshes for the iteration process. The effect of the intermediate region on the excavation region is thus computed and stored; these contributions will remain unaltered for the rest of the processing. Effectively, the intermediate region is eliminated from the problem, only the excavation area is left for further processing.

4.2 Scaling procedure for large configurations

When the configuration is large and excavations are present throughout, the final solution is not without difficulty. One approach is to compress the finer details into larger blocks of averaged data. This would lead to a coarse solution, on the scale of the blocks, containing the averaged input data. Such a solution would be of little use when information is required on the same level of detail as the input information.

It would be, however, also inadequate and unsatisfactory to single out a particular area and ignore the rest of the environment.

Apart from the possibility of ignoring some distant, isolated excavation, there is no room for the elimination of other contiguous excavations. Making imaginary cuts through the excavated area introduces topological changes that could completely upset the true closure-ride distribution and lead to a solution of a very different problem.

The lumping technique treats near influences by small blocks and remote influences by large blocks. The application of this idea is responsible for considerable structural complication in a program. However, improvements in the results fully justify the time spent on its implementation.

The same idea may be used, in a different form, for the solution of the problem caused by the large size of the configuration. A finer solution may be arrived at in a limited area, when the remote influences are taken into account in a coarser way. The coarse contributions could be determined in an overall coarse solution, obtained as a first step. In the limited area, a smaller mesh of quantization allows a more detailed description of this area. This procedure may be designated as a 'scaling step', meaning the reduction of mesh size.

Several scaling steps may be executed in succession; at each step the area retained for further detailed analysis and the mesh size are reduced and a new solution is computed. The influence of the dropped out regions is retained on the right hand side of the new system equations and remains unchanged during iteration. The process is additive: at each step a new region drops out and its influence is accumulated with those of the previously dropped out areas.

At the end of the scaling process an ultimate solution is obtained that is valid in a certain area, described with a certain amount of detail. The choice of the area for detailed analysis and the degree of detail in its description is left to the user.

4.3 Waste filling and support

The behavior of waste is modeled in two phases:
(i) No reaction of the waste is to be expected until a certain amount of compression has occurred, that is, after the roof and floor converged.
(ii) Elastic reaction with approriate elastic coefficients. The computation is carried out using the same expressions as for the compressible seam kernels.

In the case of support the kernels may have the same expressions as for the waste, however, appropriate modulus values for steel have to be selected.

4.4 Non-linear seam behavior

The treatment is in three phases:
(i) Elastic behavior until the peak in the stress/strain curve is reached. This critical strain will be handed to the program, which will be compared to the roof-to-floor convergence of the seam. If the convergence exceeds the critical value, then phase (ii) will be implemented.
(ii) The seam collapses and the rock becomes free of stress, satisfying the boundary conditions of the excavated face. The kernels are the usual, 'mined' kernels of the rock. Further, the seam behaves

935

like waste; after a certain amount of compression elastic reaction will reappear, as in the case of phase (ii) of waste filling.

(iii) Elastic reaction with appropriate elastic coefficients. The elastic modulus would be much lower than that in phase (i). For parts of the seam adjacent to the excavation face no phase (iii) is envisoned, it is assumed that these parts of the seam remain in a collapsed state.

5 CONCLUSIONS

A computer code, developed on the basis of principles outlined in this paper, is capable of modeling extensive mining excavations in a single seam. One very useful feature is the scaling facility, combined with the retention of the influence of the surrounding excavations. This feature allows the detailed analysis of workings on an enlarged scale, without the danger of oversimplifying the true mining geometry. This is of particular use, when extensive pillared areas need be analysed.

Major improvements of the method include modeling the convergence in the unworked parts of the seam and the inclusion of the excavation faces in the solution of the general mining problem.

Other useful features are: modeling of the general ground surface, variable seam width, non-linear seam behavior, waste filling and support.

REFERENCES

Salamon, M.D.G. 1964. Elastic analysis of displacements and stresses induced by the mining of seam or reef deposits - Part I. J.S.Afr.Inst.Min.Metall. 64:128-149.

Salamon, M.D.G. 1964. Elastic analysis of displacements and stresses induced by the mining of seam or reef deposits - Part IV. J.S.Afr.Inst.Min.Metall. 65:319-338.

Plewman, R.P., Deist, F.H. and Ortlepp, W.D. 1969. The development and application of a digital computer method for the solution of strata control problems. J.S.Afr.Inst.Min.Metall. 70:33-34.

Cook, N.G.W., Hoek, E., Pretorius, J.P.G., Ortlepp, W.D. and Salamon, M.D.G. 1966. Rock mechanics applied to the study of rockbursts. J.S.Afr.Inst.Min.Metall. 66:435-528

Moris, J.P.E. 1975. SHAMIP, A computer program for elastic analysis of large size, tabular, mono-planar, shallow, hard orebodies. Research report No: 51/75, Chamber of Mines of South Africa, Johannesburg.

Rock mass classification by fuzzy sets

V.U.NGUYEN
University of Wollongong, New South Wales, Australia
E.ASHWORTH
South Dakota School of Mines & Technology, Rapid City, USA

1 INTRODUCTION

It is widely recognized that subjectivity plays an important role in mining geomechanics in general and is the basis of a number of criteria employed in many different rock mass classification systems.

Subjective uncertainty results mainly from the use of descriptive and sometimes ambiguous phrases in the processing of geotechnical information required in rock mass classification, e.g. "highly weathered rock", "very large inflow of water" . For many other classes of criteria that can be treated as quantitative, such as unconfined compressive strength, slaking potential, etc., it can be recognized that the numerical values of these criteria already posess some inherent uncertainty associated with test or observation errors customarily dealt with by statistics and probability theory. Furthermore, some index values for these criteria may lie in the boundary or cloudy region between two adjacent classes , and yet by the conventional scores summation method , we normally assign a fixed numerical score to an item within a corresponding range regardless of the relative position of the item value in the range.

In this paper, we present the application of fuzzy set theory and in particular, the Bellman-Zadeh aggregation procedure in obtaining a rock mass classification rating from the CSIR classification system with incorporation of expert knowledge. Numerical examples are given to illustrate the proposed procedure.

2 FUZZY SETS

2.1 Description

The notion of fuzzy sets was first introduced by Zadeh (1965) to model real life classes in which there may be a continuum of grades of membership. Fuzzy sets underlie much of our ability to make decisions based on ambiguous and imprecise information, and fuzzy set theory is said to be a generalization of ordinary or classical set theory. It is recalled that an ordinary set or a crisp set is a collection of objects having some common property, e.g. a class of shield-type supports, a group of longwall panels, etc. Suppose we want to define a class of "highly weathered rock". To do that, we may first ask ourselves : "How weathered is highly weathered ?", and we can recognize that a satisfactory answer to this question is largely based on our subjective judgement, at least until there is a universal agreement on some objective rating index to describe the degree of weathering. Such a class or stratum of highly weathered rock is thus delineated by a cloudy or imprecise boundary and is said to represent a fuzzy set which admits the possibility of partial membership in it (Figure 1). Through fuzzy set theory, descriptive words, or phrases such as "low caving potential", "highly slaking rock", or proposition of the type "If A then B" (e.g. if the floor comprises highly swelling rock, it would heave easily following water inrushes), can be modelled or interpreted by the use of membership functions and linguistic variables that the membership functions serve to describe.

Let $U = [x]$ denote a space of objects or a universe of discourse. a fuzzy set of A in U is a set of ordered pairs :

$$A = [(x, \mu_A(x))]$$

$$x \varepsilon A \text{ , and } A \subset U$$

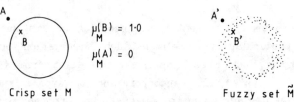

Crisp set M $\qquad\qquad$ Fuzzy set M̃

Figure 1. The concept of a fuzzy set

938

where $\mu_A(x)$ is termed the "grade of membership of x in **A**", which may take on values in the range of 0-1. For example, after a testing program, we conclude that the roof stratum has very high slaking potential. In fuzzy set grammar, "very high" is represented as a linguistic variable, say, with a central value of 0.9. The fuzzy set A describing a stratum with very high slaking potential can thus be written as:

$$A = [0.5 \mid 0, 0.6 \mid 0.2, 0.7 \mid 0.6, 0.8 \mid 0.8, 0.9 \mid 1.0, 1.0 \mid 0.8]$$

in which 0.5, 0.6, 0.7, 0.8, 0.9, and 1.0 are the various values assumed by the linguistic variable "very high" : 0, 0.2, 0.6, 0.8 , 1.0 and 0.8 are the respective grades of membership or degrees of belief and | is a delineator.

2.2 Fuzzy set operations

The basic mathematical operations on fuzzy sets can be summarized as follows :
* the UNION of two fuzzy sets A and B, i.e. A U B, results in membership levels :

$$\mu_{A \cup B}(x) = [\mu_A(x) \vee \mu_B(x)] = \max[\mu_A(x), \mu_B(x)] \qquad (1)$$

* the grade of membership for the INTERSECTION of A and B is :

$$\mu_{A \cap B}(x) = [\mu_A(x) \wedge \mu_B(x)] = \min[\mu_A(x), \mu_B(x)] \qquad (2)$$

* the operation NOT A, or the compliment of a fuzzy set A is :

$$\overline{A} = [(x \mid \mu_{\overline{A}}(x))] \qquad (3)$$

where $\mu_{\overline{A}}(x) = 1 - \mu_A(x)$
* the fuzzy RELATION , R, from a fuzzy set $A = [x \mid \mu_A(x)]$ and a fuzzy set $B = [y \mid \mu_B(y)]$ is defined as a set having dual membership in both A and B, with grade $\mu_R(x, y)$, i.e.

$$R = \int_{A \times B} [(x, y) \mid \mu_R(x, y)] \qquad (4)$$

where

$$\mu_R(x, y) = [\mu_A(x) \wedge \mu_B(y)] = \min[\mu_A(x), \mu_B(y)] \qquad (5)$$

* the fuzzy set COMPOSTION of A′ and R is a fuzzy subset B′ :

$$B' = A' \circ R \qquad (6)$$

where each element of B' is constructed from :

$$\mu_{B'}(y) = \max[\min(\mu_{A'}(x), \mu_R(x, y))] \qquad (7)$$

which can be interpreted as a matrix multiplication of A' and R in the fuzzy set framework with multiplication being replaced by min and addition by max.

For examples of these fuzzy operations, see Nguyen (1985).

3 FUZZIFIED ROCK MASS CLASSIFICATION

3.1 Classification procedure

Consider now the CSIR rock mass classification system (Bieniawski, 1980), in which there are five different classes, I to V, each being related to the stand-up time of an active unsupported span. The designation of a rock mass to any of the five classes is based on a total rating of five basic criteria pertinent to : rock strength, RQD, discontinuities spacing, condition of discontinuities, and groundwater. Each individual rating is assessed where possible from the result of investigation or laboratory tests, and the rating on each criterion is a fixed numerical score for each different range of test results, regardless of the relative position of the test result to the boundaries of the range for each particular score. The ratings for criteria on discontinuities and groundwater conditions are largely subjective.

The fuzzy aggregation procedure proposed by Bellman and Zadeh (1970) for multicriteria decision modelling is applied as an alternative derivation of Bieniawski's geomechanics classification for a rock mass in which expert knowledge is duly incorporated. It can be reported here that, from the numerous results of Mining Engineering students' tutorial excercises at the University of Wollongong (1984), the fuzzy approach always results in either the same rock classification as that obtained by the CSIR procedure or a more conservative classification accounting for subjective

940

uncertainty on qualitative data or data that are close to the range boundaries.

Recall that in the CSIR system we have five criteria ($j = 5$) and five different rock classes ($i = 5$). In the fuzzy framework a fuzzy binary relation $A_j \times B_i$ can be established as a table in lieu of the CSIR table of scores as given by Hoek and Brown (1980) . According to Bellman and Zadeh (1970), for a pessimistic or conservative aggregation, the synthesized class is the class having an aggregated membership grade of :

$$\mu_R = V_{i=1}^5 [\Lambda_{j=1}^5 \mu_{ij}] \tag{8}$$

in which V and Λ denote max and min operations, respectively. The fuzzy aggregation procedure applied in obtaining a rock mass classification is best illustrated by the following example.

3.2 Example

Consider a rock mass in which a roadway is to be driven. The parameter values or descriptions associated with the five criteria are given in Table 1. Assuming negligible effects of discontinuity strike and dip orientation it follows from Table 1 that the rock mass has a total score of 70 (in the range 61–80) and belongs to Class II (Good rock) in accordance with the CSIR Table given in the text by Hoek and Brown (1980). A close inspection of individual numerical and qualitative ratings given in Table 1 would suggest however that most of the results lie in the regions near the boundaries between two adjacent score classes, and yet the class score for each criterion assumes a uniform value regardless of any judgement on the accuracy of test results or observations .

In the framework of fuzzy sets, we can now transform the scores summation table (Table 1) into a fuzzy binary relation between criteria and rock classes as shown in Table 2. The dual membership grades in Table 2 signify that for each particular numerical or qualitative result associated with a criterion, the

rock mass can be accordingly grouped or said to belong to each
class with a different degree of belief or support, derived by
our subjective and expert judgement. For engineering purposes
at present, the derivation of membership grades can be obtained
by scaling from some central or limiting value. For example, for
criterion (ii), an RQD of 50 would likely correspond to a membership
grade of 0.80 (= 50/62.5) in Class III having a range of 50-75 and a
central value of 62.5. Applying the min-max scheme to Table 2, i.e.
taking minima down the columns and maximum from the resulting row
, we obtain an optimum membership grade of 0.62 yielding a Class
II for this rock. The result is thus identical to that obtained
by the scores summation procedure.

To illustrate sensitivity of the fuzzy procedure, we suppose
that instead of getting RQD = 50, we have RQD = 73. The fuzzy
vector for criterion (ii) becomes :

$$[\mu_{(ii)}] = [I \mid 0.65, II \mid 0.77, III \mid 0.87, IV \mid 0.62, V \mid 0.40]$$

Criterion	Value or Description	CSIR rating
(i) UCS	245 MPa	12
(ii) RQD	50	13
(iii) Joint spacing	300mm	10
(iv) Joint conditions	< 1mm , MW	25
(v) Groundwater	9l/min/10m	10
	TOTAL=	70

Table 1. Ratings summation for Example 1 by the CSIR method

Replacing the row corresponding to criterion (ii) in Table 2
and performing the same Bellman-Zadeh procedure, we obtain the
final optimum membership grade of 0.66 corresponding to Class II
which is also the class obtained by scores summation.

Class / Criterion	I	II	III	IV	V
(i)	0.75	0.82	0.60	0.42	0.20
(ii)	0.55	0.62	0.80	0.71	0.65
(iii)	0.50	0.66	0.90	0.80	0.60
(iv)	0.65	0.80	0.70	0.40	0.22
(v)	0.64	0.81	0.75	0.60	0.32
Min.	0.50	0.62	0.60	0.40	0.20
Max.		0.62			

Table 2. Rock classification by the use of membership grades

If we further alter the UCS result (criterion (i)), say UCS = 99 MPa, the membership vector for criterion (i) may become :

$$[\mu_{(i)}] = [I \mid 0.63, II \mid 0.70, III \mid 0.76, IV \mid 0.45, V \mid 0.25]$$

It can be recognized that for UCS = 99 MPa the total score is 65 obtained by the CSIR procedure, and the rock accordingly still belongs to Class II. By the fuzzy procedure however, the maximum degree of support is now 0.70 which would put the rock into Class III. The shift of determining membership grade has been centered on criterion (iv) (see Table 2) and yet the mechanism for this shift is undeniably due to the numerical value and associated membership grades in criterion (i).

4 CONCLUDING REMARKS

In this paper, we have proposed the use of fuzzy set theory to model our subjective or possibilistic judgement on various rock classification criteria and to obtain a final rock classification through aggregation of the degrees of support that we have assigned to the criteria based on numerical values or qualitative descriptions associated with these criteria.

The fuzzy approach has been shown to give results in excellent agreement with the conventional scores summation scheme and yet it can incorporate expert judgement on the various criteria concerned. As a result of space limitation however, many interesting details of fuzzy set applications in rock mass classification and mining geomechanics in general, have not been dealt with in the present paper. These include the Norwegian Q-index system (Barton et al., 1974), non-interactivity among fuzzy criteria, rules of assigning membership grades, etc. The illustrative example using the CSIR classification system indicates the applicability, viability and simplicity of fuzzy set operations in an important area of decision making processes in mining geomechanics. Further work on fuzzy set application in mining geomechanics is therefore suggested.

REFERENCES

1. Barton, N., Lien, R., and Lunde, J. 1974. Engineering classification of rock masses for the design of tunnel support. Rock Mech., Vol. 6, No. 4, pp 189-236.

2. Bellman, R.E. and Zadeh, L.A. 1970. Decision making in a fuzzy environment. Management Sci., Vol. 17, No. 4, pp B141-B164.

3. Bieniawski, Z.T. 1980. Current possibilities for rock mass classification as design aids in mining. 1980 AIME Fall Meeting at Minneapolis, Minnesota (October). SME Preprint.

4. Hoek, E. and Brown, E.T. 1980. Underground excavations in rock. Inst. Min. Metall., London (U.K.) 527 pp.

5. Nguyen, V.U. 1985a. Tender evaluation by fuzzy sets. ASCE Jour. Engineering Construction and Management (in press).

6. Nguyen, V.U. 1985b. Some fuzzy set applications in mining geomechanics (submitted to Int. Jour. Rock Mech. & Min. Eng. Sci.).

7. Zadeh, L.A. 1965. Fuzzy sets. Information and Control, Vol. 8, pp 338-353.

The asymmetric stress distribution around a slotted cylinder in a poroelastic medium

E.P.FAHRENTHOLD
University of Texas, Austin, USA

J.B.CHEATHAM, Jr.
Rice University, Houston, Texas, USA

1 INTRODUCTION

The distribution of rock stresses around a slotted casing may be studied through the application of complex variable methods to poroelasticity. Rice and Cleary (1976) formulated the coupled poroelasticity
problem using complex variables, and applied it to suddenly pressurized
cylindrical and spherical cavities. Herein the two-dimensional analysis
of elasticity problems with body forces is employed to solve several
uncoupled porous media problems under transient radial flow conditions.
Specifically the rock stresses around open, fully supported, and partially supported well bores are considered (Fahrenthold 1984). The
case of a well bore supported by a liner with a single slot may be considered a two-dimensional analog to the perforated casing problem.

2 PROBLEM STATEMENT

The objective of this elastic analysis is to determine the stress distribution in an infinite body of porous elastic solid containing a
circular hole. The boundary conditions are a specified constant state
of stress at infinity and zero displacement or radial stress on the
boundary of the hole. The zero displacement condition represents the
presence of a liner or casing along all or part of the cavity wall.

3 METHOD OF SOLUTION

Two-dimensional elasticity problems with body forces, like the one just
described, may be solved using the method of complex variables.
Mushkhelishvili (1975) and Green and Zerna (1968) describe the development and application of this method. Timoshenko and Goodier (1970)
employ it in the solution of thermoelastic problems, which are similar
to poroelastic problems of the type considered here.

4 THE EQUATIONS OF EQUILIBRIUM AND THE STRESS-STRAIN RELATIONS

The total stress τ_{ij} on the solid/fluid mixture must satisfy the equations of equilibrium for a plane problem without body forces. Define

x and y to be rectangular coordinates in the plane of interest, related to the complex variable z by

$$z = x + iy, \quad i = \sqrt{-1}. \tag{1a}$$

In terms of the polar coordinates r and θ

$$z = re^{i\theta}. \tag{1b}$$

The total stress on the mixture is a function of the effective stress σ_{ij} (Nur and Byerlee 1971), the pore pressure P, and an experimentally determined constant α, and can be written

$$\tau_{ij} = \sigma_{ij} - \delta_{ij} \alpha P \tag{1c}$$

where δ_{ij} is the Kronecker delta and tension is taken as positive.

The effective stress determines the strain in the porous solid, so that the pertinent stress-strain relations are

$$\sigma_{ij} = 2\mu e_{ij} + \delta_{ij} \lambda e \tag{2a}$$

where μ and λ are Lamé coefficients for the porous solid, the e_{ij} are components of the strain in the porous solid, and

$$e = e_{kk} \tag{2b}$$

with the repeated index indicating a sum over

$$i = x, y, z. \tag{2c}$$

The plane strain poroelastic problem takes the form of a conventional elasticity problem with body forces when written in terms of the effective stress σ_{ij} (Lubinski 1954). Thus the established methods of complex variables may be applied without modification to the problem of interest.

5 STRESSES AND DISPLACEMENTS EXPRESSED IN TERMS OF COMPLEX POTENTIAL FUNCTIONS

The elastic strains in the porous solid e_{ij} are determined from the displacements in the x and y directions, u and v. If the strain-displacement equations are combined with the constitutive and equilibrium relations, England (1971) shows that there exists a general solution for the displacements that depends on three functions: $\Omega(z)$ and $\omega(z)$ are complex potentials whose form must be determined for the particular boundary value problem under consideration, while X(z) is derived from the given body force distribution. The general solution for the displacement is

$$2\mu(u + iv) = \hat{k} \, \Omega(z) - z \, \overline{\Omega'(z)} - \overline{\omega(z)} - \frac{\mu}{2(\lambda + 2\mu)} X(z) \tag{3}$$

where a horizontal bar denotes the complex conjugate, the prime denotes differentiation with respect to z, and

$$\hat{k} = \frac{\lambda + 3\mu}{\lambda + \mu}. \tag{4a}$$

948

The stresses produced by the displacements (3) can be determined, the result being

$$\sigma_{xx} + \sigma_{yy} = 2[\Omega'(z) + \overline{\Omega'(z)}] - (\frac{\lambda + \mu}{\lambda + 2\mu}) V(z) \qquad (4b)$$

$$\sigma_{xx} - \sigma_{xx} + i2 \sigma_{xy} = -2[z \overline{\Omega''(z)} + \overline{\omega'(z)}] - \frac{\mu}{(\lambda+2\mu)} \frac{\partial X(z)}{\partial \overline{z}} \qquad (4c)$$

where the double prime indicates the second derivative with respect to z and V(z) is the body force potential

$$V(z) = \frac{\partial X(z)}{\partial z}. \qquad (5)$$

With stresses and displacements expressed in terms of the complex potentials $\Omega(z)$, $\omega(z)$, V(z) and the particular integral X(z), it is necessary to determine these functions for the problem in Section 2. The body force potential (V(z)) and the particular integral (X(z)) are calculated from the pore pressure distribution.

6   THE PORE PRESSURE DISTRIBUTION

If the well bore is taken to be a circular hole of radius R in an infinite medium, then the pore fluid flow field can be described by the constant terminal rate solution (Dake 1978) for the pore pressure

$$P = P_\infty - \hat{Q} \int_\epsilon^\infty \frac{e^{-s}}{s} ds \qquad (6a)$$

$$\hat{Q} = \frac{Q\bar{\mu}}{4\pi kh} \qquad (6b)$$

$$\epsilon = \frac{n\bar{\mu}cr^2}{4k\tau} \qquad (6c)$$

where P_∞ is the initial reservoir pressure, Q is the fluid volumetric flow rate, k is the formation permeability, h is the formation thickness, n is the formation porosity, c is the fluid compressibility (assumed small and constant), and τ is the time after the onset of production from the well. The quantity $\hat{Q}$ represents the rate at which fluid is being produced from the given reservoir, while ϵ is determined by the particular combination of radial position (r) and time (τ) for which the pressure is desired. This pore pressure distribution yields a potential function

$$V(z) = -2\alpha P \qquad (7)$$

and a particular integral

$$X(z) = z(V(z) - 2\alpha\hat{Q} \frac{e^{-\epsilon}}{\epsilon}). \qquad (8)$$

7   THE ROCK STRESSES AROUND AN OPEN WELL BORE

Consider the stress distribution in the porous solid around an open well bore of radius R. Given a uniform stress state and zero rotation at infinity

949

$$\sigma_{xx} = \sigma_{yy} = -\sigma_\infty \tag{9a}$$

$$\sigma_{xy} = 0 \tag{9b}$$

the form of the functions $\Omega(z)$ and $\omega(z)$ may be determined as

$$\Omega(z) = Az \tag{9c}$$

$$\omega(z) = -(\hat{P} + 2A)\,\frac{R^2}{z}. \tag{9d}$$

where

$$A = -\tfrac{1}{2}[\sigma_\infty + (\frac{\lambda + \mu}{\lambda + 2\mu})\alpha P_\infty], \quad \bar{\epsilon} = \frac{m\bar{\mu}cR^2}{4k_T}, \tag{9e}$$

and

$$\hat{P} = (\frac{\lambda + \mu}{\lambda + 2\mu})\alpha P_w - (\frac{\mu}{\lambda + 2\mu})\alpha\hat{Q}\,\frac{e^{-\bar{\epsilon}}}{\bar{\epsilon}}. \tag{9f}$$

8   THE ROCK STRESSES AROUND A FULLY SUPPORTED WELL BORE

The stress distribution around a cased well bore may be estimated by taking the boundary condition on the rock around the casing to be that of zero displacement. The complex potentials are in this case

$$\Omega(z) = Az \tag{10a}$$

$$\omega(z) = [2\mu\hat{D} + (\hat{k} - 1)AR](R/z) \tag{10b}$$

where

$$\hat{D} = \frac{\alpha R}{2(\lambda + 2\mu)}\,(P_w + \hat{Q}\,\frac{e^{-\bar{\epsilon}}}{\bar{\epsilon}}). \tag{10c}$$

9   THE ROCK STRESSES AROUND A PARTIALLY SUPPORTED WELL BORE

The principal obstacle in the analytical study of rock stresses around casing perforations is the difficulty in describing simultaneously the unstressed rock surface adjacent to the perforation and the supported rock surface cemented to the casing. However for the two-dimensional analog of the perforation problem, complex variable methods allow the study of the mixed boundary value problem of a well bore supported along only part of its circumference.

Again take the well bore to lie in an infinite porous solid with the pore pressure distribution given previously. The effect of partially supporting the wall of the well can be estimated by negating the displacement obtained in Section 7 over all but a single arc of the well bore.

The solution to the stated problem is obtained by superimposing on the stresses in Section 7 the stresses obtained for the following mixed boundary value problem.

Consider a circular hole of radius R in an infinite medium with zero stress and rotation at infinity. Along the circular hole the boundary conditions are

$$\sigma_{rr} + i\sigma_{r\theta} = 0 \qquad \text{for} \quad t = Re^{i\theta} \quad \text{on } L' \qquad (11a)$$

$$u + iv = f(t) \qquad \text{for} \quad t = Re^{i\theta} \quad \text{on } L \qquad (11b)$$

where the arcs L and L' are defined by

$$L \quad : \quad r = R, \ |\theta| < \phi \qquad (11c)$$

$$L' \quad : \quad r = R, \ |\theta| > \phi, \ -\pi \le \theta \le \pi. \qquad (11d)$$

The slot in the liner is along L' where the effective radial stress is zero. From the stress boundary value problem of Section 7 the displacement on L' must be

$$f(t) = \hat{u}t \qquad (11e)$$

where

$$\hat{u} = \frac{1}{2\mu} \ [(\frac{\lambda + 2\lambda}{\lambda + \mu})\sigma_\infty + \alpha(P_\infty - P_w)]. \qquad (11f)$$

England (1971) shows that the solution for the mixed boundary value problem has a general form

$$\sigma_{rr} + \sigma_{\theta\theta} = 2[\Omega'(z)] + \overline{\Omega'(z)}] \qquad (12a)$$

$$\sigma_{rr} + i\sigma_{r\theta} = \Omega'(z) - \frac{R^2}{z\bar{z}}\Omega'(\frac{R^2}{\bar{z}}) + (1 - \frac{R^2}{z\bar{z}})[\overline{\Omega'(z)} - \bar{z}\ \overline{\Omega''(z)}]. \qquad (12b)$$

In this case the function $\Omega'(z)$ may be calculated as $(\gamma = \frac{1}{2} + \frac{i}{2\pi}\ln\hat{k})$

$$\Omega'(z) = \frac{2\mu\hat{u}}{(1 + \hat{k})} - [\frac{2\mu\hat{u}}{(1 + \hat{k})}(z - \gamma Re^{i\phi} - (1-\gamma)Re^{-i\phi}) +$$

$$\frac{\hat{X}}{2\pi(1 + \hat{k})} \ (1 + \frac{R}{z}ke^{-2\phi\beta})](z - Re^{i\phi})^{-\gamma} \ (z - Re^{-i\phi})^{\gamma - 1} \qquad (13)$$

where $\hat{X}$ is the resultant force over the arc L, a real number by symmetry.

The form of $\Omega'(z)$ produced by this solution leads to singularities of the stresses at the ends of the arc L', that is at the edges of the slot. This phenomenon is not uncommon at points where the boundary conditions change in type.

Substituting (13) into equations (12) gives a stress distribution which, superimposed on the results of Section 7, describes the rock stresses around a partially supported well bore under nonsteady flow conditions.

10 NUMERICAL EXAMPLES OF THE ELASTIC STRESS DISTRIBUTION AROUND OPEN AND FULLY SUPPORTED WELL BORES

To illustrate the solutions in Sections 7 and 8, consider the following example:

$$\frac{\sigma_\infty}{P_\infty} = \frac{1}{10} \qquad (14a)$$

$$\frac{\hat{Q}}{P_\infty} = \frac{1}{50} \qquad (14b)$$

$$\alpha = 1 \qquad (14c)$$

$$\nu = .25 \qquad (14d)$$

where ν is Poisson's ratio for the porous solid. Poisson's ratio determines the value of the coefficients (Malvern 1969)

$$\frac{\lambda + \mu}{\lambda + 2\mu} = \frac{1}{2(1 - \nu)} \qquad (14e)$$

$$\frac{\mu}{\lambda + 2\mu} = \frac{(1 - 2\nu)}{2(1 - \nu)} \qquad (14f)$$

The nondimensional effective stresses

$$\frac{\sigma_{rr}}{P_\infty}, \quad \frac{\sigma_{\theta\theta}}{P_\infty}, \quad \frac{\sigma_{zz}}{P_\infty} \qquad (15a)$$

were calculated for the region

$$1 \leq \frac{r}{R} \leq 5 \qquad (15b)$$

for a time corresponding to

$$\bar{\varepsilon} = 4 \times 10^{-4} \qquad (15c)$$

which represents a well pressure

$$\frac{P_w}{P_\infty} = 0.597. \qquad (15b)$$

With the rock in plane strain,

$$\sigma_{zz} = \nu(\sigma_{rr} + \sigma_{\theta\theta}). \qquad (16)$$

The effective stress distribution for an open well bore is shown in Figure 1. The maximum principal stress difference occurs at the well bore and increases in magnitude as the drawdown increases. The order of the principal effective stresses at the well bore is

$$\sigma_{rr} > \sigma_{zz} > \sigma_{\theta\theta}. \qquad (17a)$$

The effective stress distribution for a fully supported well bore is shown in Figure 2. Again the maximum principal stress difference occurs at the well bore and increases as the drawdown increases. The order of the principal effective stresses at the well bore is

$$\sigma_{\theta\theta} = \sigma_{zz} > \sigma_{rr}. \qquad (17b)$$

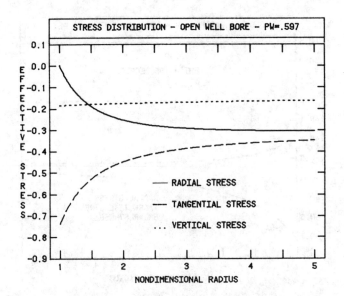

Figure 1. Open well bore: radial variation of the effective stress

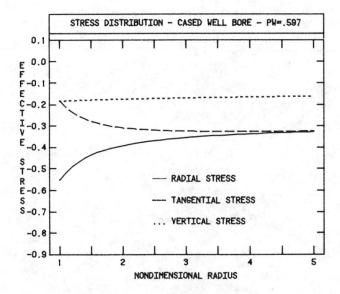

Figure 2. Cased well bore: radial variation of the effective stress

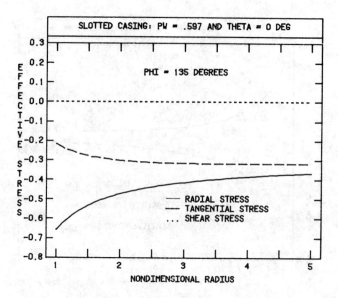

Figure 3. Slotted casing: radial variation of the effective stress along the line θ=0.

11 NUMERICAL EXAMPLE OF THE ELASTIC STRESS DISTRIBUTION AROUND A PARTIALLY SUPPORTED WELL BORE

The solution derived in Section 9 for the elastic stresses in rock around a slotted casing may be illustrated with the particular example

$$\frac{\sigma_\infty}{P_\infty} = \frac{1}{10} \tag{18a}$$

$$\frac{\hat{Q}}{P_\infty} = \frac{1}{50} \tag{18b}$$

$$\alpha = 1 \tag{18c}$$

$$\nu = .25 \tag{18d}$$

$$\phi = \frac{3\pi}{4} \tag{18e}$$

$$\hat{X} = 2P_w R\sin(\pi - \phi) \tag{18f}$$

at a well pressure

$$\frac{P_w}{P_\infty} = .597. \tag{18g}$$

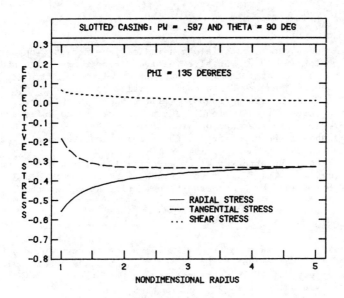

Figure 4. Slotted casing: radial variation of the effective stress along the line θ=π/2.

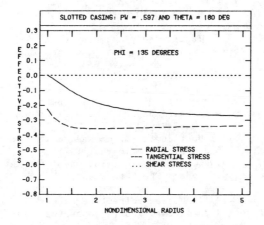

Figure 5. Slotted casing: radial variation of the effective stress along the line θ=π.

Radial, tangential, and shearing stresses are shown as a function of the nondimensional radius

$$\rho = \frac{r}{R} \qquad (19a)$$

along the radial lines

$$\theta = 0, \frac{\pi}{2} \text{ and } \pi. \tag{19b}$$

Figure 3 shows the stresses along a radial line directly opposite the casing slot ($\theta = 0$). Radial effective stresses are large and compressive as in the case of a fully supported well bore.

Figure 4 shows the stresses along a radial line closer to the slot ($\theta = \pi/2$). With the casing support still present in this area, the form of the stress distribution is again similar to the fully supported case. However, note the introduction of large shearing stresses near the casing due to the asymmetry of the problem and the bonding of the rock to the casing surface.

Figure 5 shows the stresses along a radial line through the center of the slot ($\theta = \pi$). The form of the stress distribution is similar to the open well bore case, with zero radial effective stress at the slot.

12 CONCLUSION

Qualitatively the results of the mixed boundary value problem are as expected. The analysis of the slotted casing problem provides insight as to the effects of casing perforations on the stress distribution in rock near a producing well bore.

REFERENCES

Dake, L.P. 1978. Fundamentals of reservoir engineering. New York: Elsevier Scientific Publishing Company.

England, A.H. 1971. Complex variable methods in elasticity. New York: John Wiley and Sons, Inc.

Fahrenthold, E.P. 1984. Elastic and plastic stresses in a porous medium containing spherical or cylindrical cavities. PhD Thesis, Rice University.

Green, A.E.& W. Zerna, 1968. Theoretical elasticity. Oxford: Oxford University Press.

Lubinski, A. 1954. The theory of elasticity for porous bodies displaying a strong pore structure. Proc. Second U.S. National Congress of Applied Mechanics. ASME: 247-256.

Malvern, L.E. 1969. Introduction to the mechanics of a continuous medium. Englewood Cliffs, New Jersey: Prentice-Hall, Inc.

Mushkhelishvili, N.I. 1975. Some basic problems of the mathematical theory of elasticity. Leyden, The Netherlands: Noordhoff International Publishing.

Nur, A.& J. Byerlee. 1971. An exact effective stress law for elastic deformation of rock with fluids. Jour. geophysical research. 76(No.26): 6414-6419.

Rice, J.R.& M.P. Cleary. 1976. Some basic stress diffusion solutions for fluid-saturated elastic porous media with compressible constituents. Review of geophysics and space physics. 14(No.2):227-241.

Timoshenko, S.P.& J.N. Goodier. 1970. Theory of elasticity. New York: McGraw-Hill Book Co.

Detection of yield and rupture of underground openings by displacement monitoring

S.M.MALONEY & P.K.KAISER
University of Alberta, Edmonton, Canada

ABSTRACT

A series of laboratory tests on small circular openings were conducted on a naturally jointed material to establish the limitations of current underground monitoring techniques in evaluating the stability of openings in overstressed ground. The rate of convergence was found to be a suitable indicator for the detection of instability modes of underground openings but radial strain measurements by extensometers were required to identify the actual failure process, its location, extent and direction of propagation. As the convergence rate measured during excavation is a function of both the time-dependent rock mass properties and the rate of tunnel advance, separation of these two effects is required prior to stability assessment. Expressions allowing such a separation were developed and verified during testing. The significance of these findings with respect to current monitoring techniques is also discussed.

1 INTRODUCTION

The observational approach to tunnelling is becoming more popular because major benefits in terms of cost savings and increased safety can be achieved. For underground excavations in soil or rock and regardless of their intended use, monitoring is required to evaluate ground and support performance. Monitoring techniques are employed for a variety of reasons of which the assessment of opening stability and the verification of the assumed mode of opening behaviour, elastic, yielding, unstable rupture, etc., are paramount. Unfortunately, field monitoring alone is not sufficient for the development of a reliable predictive capability. A consistent framework for the interpretation of the measurements must exist and needs to be verified by monitoring. In the field, a multitude of variables influencing opening performance complicate analyses. Controlled environmental conditions are essential for the development of rational evaluation techniques. One means by which this may be achieved is the simulation of field conditions in laboratory scale models.

In such tests, the response of an excavation to pre-determined stimuli may be observed and a clearer picture of the overall behaviour of underground excavations may emerge. When coupled with observation techniques that correspond with those normally used in the field, back analysis techniques can be developed and verified. This paper reports on a laboratory investigation wherein attention was focused on the evaluation of opening stability by deformation monitoring and on the response of instrumentation to tunnel advance activity.

Detailed descriptions of the test facility and typical results have been presented by Kaiser and Morgenstern (1981a,b). This test facility was developed for physical modelling of the time-dependent processes controlling the behaviour of underground openings. Samples (600x600x200 mm) of a naturally jointed, heterogeneous rock mass (coal) were instrumented with radial extensometers installed in every 45° sector of two concentric rings. After tunnel excavation, the convergence of the tunnel walls along four diameters (parallel and perpendicular to the major joint set and parallel to the applied stresses) were measured by convergence gauges inside the tunnel. The behaviour of circular tunnels before and during yield; and during rupture propagation processes was described by Kaiser & Morgenstern (1982) and Kaiser et al. (1985).

The samples prior to tunnel excavation were loaded both uniformly and non-uniformly (with unequal lateral pressure) to determine the time-independent and time-dependent rock mass properties. Two loading paths were followed in the course of the investigation:
  1. External loading - the sample containing a pre-existing, unsupported, circular tunnel was loaded; and
  2. Excavation simulation - a circular tunnel was excavated and subsequently widened in a pre-stressed sample.
Only the latter loading path reflects the actual conditions underground.

It is the objective of the selected test results presented in the following to establish the limitations of current underground monitoring techniques, particularly convergence measurements, for the assessment of the stability of underground openings in overstressed ground.

2 PRESENTATION AND INTERPRETATION OF TEST RESULTS

2.1 Identification of Zones of Overstressed Rock

The material property distribution within a coal sample is very non-uniform (Kaiser and Maloney, 1982). As a result of spatial variations, the strain recorded locally by extensometers varies widely. The range of extensometer response recorded under uniform loading of an intact specimen is presented in Figure 1 for a typical sample (MC-7). Three stress-strain curves are shown as representative examples of extreme and average behaviour. Similar variations, possibly to a somewhat lesser extent, must be expected in the field. Observed strains are much in excess of those predicted using an average value of Young's modulus E = 1.5 GPa and Poisson's ratio of 0.23 (Kaiser et al., 1983a) of 0.46% at 10 MPa field stress. The principal cause for the additional deformation must be attributed to the extreme non-linearity of the stress-strain relationship at low stresses (due to crack closure under load application or crack opening under stress relaxation). From a detailed investigation of the extensometer response, it became evident that strains and displacements strongly depend on local material properties, stress level and orientation with respect to intersecting discontinuities. The detection of abnormal behaviour from strain measurements recorded by extensometers is, both in the tests and in the field, complicated by these influences.

The total accumulated ground displacement or radial strain can seldom be determined in the field due to the impracticality of placing instrumentation ahead of the face or the limited access to the face during tunnel advance. Hence, it was found beneficial to use the rate rather than the magnitude of deformation as an indicator of tunnel or ground performance (Cording et al., 1975; John, 1977; Lane, 1977). For this reason, the following interpretation of test results relies on the time-dependent observations presented in double logarithmic plots of deformation or strain rate versus time.

The time-dependent response of an opening in a rock mass depends, to a large extent, on the intensity of the applied load. At low stress levels, terminating (primary) creep will lead to a finite creep strain whereas at high stress levels a transition from primary to tertiary creep with increasing creep rates leading to yielding or propagation of a rupture zone will be observed. In actual tunnelling situations, initiation of yielding will not necessarily lead to collapse (rupture) of the opening wall but to a change in the rate of deformation due to a change in the rock mass structure and hence, its deformation properties and support capacity. It would therefore seem likely that there are strain rate boundaries separating the various modes of behaviour. Three such creep rate functions have been selected to delineate typical modes of tunnel behaviour (Kaiser et al., 1983b):

1. Critical creep rate CCR(t) - creep rate below which only steadily decelerating creep and no yielding occurs;
2. Post-yield creep rate PCR(t) - creep rate reached after propagation of a yield zone has terminated; and
3. Unstable propagation rate UPR(t) - creep rate indicative of unstable propagation where no stable equilibrium can be reached (typical for near surface openings or tunnels in cohesionless materials).

Appropriate CCR and PCR functions for the test material were determined from the closure rates recorded during an external loading test conducted by Guenot (1979) and are presented in Figure 2. A linear CCR(t) was chosen to follow the upper limit of the creep curves (shaded region) at stress levels where no yielding could be identified. The PCR(t) was assumed to be parallel to the CCR(t) and was drawn touching the highest rates measured during the test at 14 MPa when stable yield zone propagation was observed. The UPR(t) could not be accurately located as no tests leading to collapse were executed. Comparison of closure rates measured during external loading tests and excavation simulation tests (Sample MC-7; Maloney, 1984) indicates that these functions are applicable to both situations. Similar creep rate functions were developed for the radial strain rate based on the assumption that the ratio of the radial strain rate function to the tunnel closure rate function would correspond to the ratio of the elastic radial strain to the elastic tunnel closure. Global radial strain rate functions, however, are much more difficult to apply because of the dependence of radial strain on local material properties.

A total of five excavation simulation tests on two specimens, Samples MC-6 and MC-7, were performed to evaluate the behaviour of the tunnel during face advance. The deformation processes involved could only be determined from extensometer measurements because tunnel convergence could not be recorded during excavation.

Figure 3 presents the extensometer response during the excavation of a 108 mm diameter tunnel in Sample MC-6. Immediately apparent is the large variation in strain development. The majority of extensometers (12 of 16) respond in a similar manner (shaded area) while the remaining extensometers display anomalous behaviour. The response of the instrument located in the outer ring (#9) can be related to a local zone of higher stiffness while the others are related to yield processes. Similar conclusions can be drawn from Figure 4 where the creep rates during and after excavation are presented. Tunnel closure rates (inset) show that propagation of a yield zone, approximately perpendicular to the major joint set as indicated by the extensometers, continued to the end of the test at 25 hours. Initially the closure rate parallel to the major joint set (Orientation C) did not exceed the CCR(t), however, after 9 hours of creep the rate in this orientation experienced a sudden jump to the rate recorded by the other gauges, close to PCR function.

Of particular interest in Figure 4 is the shape of the radial strain rate versus time curve. Initially the strain rate is dominated by the change in stress field due to the face advance (up to t = 0.27 hrs). Later, it is controlled by the creep of the rock and stress redistribution due to yield propagation. This is further demonstrated in Figure 5 (during widening of the tunnel to 152 mm diameter) where interruptiions in the excavation sequence are clearly indicated by rapid drops in strain rate approaching the long term creep rate curve. During field monitoring the tunnel closure and strain rate curves would show similar behaviour. This must be considered when applying closure rate criteria to assess opening performance. It is necessary to separate the effects of face advance (see Section 2.2) and time-dependent rock deformation on the deformation rate (Panet and Guenot, 1982; see also contribution by Panet, Guenot and Sulem to this conference).

Figures 6 and 7 present the radial strain and tunnel closure rates recorded behind the face during the tunnel widenings performed on

Sample MC-7. Yielding near this excavation was of a very localized nature as only Extensometer 6 displayed anomalous behaviour. According to the strain rate criterion, a yield zone beginning at approximately 9 hours continued to propagate throughout this test and throughout the subsequent widening test. This propagation of a very localized yield zone was not detected by tunnel closure measurements. They suggested that yielding had occurred (rates exceeded the CCR) but give no indication of yield zone propagation, particularly in Test MC-7.13 (Figure 7) where the PCR is not reached. This suggests that the rate criteria may require some adjustment for this particular sample. Furthermore, not all tunnel closure rates exceeded the CCR in these two tests. This demonstrates the need for multi-directional tunnel closure measurments if convergence gauges are to be used for safety evaluation.

The closure rate criteria presented in Figure 2 generally proved successful in the assessment of opening stability, however, they provided no insight into the yield process, its location, extent and direction of propagation. Extensometers or multiple convergence gauges are needed to localize yield zones. This is further evidenced by Figure 8 where the development of yield zones, as determined from extensometer measurements (shaded areas), is contrasted with the measured tunnel closure (convergence normalized to the convergence predicted by linear elasticity). In Test No. 5.05 for instance, the maximum closure is approximately perpendicular to the yield zone whereas in Tests No. 5.10 and 5.11, it is almost parallel to it. Also, in Sample MC-6 a gradual propagation and change in shape of the yield zone is reflected by little change in the magnitude of tunnel convergence but a significant reorientation of the direction of major and minor convergence. This illustrates well that convergence measurments do not clearly reflect the mode of tunnel behaviour or yield zone propagation.

2.2 Near Tunnel Face Behaviour

Expressions for both the radial strain and tunnel closure rates due to face advance alone were developed by Kaiser et al. (1983a) based on earlier work by Panet and Guenot (1982). These expressions are applicable to the region behind the tunnel face. In a linearly elastic medium the rates are given as follows:

$$\epsilon'(t) = \frac{2\,u(\infty)\,d'}{k r^2} \left[\frac{ka}{ka + d't} \right]^3 \qquad \dots\dots\dots 1$$

$$u'(t) = \frac{-2\,u(\infty)\,d'}{ka} \left[\frac{ka}{ka + d't} \right]^3 \qquad \dots\dots\dots 2$$

where

$\epsilon'(t)$ = radial strain rate at time t;

$u'(t)$ = tunnel closure rate at time t;

d' = rate of tunnel advance;

k = 0.84 (found by curve fitting);

a = tunnel radius;

r = radial distance to point of measurement; and

$u(\infty)$ = ultimate elastic tunnel wall convergence (i.e., the difference between the convergence recorded when the face is at the measuring station and when the face is at an infinite distance from the station. During widening the differential tunnel convergence is substituted).

The predicted strain rates due to face advance alone are shown on Figures 6 and 7 as dashed lines. Given the variability in strain response due to material heterogeneity it must be concluded that the strain rate resulting

960

from the advance of the tunnel face is accurately represented by the above expressions.

The development of radial strain during the excavation and subsequent widenings of a tunnel in a pre-stressed sample (MC-7) are presented in Figure 9. Strains have been normalized to the value at the end of tunnel excavation or widening. In this manner, the significant variation in strain magnitude which was observed during these tests will not dominate.

There is a considerable degree of non-uniformity in the pattern of strain development. During the excavation of the 42 mm diameter tunnel (Figure 9a), Extensometers 7 and 8 were experiencing an increase in compressive strain at the time of face arrival, whereas the others were undergoing extensional straining as expected (Extensometer 2 showed no response to the tunnelling activity and has not been included in this figure). All extensometers had recorded varying degrees of compressional strain ahead of the face (from 4 to 68% of the extensional strain) reflecting the 3-dimensional nature of the response in the near face zone. At the time of face arrival up to 38% of the total extensional strain had occurred (Extensometers 1 and 5). During subsequent widenings (to 108 mm, Figure 9b, and to 152 mm, Figure 9c) the percentage of straining ahead of the face increased to 35.8% (range of 17 to 54%) and 60.9% on average (range of 29 to 79%), respectively. This is more clearly shown in Figure 10 where the range of strain (normalized as before) is plotted as a function of the distance behind the tunnel face together with the predicted curve (Eqn. 1) for linear elastic ground.

The increase in strain development ahead of the face results from overstressing of the already weakened rock cylinder to be excavated during the subsequent widening. This process, in addition to yielding of the tunnel walls ahead of the face, effectively shifts the tunnel deformation ahead of the face. In a real tunnelling situation, proportionally less loading of the tunnel support would occur during widening than during the opening of a pilot because more displacement would have dissipated at the point of support installation.

CONCLUSIONS

The response of a given monitoring system to an induced stress change is often compared to predictions made by relatively simple continuum models that seldom reflect the heterogeneous nature of a jointed rock mass. The variation in instrument response in such a material was found to be dominant rendering impractical the application of a universal displacement criterion. The test results presented demonstrate, however, that judgement can be based on an indicator of change in behaviour that considers the rate of deformation at a given location. Modes of instability like rock mass yielding are associated with significant changes in deformational behaviour during the yield initiation and rupture propagation phases. The deviation from a critical deformation rate was found to be a successful measure for stability evaluation.

In practice, the problem of determining site specific closure rate functions remains to be solved. However, by regular monitoring of rates in stable, intermediate and unstable sections of an opening, one should be able to determine appropriate values. These must, however, be related to the construction and support installation history.

As the convergence rate measured during tunnelling is a function of both the rate of tunnel advance and the time-dependent rock mass properties, separation of these components is necessary before comparison with the design criteria. Expressions developed by Kaiser et al. (1983a) have been used successfully to separate the two closure rate components and are recommended for verification on case histories.

Closure rates in excess of the closure rate functions, while indicating processes of rock overstressing, were found to be insensitive to the extent and shape of the deformation field around the excavation. The non-axisymmetric nature of the yield process, even under a uniform stress field, was not always readily identifiable from the convergence records. Measurements of radial strain are necessary to delineate the location and extent of the yielding or softening zone. Furthermore, tunnel closure rates or radial strain must be recorded in several directions and regularly to ensure correct interpretation of the mode of abnormal behaviour.

These conclusions must be respected when designing the instrumentation layout for a monitoring system to evaluate the safety of an underground opening or for the verification of assumed design models. In both cases, it is of foremost importance to establish the failure mechanism or mode of behaviour. Too much effort is expended in back analysis techniques that assume a mode of behaviour rather than in the verification of the assumed mode. The test results show that it is often necessary to use the instrumentation to delineate zones of yielding and rupture before it is possible to evaluate the observed tunnel convergence records.

ACKNOWLEDGEMENTS

Financial support for this project through the Alberta-Canada Energy Resources Research Fund, a joint program of the Federal and Alberta governments and administered by Alberta Energy and Natural Resources, is gratefully acknowledged.

REFERENCES

Cording, E.J., Hendron, A.J., Hansmire, W.H., et al. 1975. Methods of geotechnical observation and instrumentation in tunnelling. Report for National Sciences Foundation. 2 volumes, 566p.

Guenot, A. 1979. Investigation of Tunnel Stability by Model Tests. M.Sc. thesis, Department of Civil Engineering, University of Alberta, 217p.

John, M. 1977. Adjustment of program of measurements based on the results of current evaluation. International Symposium on Field Measurements in Rock Mechanics, Vol. 2, p.639-656.

Kaiser, P.K. & Maloney, S.M. 1982. Deformation properties of a subbituminous coal mass. International Journal of Rock Mechanics and Mining Sciences & Geomechanics Abstracts, Vol. 19, p.247-252.

Kaiser, P.K. & Morgenstern, N.R. 1981a. Time-dependent deformation of small tunnels - I. Experimental facilities. International Journal of Rock Mechanics and Mining Sciences & Geomechanics Abstracts, Vol. 18, p. 129-140.

Kaiser, P.K. and Morgenstern, N.R., 1981b. Time-dependent deformation of small tunnels - II. Typical test data. International Journal of Rock Mechanics and Mining Sciences & Geomechanics Abstracts, Vol. 18; p. 141-152.

Kaiser, P.K. & Morgenstern, N.R. 1982. Time-independent and time-dependent deformation of small tunnels - III. Prefailure behaviour. International Journal of Rock Mechanics and Mining Sciences & Geomechanics Abstracts, Vol. 19, p. 307-324.

Kaiser, P.K., Maloney, S.M. & Morgenstern, N.R. 1983a. Support Design for Underground Cavities in Weak Rock. Part III, Energy Resources Research Fund, Contract U-80-3, 179p.

Kaiser, P.K., Maloney, S.M. & Morgenstern, N.R. 1983b. Time-dependent behaviour of tunnels in highly stressed rock. 5th International Congress on Rock Mechanics, Melbourne, pp. D329-336.

Kaiser, P.K., Guenot, A. & Morgenstern, N.R. 1985. Deformation of small tunnels - IV. Behaviour during failure. International Journal of Rock Mechanics and Mining Sciences & Geomechanics Abstracts (in press).

Lane, K.S. 1977. Instrumented tunnel tests: A key to progress and cost saving. Underground Space, Vol. 1, No. 3, p. 247-259.

Maloney, S.M., 1984. An Assessment of Deformation Monitoring Practice in Underground Excavations in Weak Rock by Model Tests. M.Sc. thesis, Department of Civil Engineering, University of Alberta, 282p.

Panet, M. & Guenot, A. 1982. Analysis of convergence behind the face of a tunnel. Tunnelling '82, The Institution of Mining and Metallurgy, p. 197-204.

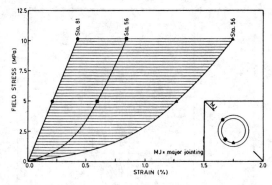

Figure 1 Variation in extensometer response during loading of intact specimen to 10 MPa — Test MC-7.02

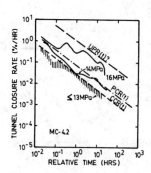

Figure 2 Typical tunnel closure rates during Test MC-4.2

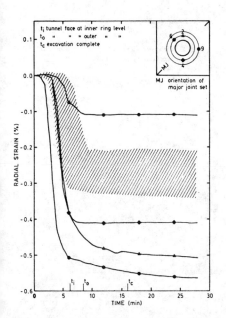

Figure 3 Development of radial strain — 108 mm tunnel excavation, Test MC-6.02

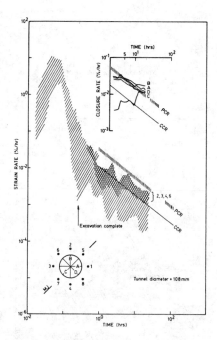

Figure 4 Measured radial strain and tunnel closure rates during 108 mm tunnel excavation Test MC-6.02

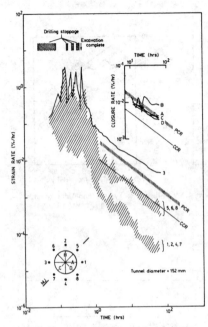

Figure 5   Measured radial strain and tunnel closure
rates during widening to 152 mm — Test
MC-6.05

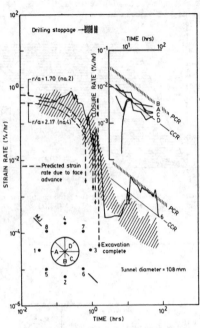

Figure 6   Measured radial strain and tunnel closure
rates during widening to 108 mm — Test
MC-7.10

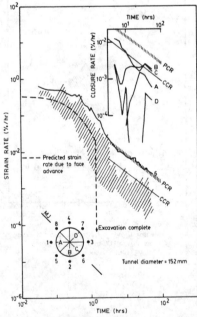

Figure 7   Measured radial strain and tunnel closure
rates during widening to 152 mm — Test
MC-7.13

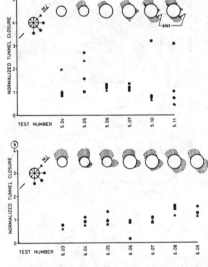

Figure 8   Development of yield zones and corresponding
tunnel convergence (normalized to the convergence in a linearly elastic material) — Samples
MC-5 and MC-6

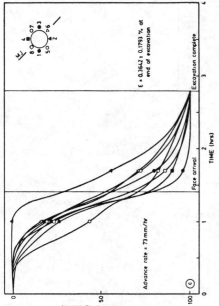

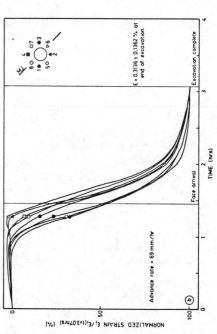

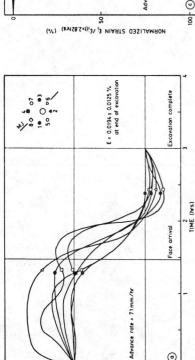

Figure 9 Development of radial strain around the opening a) Excavation of 42 mm tunnel — Test MC-7.08; b) Widening to 108 mm — Test MC-7.10; and c) Widening to 152 mm — Test MC-7.13

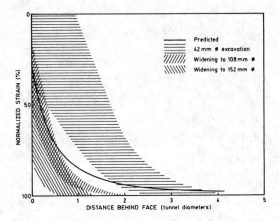

Figure 10 Comparison of the measured development of radial strain
with that predicted for a linearly elastic material

966

Geostatistical approach to roof fall prediction

T.CYRUL
Strata Mechanics Research Institute, Polish Academy of Sciences, Krakow, Poland
KOT F.UNRUG
University of Kentucky, Lexington, USA

1 INTRODUCTION

Roof falls are among the most costly and dangerous phenomena confronting the U.S. underground mining industry. To date, a number of theories have been developed that address roof behavior, most of which are of the deterministic type (Wright 1973).

The number of factors effecting roof behavior, as well as the complexity, is the reason that the deterministic approach to roof behaviour evaluation is very often far from reality.

It is obvious that when dealing with roof behaviour we cannot overcome the scale effect. The mechanical properties of rocks, which play a decisive role in the deterministic models of roof behaviour, besides their local variability, exhibit very quantitative and qualitative differences over large areas subjected to mining. Frequently, of even more importance are unexpected variabilities of geological factors (stratification, discontinuities, zones of weakness, etc.) which may have a very irregular spatial distribution. Moreover, the geometry of mining excavations that extend over large areas and are usually not regular, contribute substantially to the complexity of the roof behaviour.

To deal with such variable conditions effectively, in the deterministic sense, one must analyze each mining structure (intersection, pillar, etc.) individually. This of course is unacceptable. In practice, the deterministic model of a given phenomenon, with the input data collected from a few locations, is extended over a large area uniformizing the real conditions. As a result of such a procedure, unrealistic discrepancies of the investigated feature occur, both in a quantitative and qualitative sense.

An alternative to the deterministic models, which must be verified by measurements, is monitoring, which seems to be the only alternative to control and predict behaviour of mining structures. However, the measurement data, due to the above-mentioned conditions, are usually very scattered both in time and distance, ultimately causing frustration of those mining engineers thinking in the deterministic mode. Thus, a conclusion arises, that we can mush easily sense to complex reality that we can deal with it in engineering practice. Therefore, there is a constant need for new approaches which may contribute to improvement of efficiency of dealing with mining problems.

In this paper, a new approach to characterization of roof behavior is presented. No assumptions concerning rocks and roof conditions are made, except for the assumption that the measuring equipment perform properly.

The approach is based on monitoring of the roof behavior established by measurements extended over a large area. The quantities to be measured may be of different types (for example: torque, sag, strata separation, load carried by roof bolts, etc.). The original of the approach is the geostatistical method of the data evaluation which exposes the spatial variability of the real roof conditions.

Due to very limited space, the principles of geostatistics will not be discussed. Instead, we recommend the fundamental references on the subject (Matheron 1963), (Matheron 1971), (David 1977), (Journel & Huijbregts 1978).

Because geostatistics originate from ore reserve estimations, in the references, objects that are investigated are assays or grades. To the best knowledge of the authors, geostatistics has not yet been applied to rock mechanics, therefore the term "grade" when used in the literature can be replaced by thickness, bolt load, porosity, etc.

2 THEORY

After mining excavation is performed, the roof rocks tend to deform into the excavation. Stiffness of the strata, as well as the stress field, determine the magnitude of derformation.

The most common underground coal mining opening is an entry which is supported by roof bolts, Fig. 1.

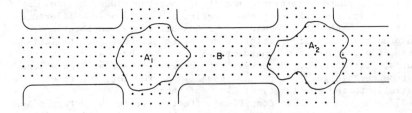

Figure 1. Scheme of the creation of roof falls at intersections.

It is assumed that the roof bolts perform perfectly, i.e., any changes in roof behaviour will affect the load carried by the bolts subjected to the change. According to the statistics of roof falls, falls occur most frequently at intersections.

Let us, therefore, imagine a sequence of intersection along the entry, as shown in Figure 1. Let us further assume that the roof falls are going to occur at the intersections. The roof falls are localized by the closed lines which surround both regions, A, of rocks equivalent to the size of the roof falls.

Roof falls usually occur suddenly; however, they very rarely occur immediately after execution of the excavation. Thus, roof falls are preceded by certain processes in the roof. There is very little known about the mechanism of this process, but in the proposed approach it is not necessary to know much about it to preduct the changes that are occurring in the roof. Assuming that each roof bolt is a monitoring device, the readings from the bolts within region A of Fig. 1 should differ on the

average from those in region B. By employing classical statistics, we
can evaluate these differences by analysing the distribution of readings
taken in region A, region B, or in both together. As a measure of the
differences in readings, statistics offer a variance, which has the form

$$V = \frac{1}{N} \sum_{i=1}^{N} (\overline{L} - L_i)^2 \tag{1}$$

where N - number of bolts taken into consideration
      L - the mean load
      L_i - an arbitrary reading

The variance and the distribution of readings do not contribute very
much to our understanding whether the roof fall is eminant or not, since
the variance does not consider localization of the bolts, and consequently does not expose the spatial variability of the bolts load.

Rock structure can be characterized by the spatial distribution of a
certain number of measurable quantities called "regionalized variables".
The load carried by the roof bolts is an example of the regionalized
variable l(x) in horizontal space.

Geostatistical theory is based on the observation that the variabilities of all regionalized variables have a praticular structure. The indications, l(x) and l(x+h), from the bolts at points x and x+h are auto-
correlated depending on the vector h (in modulus and direction) which
separates the two points, and on the load considered.

Direct study of the mathematical function l(x) in impractical because
of its high spatial variability. Moreover, the spatial autocorrelation
between two neighbouring values, l(x) and l(x+h), makes it unacceptable
to assume that all the numerical values, l(x), l(x'), as independent
realizations of the same randome variable L. Therefore, the concept of
random function has been utilized in geostatistics to express the random
variables, $L(x_i)$, defined at each point, x_i, of the region, R. The
random variables, $L(x_i)$, are correlated and this correlation depends both
on the vector h separating two points, x and x+h, and the nature of the
variable itself.

At any point, x_i, the true load, $l(x_i)$, is considered as one particular
realization of the random variable, $L(x_i)$, over the region R (for example,
deposit, section of an entry, etc.). Similarly, the set of the load
indications, $[l(x_i), \forall\, x \in R]$, defining roof conditions in region, R, is
considered as one particular realization of the random function, $[L(x_i),
\forall\, x \in R]$.

Geostatistics has been successfully used in solving a variety of practical problems. Depending on the problem, certain restrictions are
introduced which create a set of geostatistical tools enabling analysis
of the spatially scattered quantities. One of the most powerful tools
of geostatistics is variogram, which is defined as the expectation of the
random variable, $[L(x)-L(x+h)]^2$, i.e.,

$$2\gamma(x,h) = E\{[L(x) - L(x+h)]^2\} \tag{2}$$

To overcome serios problems, the intrinsic hypothesis is used in many
practical applications. The hypothesis makes it possible to calculate
an estimator of the function, $2\gamma(x,h)$, from the available measurement
data. The estimator, $2\gamma^*(h)$, is the arithmetic mean of the squared
differences between two experimental measures, $[l(x_i+h)$, or any two
points separated by the vector h; i.e.,

$$2\gamma^*(h) = \frac{1}{N(h)} \sum_{i=1}^{N(h)} [\ell(x_i) - \ell(x_i + h)]^2 \qquad (3)$$

where $N(h)$ is the number of experimental pairs of bolt indications separated by the vector h. Because $2\gamma^*(h)$ is a function of vector h, it is possible to calculate the variogram in different directions. Differences in the variograms shapes in different directions allow for concluding anisotropies of the phenomenon under consideration.

There are a number of variogram models which describe spatial distribution of different quantities and different shapes. While discussing our data we deal with one of them.

3 COLLECTION OF THE DATA

The data were collected in the Martin Co. Coal Company mine in the Eastern Kentucky. According to the above model of roof behaviour, we faced question of its verification. Because any field measurement program is very time and money consuming, at the beginning the roof bolt torque was chosen as a quantity to be measured. The authors realize that torque is a very unprecise method of measurement; however, its simplicity alows to collect a sufficient amount of data with very litle effort.

The torque was measured along four lines, L1, L2, L3, L4, as shown in Fig. 2. Lines L1 and L2 were mutually parallel and had a total length of 87.6m each, containing 73 bolts 1.2m apart. Lines L3 and L4, mutually parallel,

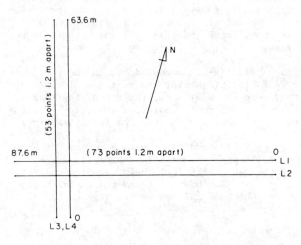

Figure 2. Configuration of the lines along with
the torque was measured.

were almost perpendicular to L1 and L2. Each of the measurement lines were extended over several intersections and breaks between the. Fig. 3 shows the fragment of the mine in which the measurements were performed. The measurement lines are shown in the entries.

970

Figure 3. Fragment of the field situation.

4 DISCUSSION OF THE DATA

To solve many practical problems using geostatistics, many computations
are usually involved. Some problems involve serious questions of
sampling, computations of one-directional and multidirectional variograms,
fitting models, estimation, etc. In this paper only one of these
procedures will be discussed, namely: unidirectional variogram. The
data that have been collected show a certain spatial structure and
the variograms show visible regularity which cannot be accidental.

Let us, however, start with Fig. 4, in which the row data are presented. The absolute values of the torque are shown on the vertical
axis, and the consecutive number of bolts along lime L1, are indicated
on the horizontal. The Scatter of the data is substantial; however,
a certain tendency of the scatter is also visible.

The histogram of the data collected along line L1 is shown in Fig. 5.
The histogram is almost symmetrical, and except for a few peaks, is very
flat. The most frequent magnitude of the torque is similar to the mean
value. There are a few more lower magnitures of torque than the mean
value, which cause a slight positive skewness.

In Fig. 6, the variogram of the data along line L1 is presented. The
boxes and the breakes between them in the bottom part of each variogram
refer to pillars and breaks in the reality. They are presented to scale.
The variogram at the top of the figure taken into consideration all data
along line L1, and is very reliable due to the large number of pairs prescribed to each point of the variogram. It shows regular oscillations
of the variogram as a function of the distance, h. The amplitude of the
oscillations indicates spatial structure of the load carrie by the bolts
along line L1. In geostatistics, the so-called hole-effect models are
prescribed to this kind of spatial variability. One should notice that
the extrema of the experimental variogram fit very well to the geometry
of mining excavations (pillars and intersections). To expose this coin-

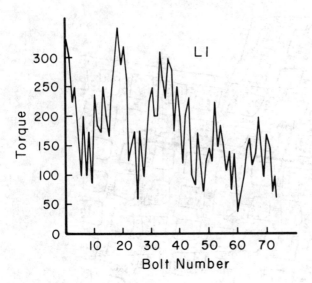

Figure 4. Bolt load distribution along line Ll

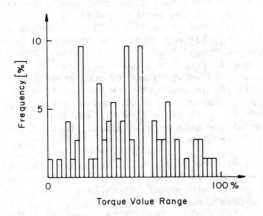

Figure 5. Histogram of the readings along line Ll

cidence, the variograms for shorter sections of line Ll are also presented. They are less reliable due to the fever number of pairs taken for
calculations; however, with a change of scale of the distance, the hole
effect and its matching with the geometry of intersections and pillars
is more pronounced than in the upper graph.

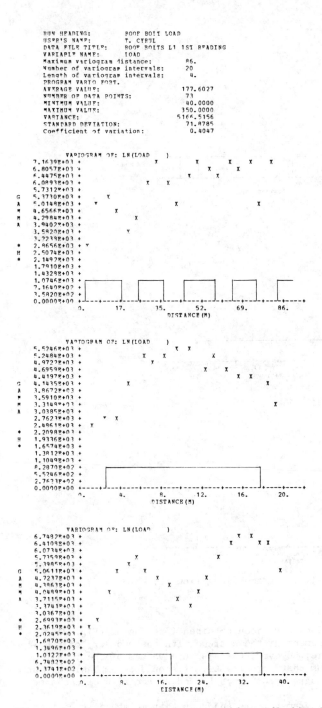

Figure 6. Experimental variograms along the line L1

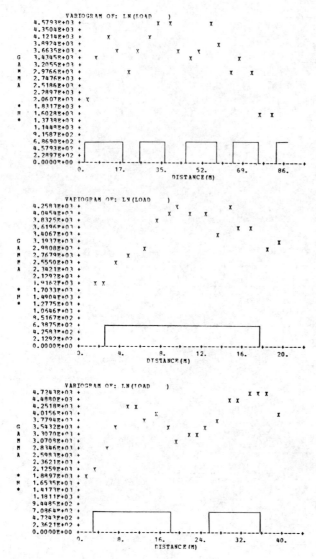

Figure 7. Experimental variograms along line L2.

Very similar relations have been obtained for line L2 (Fig. 7). The oscillations and agreement of the extreme with the geometry of the intersections is visible; however, the absolute values of the variogram amplitudes idffer from that for line L1. It should be emphasized that the experimental variograms for lines L3 and L4 are also of the same type.

Looking at the variograms, it is apparent that in the part of the observation line corresponding to the intersections, a minimum vari-

974

ance is observed. The full physical explanation of this phenomenon is not possible at this stage of the research being done, because the amount of data gathered are not sufficient to draw a firm conclusion. It should be pointed out that grades of minerals in a given volume which are the object of statistical analysis in ore reserve evaluation have unique physical interpretation. Rock mechanics phenomena, inspite of the lack of experience in geostatistical analysis in this area, seem to be more complex, mainly due to the fact that the process of data collection is subjected to a number of unknown factors.

In our case, the mine roof in the entire area was composed of massive sandstone with no history of roof problems. This part of the mine is also fairly new and the measurements were performed approximately one year after the bolts had been installed. The bolts were 1.5m long with mechanical anchors. Overall roof conditions can be considered good and uniform over the site area. The variograms are very regular and fit the geometry of the excavations, suggesting that the uniform roof conditions which originate from the personal judgement are not supported by the measurements. In the roof, there exist spatial variability of conditions which affect the load carried by the bolts. This spatial variability is visible in terms of absolute values of the load (Fig. 4), and the spatial correlations (variograms). A few of the variograms taken at intersections indicate that within intersections conditions affecting bolt load are more uniform than between them. It is possible that the bending moment in the roof strata within the intersections is larger, producing more tension on the bolts, while at the same time diminishing scatter of the tensions originating from the installation and random bleeding of the bolts.

5 CONCLUSIONS

The first application of geostatistics to the analysis of roof conditions seems to be successful and promising. Not clear physical interpretation of the variograms should not be exaggerated, causing skepticism for further applications of geostatistics to rock mechanics. Clear qualitative relations of the variograms and the site geometry should encourage further studies to widen the applications of geostatics.

REFERENCES

David, M., 1977. Geostatistical ore reserve estimation. Elsevier.
Matheron, G., 1963. Principles of geostatistics. Economic Geology. 50: 1246-1266.
Matheron, G., 1971. The theory of regionalized variables and its applications. Les Cashierdu Centre de Morpholigie Mathematique, Fasc.5, CG Fontainebleau.
Journel, A.G. & Huijbregts, Ch.J. 1978. Mining geostatics,.Academic Press.
Wright, F.D., 1973. Roof control through beam action and arching. SME Mining Engineering Handbook, Vol.1; 13.7.

Mine subsidence hazard detection technique for Pennsylvania's anthracite coalfields

SWAPAN BHATTACHARYA & MADAN M.SINGH
Engineers International Inc., Westmont, Illinois, USA

NOEL M.MOEBS
US Bureau of Mines, Pittsburgh, Pennsylvania, USA

1 INTRODUCTION

The anthracite coalfields of northeastern Pennsylvania have been extensively undermined for the past 200 years or more. Numerous instances of
surface subsidence effects due to the abandoned mines have been reported
and the threat continues.

Several subsidence control and mitigation measures have evolved in
recent years. Of these, one of the most effective methods involves the
backfilling or flushing of the mine voids with mine waste or other suitable material to support the overlying rock strata. However, due to the
excessive capital expenditure and the associated technical difficulties
in the implementation of these control techniques, their application
have been severely limited to small localized areas. It has, therefore,
become necessary to identify areas within the anthracite region that
have the potential for imminent subsidence activity. This would enable
the appropriate authorities and planners to direct their limited resources more efficiently toward the prevention or control of subsidence
damage.

This paper presents a methodology to screen potential sites in the
anthracite coalfields to determine which sites would be most appropriate
to monitor for impending subsidence activity, and provides an integrated
monitoring plan for subsidence detection using surface geophysical
techniques.

2 STUDY AREA

The study area comprises of the Northern Anthracite Field (NAF) located
in the northeast corner of the state and extending over the Lackawanna
and Luzerne Counties (Figure 1). The NAF is an elongated canoe-shaped
basin containing two major synclinal folds separated by a transverse
anticline. The bedrock in the basin is predominantly composed of sandstones, shales, conglomerates, and up to 18 mineable anthracite coal
seams, overlain by unconsolidated glacial and alluvial deposits. The
thickness of the coal beds range from a few mm (in.) to as much as 8 m
(27 ft), totaling nearly 30 m (100 ft) in aggregate thickness.

The mineable coal beds in the NAF have all been mined to various degrees; the predominant mining technique being room-and-pillar with hap-
hazard pillar "robbing." The deterioration of these mine structures
over time have led to numerous subsidence expressions at the surface

977

including land surface depressions as much as 60 m (200 ft) in diameter
and 27 m (90 ft) deep (Ash 1950). However, the situation is most critical where mining occurred within 30 m (100 ft) of the surface. An additional factor affecting subsidence is the presence of thick alluvium
which fills a deeply eroded paleo-channel of the Susquehanna River. The
erosion within the paleo-channel removed some of the suppporting roof
rock above the mines making these areas more prone to collapse.

The subsidence problems in the NAF have been accentuated by the considerable surface development and urbanization over most of the mined
out area. This aspect also serves as a deterrent to the application of
many subsidence monitoring options available today.

3 SITE SELECTION METHODOLOGY

Since extensive areas within the NAF are underlain by abandoned mine
workings and the potential for surface damage exists over the entire
area, a rational procedure for prioritizing monitoring sites is needed.
The proposed site selection methodology is based on the premise that
these sites should be located in areas characterized by high subsidence
risk. Subsidence risk (R_i) for an individual subsidence event i may be
expressed as:

$R_i = P_i \times C_i$ where
P_i = probability or likelihood of subsidence occurrence
C_i = consequence or impact of subsidence on surface features.

Obviously, given the uncertain nature of subsidence development and the
absence of rigorous analytical techniques for defining subsidence potential and impact, the subsidence risk for a given situation cannot be expressed in strict quantitative terms. Instead, it may be represented in
purely qualitative or semi-quantitative form using an empirical approach.
In this way, various sites within an extensively undermined area may be
ranked on the basis of the relative subsidence risks associated with
each site.

In the NAF, the major controlling factors in the evaluation of subsidence potential include the thickness and competency of overburden and
interburden, degree of extraction, mine pool elevation, surface drainage
characteristics, and the time period of mine abandonment. The consequence or impact of subsidence is dependent on the severity of the subsidence event and the degree of surface development. Due to the wide
range of subsidence severity observed in the NAF, its impact was assumed
to be solely a function of the surface development or the intrinsic
value of the affected area.

The flow chart in Figure 2 illustrates the logic of the proposed
methodology. Based on this methodology, high risk areas within the
anthracite fields were delineated and six potential monitoring sites
were selected.

4 SELECTION OF MONITORING SYSTEM

There is a wide range of tools and techniques available today that could
be used for the purpose of detecting incipient collapse; but none of the
methods have proved entirely successful, and all of them fail under
certain conditions. Consequently, the key to successful implementation
is to recognize that every investigation requires a tailored, site-
specific, systems approach, taking into consideration all the critical
variables characteristic to that application.

In this study, the most effective monitoring system was determined through a series of steps. The first step involved defining the type of mine subsidence problem. Evidence for mine subsidence is not always expressed at the ground surface and the evidence in the near surface can be very subtle. For the purposes of classification, we have grouped mine subsidence into four stages of development as shown in Figure 3. Of the four classes of subsidence shown, Classes II and III are of greatest interest in this study since these involve situations where ground instability has not manifested itself at the surface.

The second step was to define a range of monitoring methods potentially applicable to this study. More than 30 available methods were identified, covering a wide array of techniques and represented state-of-the-art experience.

The third step consisted of narrowing the range of all possible methods to those that are specifically applicable to the types of subsidence being considered in this study. This was achieved by evaluating the various techniques as to their potential for detecting subsidence within each of the scenarios of mine subsidence development identified in the first step (see Table 1). Airborne and subsurface techniques were eliminated due to the former's inability to detect localized subsidence and the latter's excessive cost and experimental nature. The narrowed list of techniques were evaluated against a set of selection criteria (Table 2) to determine their relative potential for the required application. For this purpose, a comprehensive "capabilities matrix" was developed encompassing all the above techniques and selection criteria. The matrix is not included here due to space limitations; the interested reader may refer to Bhattacharya and Singh (1985).

The final selection of the candidate monitoring system was based on the results of the above analysis and the subjective evaluation of specific geologic, hydrogeologic, mining, and cultural characteristics of the study area. Past experience has shown that reliance on a single method can lead to failure under certain circumstances. We therefore propose a range of techniques that both complement and supplement one another, and bring about an economical and technically optimum solution. The integrated monitoring plan consists of the following techniques in combination:

● ground penetrating radar (GPR)
● electromagnetics (EM)
● in situ displacement sensors (tiltmeters)

5 DESCRIPTION OF MONITORING SYSTEMS

Both GPR and EM techniques rely on the identification of near surface indicators (NSI) for the prediction of incipient collapse. NSI refers to subtle, near-surface changes in soil conditions which are caused by infiltration and subsidence over a deeper lying void. These indicators generally occur long before subsidence or collapse occurs and hence provide an early warning of impending instability. The use of NSI has been found extremely effective in past studies when used in conjunction with continuous sampling geophysical methods (Benson and LaFountain 1984). The principal types of NSI accompanying coal mine subsidence include soil piping, vegetation stresses, changes in electrical properties of soil, and microsubsidence.

GPR uses high frequency radio waves to acquire subsurface information. The radar signals are generated by an antenna and are radiated downward into the ground. The waves are reflected back by interfaces of materials

979

to receivers on the surface. This produces a continuous cross-sectional "picture" or profile of shallow subsurface conditions. Unlike most other techniques, GPR sensors are not required to be in physical contact with the earth. The transmitter and receiver can be simply pulled along the land surface. GPR offers the capability to provide the greatest resolution of subsurface details. Its usefulness is, however, dependent on the degree of radar penetration which is very site specific. Although radar may penetrate to a depth of 15 m (50 ft) or less, it has the ability to detect minute NSI due to its high resolution capability.

The EM method provides a means of measuring the electrical conductivity of subsurface materials, which provides information on changes of soil moisture content, thickness of rock and soil layers, and structural features such as fractures, voids, and piping activity. Like radar, the EM technique offers the capability for a high resolution survey which may locate anomalous conditions associated with the subsidence. Because the data can be gathered continuously along profile lines to depths of 6m and 15 m (20 and 50 ft), high density site coverage is feasible. The survey technique is similar to a GPR traverse. The technique is non-destructive and can penetrate through paved roads, concrete and rock. Meaningful EM data acquisition is limited by the presence of buried pipes and cables, metal fences, railroad tracks, steel reinforced structures, and electrical sources, however, it is better suited than resistivity to areas where cultural noise is a factor.

Tiltmeters measure differential movement in the subsurface and are capable of maintaining a continuous record of deformations over time. Since both GPR and EM equipment are only capable of indirect detection of subsurface movement, tiltmeters can provide the much-needed confirmation of the EM and radar results.

6 CONCEPTUAL MONITORING PLAN

The conceptual plan involves an integrated systems approach for best results. Before commencing monitoring work, the survey plan should be well laid-out on the basis of aerial photos, mine maps, geological sections, and topographic profiles of the site. In order to optimize the use of the different techniques, the sites should be examined with a site-wide technique as a reconnaissance tool. The results of the reconnaissance can then be used to locate shorter, more detailed traverses. Also, the sequence of measurements should be updated in a time sequence (on the order of months) to detect temporal variations. In addition, a long-term monitoring device should monitor the site continuously.

The conceptual plan requires that the different methods be performed in the proper sequence. This consists of EM measurements followed by GPR and the installation of tiltmeters. The EM technique is ideally suited for reconnaissance surveys because of its portability. Large portions of a site can be covered by walking or using a truck-mounted system.

After the EM survey has been completed, areas of anomalous subsurface properties should be compared with zones of ground disruption. In those areas where EM data appear to indicate anomalous subsurface properties, radar traverses should be made to detail the occurrence. In order to determine the continuous nature of the subsidence, tiltmeters should be installed. Their locations will depend on the size of subsidence features and extent of the monitoring site.

The spacing for the traverses will vary with the actual site conditions. These conditions may range from traverses on 7.5 m to 15 m (25 to 50 ft) centers, to single traverses down roads or alleys. However, attempts should be made to gather as much data in an area as possible by completing parallel lines or discontinuous segments to in-fill difficult access areas. For example, EM traverses located in streets should be done in a minimum of two and ideally three parallel lines spaced over the width of the street; lines between houses or through short open areas should be used to gather data for contouring. Radar traverses will be coincident with EM where anomalous EM readings are detected and on a denser spacing to define the suspected feature. Radar traverses should be made parallel to the suspected subsidence feature as well as perpendicular to it. The traverses should be long enough to pass from undisturbed to disturbed zones and off again in the case of the perpendicular traverses. The parallel traverses should traverse the length of the feature. Antenna selection for the radar system will depand on the response of the antenna to the site surface. It is advisable to have several antennae (80, 120 and 300 MHz) on site and to evaluate the success of the various types before selecting one for production work.

Both EM and radar measurements should be repeated over the site to provide temporal changes in NSI characteristics. It is recommended that measurements be taken on a quarterly basis over a period of long enough to define the rate of change in the NSI. This period may vary between sites but is likely to be one to three years. The data collected during each survey should be fed into the computer to compare with baseline data. Data interpretation will be on the basis of computer output and raw field data plots of the monitoring results.

7 CONCLUSION AND RECOMMENDATION

The subsidence monitoring scheme proposed appears to be a potentially viable technique for early detection of subsidence in the NAF. However, field verification of the technique is critical in the evaluation of its limits of applicability.

REFERENCES

Ash, S.H. 1950. Buried valley of the Susquehanna River – anthracite region of Pennsylvania. U.S. Bureau of Mines Bulletin 494, 27 pp.
Benson, R.C. & L.J. LaFountain 1985. Evaluation of subsidence or collapse potential due to subsurface cavities. To be published.
Bhattacharya, S. & M.M. Singh 1985. Development of an integrated system of monitoring for the detection of imminent subsidence. Final report on U.S. Bureau of Mines Contract No. J0134022, in preparation.

ACKNOWLEDGEMENTS

The authors would like to express their gratitude to the U.S. Bureau of Mines for support of this work under Contract No. J0134022. The technical help received from Technos, Inc. is also acknowledged. The authors appreciate the support of Engineers International, Inc. in the preparation and publishing of this paper. The views and conclusions contained in this paper are those of the authors and do not represent the official position of the Bureau of Mines or the U.S. Government.

Table 1. Available instrument systems and their applicability.

Sensor System	Characteristic of Cavity			
	Class I	Class II	Class III	Class IV
Airborne Sensors	None Applicable	Thermal Imagery	Thermal Imagery Black and White Photography Color Photography Infra-Red Photography	Thermal Imagery Black and White Photography Color Photography Infra-Red Photography Radar Imagery Satellite Imagery Multispectral Satellite Imagery
Surface Sensors	Seismic (various) Resistivity (various) Micro-gravity Standard Gravity Electromagnetics	Seismic (various) Resistivity (various) Micro-Gravity Standard Gravity Electromagnetics Ground Penetrating Radar	Seismic (various) Resistivity (various) Micro-Gravity Standard Gravity Electromagnetics Ground Penetrating Radar Thermal Imagery	Seismic (various) Resistivity (various) Micro-Gravity Standard Gravity Electromagnetics Ground Penetrating Radar Thermal Imagery Visual/Leveling Geochemical
In Situ Sensors	None Applicable	Piezometer/Water Table Sensors Thermal Sensors	Piezometer/Water Table Sensors Thermal Sensors Micro-Acoustic Displacement/Pressure Sensors	Piezometer/Water Table Sensor Thermal Sensors Micro-Acoustic Displacement/Pressure Sensors
Subsurface Sensors	Acoustic (Sonar) Seismic Ground Penetrating Radar Gravity Magnetics Electromagnetics Dyes/Tracers Borehole Camera/Visual Conventional Logging Tools Geochemical Nuclear	Acoustic (Sonar) Seismic Ground Penetrating Radar Gravity Magnetics Electromagnetics Dyes/Tracers Borehole Camera/Visual Conventional Logging Tools Geochemical Nuclear	Acoustic (Sonar) Seismic Ground Penetrating Radar Gravity Magnetics Electromagnetics Dyes/Tracers Borehole Camera/Visual Conventional Logging Tools Geochemical Nuclear	Acoustic (Sonar) Seismic Ground Penetrating Radar Gravity Magnetics Electromagnetics Dyes/Tracers Borehole Camera/Visual Conventional Logging Tools Geochemical Nuclear

Table 2. List of selection criteria.

• REGIONAL AND SITE SPECIFIC APPLICABILITY	• TRAVERSE SPEED
• OPERATING PRINCIPLE	• SENSITIVITY TO ENVIRONMENT
• RANGE/DEPTH OF INVESTIGATION	• SUSCEPTIBILITY TO NOISE
• RESOLUTION	• EQUIPMENT COST
• ACCURACY	• EASE/COST OF INSTALLATION
• POWER REQUIREMENTS	• EASE/COST OF DATA REDUCTION
• REPEATABILITY	• REQUIRED SKILL FOR OPERATION
	• CREW SIZE

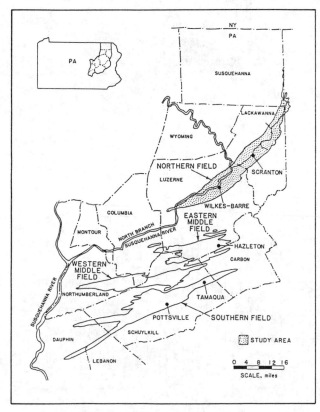

Figure 1. Map of study area.

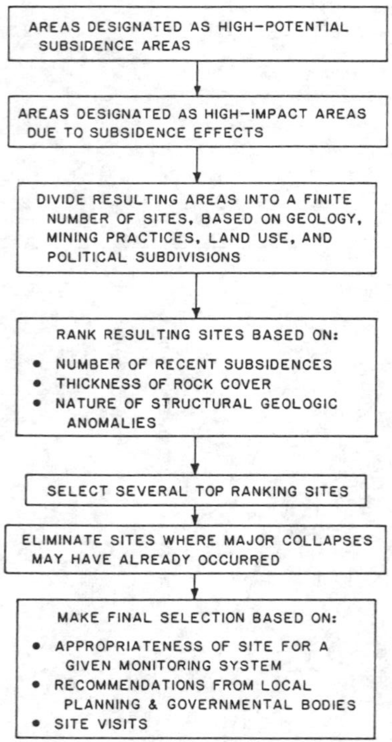

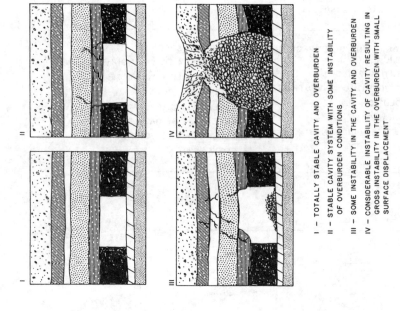

I – TOTALLY STABLE CAVITY AND OVERBURDEN

II – STABLE CAVITY SYSTEM WITH SOME INSTABILITY OF OVERBURDEN CONDITIONS

III – SOME INSTABILITY IN THE CAVITY AND OVERBURDEN

IV – CONSIDERABLE INSTABILITY OF CAVITY RESULTING IN GROSS INSTABILITY IN THE OVERBURDEN WITH SMALL SURFACE DISPLACEMENT

Figure 3. Classes of cavity stability.

AREAS DESIGNATED AS HIGH-POTENTIAL SUBSIDENCE AREAS

AREAS DESIGNATED AS HIGH-IMPACT AREAS DUE TO SUBSIDENCE EFFECTS

DIVIDE RESULTING AREAS INTO A FINITE NUMBER OF SITES, BASED ON GEOLOGY, MINING PRACTICES, LAND USE, AND POLITICAL SUBDIVISIONS

RANK RESULTING SITES BASED ON:
• NUMBER OF RECENT SUBSIDENCES
• THICKNESS OF ROCK COVER
• NATURE OF STRUCTURAL GEOLOGIC ANOMALIES

SELECT SEVERAL TOP RANKING SITES

ELIMINATE SITES WHERE MAJOR COLLAPSES MAY HAVE ALREADY OCCURRED

MAKE FINAL SELECTION BASED ON:
• APPROPRIATENESS OF SITE FOR A GIVEN MONITORING SYSTEM
• RECOMMENDATIONS FROM LOCAL PLANNING & GOVERNMENTAL BODIES
• SITE VISITS

Figure 2. Flow chart of site screening methodology.

Application of geophysical exploring methods for observing rock failure in the mining of coal seams menaced by water-bodies

LIU ZONGCAI, SUN ZHENGPENG, GAO HANG, LI BAIYING, YU SHIJIAN,
LI JIAXIANG & ZENG RUIHUA
*Special Mining Research Department, Shandong Mining College, Taian,
People's Republic of China*

INTRODUCTION

There are several tens of billions of tons of coal resources menaced
by ordovician karst confined-water in China. The main menace to the
safe mining of these seams is floor water-irruption. Accidents of
floor water-irruption take place frequently in these mines and with
the increase of mining depth, the hydraulic pressure of confined-
water gets higher and accidents involving floor water-irruption tend
to increase. The safety of production in coal mines was affected by
the floor water-irruptions. Solving the problem of coal-mining above
the confined-water bodies is now one of the important subjects in
China.

Based on the investigations of much floor water-irruptions data,
we think that the existence of confined-water is the prerequisite
condition for floor water-irruption, and the effective thickness,
strength, mechanical properties of the floor, geological structure
and mining effects are the main factors for floor water-irruption.
Among these factors, mining is the only man-made factor and can be
controlled. Then, during the process of mining, how will these factors change? What is the regularity of change? We can settle these
problems only by comprehensive observations in-situ.

Seam 5 in Mine 3 of the Jingxing Mining Bureau of Hebei Province
is close to the ordovician limestone which contains a great deal of
karst water, and the water can appear in the drill-hole only several
meters deep from the floor. In addition, the geological structures
and hydrological conditions of this area are very complicated.The
water-irruptions took place 4 times in this area and it was considered an "unmimable area". On such a place, it is better to do the
damaging tests and comprehensive observations of the floor by making
use of the present drifts, equipment and persons.If successful, we
can create a new method for mining coal above confined-water. Therefore, this work is very significant in theory and in practice.

SELECTION OF OBSERVING METHODS

The purpose of observing is to learn the floor stress change regu-
larities and the floor damaged depth due to the effects of coal-
mining, and finally to direct the "Mining With Water-Pressure".The
selecting principle for observing methods is that on one hand, the

method is available and on the other, the equipment is usable in underground mines. The following six kinds of methods were selected for the comprehensive observations by repeat investigations.

1. The drill-hole ultrasonic method:
It was applied to observe the floor damaged depth due to the effects of mining.

2. Relative stress measuring.
It was used to observe the floor stress changes(including the maximum extra shear stress and the direction of the maximum extra principal stress) and the floor damaged depth due to the effects of mining.

3. Water-drain (or water-injecting):
It was used to observe the floor damaged depth due to mining.

4. Single prop pressure cell:
It was used to measure the appearance of rock pressure of the roof.

5. The roof moving instrument:
It was used to measure the roof convergence.

6. The audio-frequency geoelectric field method:
It was used to explore the confined-water in the mined drifts before mining (This part was deleted since it has no relation with this paper).

THE STATE OF THE TESTING FACE AND THE LAYOUT OF COMPREHENSIVE OBSERVATIONS

Face 5701 in Mine 3 of the Jingxing Mining Bureau was selected for testing. In this face, the west boundary is the Jiaochang Fault (D=120m), the east boundary is the Fault F3 (D=3 to 5m), near the Shuijiaxu Fault (D=120m). There are two faults (D=1 to 5m) whose strikes are about south-north, and there exist hidden faults under the seam. In the mining area there are 5 karst-collapses with different dimensions. The hydrological conditions are very complicated. This area is in the runoff region of the Weizhou Springs, and the entry of the Ordovician karst water of Jingxing Coal Basin. The faults make the distance of seam to limestone short (10 to 30m generally, 8.6m at least).

Because of the complicated conditions, the dimensions of the face should be diminished so that the rock pressure may be diminished and the floor damaged depth can be smaller and the probability of water-irruption will be less. Therefore, the breadth of face was 20 to 30 meters, 150 meters in length, and the blasting method and roof falling were applied.

In order to apply the ultrasonic method, stress measurement and water-drain (or water-injecting), the floor holes were drilled. Because of observations before and after mining, an observation roadway (100 meters long, out of conveyer roadway, i.e. 20 meters west out of Face 5701) was extracted, since the deepest parts of floor damage are situated at the lower section of the face. There are two observation sites, one includes an ultrasonic hole, a water-drain hole, a prop pressure cell and a convergence instrument; the other includes an ultrasonic hole, a water-drain hole, three stress holes, a prop pressure cell and a convergence instrument. Near the south mining-stopping line there is a water-drain hole (Shown in Figure 1).

986

PRINCIPLES, RESULTS AND EXPLAINATIONS OF COMPREHENSIVE OBSERVATIONS

1. Observation of drill-hole ultrasonic:

The ultrasonic rock-parameter instrument (SYC-2) was used. It has been proved that when travelling in different rockmass, the ultrasonic has different velocity and in rockmass with different stress

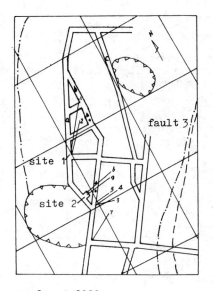

a. observation roadway

b. conveyer roadway

c. material roadway

fault 3

site 1

site 2

── 6 soundwave observation hole

▲ convergence instrument

• prop pressure cell

scale   1:2000

Fig. 1 Layout of comprehensive observation

states, the ultrasonic velocity becomes different. The stress state of floor in the advance of mining is shown in Fig.2. The floor in front of the coalwall, acted region by the front abutment pressure, is a compressive area, the floor in front of the gob is an expansive area and the floor back of the gob, acted upon by the back abutment pressure, is a compressive area. The boundary between the compressive and expansive area is a shear plane. In the compressive area, ultrasonic velocity is higher, and in the expansive area ultrasonic velocity is lower. Because a point in the floor undergoes the process of "Compression-Expansion-Compression" during the process of mining, its ultrasonic velocity will undergo a process of "higher-lower-higher". Observe the floor with the ultrasonic before and after mining and compare the results to identify the floor damaged depth due to the mining effects.
    The field ultrasonic velocity curves of Face 5701 in Mine 3 of the Jingxing Mining Bureau is shown in Fig.3. It is clear from the figure that during the mining the ultrasonic velocity of the floor 3m up to the seam is higher in the compressive area, lower in the expansive area and higher in the back compressive area, with the

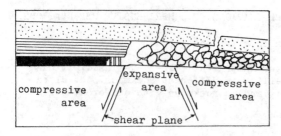

Fig.2 State of floor stress

tendency of "higher-lower-higher". The ultrasonic velocity of the
floor 3m down is not clear, with no process of "higher-lower-higher".
Therefore, the floor damaged depth is 3 meters.

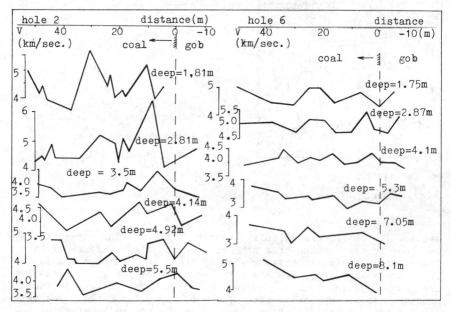

Fig. 3 Ultrasonic velocity curve

2. Relative stress measurement:

The simple stress instrument of 75-1 was used to measure the floor
stress during mining. When the floor stress varies, the sensor will
vary also, representing the variance of electric current. By measuring the current and calculating with the formulae, the maximum
extra shear stress τ_m and direction of maximum extra principal
stress θ may be identified.
   The field curve of maximum extra shear stress in Face 5701 is
shown in Fig.4. It is clear from the figure that in the floor with

988

$$\mathcal{T}_m = \frac{1}{4B} \sqrt{(\Delta I_1)^2 + (\Delta I_2)^2}$$

$$\theta = \frac{1}{2} \tan^{-1} \frac{\Delta I_2}{\Delta I_1}$$

36 meters front of coalwall, the value of $\mathcal{T}_m$ is zero (i.e. no mining effect), the closer the distance to the coalwall, the larger the value of $\mathcal{T}_m$ and the maximum value of $\mathcal{T}_m$ is on 6.2 meters back of the coalwall. In the gob, the farther the distance to the coalwall, the smaller the value of $\mathcal{T}_m$. The direction of maximum extra principal is about at a $30°$ angle with the horizontal plane. Therefore, we mastered the stress field of the mining face.

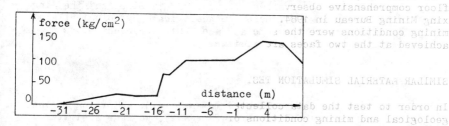

Fig. 4 Curve of shear stress

3. Measurements of water-drain (or water-injecting):

The principle of this method is very simple. Drill a hole in the floor before mining and put the steel pipes in the hole except the part of measuring depth. When water flows out from the hole, observe the amount of water-drain every day; when there is no water in the hole, observe the amount of water-injecting every day. According to the amounts of water-drain (or water-injecting) during mining, we may analyse the floor damaged depth after mining. Figure 5 is the curve of water-amounts of Hole 1 and Hole 7 with the advance of face.

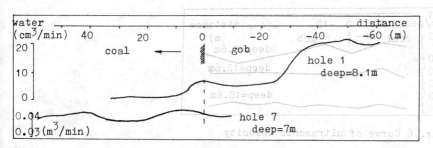

Fig. 5 Curve of water amount variance

It is clear from Fig.5 that for Hole 1 (8 meters deep) the amount of water-drain does not vary greatly with the advance of mining and for Hole 7 (7 meters deep) the amount of water-drain does not vary greatly either, which indicates that the floor damaged depth does not extend to the depth of Hole 1 and Hole 7.

4. Measurement of single prop pressure and convergence:

At the first observation site, the point of the maximum value of single prop pressure is on 5 meters at the front of the coalwall (value of pressure is 6.5 tons, subsidence value of roof is 25mm, amount of floor rising is 38mm). At the second observation site, the point of the maximum value of single prop pressure is on 6 meters at the front of the coalwall (pressure value is 5 tons, convergence is 73mm). The farther the distance to the coalwall, the smaller the pressure (The point on 50 meters at the front of coalwall, the pressure is zero).

The results mentioned above indicated that the appearance of rock pressure due to coal-mining is small and of little extent.

In order to prove the data achieved at Face 5701, we did another floor comprehensive observation at Face 4707 in Mine 1 of the Jingxing Mining Bureau in 1984. Here the geological, hydrological and mining conditions were the same as Face 5701. The conclusions achieved at the two faces are similar.

SIMILAR MATERIAL SIMULATION TEST

In order to test the data collected in the field, according to the geological and mining conditions of Face 4707, we made a similar material simulation test. Take the longitudinal profile of a long-wall face as a plane strain problem, doing tests in the plane model frame (4 meters long, 24 cm wide and 2.2m high). The mining thickness of seam is 3 meters. With the advance of face, the comprehensive observations were still applied to observe the floor (example: ultrasonic, stress measuring and floor movement methods).

1. Ultrasonic observation:

Fig.6 shows the floor ultrasonic velocity curves at different depth. The first curve (2.6m deep) varies obviously, with the process of "high-low-high". And the other two curves do not vary obviously. In

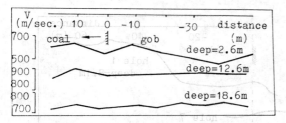

Fig. 6 Curve of ultrasonic velocity

order to review the floor with ultrasonic velocity, we introduced the Fissure Coefficient K_R:

$$K_R = (\frac{V'_{ep}}{V_{ep}})^2$$

where Vep' is the ultrasonic velocity of measured rock
     Vep is the ultrasonic velocity of full rock
Calculated results indicated that the minimum K_R at the depth of
2.6 meters is 0.72, depth of 12.6 meters 0.84, depth of 18.6 meters
0.90. Therefore, according to this variance gradient, the minimum
K_R at the depth of 4 meters is o.75. If the value of 0.75 is used
as critical fissure coefficient to defime the floor damaged depth,
then the floor damaged depth of this face is 4 meters.

2. Measurement of floor stress

The resistance-strain method was used to observe the floor stress.
Fig. 7 is the curve of floor extra stress at different depths. It
is clear that in the front of the coalwall the floor stress increases,
at the coalwall the floor stress becomes minimal and in the gob the
floor stress tends to increase (lower than in front of coalwall).

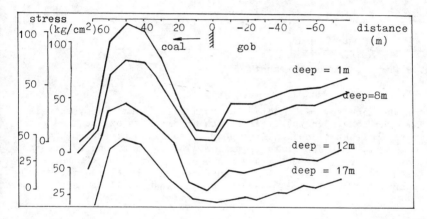

Fig. 7 Curve of floor extra stress

The smaller the depth from the seam, the larger the value of floor
stress and the larger the difference of the maximum and minimum
stress. From the point of view of the face advancing, the stress of
a point in the floor varies from lower to higher to lower again. In
this variance process, the energy accumulated in the floor will release to the failure of rockmass. The larger the difference between
the maximum and minimum stress, the stronger the failure of rock-
mass.

3. Observation of floor movement:

The optical lenses were used to measure the movement of floor rock-
mass. Fig.8 is the curve of floor movement at different depths. The
observation points at 10 meters out of the stopping-cut-line and 10
meters out of the face cut appear as subsidence (shown in Fig. 8-a
and Fig.8-b). The maximum subsidence of the floor at 10 meters out
of the stopping line (2.5 meters below the seam) is 19.4mm, 7.5m
below is 15.3mm. The maximum subsidence of the floor at 10 meters

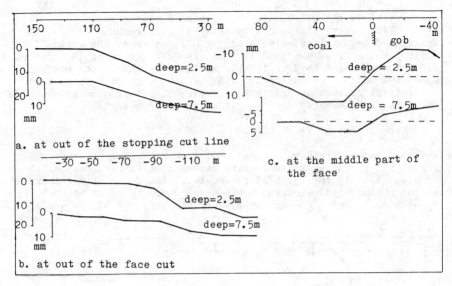

a. at out of the stopping cut line

c. at the middle part of the face

b. at out of the face cut

Fig. 8 Curve of floor movement

out of the face cut (2.5m below the seam) is 17.8mm; 7.5m below is
10.7mm. The points in the floor of the middle part of the face, when
they are in front of coalwall, appear as subsidence; when behind
the coalwall, they appear to be rising. The maximum compressive and
expansive values (2.5m below the seam) are 10.6mm, at 7.5m below they
are 4.4mm and 6.6mm. According to the gradient above, the movement
of observation points (13 meters below the seam) will be zero.

CONCLUSIONS:

Face 5701 and Face 4707 have been mined out safely. For these faces
severely menaced by Ordovician karst confined-water, with complicated
geological and hydrological conditions and the tendency of water-
irruption, and considered an "unminable area", this first successful
mining using short wall faces is of great significance. A new way
for coal-mining above the Ordovician karst confined-water was
created.
    The results achieved by field comprehensive observations are the
base of "Mining with Pressure". The floor damaged depth of these
two faces is 3 to 4 meters. The results achieved by similar material simulation test identify with the results achieved by field
observations.
    Based on the successful mining of these two faces and the results
achieved both by field observation and similar material simulation
test, for the seam menaced by confined-water, the short-wall face
or strip face may be used to ensure the safety of mining.

Stresses and strains on the common boundary surface and strength of composite rock masses acted by three-dimensional compressive stresses

TAN XUE SHU, XIAN XUE FU & CAO WEI
Department of Mining Engineering, Chongqing University, People's Republic of China

ABSTRACT

Composite rock mass is one kind of the universal underground rock masses. In this paper, the authors use the continuous condition of deformation, the equilibrium condition of static force and the principle of superimposition to analyze and calculate the stresses and strains on the common boundary surface of the composite rock mass acted by three-dimensional compressive stresses, then point out the destroying mechanism and condition of the composite rock mass.
    Rock specimens of limestone and clay mudstone are subjected to a triaxial compression test, respectively. Then, the two kinds of rock specimens are glued together and tested again in the same way. Good agreement is obtained by comparing the results theoretically calculated with the experimental ones. The conclusions in this paper have a value of reference in investigating the strength of composite rock masses.

INTRODUCTION

Underground composite rock mass is composed of rocks with different properties, a common boundary surface existing between any two kinds of rock. Therefore, the mechanical properties of the rock mass are contributed by the properties of an individual rock as well as the properties on the interface. Underground composite rock mass, generally acted by three-dimensional compressive stresses caused from the pressure of the above rock layers and geologically structural stresses, will be first destroyed often on the interface of rock to rock rather than in rock bodies. So the interface is reasonably considered as a weak face. Analysing the stresses and strains on the interface is primary in the study of the destroying mechanisms and conditions of the composite rock mass.

STRESSES AND STRAINS ON THE INTERFACE

The model of composite rock mass, shown in Fig 1(a), is composed of three layers of rock and subjected to three-dimensional compressive stresses $\sigma_1, \sigma_2, \sigma_3$. The modules of elasticity and Possion's ratios of Rock A and Rock B are repressed by E_a, μ_a, and E_b, μ_b, respectively. Suppose

$$E_a > E_b$$
$$\mu_a < \mu_b \qquad\qquad (1)$$

Formula (1) means that the deformation in Rock B is larger than that in Rock A under a certain force.

Again supposing Rock A and Rock B are tightly stuck. It means that no relative deformation occurs on the interface.

According to the superimposed principle of mechanics, the model acted simultaneously by σ_1, σ_2, σ_3, shown by Fig 1(a), can be changed into three models acted by longitudinal stress σ_1, side stresses σ_2 and σ_3, respectively, shown in Fig 1(b), 1(c), 1(d).

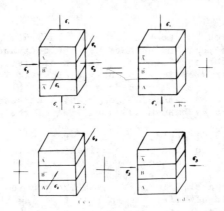

Figure 1. Action of forces and super-imposition of the model.

On the interface of Rock A and Rock B of composite rock mass under the action of σ_1, σ_2, σ_3, respectively, shown in Fig 1, horizontal restraint will occur on the interface because of the nonuniformity of horizontal strains. As a result, additional stresses will produce on the interface. Analysis and calculation are performed to the cases shown in Fig 1(b), 1(c), 1(d), respectively, by use of the continuous condition of deformation and equilibrium condition of static force (Tan Xue Shu 1984). Relationship between stresses and strains on the interface is got. Superimposed principle and mathematical simplication are used to the above results and total stresses on the interface of the specimen acted simultaneously by σ_1, σ_2, σ_3 can be written as follows.

$$\sigma^*_{1a} = \sigma_1$$
$$\sigma^*_{2a} = -K_2\sigma_3 + (\sigma_2 + K_1\sigma_2) - K_3\sigma_1 \qquad\qquad (2)$$
$$\sigma^*_{3a} = -K_2\sigma_2 - (\sigma_3 + K_1\sigma_3) - K_3\sigma_1$$

$$\sigma_{1b}^* = \sigma_1$$
$$\sigma_{2b}^* = K_2\sigma_3+(\sigma_2-K_1\sigma_2)+K_3\sigma_1 \tag{3}$$
$$\sigma_{3b}^* = (\sigma_3-K_1\sigma_3)+K_2\sigma_2+K_3\sigma_1$$

Here
$$K_1 = \frac{E_a^2(1-\mu_b^2)-E_b^2(1-\mu_a^2)}{(E_a+E_b)^2-(E_a\mu_b+E_b\mu_a)^2}$$
$$K_2 = \frac{2E_aE_b(\mu_b-\mu_a)}{(E_a+E_b)^2-(E_a\mu_b+E_b\mu_a)^2} \tag{4}$$
$$K_3 = \frac{(E_a\mu_b-E_b\mu_a)(E_a\mu_b+E_b\mu_a+E_a+E_b)}{(E_a+E_b)^2-(E_a\mu_b+E_b\mu_a)^2}$$

ANALYSIS AND DISCUSSION

Sttesses on the interface of composite rock mass will change because of the restraint of horizontal strains. In Formulas (2) and (3), if

$$\sigma_3(1+K_1) < K_2\sigma_2+K_3\sigma_1 > \sigma_3(K_1-1)$$
$$\sigma_2(1+K1) < K_2\sigma_3+K_3\sigma_1 > \sigma_2(K_1-1) \tag{5}$$

we have

$$\sigma_{3a}^*< 0 \qquad \sigma_{2a}^*< 0 \qquad \sigma_{1a}^* > 0$$
$$\sigma_{3b}^*> 0 \qquad \sigma_{2b}^*> 0 \qquad \sigma_{1b}^*> 0 \tag{6}$$

This means that, on the interface, the state of stress in Rock A changes from three-dimensional compression into triaxial compression tension and in Rock B unchanges in directions but changes in values, from σ_1, σ_2, σ_3 to σ_{1b}^*, σ_{2b}^*, σ_{3b}^*, respectively.

In the composite rock mass under three-dimensional uniform compression, the original relation of three principal stresses can be written as $\sigma_1>\sigma_2>\sigma_3$. But it is not true on the interface that $\sigma_{1a}^* >\sigma_{2a}^*>\sigma_{3a}^*$(or $\sigma_{1b}^*>\sigma_{2b}^*>\sigma_{3b}^*$). The order of the principal stresses may be changed. For example, in Formula (2), $\sigma_{3a}^*>\sigma_{2a}^*$ will be true if $(1+K_1+K_2)<0$. The condition of strength will change. In Eq. (2), (3), if $\qquad \sigma_{1a}^*+\sigma_{2a}^*+\sigma_{3a}^*<\sigma_1+\sigma_2+\sigma_3$
$$\sigma_{1b}^*+\sigma_{2b}^*+\sigma_{3b}^*>\sigma_1+\sigma_2+\sigma_3 \tag{7}$$
the average normal stress in Rock A will decrease. As a result, its strength will subsequently decrease. Reversely, the average normal stress in Rock B will increase and its strength will increase.

If the specimen is only acted by longitudinal stress σ_1, shown in Fig 1(b), it can be known from analysis and calculation that the state of stress in Rock A near the interface will change from uniaxial compression into three-dimensional compression-tension and in Rock B into three-dimensional compression. In this case, if the strength of Rock B is equal to or larger than that of Rock A, destruction will first take place in Rock A(Tan Xue Shu 1984).

In above analyses, whether the individual component of stresses is satisfied with Formulas (5) and (6) depends on the values of K_1, K_2, K_3 which, according to Fofmula (4), subsequently depend on the modules of elasticity and Possion's ratios of the rocks. So, whether Formulas (5), (6), (7) are true depends on the mechanical properties of Rock A and Rock B.

In order to compare the theoretical results with experimental ones, we chose two kinds of rock, Rock A(limestone) and Rock B(clay mudstone), from the coal-bearing layers in a coal area. Modules of elasticity, Possion's ratios, internal cohesions, internal friction angles are got from pre-tests and listed in Table 1.

Table 1. The mechanical properties of Rock A and Rock B

Name of rock	Elastic module $E \times 10^9 Pa$	Possion's ratio μ	Internal cohesion $K \times 10^5 Pa$	Internal friction angle	$Sin\phi$	$\dfrac{1+Sin\phi}{1-Sin\phi}$	$\dfrac{2KCos\phi}{1-Sin\phi}$
Limestone (Rock A)	128	0.29	100	44°	0.69	5.55	471
Clay mudstone (Rock B)	117	0.34	53	42°	0.67	5.10	373

It can be known from Table 1 that the module of elasticity is larger and Possion's ratio is smaller, respectively, of Rock A than of Rock B, which satisfies with Formula (1).

According to the composition shown by Fig 1, the specimen of composite rock mass is made which is a solid square-column with a cross area of 50x50 sq.mm and a height of 120 mm. The specimen is struck from Rock A, situated at two ends of the column, and Rock B, in the medial section of the specimen. Every section of Rock A or Rock B is about 40 mm high. Triaxial compression tests are done on the specimen. The results are shown in Table 2.

Table 2. Strength of composite rock mass in longitudinal compressive loading

Side compressive stress $(\sigma_2=\sigma_3)$ $(10^5 Pa)$	Experimental Composite specimen $(10^5 Pa)$	Calculating Limestone $(10^5 Pa)$	Clay mudstone $(10^5 Pa)$	Composite specimen $(10^5 Pa)$
60	575	610	953	610
90	726	738	1167	738
120	1232	865	1380	865
150	947	992	1594	992

Mohr linear condition of strength, from Mohr theory of strength, can be written as follows(J.C. Jeager, N. G. W. Cook 1981).

$$\sigma_{1j} = \frac{1+Sin\phi}{1-Sin\phi} \sigma_{3j} + \frac{2KCos\phi}{1-Sin\phi} \tag{8}$$

hear K and ϕ represent the internal cohesion and internal friction angle, respectively.

In Formulas (2) and (3), if $\sigma_2=\sigma_3$, we get $\sigma_{2a}^*=\sigma_{3a}^*$ and $\sigma_{2b}^*=\sigma_{3b}^*$. If the stresses on the interface reach limiting equilibrium, taking σ_{1a}^*, $\sigma_{2a}^*=\sigma_{3a}^*$, σ_{1b}^*, $\sigma_{2b}^*=\sigma_{3b}^*$ into Formula (8), we obtain the limiting strength in longitudinal direction of Rock A and Rock B, respectively.

$$\sigma_{1aj}^* = \frac{\dfrac{1+Sin\phi_a}{1-Sin\phi_a}(1+K_1-K_2)\sigma_3+\dfrac{2KCos\phi_a}{1-Sin\phi_a}}{1+K_3\dfrac{1+Sin\phi_a}{1-Sin\phi_a}} \qquad (9)$$

$$\sigma_{1bj}^* = \frac{\dfrac{1+Sin\phi_b}{1-Sin\phi_b}(1-K_1+K_2)\sigma_3+\dfrac{2KCos\phi_b}{1-Sin\phi_b}}{1-K_3\dfrac{1+Sin\phi_b}{1-Sin\phi_b}} \qquad (10)$$

Using Formula (4) and the results in Table 1 and simplifying Formulas (9) and (10), we have

$$\sigma_{1aj}^* = (5.59\sigma_3+471)/1.32 \qquad (11)$$

$$\sigma_{1bj}^* = (5.06\sigma_3+373)/0.71 \qquad (12)$$

From Formulas (11) and (12), the longitudinal limiting compressive strength in the interface is calculated and the results are listed in Table 2.

It can be seen from Table 2 that the internal cohesion and the internal friction angle are larger in Rock A than in Rock B. It follows that, according to Mohr condition of strength, the strength of Rock A is greater than that of Rock B. On the other hand, it can be seen from Table 2 that, because of the restraint of horizontal strains caused by the sticking of Rock A and Rock B, the strength of Rock A is lower than that of Rock B. It is clear that the strength of Rock A decreases and of Rock B increases after sticking and destruction will first occur in Rock A. It is reasonable to take the strength of Rock A as that of composite rock mass in Table 2. The composite rock mass under false-triaxial compressive stresses will be stable and safe only when external longitudinal stress σ_1 is smaller than σ_{1aj}^*.

A fact, from Table 2, which must be mentioned is that the theoretical results are in comparitive agreement with the experimental ones, but differences still exist and get larger especially when the side stress is higher.

What should be explained is that, in Table 2, the longitudinal compressive strength of Rock A, σ_{1aj}^*, has been taken as that of the composite rock mass, σ_1. In fact, σ_{1aj}^* only represents the initial strength of the rock mass because the rock mass can take certain amount of load after Rock A has been destroyed. The composite rock mass is completely destroyed only when both Rock A and Rock B are destroyed.

REFERENCES

Tan Xue Shu, 1984, The investigation of strength theory of composite rock mass, J. of Mining Technology
J. C. Jeager, N. G. W. Cook, 1981, Fundamentals of rock mechanics, The Publishing House of Science

Blast induced subsidence in the craters of nuclear tests over coral*

DONALD E.BURTON, ROBERT P.SWIFT, H.DAVID GLENN & JON B.BRYAN
Lawrence Livermore National Laboratory, California, USA

ABSTRACT

The craters from high-yield nuclear tests at the Pacific Proving Grounds are very broad and shallow in comparison with the bowl-shaped craters formed in continental rock at the Nevada Test Site and elsewhere. Attempts to account for the differences quantitatively have been generally unsatisfactory.

We have for the first time successfully modeled the Koa Event, a representative coral-atoll test. On the basis of plausible assumptions about the geology and about the constitutive relations for coral, we have shown that the size and shape of the Koa crater can be accounted for by subsidence and liquefaction phenomena. If future studies confirm these assumptions, it will mean that some scaling formulas based on data from the Pacific will have to be revised to avoid overestimating weapons effects in continental geology.

1. INTRODUCTION

To understand the effectiveness of nuclear weapons, one must be able to predict the effects of near-surface detonations of relatively high-yield nuclear devices (several hundred kilotons) on targets embedded in various kinds of rocks and soils. However, all of the high-yield explosive cratering events in the U.S. data base took place at the Pacific Proving Grounds (PPG). The PPG are located at the Enewetak and Bikini atolls. The geology of these coral atolls is unlike that of any continent. The matter is not academic; empirical formulas used until recently to predict the size and shape of weapon craters [Cooper 1977] are based on data from the PPG. We now believe that these formulas greatly over-estimate surface-burst effectiveness in typical continental geologies.

There have been so few above-ground and shallow-buried nuclear events that it has been necessary to develop numerical techniques to extrapolate beyond known craters to predict the effects of new weapons and new geologic settings. Some doubt remains about the completeness of such

*Work performed under auspices of USDOE by LLNL under No. W-7405-Eng-48.

models because of their inability to reproduce the very shallow, saucer-shaped craters formed in coral at the PPG. Calculated crater volumes in studies by some investigators are only about 20 to 25% of those observed in coral, and none have reproduced the shapes associated with these events. For example, Figure 1 contrasts the result of a typical numerical simulation [Schuster 1983] with the profile of the Koa event crater [Ristvet 1978] which has a volume of 2.11×10^7 m^3 and radius of about 600 m.

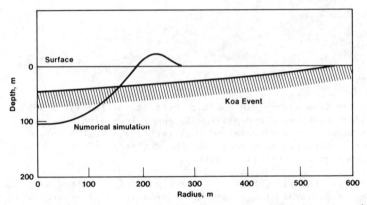

Figure 1. Profile of a Pacific Proving Ground Crater (Koa Event) contrasted with the crater resulting from a typical numerical simulation (Schuster 1983).

Various physical mechanisms have been postulated for the size and shape of the Pacific craters. In this work, we have developed a multiphase constitutive model based on mixture theory [Swift 1984], introduced it into our two-dimensional continuum dynamics code TENSOR [Burton 1977, 1982], and applied it to a simulation of the Koa Event. Our studies [Burton 1984] attribute the large crater volumes to late-time subsidence. As the pore fluids migrate upwards through the fractured coral, the coral consolidates to a volume comparable to that attained during shock passage. This leads to surface subsidence which enlarges the early bowl-shaped transient crater. Our model also predicts shock liquefaction; liquefied coral can be expected to slump and transform a transient bowl-shaped crater into the saucer shape observed.

2.   CONSTITUTIVE RELATIONSHIPS FOR MIXTURES

The constitutive model assumes a solid containing two types of flaws: pores considered to be preexisting, isotropic, and homogeneous, and cracks that are induced during the calculation and treated using an anisotropic algorithm. Although we make a logical distinction between crack and pore pressure, the assumption of pressure equilibrium between the two types of flaws reduces the system to three components (solid, water, and air). The following describes the types of relationships which govern the system response.

Kinematic Conditions. The kinematic conditions needed for a solid (s), water (w), air (a), multiphase material are

$$M_s = \rho_s (1-\phi) V, \quad M_w = \rho_w S \phi V, \quad \text{and} \quad M_a = \rho_a (1-S) \phi V \tag{1}$$

in which M_i is mass, ρ_i is density, V is volume, and the saturation, porosity, and the constituent porosities are defined by

$$S = \phi_w/\phi, \quad \phi = \phi_w + \phi_a, \quad \text{and} \quad \phi_i = V_i/V. \tag{2}$$

Constituent Response Laws. The constituent response laws are normally given as tabular functions in terms of pressure vs density, while the low pressure water and air responses are represented by adiabatic gas law approximations,

$$\sigma_w = \sigma_w (\rho_w), \quad \sigma_a = \sigma_a (\rho_a), \quad \sigma_s = \sigma_s (\rho_s) \tag{3}$$

Constraints. Pressure equilibrium is assumed between the water and air and between the pores and cracks. These constraints can be recast as functions of S and ϕ or

$$\sigma_w(\phi,S) = \sigma_a(\phi,S) \quad ; \tag{4}$$

Effective Stress Law. The final volumetric relationship is provided by the effective stress law. The classical concept of effective stress is due to Terzaghi (1943) and suggests that the bulk response of a porous solid can be separated into that due to the pore fluid and that due to an "effective" stress defined as

$$\sigma_e = \sigma - \sigma_f \tag{5}$$

with $\quad \sigma_f(\phi,S) = S\sigma_w + (1-S) \sigma_a.$ \hfill (6)

where σ is the total stress tensor. The Terzaghi effective stress has been shown to satisfy a response law of the form [Swift 1984]

$$\dot{\sigma}_e = K (\dot{\epsilon} - \frac{\dot{\sigma}_f}{K_s}), \tag{7}$$

where K and K_s are the drained and solid bulk moduli and $\dot{\epsilon} = \dot{V}/V$ is the volumetric strain rate and the term in parentheses appears as an effective strain rate.

Although the effective stress response law for σ_e is convenient for purposes of understanding, it has several embedded singularities that must be removed in the numerical implementation. It was shown that the response law reduces to the following form [Swift 1984]

$$(1-\phi)(1-\phi - \frac{K}{K_s})[\dot{\epsilon} + \frac{\dot{\sigma}_f (S,\phi)}{K_s}] - [1 - \phi + \frac{\sigma_e (S,\phi)}{K_s}] \dot{\phi} = 0 . \tag{8}$$

The model presently employed in the TENSOR code treats pore collapse and shear failure independently, along with tensile failure algorithms that produce volume dilatancy. In the above form the theory is reduced to solving two equations [Eqns. (4) and (8)] simultaneously for saturation, S, and total porosity, ϕ, at each time step. This is done using a modified Newton-Raphson iteration scheme.

3. SHOCK INDUCED CONSOLIDATION

The presence of water in the coral pores profoundly affects both the transient and late-time material response and leads consolidation and liquefaction. When coral is dry it transmits shock poorly; the collapse of its pores attenuates the shock rapidly with distance, concentrating damage to the region near the source. Pores filled with water transmit shock better than air-filled pores, so the shock travels with less attenuation and can damage larger volumes of coral far from the source.

Figure 2 illustrates typical responses of drained and undrained coral. The drained coral matrix starts with an initial effective stress shown at point A. As the shock wave traverses the material, it first compresses drained coral to point B (irreversibly compacting it) and then unloads down the release path to the axis (where the coral fails in tension) and then to point C.

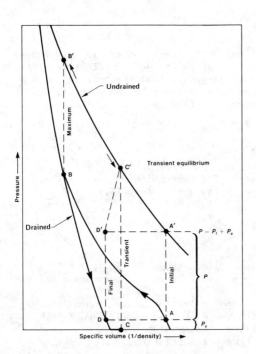

Figure 2. Curves illustrating the compaction and liquefaction processes in terms of the relationship between the responses to shock of drained and undrained coral.

The mixture theory of Section 2 enables us to describe the response of undrained coral in terms of the drained coral response at corresponding volumetric strains. For undrained coral, the shock response would be to move from point A' to the shocked condition (point B') corresponding to the strain in drained coral (point B). The corresponding degree of unloading for the undrained material is point C', at

1002

which time the material is in a transient equilibrium state with respect to total stress. The dynamic calculation is stopped at this point.

Final equilibrium with respect to effective stress occurs by porous flow. Although we are not at present modeling porous flow, we can infer the net effects using our model by assuming that the effective stress reloads approximately back to its initial value. Because the release path BD is steep compared to BA, volume errors resulting from the effective pressure approximation are relatively small. For instance, if a calculation is stopped at point C' (corresponding to the specific volume at point C for dry coral), the net consolidation or volume change for each zone can be determined by going from point C back to point D. The final state for the system is point D'.

The surface subsidence profile is determined by adding the volume changes for all the zones vertically. We can then calculate the total volume of the subsidence crater by integrating over the subsidence profile.

4. SIMULATING THE KOA EVENT

We used the large crater produced by the Koa Event (2.11×10^7 m^3 in apparent crater volume) as a test case for our mixture model. The 1.3 Mt Koa device was detonated in a tank of water placed on a concrete pad poured over coral sand. We modeled the various layers of coral below the ground surface to a depth of 1300 m using measured densities and compressional velocities. Five types of coral were identified and the geologic profiles were obtained for the bulk density and compressional velocity as a function of depth. These profiles were constructed from density logs, core samples, and seismic velocity records.

The calculation was begun with an Eulerian code, which treats the radiation-hydrodynamic energy transfer at early times. The Eulerian code was run to a time of 1 ms and then linked to the Lagrangian code TENSOR. We mapped the pressures, densities, and velocities calculated by the Eulerian code onto a larger grid that extended to a depth of 50 m and a radius of 200 m and continued the calculations with the TENSOR code. After the link, the airblast loading on the ground surface was approximated by a pressure boundary condition due to Brode (1970). We repeated this overlay procedure six times. The final TENSOR grid extended to a depth of 1300 m and a radius of 1400 m.

Figure 3 illustrates the overlaying process, the scale of the problem, and the propagation dynamics of the ground shock. The small black square around the origin at the upper left rear represents the region depicted at early times < 1 ms. The six TENSOR grids appear arrayed along the time axis according to the times of the ground-shock pressure contours shown (2, 10, 57, 133, 280, and 500 ms). The boundaries of the final TENSOR grid extend beyond the border of the figure.

At about 45 deg from the surface, the effect of downward-traveling rarefaction waves generated by the free surface is evident in the shape of the pressure contours. The confinement of the peak pressures to a conical region about the symmetry axis is important to the subsidence interpretation that follows.

Figure 4 shows contours of volumetric consolidation in relation to the various coral layers in the TENSOR mesh. These contours were obtained as discussed previously, by assuming the equality of initial and final effective stress (points A and D in Fig. 2). Note that the

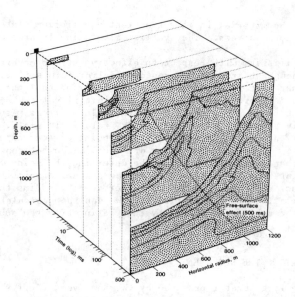

Figure 3. The complete calculation of the Koa Event, starting with the Eulerian calculation (small square at the origin of the back plane) and continuing through six successive remappings to larger grids and TENSOR calculations. Pressure contours are shown for times of 2, 20, 57, 133, 280, and 500 ms.

shape of the contours corresponds to the shock-propagation contours of Fig. 3 that exhibited the strong influence of rarefaction effects off the free surface. Most of the consolidation occurred within the observed crater radius, but significant contributions occurred for the relatively porous layer at a depth between 610 and 760 m.

Figure 5 presents the Koa Event crater profile, measured along the reef, and at various phases of our calculation. The dashed curve represents the transient crater profile in the calculation at a time of 676 ms. The transient crater radius at this time was about 100 m.

Although the ground motion continues until at least 3.3 s [Schuster 1983], we terminated the calculation at 676 ms because we had carried it far enough to address the subsidence issue, which is governed primarily by the magnitude of the peak stress. We plan additional calculations out to later times, but for this study we have simply made a ballistic extrapolation to arrive at the solid profile shown in Fig. 5.

Combining our subsidence contribution with the ejecta profile, we obtain a third profile with a crater volume of 2×10^7 m^3, which is in excellent agreement with that of the actual crater, even though it has a different shape. Significant vertical displacements occur out to a radius of 500 m before rapidly tapering off.

The indicated crater shape is an artifact of assuming that the subsidence is only vertical. The constitutive model predicts that the shear strength of the liquefied material will be insufficient to support a crater of this depth, so that at some time there would be a

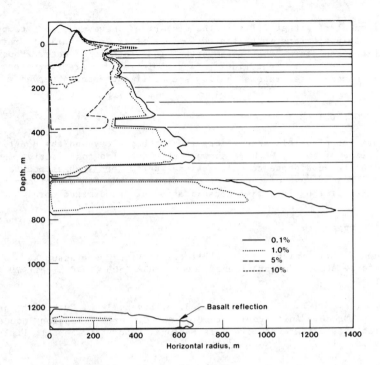

Figure 4. Consolidation contours within the various coral layers.
Numbers indicate volume change in percent. The consolidation in any
given zone is a function of the local porosity and the peak shock
stress.

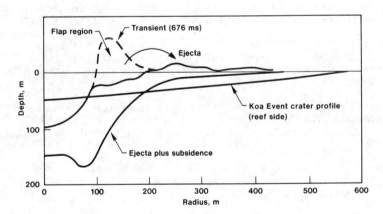

Figure 5. Actual and calculated profiles for the Koa Event crater.
Long and short dashes respectively represent the calculated transient
profile and the EJECT calculation of throw-out. The solid curve is the
crater profile resulting from vertical subsidence, which closely
matches the volume of the observed Koa Event crater.

horizontal flow that fills in the crater. We have made no attempt to model this slumping in this study, since it is the transient crater, not its final form, that is important in strategic effects. However, it does seem clear that liquifaction would rapidly transform the bowl-shaped crater into a shallow saucer like the one observed.

5. CONCLUSIONS

Based on plausible assumptions about the geology and the constitutive relations of coral, we have shown that a detailed constitutive model can relate subsidence to calculational parameters such as peak effective stress. Most of the observed volume of the Koa crater can be accounted for by late time consolidation of the damaged coral.

6. REFERENCES

Brode, H. L., "Height of Burst Effects at High Overpressures," Defense Atomic Support Agency Report DASA 2506 (1970 with 1979 update).

Burton, D. E., L. A. Lettis, Jr., J. B. Bryan, T. R. Butkovich, and A. L. Bruce, "Anisotropic Creation and Closure of Tension Induced Fractures", Lawrence Livermore National Laboratory Report, UCRL-79578. (1977).

Burton, D.E., L.A. Lettis, Jr., J. B. Bryan, and N.R. Frary, "Physics and Numerics of the TENSOR Code," Lawrence Livermore National Laboratory Rept. UCID-19428 (1982).

Burton, D.E., R.P. Swift, J.B. Bryan, and H.D. Glenn, "Subsidence in the Craters of Nuclear Tests at the Pacific Proving Grounds," Lawrence Livermore National Laboratory Report UCRL-91583, (1984).

Cooper, H.F. Jr., "A Summary of Explosion Cratering Phenomena Relevant to Meteor Impact Events," in Impact and Explosion Cratering, Pergamon Press (New York), D.J. Roddy, R. D. Pepin, and R.B. Merrill (eds.), (1977).

Ristvet, B. L., "Geologic and Geophysical Investigations of the Eniwetok Nuclear Craters," U.S. Air Force Weapons Laboratory, Kirtland Air Force Base, Albuquerque, NM, Rept. AFWL-TR-77-242, (1978)

Schuster, S.H., and V. E. Koit, "Initial KOA Calculations," Seventh Meeting of the DNA Ad Hoc Cratering Working Group, R&D Associates, Marina del Rey, CA, November (1983).

Swift, R.P., and D. E. Burton, "Numerical Modeling of the Mechanics of Non-linear Porous Media Under Dynamic Loading," Lawrence Livermore National Laboratory Report UCRL-53568 (1984).

Terzaghi, K., Theoretical Soil Mechanics, Wiley, New York, (1943).

A blocky physical model of longwall caving under strong roof conditions

M.B.WOLD
Division of Geomechanics, CSIRO, Australia

ABSTRACT

A well scaled, blocky physical model was used to study the feasiblity of longwall coal mining under strong and massive sandstone roof conditions at Moura, Queensland. Coal seams were progressively mined from the model while loads were measured on an instrumented model support, and roof caving and goaf formation mechanisms were measured using high precision photogrammetry. Caving spans and height, bulking factor, angle of break, support loads and their interaction with the structural geology are discussed with respect to predicted mine behaviour.

1 INTRODUCTION

The extraction of coal by longwall mining from beneath strong and massive roof strata presents the miner with geotechnical problems involving large caving spans and heights. These imply heavy loads on powered supports, pillars and abutments, the possibility of floor heave at the face and in the access roadways, and the danger of air-blasts from sudden failure of large spans. The need to cope with these geological conditions in some coalfields in Australia has led to the introduction of powered supports with capacities as high as 900 tonnes (Lama et al,1984).

At the Moura mine in the Bowen Basin, Queensland, strip mining and underground mining of several coal seams takes place in the strong, massive sandstones of the Baralaba coal measures. The introduction of longwall mining is under consideration by the operators, Thiess Dampier Mitsui,Pty. Ltd., and to investigate the feasibility of caving of the sandstone roof strata, the CSIRO Division of Geomechanics undertook a physical modelling study (Wold,1984).

Physical modelling methods are particularly useful in providing insights into the inelastic and failure regimes of discontinuous rock masses (e.g. Barton, 1979). Care must be taken that the visual impact of model behaviour does not overshadow the quantitative factors which govern that behaviour. The validity of the conclusions depends on the accuracy with which the boundary conditions, material properties, body forces and structural features are modelled, and on the accuracy of measurement of the response during testing. Frequently it is not possible to correctly scale all the desired parameters, and the consequent distortions in behaviour need to be assessed when applying the model results to the prototype.

The geomechanical parameters simulated in the Moura model test were
based on stratigraphic and structural observations, rock stress
measurements, and laboratory testing of joints and intact rock samples
(Nguyen et al,1983). The model was constructed from artificial rock-
like materials specially developed to satisfy the scaling requirements.
It contained more than 8000 blocks, representing rock units ranging in
size from 1m x 2m to 2m x 4m, and was excavated while under loads which
simulated the pre-mining stresses. Loads on an instrumented model
longwall support were measured and roof caving and goaf formation were
recorded and measured using high precision photogrammetry. Results are
interpreted in terms of predicted mine behaviour.

2 GEOMECHANICAL CONDITIONS AT THE MOURA MINE

Five seams are mined from the Baralaba coal measures by open pit or
underground methods. The seams are from 1.5 to 7m thick and have been
named from the top of the sequence as A,B,C,D and E. Two underground
mines are operating in C and D seams, with access via portals in
previously stripped pits. The C seam workings are directly above the D
seam workings.

The strata have a regional dip to the west of about 8 degrees, and are
mainly siltstones and shales at the upper levels and sandstones at the
lower interseam levels. The B-C interseam, which form the roof of the
proposed longwall blocks, contains sandstone up to 50m thick. An
analysis of bedding plane fractures in vertical bore cores showed that
the thickest units of about 3m, tend to occur near the middle of the
interseam. The C-D interseam contains up to 30m of sandstone, with unit
thicknesses of about 4m but up to 7m. The dip of the fractures generally
parallels the regional dip and particular thickness patterns tend to
extend linearly down dip.

Vertical jointing is well developed with a primary set of smooth
parallel joints of about 2m spacing with vertical persistance of up to
30m, striking N-N-W. A second vertical joint set, rougher, less
extensive and less well defined, strikes E-W. Laboratory shear testing
showed the smooth primary joints to be cohesionless with an angle of
friction in the range 20-35 degrees, in contrast to the rougher
secondary joints which produced a high apparent angle of friction.

Pre-mining stresses were measured at two underground sites by
overcoring and hydraulic fracturing. The major and minor principal
stresses σ_1 and σ_3, lie in the plane of the strata. σ_3 is directed E-W
and is slightly less than the near-vertical intermediate principal
stress σ_2, which corresponds in magnitude with the depth of overburden.

3 DESIGN OF MODEL

3.1 Construction and loading

A vertical ENE-WSW section representing a plane 200m wide and from 100m
to 300m below ground level was modelled at a length scale of 1:150. The
model was 1.25m square and 150mm thick. The chosen plane is normal to
the strike of the primary joint set and approximately parallel to the
regional dip, in which direction variations in the lithology and
structure are relatively minor. The semi-horizontal joint structure of
the model, based on the bedding plane fracture analysis, was simplified
to produce rock unit thickness classes of 1, 2, 3 and 4m. The major

vertical joint set was spaced regularly at 2m, with each joint plane
essentially continuous over the full height of the model. The idealized
lithological and structural features are shown in Figure 1, looking
south.

The model was made from sand-water-plaster materials, from which a
range of strengths and deformation moduli were obtained to simulate the
properties of the sandstone, shale and coal. The material properties are
given in Table 1 for the model and prototype (in parenthesis).

Table 1. Mechanical properties of Moura model and prototype.

PROPERTY	SANDSTONE	SHALE	COAL
unconfined compressive strength MPa	0.87 (90)	0.65	0.20
tensile strength MPa	0.15 (25)	0.10	
Young's modulus GPa	0.53 (14)	0.30	0.15
specific gravity	2.6 (2.4)	2.6 (2.4)	
friction angle, joints. degrees	24-32 (20-35)	24-32	
cohesion, joints	0 ($\sim$0)	0	

The model was loaded biaxially to produce a lithostatic stress field,
which represented the measured stresses in the chosen plane (Fig.1). The
vertical component of load from 100m to 300m arises from body forces,
with a surcharge applied to the top of the model corresponding to 100m
of overburden. The external loads were applied through a low-friction
system of seven vertical platens and eight pairs of horizontal platens
which could rotate and translate independently on ball race rollers. The
model was supported on its base by a semi-flexible array of passive
platens. The loading system could accomodate large boundary deformations
and curvatures, while maintaining the required loading distribution. No
load was applied to the front and rear faces of the model, to allow
block movement and stress re-distribution without frictional restraint.

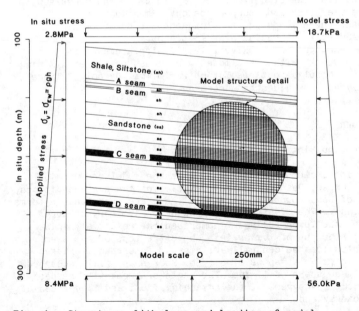

Fig. 1. Structure, lithology and loading of model.

3.2 Similarity requirements

Adequate similarity for modelling the jointed rock required that the dimensionless quantity $\sigma/\rho Lg$, and the angle of friction of the joints ϕ_j, be equal for the model and prototype; where σ = stress, ρ = density, L = length and g = acceleration due to gravity. With scale factors of unity for angle of friction, density and gravity, similarity was achieved by making the scale factor for stress equal to that for length; i.e. 1:150. Similarity for the intact blocks required the following dimensionless quantities to be equal in the model and prototype: σ_c/σ; σ_t/σ; $\rho g L/E$; σ_c/E; ν; ρ; where in addition to the previously defined quantities, σ_c = unconfined compressive strength, σ_t = tensile strength, E=Young's modulus, ν=Poisson's ratio, ϕ=angle of friction.

Assuming that the bedding plane fracture surfaces had similar frictional properties to the primary joint set, and neglecting any groundwater effects, the model was adequately scaled to simulate the jointed blocky structure, and the tensile strength of the individual blocks. However, the vertical joints in the model were rougher than required. For simulation of deformation and shear failure within the individual blocks, the model was stronger but less stiff than required, implying exaggerated deformations within the model blocks. This was not expected to significantly affect the caving performance of the model.

4 EXPERIMENTAL PROCEDURE

Following load cycling to consolidate the model and imposition of the required boundary stresses, the major portion of C seam (Fig.1) was progressively mined in steps equivalent to 1.5m. D seam was then similarly excavated. At the mining face a mechanized model support provided scaled setting loads, and was instrumented to measure the force vector and its line of action. Setting loads in the range 400 to 790 tonnes were used (assuming support canopy dimensions of 1.5m x 4.0m), and these loads and the load changes during mining and caving were measured to a precision of ±5 tonnes.

Using precise photogrammetry (Rivett,1983), displacements and rotations of 400 blocks within the model were measured for each mining and caving event. Displacement resolution was 0.1mm. Dynamic failure modes were analysed from video tape records.

5 MODEL BEHAVIOUR

5.1 Caving spans, bulking factor, caving height

In all, 130 mining cycles were carried out on the model and 9 major caving falls occurred. Despite the complexities of the test conditions, clear patterns of behaviour were evident. These are described in terms of mine dimensions. The first falls, at spans of 48m for the upper (C) seam and 30m for the lower (D) seam, comprised the relatively thin strata units to a height of 10m or less above the tops of the seams. The more massive units located centrally within the interseams, bridged across and failed later at spans of 65-75m. Subsequent falls occurred fairly regularly at spans of 11-19m. The angle of break with respect to vertical was about 25 degrees at the advancing face, and 18 degrees at the starting roadway end.

Representative caving development is shown for the third fall (Fig.2), which took place after 18m of face advance, at an overall span of 81m. The caving zone extended to 54m above the top of the seam, or 12 times the seam thickness. Before the fall, the thin strata to 10m above the coal spanned from the support to the goaf as a beam with built-in end at the support and simply supported at the goaf, rather than as a cantilever. The beam maintained its integrity while gradually deflecting away from the massive sandstone above it, showing that significant support may be provided by the unconsolidated goaf close to he face. Vectors of block displacement (Fig.3) show that just before the fall, movement was confined to a relatively narrow band of rock running up at 15-30 degrees to vertical from the rear of the support. Failure initiated in tension at the base of the immediate-roof beam, with the massive strata above bridging temporarily before collapsing. (Fig.4).

The bulking factor, K, varied within the goaf depending on the size of the rock units, their height above the seam, and the degree of consolidation. The vertical expansion factor was always greater than the horizontal factor: the unconsolidated immediate roofs of both C and D seams had vertical factors of 1.24 - 1.25 and a horizontal factor of 1.03, producing K = 1.32 (assuming similar horizontal expansion in the third direction). In the higher goaf including the more massive strata, and in consolidated areas, the vertical expansion factor ranged from 1.04 to 1.07 and the horizontal factor was less than 1.01. This produced K = 1.05 - 1.09, implying caving heights of 10 to 20 times the mining thickness.

Fig. 2. Caving zone after 3rd fall, C seam.

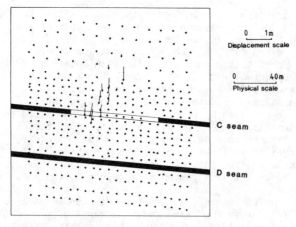

0   1m
Displacement scale

0   40m
Physical scale

C seam

D seam

Fig. 3. Displacements before 3rd fall,
7m face advance C seam.

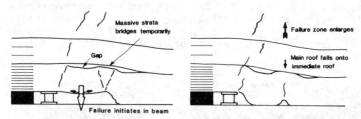

Massive strata
bridges temporarily

Gap

Failure initiates in beam

Failure zone enlarges

Main roof falls onto
immediate roof

Fig. 4. Failure mode for 3rd fall, C seam.

5.2 Support loads

The increments of normal load on the support produced by each mining
step were variable, but tended to increase as the span increased. After
the first fall, periodic "weighting" developed with a period of 5-7
mining cycles, as is often seen in practice (e.g. Peng and Chiang,
1984). For C seam, the range of load increments was about 20-180 tonnes,
with variable shear loads of up to 55 tonnes. Similar increments
occurred for D seam, but once failure of the massive strata bridging
across the immediate roof had begun, the increments became larger -
typically exceeding 200 tonnes. An extreme load of about 2500 tonnes was
produced during sudden failure of the complete bridge. This failure re-
mobilised the goaf above the previously mined upper seam which then
contributed to support loading as mining continued (Fig.5).

6 DISCUSSION AND CONCLUSIONS

The strong and massive sandstone strata within the interseam intervals
played a dominant role in the caving behaviour. The most massive units
bridged across the the goafs produced by caving of the relatively
thinner units which lay directly over the seams. Failure of these
bridging strata generated high support loads analogous to the "first
weight" experienced at typical spans of 70-120m in Australian longwalls.

1012

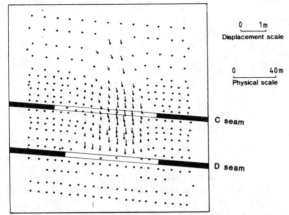

0 1m
Displacement scale

0 40m
Physical scale

C seam

D seam

Fig. 5. Displacements for 9m face advance, D seam,
after failure of interseam bridging strata.

The spatial distribution, orientation and mechanical properties of the
joints determines the "massiveness" of the strata. Preliminary model
tests showed that the tensile strength of the strata units, and cohesion
and friction on joints, had a critical effect on the ability of blocky
strata to form composite beams which could bridge over large spans. Any
cohesion on the horizontal bedding plane fractures increased the
effective depth of the beams and greatly increased their bending
strength and stiffness. However, although the tensile strength of the
intact material was high, the vertical joints produced tensile strengths
of the strata units approaching zero. Friction and interlocking on the
vertical joints enabled maintenance of beam flexural strength.

At Moura, the smoothness and low friction of the major joint set are
likely to contribute significantly to the cavability of the interseam
strata. Similar properties in the sub-horizontal fractures and bedding
planes would be desirable from this point of view. In the gathering of
pre-development data, the mapping and measurement of mechanical
properties of joint and fracture systems should receive high priority.
Horizontal stress, which in Australia is often higher than vertical
stress, would tend to increase the stability of the bridging strata by
counteracting the development of tensile stresses in the lowest
competent unit. However, any local span from the support to the goaf
would be horizontally stress-relieved and thus become more susceptible
to tensile failure. The extraction of longwall blocks perpendicular to
the primary vertical joint set and in the direction of the minor
principal stress, as modelled, would provide the best prospect for
controllable caving. The model results suggest that this could be
achieved.

The mode of caving development implied that an immediate roof block
was defined by the caving height and caving angle as described by Wilson
(1975). With the low bulking factor and consequent large caving height
produced by the strong sandstone, this type of analysis would suggest
very heavy support loading. However, the model showed that the newly
formed goaf supplied substantial normal and shear components of support
to the overhanging immediate roof block (Fig.6), decreasing the powered
support requirements. Similarly at the lower level of the goaf directly
behind the support, the local roof beam was supported at its far end by

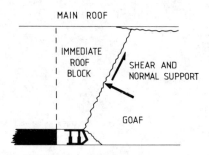

MAIN ROOF

IMMEDIATE
ROOF
BLOCK

SHEAR AND
NORMAL SUPPORT

GOAF

Fig. 6. Partial support of
immediate roof block by goaf.

the goaf, rather than forming a cantilever. In this overall situation
the powered support could yield away from excessive loads. However, the
development of very large dynamic loads during brittle failure of strong
bridging strata has caused damage to support systems. In these
conditions hydraulic systems should have the capacity to rapidly dump
large volumes of fluid to relieve high dynamic pressure.

In the strong roof conditions found in Australia and the USA,
lemniscate shield type supports are generally used to cope with
horizontal forces on the support. For design purposes, laboratory
testing of full size supports is carried out, but underground
measurement to determine load vectors on supports has been difficult
(Barczak and Carson,1984). The model techniques may be useful for this
purpose, although further refinement is required to improve the
similarity between model and prototype supports.

Overall, the model results compare well with behaviour experienced in
real mines, providing evidence that with proper scaling of in situ
conditions, useful quantitative predictions of mine behaviour are
possible.

7 REFERENCES

Barczak,T.M. and Carson,R.C. 1984. Technique to measure load vector on
    shield supports. 25th Symposium on Rock Mechanics, p. 667-679.
    Evanston, Illinois.
Barton,N.R. 1979. Model studies of very large underground openings at
    shallow depth. Proc. 4th Congr. Int. Soc. Rock Mech., Montreaux.
Lama,R.D.,Blackwood,R.L.,Hebblewhite,B.K.,Bhattacharyya,A.K. 1984.
    Monitoring the effect of massive sandstone roof in a longwall
    operation at West Cliff Colliery. The Coal Journal, August.
Nguyen,V.V.,Enever,J.R. and Mallett,C.W. 1983. A study of site
    conditions affecting roof caving potential in an area of massive
    sandstone. CSIRO Aust.,Div. Geomech., Geomechanics of coal mining
    report No. 45.
Peng,S.S. and Chiang,H.S.,1984. Longwall mining. New York. Wiley.
Rivett,L. 1983. The role of photogrammetry in surveillance surveys.
    Symposium on the surveillance of engineering structures, University of
    Melbourne. November.
Wilson,A.H. 1975. Support load requirements on longwall faces. The
    Mining Engineer, p.479-491. June.
Wold,M.B. 1984. Physical model study of caving under massive sandstone
    roof conditions at Moura, Queensland. CSIRO Aust., Div. Geomech.,
    Geomechanics of coal mining report No. 57.

Finite element techniques for the determination of rock salt material properties from in situ and laboratory penetrometer data

STEPHEN NIOU & SHIANN-JANG CHERN
Serata Geomechanics Inc., Richmond, California, USA

SHINJI KIKUCHI
Japan Development & Construction Co. Ltd, Tokyo, Japan

ABSTRACT

Laboratory biaxial indentation tests have been used to examine rock salt behavior in response to a point loading. The results were compared with borehole penetrometer data acquired in situ. Comparison of these two sets of results illustrates the applicability of the borehole penetrometer for in situ determination of rock salt material properties. Finite element simulations were conducted to evaluate the salt material property parameters by modelling material behavior, which requires an assumption of continuity between the applied surface of the indention and the salt.

1 INTRODUCTION

Determination of material properties of rocks has long been an important need in mining engineering. Laboratory methods such as the uniaxial loading test and triaxial loading test are common means of obtaining rock properties. However, recent investigation (Cook, Hood, Tsai) indicates that indentation tests can be applied for rock testing, as rocks respond differently under the indentor. Invesitgation (Serata & Bellman) also reveals correlations between results of uniaxial loading tests and indentation tests with regard to the determination of mechanical property parameter values (Fig. 1). These recent works indicate that indentation tests can be made to produce information about mechanical properties just as can more common testing methods. Serata and Bellman have also shown that indentation tests can be conducted either in situ or in the laboratory. Test results of in situ and lab indentation tests reveal the same order of magnitude.

This paper illustrates an application of the penetrometer to obtain in situ properties of rock salt. A finite element code, REM, was used to convert field data to coefficients of rock properties. To evaluate the accuracy of the in situ penetrometer, a similar penetrometer test was conducted in the lab, using specimens obtained from the test site. The lab test was conducted under biaxial loading conditions. REM was again used to convert the indentation data to material properties. Two sets of rock properties were then compared to show the applicability of the field penetrometer tests.

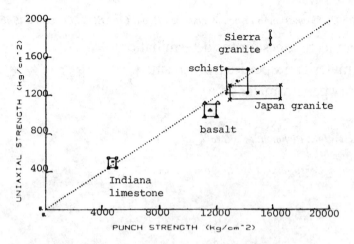

FIG. 1.
Relation
between
indentation
punch
and uniaxial
strengths
of various
types of rock.

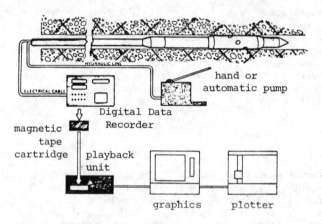

FIG. 2.
Field penetrometer
measuring system.

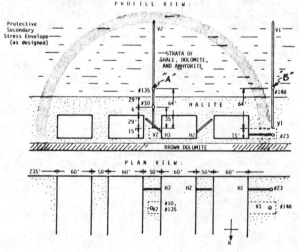

FIG. 3.
Locations of in situ
penetrometer test.

2 DESCRIPTION OF IN SITU PENETROMETER TESTING

The borehole probe body is a cylinder 1 m in length and 92 mm in diameter. The probe has 8 independently acting loading pistons, deployed in 4 radial directions at 90° intervals, and spaced 5 cm between the centers. The 8 pistons are loaded by the same hydraulic fluid and conduct 8 separate loading tests simultaneously. Linearly variable deformation transducers (LVDTs) are used to monitor piston movement. Detailed descriptions of the penetrometer and its data acquisition system are found in the references (Serata, McNamara, Tsai, 1983; Serata & Bellman, 1984). The entire system of the in situ indentation test is shown in Fig. 2.

The in situ penetrometer test was conducted in the 4-room test entry system of the Sifto salt mine, Goderich, Ontario. Data for this presentation were obtained at two critical locations, A and B, as shown in Fig. 3. There, the piston loading was applied with 10 minutes of increasing load, 5 minutes of creep loading at the maximum load, and 0.5 minutes of unloading. Figs. 4 and 5 illustrate the resulting pressure-displacement (p-D) curves.

3 LABORATORY INDENTATION TEST

The biaxial testing stand used for the laboratory indentation tests is equipped with two sets of flat jacks, providing biaxial confinement to the rectangular specimen. The indentor loading is applied against the exposed surface of the specimens, which are preloaded laterally by the two sets of flat jacks. A typical test procedure includes 3 loading and creep cycles with 5 minutes of loading and 10 minutes of creep at the maximum loading.

The size of the rock sample is 100x100 mm faces with 85 mm height. Before testing, confining pressures are applied to the sides of the sample for 30 minutes. The indentor is lowered, and 3 loading-creep cycles are applied to the rock. Test results are given in the p-D relation shown in Figs. 6 and 7 under two different confining pressures of 140.74 kg/cm^2 and 211 kg/cm^2.

4 FINITE ELEMENT SIMULATIONS

After obtaining the p-D curves, the next step was to convert them into corresponding material properties of the rock salt. This step was approached by using a finite element code to simulate the various loading steps of the test procedure by properly selecting material properties to match the actual p-D curves. The finite element code used in this analysis is based on the following assumptions: (1) separation of octahedral and volumetric behaviors in parallel series of linear summation; (2) in the individual series, basic behavioral components of elasticity, viscoelasticity, and viscoplasticity are superimposed in linear addition of their strains; and (3) the nonlinear nature of material properties are inherent in the individual components and are interrelated among the components.

The input meshes for laboratory and field tests can be seen in Figs. 8 and 9, respectively. An axisymmetric analysis was used for both meshes. The test procedures are closely followed in the model simulation through various stages of loading, creeping, and unloading.

1017

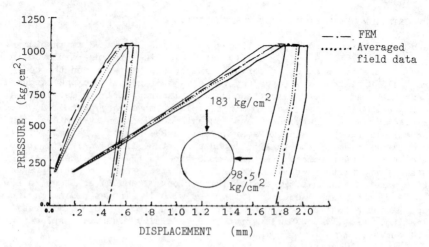

FIG. 4. Comparison with Field and FEM Simulated Punching Test Results'
at Location B.

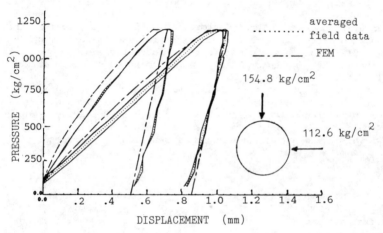

FIG. 5. Comparison with Field and FEM Simulated Punching Test Results
at Location A.

In the simulation for laboratory tests, rock properties are the only
factors adjusted for matching the desired curves, while in the simulation of field penetrometer tests, confining stresses were varied as well
as rock properties.

The field penetrometer has 8 piston heads which form 4 groups. Accordingly, 4 curves result from a single penetrometer test and these curves
are averaged into two curves. For matching the finite element model
with the field test results, the input material properties were first
adjusted to cause the simulated behavior to fall at about the middle
of the two different p-D curves. Secondly, the simulated curve of the
middle position is split by increasing the difference between the

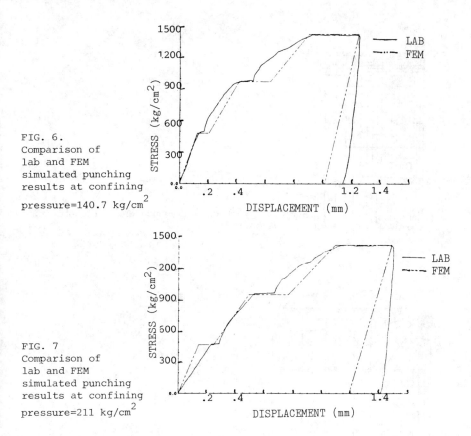

FIG. 6.
Comparison of
lab and FEM
simulated punching
results at confining
pressure=140.7 kg/cm^2

FIG. 7
Comparison of
lab and FEM
simulated punching
results at confining
pressure=211 kg/cm^2

maximum and minimum stresses, while the mean stress is left unchanged
until the pair of split curves matches with the measured pair of split
curves.

5 DISCUSSION

The simulated results from the laboratory tests under the two different
confinement pressures are plotted in Figs. 6 and 7. Rock properties
for these simulations are listed in Table 1. The simulated p-D curves
match the field data closely, as shown in Figs. 4 and 5, and material
properties used for these simulations are also listed in Table 1.
    In Table 1, it can be noticed that G_2, V_2 and V_4 are lower than what
were expected. Here, the G_2 and V_2 values disclose short-term viscoelastic properties, which are different from the commonly observed long-
term viscoelastic properties. This reflects the time period of the
test. The V_4 values mostly indicate the initial consolidation effect,
rather than the true viscoplasticity.
    Rock properties obtained from the field penetrometer and laboratory in-
dentation tests agree well with each other, as can be seen in Table 1.
This demonstrates the applicability of the field penetrometer tests.

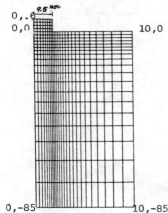

DIMENSION mm

FIG. 8. Finite element mesh for lab indentation test.

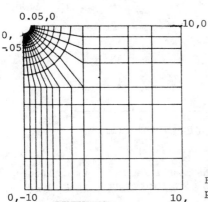

DIMENSION m

FIG. 9. Finite element mesh for field
penetrometer test.

PROPERTIES	Symbol	Unit	Lab Salt @ 140.74	Lab Salt @ 211.11	Field 60.5V2	Field 60.5V1
Shear modulus	G_1	kg/cm^2	84400	56300	39400	42200
Retarded shear modulus $(\tau_o < k_o)$	G_2	kg/cm^2	3380	2110	2110	1690
Elastoviscosity $(\tau_o < k_o)$	V_2	$kg/cm^2 \cdot day$	338	211	106	85
Plastoviscosity	V_4	$kg/cm^2 \cdot day$	105	105	141	105
Ultimate bulk modulus	K_1	kg/cm^2	116500	77400	56300	60300
Retarded bulk modulus	K_2	kg/cm^2	70370	70370	35200	35200
Hydrostatic elasto-viscosity	D_2	$kg/cm^2 \cdot day$	7040	7040	3520	3520
Unconfined octahedral shear strength	k_o^A	kg/cm^2	4.2	4.2	4.2	4.2
Ultimate octahedral shear strength	k_o^B	kg/cm^2	42	42	42	42
Maximum stress	P_o	kg/cm^2	140.74	211.11	154.8	183
Minimum stress	Q_o	kg/cm^2	--	--	112.6	98.5

TABLE 1.
Material property
parameters and
stress fields.

For the determination of in situ creep properties, the constant load of the creep test should be maintained for long-term observation. In analyzing such data for determining viscoelastic properties, the viscoelastic components modelled using a single Kelvin model should be replaced by a 3-Kelvin model.

In Fig. 4, the two averaged curves are widely spread. This might have been caused by stress fields and/or by non-homogeneity of rocks at different spots. Since the penetrometer has 8 pistons and each curve is the average of 4 piston movements, it is unlikely that the separation of curves is caused by rock non-homogeneity. It was thus decided to utilize the non-uniform stress effect in modelling the split field p-D curves. From Figs. 4 and 5, and Table 1, it is shown that the larger the difference between the maximum and minimum field stresses, the greater the p-D curve split. Thus, the field penetrometer can sense not only the material properties but also the field stresses with their orientation.

Comparing the model properties listed in Table 1, the results from simulating field penetrometer tests are not much different from those of simulating the laboratory tests. This indicates that the field penetrometer is capable of replacing the laboratory biaxial indentation tests in finding material properties of rocks with the accuracies usually required for most mining purposes.

There are important advantages of the field penetrometer over the lab tests. First, the rock material properties can be obtained with much less disturbance and more effectiveness. There is no need for sample collection, logging, shipment, and test preparation. Also, the field penetrometer can determine variation of material properties all along the test borehole at any desired intensity. However, the test results can be analyzed while the probe is still in the test borehole at site, making quality control of the measurements effective.

In the future, the authors would like to see the effects of changing piston size and shape of the piston head. Also, it would be interesting to correlate the penetrometer test data with laboratory triaxial or other tests. For the finite element code, we would like to add constitutive models of tensile failure, strain softening, and the slip joint phenomenon to closely simulate the indentation behavior.

6 CONCLUSIONS

This paper is a preliminary study on finding rock salt properties and field stresses through the penetrometer method and finite element simulation. Although the method needs further improvement, it indicates the potential of field indentation tests in finding rock properties. In addition, the finite element code provides reasonable results when converting field data to material property coefficients.

REFERENCES

Cook, N.G.W., Hood, M., & Tsai, F. 1984. Observations of crack growth in hard rock loaded by an indentor. Int. J. Rock Mech. Min. Sci 21:2.
Lindquist, P.A., & Lai, H.H. 1983. Behavior of the crushed zone in rock indentation. Rock Mech. Engng, 16, 199-207.
Serata, S., and Bellman, R. 1983. Development of the Serata stress

measuring system for application to both hard-brittle and soft-ductile grounds. Proc., 24th U.S. Symposium on Rock Mechanics.

Serata, S., McNamara, J., & Tsai, F. 1983. Field experience with a multiple piston loading borehole probe. Proc., 24th U.S. Symposium on Rock Mechanics.

Wagner, H., and Schumann, E.H.R. 1971. The stamp load bearing strength of rock: an experimental and theoretical investigation. Rock Mech. 3, Springer-Verlag, 185-207.

Wang, J.K., & Lehnoff, T.F. 1976. Bit penetration into rock -- a finite element study. Int'l. J. Rock Mech. Min. Sci., 13, 11-16.

The application of a personal computer
in a rock mechanics data acquisition system

ZBIGNIEW HLADYSZ & CHARLES A.KLICHE
South Dakota School of Mines & Technology, Rapid City, USA

1 HISTORICAL BACKGROUND

In 1981, the Mining Engineering Department at the South Dakota School of
Mines and Technology commited itself to upgrading its rock mechanics
laboratory. Originally, it was intended to make a survey of needs and
then attempt to obtain the needed funding from either state or outside
sources. Early on the survey, it was apparent that the cost of
replacing the existing laboratory equipment with the state-of-the-art
instrumentation would be at least $250,000.00. Unless we received
substantial outside funding, another method of upgrading the laboratory
had to be found. Instead of purchasing the computerized testing
machine, it was decided to put together a data acquisition system
compatible with the existing testing machine. The system decided upon
was a Digistrip III and RAMP Scanner from Kaye Instruments along with an
Apple IIe computer. Any software and additional hardware would have to
be developed in house.

2 SYSTEM COMPONENTS

2.1 Hardware

The hardware is composed of five parts: load retransmitter, bridge
conditioners, the Digistrip III, the RAMP Scanner and the Apple IIe
computer with internal modem. The system, H&K Data Acquisition System,
is shown on fig. 1. Currently, the system also uses the campus Cyber
170 mainframe computer capabilities for data reduction and plotting.

2.1.1 DC output load retransmitter

This device converts the motion of load indicating servo of the testing
machine to a DC signal that can be used to reproduce the load measured
by the testing machine. Its basic components consist of a 1 kΩ
potentiometer, geared to the load servo of the testing machine, and an
analog device which provides power supply for the potentiometer and
sends output signals. The output range is from 0 to 6.5 volts for each
load range on the Tinius Olson testing machine.

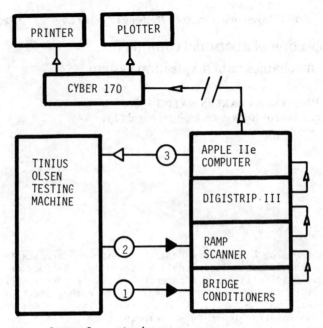

1 -- Input from strain gages
2 -- Input from load retransmitter
3 -- Manual adjustment of the rate of loading

Figure 1. H&K Data Acquisition System - System Components

2.1.2 Bridge conditioners

Bridge conditioners are used to convert the resistance output from
strain gages, attached to the rock specimen being tested, to a voltage
output. The bridge used is the model BC-8 from Kaye Instruments. Each
unit provides connections for eight input circuits. Available bridge
configurations are: 1/4 bridge - 2 and 3 wires, 1/2 bridge - 3 wires and
full bridge - 4 wires. Because the bridge is used with the Digistrip
processor, the bridge output can be scaled linearly so that the voltage
output is converted to engineering units, such as microstrain.

2.1.3 RAMP Scanner

The RAMP (Remote Analog Multiplexing Processor) Scanner performs the
function of multiplexing and converting low level DC signals to a
serial-by-bit data stream. The RAMP has a threefold job: scanning,
converting and communicating any voltage signal within the range of 1
microvolt to 24 volts DC. Currently, its primary purpose is to receive
data from the bridge conditioners and from the load retransmitter, and
transmit this data to the Digistrip III. It operates at 10 channels per
second and continuously transmits the data using a standard 30 ma
current loop interface.

2.1.4 Digistrip III

The Digistrip III is a multi-input process monitor. It is based on an internal microprocessor which must be programmed by a user with the guidelines which apply to a specific application. The instrument includes a timer and an internal printer which provides a permanent record of process data. The Digistrip III can handle up to 128 analog inputs. Its basic operations provide for the processing of inputs from strain gages, current transmitters, etc. Each input is assigned to a specific channel address. Once the appropriate instructions have been programmed into the unit, data received is automatically scaled into applicable engineering units, then printed out and/or transmitted to a computer.

In order for the instrument to process an input, a specific computation routine must be defined. These routines are called channel functions. There are 99 functions available. Functions currently in use are: milivolt scale and linear functions. Linear functions are used to define linear scaling for single input variables. A particular linear function may be assigned to one or more channel addresses. Whenever a linear function is assigned, two points X_1, Y_1, and X_2, Y_2 must be defined (fig. 2).

Once the two points are defined, the instrument automatically computes the slope and X intercept of the function. The two known points are defined for the function by programming values for: Input 1, Output 1, Input 2, Output 2.

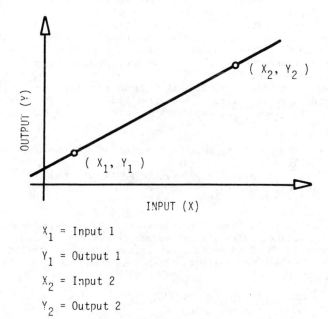

X_1 = Input 1

Y_1 = Output 1

X_2 = Input 2

Y_2 = Output 2

Figure 2. Linearization

Example:

A programmer wishes to define a linear function which will monitor
strain gage readings during a specific test over the range from 0 to
10,000 $\mu\varepsilon$. A linear function is set as follows:

Input   1: 00.000   (mV)
Input   2: 15.182*   (mV)
Output 1: 00000   ($\mu\varepsilon$)
Output 2: 10000   ($\mu\varepsilon$)

2.2 Software

Currently, to use the data acquisition system, software for both the
Apple IIe and for the Cyber 170 is required. There are two programs for
the Apple IIe. The first one, called DIGI, takes the incoming data from
the Digistrip III and manipulates it into a data file which can be read
by the Cyber 170. It reads all characters into memory using a machine
language subroutine, throws out unwanted characters, and places the
remaining characters in a file on a disk. At the present, the program
is set up for two strain gages per rock specimen. This program is used
as a regular procedure for educational purposes at the Department of
Mining Engineering.

The second program for the Apple IIe is a commercial communication
package. The communication package includes an internal modem and
communication software. The data from the Digistrip III can be directly
transmitted to the Cyber 170 without the necessity of using a computer
terminal. Previously, all data from the Digistrip III was entered via a
computer terminal. With long files, much time was spent de-bugging the
files. The communication program has the capabilities of turning the
Apple IIe into an active computer terminal for the Cyber 170 while the
data is being transmitted. This allows the operator to set up a data
file on the Cyber 170, transmit the data, verify the data, then modify
the data while in an edit mode. With the data acquisition system,
errors may only occur either as the first line of the file, or as one
of the last few lines. The important main body of the file is error
free.

The Cyber program is a very important part of the system. This program,
Program ROKTEST, uses the trasnsmitted raw data to calculate the
corrected load, the rate of loading, the secant and tangent modulus of
elasticity (or deformation), and the secant and tangent Poisson's ratio
(table 1).

The program then plots the corrected axial stress versus strains
(fig. 3.) as well as axial strains versus transverse strains. The
program corrects the load because, at last calibration, the mechanical
dial of the Tinius Olson testing machine was found to be slightly
off.

*Bridge output for gage factor = 2.045

1026

Table 1. Output Tables (Program Roktest)

SPECIMEN TESTED ON 1/3/85

2.498 IN. IS THE AVR. DIA.
5.246 IN. IS THE AVR. HT.

AXIAL STRESS (PSI)	TRANSVERSE STRAIN (MICROIN/IN)	AXIAL STRAIN (MICROIN/IN)	LOAD RATE (PSI/SEC)
574.30	6	-33	10.44
992.00	12	-69	15.47
1409.69	17	-103	13.05
1827.39	22	-138	18.16
.	.	.	.
.	.	.	.
20623.39	341	-1724	98.16

SECANT MODULUS (PSI)	SECANT POISSON'S RATIO	TANGENT MODULUS (PSI)	TANGENT POISSON'S RATIO
.174E+08	.18182	.127E+08	.18182
.144E+08	.17391	.116E+08	.16667
.138E+08	.16098	.125E+08	.13433
.132E+08	.15580	.118E+08	.14085
.	.	.	.
.	.	.	.
.120E+08	.19751	.103E+08	.16049

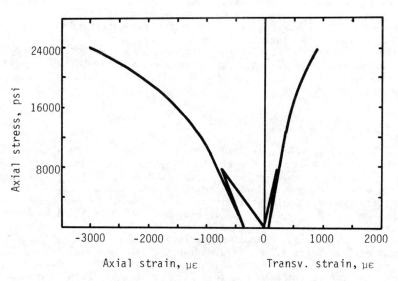

Figure 3. Output Plot (Program Roktest)

3 SYSTEM OPERATION

3.1 Menu

The Apple IIe program for the system is menu driven with a choice of 6
options as it can be seen on figure 4. When an option is chosen, a
window appears at the top of the screen. In the window (fig. 5) is
displayed the recommended rate of loading for the test and the actual
rate of loading during the test. Displayed below the window is the time
and load at each time interval as this information is received from the
Digistrip III.

```
DATA REDUCTION IS AVAILABLE FOR THE FOLLOWING TESTS:

  1. BRAZILIAN
  2. MODULUS OF RUPTURE - PRISMATIC SPECIMEN
  3. MODULUS OF RUPTURE - CYLINDRICAL SPECIMEN
  4. SHEAR - ROCK CUBE
  5. UNIAXIAL COMPRESSION
     A. WITH STRAIN GAGES
     B. WITHOUT STRAIN GAGES
```

Figure 4. Menu on the Apple IIe

When strain gages are being used during uniaxial compression, the
recommended rate of loading and the actual rate of loading are again
displayed. In addition, the time, load and strains are displayed below
the window (fig. 5) at each pre-set time interval as the information is
received from the Digistrip III. The transmission interval can be set
in increments of one minute up to 9999 minutes. An additional
possibility, which is used for the data acquisition system, is to set
the transmission interval at zero. This gives a transmission interval
of 10 seconds. The longer transmission intervals are used for long term
tests, such as creep test.

3.2 Files

At the present, two separate files are used. The first is a file
created with the Apple IIe for the incoming data from the Digistrip III.
This file is for storage of the reduced raw data on a floppy disk. The
reduced data is composed of the actual raw data with any unwanted
characters removed. Since the Digistrip III tansmits time with hours,
minutes and seconds separated by colons, and the Apple IIe does not
accept anything to the right of a colon in a normal data string, the
colon must be removed. This is accomplished using a routine which
accepts any character in a string as input. After the entire line of
data is input, the line is run through a routine which removes the
colons then stores the new line to a file on a disk. Each line of data
is reduced in this manner.

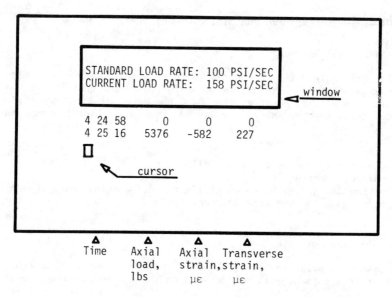

STANDARD LOAD RATE: 100 PSI/SEC
CURRENT LOAD RATE: 158 PSI/SEC

← window

| 4 24 58 | 0 | 0 | 0 |
| 4 25 16 | 5376 | -582 | 227 |

cursor

▲ Time ▲ Axial load, lbs ▲ Axial strain, με ▲ Transverse strain, με

Figure 5. Data Display on the Apple's Screen

After the test is completed, and all lines of raw data are reduced, the communication package and modem is used to transmit the data to a file on the Cyber 170 mainframe computer. The data is then edited, where necessary, to correspond with the data format for printing and plotting program on the Cyber. Once a file is set up on the Cyber computer, the program can be run at any desired time. Examples of data files are shown in table 2.

Table 2. Data Files

a. Raw data (on the Digistrip III)

4:24:58	0	0	0
4:25:06	3025	-582	227
4:25:16	4540	-1007	483
4:25:26	6580	-1452	624

b. Reduced data (on the Apple II e)

4 24 58	0	0	0
4 25 06	3025	-582	227
4 25 16	4540	-1007	483
4 25 26	6580	-1452	624

1029

4 FUTURE IMPROVEMENTS TO THE SYSTEM

4.1 Additional hardware

Additional equipment to be purchased in the future is for a continued upgrading of the rock mechanics laboratory, and not necessarily the data acquisition system. On the other hand the proposed data acquisition system can accept an input from any additional piece of instrumentation.

Needed equipment includes:

a. A new high-pressure triaxial cell.
b. A direct shear device.
c. Deformation jacket based on LVDT's for deformation measurements during uniaxial and triaxial compression.

4.2 Apple IIe software

The system is still in its infant stage as far as software is concerned. Software development will be focussed on the following objectives:

a. Additional strain gage capabilities: The program, as currently written, is for only two strain gages. Emphasis will be placed on modifying the program for "n" strain gage arrangement. This modified program will be used for the determination of directional elastic constants of anisotropic rocks.
b. Menu expansion: With the acquisition of a new instrumentation mentioned above, new options will be added to the menu.
c. Modification of Digistrip III transmission interval: The matrix of internal program options for the Digistrip III allows for data transmission at the receipt of a Control-D character. The Apple IIe program is to be modified to send a Control-D character to the Digistrip III when the computer is ready to receive the data, instead of at the current 10 second time intervals. This will allow for more points on various plots, and will therefore better indicate the behavior of the specimen being tested.
d. Determination of failure criterion: Using the input from uniaxial compresssive, tensile and triaxial or direct shear tests, failure criteria can be determined and failure envelopes can be plotted. These capabilities already exist on the Cyber 170.
e. Rate of straining: After modifications of the hydraulic circuit of the testing machine, the control of the rate of straining can be achieved. This will provide closed loop servo-controlled testing capabilities for the Tinius-Olson.
f. Eliminate the Cyber 170: A data reduction and plotting option for the Apple IIe is currently being written. This option will eliminate using the Cyber 170 mainframe computer.

5 CONCLUSIONS

Laboratory equipment is fast becoming extremely sophisticated and expensive. Many schools and laboratories can no longer afford to purchase needed equipment to upgrade their laboratories. This is the case of the rock mechanics laboratory at the South Dakota School of Mines and Technology. Instead of purchasing a new testing machine and accompanying data acquisition equipment, it was decided to put together a data acquisition system that could be used with the existing facilities. The H&K Data Acquisition System, as it currently stands, is in its infant stage of development. Much more can be done to improve the system. This work is currently underway.

The system can be adjusted to any existing rock mechanics facilities that need upgrading and expanding its capabilities.

REFERENCES

1. Tinius–Olson Manual, 1960, Tinius–Olson Testing Machine Co., Inc.
2. D.C. Output load retransmitter, 1984, Instruction No. 012373a, Tinius–Olson Testing Machine Co., Inc,.
3. Digistrip III – User's guide, 1981, Kaye Instruments, Inc.
4. RAMP/Scanner – Installation, operation and maintenance manual, 1981, Kaye Instruments, Inc.
5. Apple IIe – Manual, 198, Apple Inc.
6. Hladysz, Z., Kliche, C., 1984, A laboratory manual for rock mechanics, MinE 411, SDSM&T

Evaluation of a large sample triaxial test facility:
A progress report

MALCOLM J.REEVES
Geological Engineering, University of Saskatchewan, Saskatoon, Canada

1. ABSTRACT

An evaluation is made of the Large Sample Triaxial Test Facility
(LSTTF) housed in the laboratories of the Saskatchewan Research
Council (SRC) in Sakatoon. The 10 (ten) pressure cells will test very
large 200 mm diameter x 400 mm cores.

Data are presented to show that triaxial strength, creep and
relaxation characteristics can be determined, for 200 mm diameter
specimens, with confining stresses up to at least 50 MPa, axial loads
up to 700 tonnes and axial strains up to 15%. The research potential
of the facility is extensive.

The ability to test very large samples is important for coarsely
crystalline materials (e.g. potash), coarse granular fills (e.g mine
tailings) and fractured rocks and soils (e.g. tills).

The ability to carry out long-term tests with very large strains
under computer control is particularly applicable to creep of
evaporites; creep/flow of partially unconsolidated, heavy-oil
reservoir rocks and consolidation of tailings and fills.

2. INTRODUCTION

Ten pressure vessels were built in the late 1970's in Saskatoon at the
Saskatchewan Research Council (SRC) Laboratories. The vessels were
designed as triaxial cells to test the creep behaviour of salt, potash
and other similar "soft" rocks.

The evaluation and calibration of the laboratory was undertaken
jointly by SRC and the Geological Engineering Laboratories at the
University of Saskatchewan (GELUS) in 1983/84.

The principal objectives of the LSTTF project were three-fold :
    (1) To evaluate the triaxial hydraulic loading systems,
    (2) To evaluate the computer control and data acquisition
        systems,
    (3) To evaluate the facility as a research tool for the resource
        based industries.

The work was largely concerned with determining the practical
capabilities of the cells to perform tests; under controlled stress,
strain, temperature, stress-rate and strain rate conditions; on "soft"
rocks.

3. EQUIPMENT DESCRIPTION

A schematic representation of the LSTTF cell hydraulics and monitoring systems is shown in Fig.1. There are 10 (ten) creep cells in the facility.

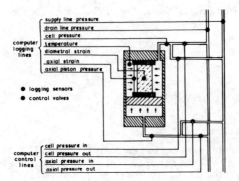

Figure 1 : LSTTF hydraulic,logging and control systems.

Each pressure vessel has a height of 1350 mm, an external diameter of 600 mm and a wall thickness of 150 mm. The internal piston for axial loading is sealed with "teflon" piston rings and has a diameter of about 430 mm. The axial load capacity is approximately 7 MN or 700 tonnes. The design specification indicates that the cells are capable of sustaining operational axial piston pressures and radial cell pressures of up to 50 MPa.

A full technical specification of the original design is provided by Chdubiak and Williams (1977) and details of modifications made during evaluation and calibration are documented by Reeves (1984).

The cells are designed for samples of diameter 200 mm with a length of 400 mm. The original design specified precast urethane sample jackets to isolate the test samples from the hydraulic fluid used to provide the radial confining pressure. In practice, these jackets were found unsuitable because of their extreme stiffness and were replaced by "ecosil" jackets (a more flexible plastic material) cast around the sample after the attachment of strain instrumentation.

The radial and axial cell pressures are completely independent and can be computer controlled. Pressure transducers sense pressure changes and adjustments can be made by actuating solenoid valves. The design specifications require that pressures be maintained constant for extended periods to within 0.4 MPa. This specification is inadequate since errors in the measurement of deviator stress on the sample can be as much as 2.0 MPa. The original pressure transducers are sceduled for replacement with sensors of greater sensitivity which measure deviator stresses to 0.25 MPa.

The current method of monitoring vertical strain was arrived at after several experimental trials. It involves the direct cementation of small, circumferential plates or "shells" to the sample surface at three equally-spaced points near the ends. These "shells" are threaded so that the rod, to which the potentiometers are attached, can be firmly anchored. The "ecosil" sample jacket is cast around the "shell" attachments with the rod passing through the jacket.

This arrangement is not ideal since the cement bond may be subject to "creep" but in practice, excellent correspondence is found between cemented resistance-wire strain gauges and pots attached in this way and problems with "slack" in the piston-platen-endpiece assembly are avoided.

Horizontal strains are monitored by resistance wire stain gauges. Attempts to develop "girth" monitors using spring loaded bands and resistance wire wraps have made little progress to date. The estimation of volumetric strains, from cell-oil volume changes sensed by the computer, has yet to be perfected but is expected to be successful.

To ensure continuity of supply all laboratory systems may be powered from d.c. batteries through a surge protector and an inverter, the battery being continually charged from the a.c. mains.

A typical configuration of data sensors involves three axial pots, five horizontal strain gauges and five hydraulic pressure sensing transducers. Many of these data signals require conditioning (amplification, offset, inversion) before they are read by a logging device. The Tecmar TM40 logger/controller card, used in an IBM-PC or COMPAQ computer, carries out all necessary control and logging functions. With external signal conditioning, the TM40 card can sample at the rate of 40 kHz (40,000 channels per second).

The software to perform logging functions is very simple. Since fast execution of code is not essential, the programs were written in Microsoft BASICA. The interval between readings can be set to any constant value or can be based on the rate of change of sensor signals. This prevents the accumulation of huge amounts of irrelevant data when slow consistent variations are logged.

Control signals are output from the Tecmar controller through an 8-bit parallel port. The solenoid valves require 110 volts a.c. supply to operate and the switching is achieved through an eight channel opto-isolated power driver card. The software to operate the control circuitry, in common with the logging software, is relatively simple. The routines fall into two distinct groups. Switch routines to open and close switches; and control routines to decide which switches to open or close. The control routines call some simple logging routines for information upon which to base decisions.

A series of auxiliary, post-test, processing routines have been written which tabulate and plot various logged parameters or functions of logged parameters.

The control/logging package is written in a form which can be readily adapted for other hardware configurations. It will log up to 16 analogue inputs and operate up to 8 control devices. Care has been taken to isolate hardware dependent code so that the software is hardware independent and transportable. The final version of the software will be self-documenting and menu-driven.

4. TEST SPECIMENS

An aluminium test-piece comprising a 250 mm diameter x 300 mm cylinder was instrumented with 5 x 50 mm length resistance-wire strain gauges (3 vertical, 2 horizontal) placed symmetrically on the cylinder surface at about the approximate mid-point in the axial direction. The test cylinder was tested for elastic response by loading in the 400 tonne Tinius-Olsen compression machine at GELUS. The derived elastic parameters agreed very closely with the expected values. This test-piece was used as a "load-cell" in the calibration of the LSTTF hydraulic cells.

Evaporite test specimens were obtained with a 200 mm internal diameter carbide "toothed" coring bit which proved an excellent cutting tool giving almost 100% recovery. The rough cores were wrapped in heavy duty plastic sheeting with one end exposed and cut with a 900 mm diameter diamond saw blade. Water was used as a cutting lubricant on the "offcut-side" of the blade only. The sawn faces obtained in this way were close to parallel. Grinding to give more precisely parallel faces would be desirable for material property testing, but for the series of tests designed to evaluate the test rig, non-parallel faces were deliberately used in an attempt to induce asymmetric loads and check the effectiveness of the hollow-ground self levelling platens. Normally cores were instrumented with three axial potentiometers together with three axial and three diametral resistance-wire strain gauges cemented to the rock surface.

The origin and approximate mineralogical compositions of the evaporite cores used in the initial test programme are given in Table 1. Analyses are composite syntheses of both chemical and X-ray diffraction results and may not be totally representative of the average composition of the very large cores tested.

Table 1 : Approximate mineral composition of test specimens

I.D.	Locality	Insol.	Carnalite	Anhydrite	Halite	Sylvite
R1	PCS Rocanville	2	2	Tr	85	11
C0	PCS Cory	3	1	Tr	34	62
C1	PCS Cory	2	1	-	40	57
C2	PCS Cory	6	2	Tr	25	67
C3	PCS Cory	8	1	Tr	42	49
V1	Cominco Vanscoy	7	1	Tr	50	42

5. CALIBRATION TESTS

A number of uniaxial tests were carried out on the 400 tonne capacity Tinius-Olsen compression machine at GELUS, to determine the load-deformation behaviour of both the aluminium test cylinder and the evaporite test specimen R1. Similar tests were repeated in the LSTTF to check that the axial piston loads were fully transferred to the test specimen. The correspondence of tests results between GELUS and LSTTF, together with the direct measurement of piston friction, gave some confidence that the LSTTF cell transfers the axial load to the test specimen without significant losses in friction.

6. PRESSURE TESTS

Several series (#1-#3) of pressure tests were designed to discover and rectify any significant leaks in the pressure vessels and hydraulic "plumbing" systems. The tests were carried out with the aluminium test cylinder acting as a "load cell".

The pressure test series led to the elimination of the ten small, temperature-sensitive, accumulators from the hydraulic circuits in favour of direct control using a single large main accumulator. Feedthrough design for sensor cables was also modified after several failures at pressures in excess of 40 MPa.

With the modified systems it is found that the magnitude of the daily pressure loss is insignificant. The pressure test series have shown that the cells can be maintained at constant pressure over extended periods and that very few pressure adjustments are necessary. Axial piston pressures and radial cell pressures up to 50 MPa have been maintained constant within instrumental sensitivity for periods exceeding 200 hours.

The only leakage problems encountered are at very low pressures (less than 5 MPa), when the endpiece seals tend to seep due to insufficient "seating" load. The seepage rates are very small and the computer can readily adjust the pressure in these situations.

7. SYMMETRY OF LOADING TESTS

Test series #4 was carried out on the aluminium test cylinder. The tests comprised a sequence of loading and unloading experiments involving incrementing the axial piston pressure at constant confining pressure. These tests were designed to check out the symmetry of loading and the automatic logging procedures for pressures, displacements and strains.

A second series (#5) of stress-strain response curves were determined for the aluminium cylinder at constant axial pressure by incrementing the confining pressure to restore hydrostatic conditions.

The series demonstrated that a symmetric strain distribution is achieved for the "stiff" aluminium cylinder. Stress-strain curves for a large number of tests over a wide range of confining pressures have established the precision and accuracy of the hydraulic loading system.

8. TRIAXIAL LOAD TESTS ON EVAPORITES

Five series (#6-#10) of tests were carried out on evaporite cores. Each core was eventually failed either by creep or axial pressure increase at constant confining pressure. Test results are summarized in Table 2 and Fig.5.

In test series #6 after 5 load-unload cycles at confining stresses of 0, 10, 20, 30 and 40 MPa with a maximum deviator stress of 6.4 MPa applied at the rate of 0.06 MPa/min, the core was finally loaded to failure. Little or no "barrelling" was observed in the failed core.

In test series #7, after 5 load-unload cycles at confining stresses of 0, 10, 19, 25 and 25 MPa with a maximum deviator stress of 6.6 MPa applied at the average rate of 0.06 MPa/min, the core was allowed to creep at constant confining stress (25 MPa) and deviator stress (6.2 MPa). The period of creep was 192 hours and the strain-time curves are shown in Fig.2. The "steady" axial creep rate was about 240 microstrains per day (or 2.8×10^{-9} /sec). Following the creep phase of the test, the core was loaded to failure. The "barrelling" observed in the failed core was attributed to the large rapid strains accumulated during the final phase of loading.

In test series #8, during the early loading phase (at a confining stress of 10 MPa and an axial stress of 23.6 MPa) an "o" ring failure occurred in a control solenoid valve. Hydrostatic stress at 10 MPa was maintained until the test could be continued. The sample was eventually loaded to failure at a rate of 0.29 MPa/min. The failed core showed extreme "barrelling".

Table 2: Evaporite core conditions at failure

Test Series #	Axial Stress (MPa)	Confining Stress (MPa)	Minimum Creep Rate (/sec)	Time of Creep (hrs)	Stress Rate (MPa/sec)	Axial Strain (%)	Radial Strain (%)	Core I.D.
6	73.4	40.0	–	–	2×10^{-3}	4.2	1.5	R1
*(7)	31.2	25.0	3×10^{-9}	192	–	0.5	0.1	C1 *
7	75.9	25.0	–	–	2×10^{-3}	11.6	4.4	C1
8	48.6	10.0	–	–	5×10^{-3}	4.4	6.6	C2
9	36.4	10.0	1×10^{-6}	7	NA	6.0	8.1	C3
10	29.5	10.0	4×10^{-9}	2500	NA	8.6	2.7	V1

*(7) Data for creep phase of test series #7 prior to failure

In test series #9, the erratic behaviour of the vertical strain gauges during rapid creep (Fig.3), highlights the advantages of the linear potentiometers for vertical strain measurement which, in contrast, yielded very consistent data. The sample was confined at 10 MPa and the axial stress was raised at 0.29 MPa/min to 36.4 MPa. Both confining and axial stresses were maintained constant to allow the sample to creep. Failure occurred after only 6.9 hours. The core showed extreme "barrelling" with much spalling from the surface.

Test series #10 includes the longest test carried out in the LSTTF and shows "steady-state" creep with little sign of "strain-hardening" after more than 1500 hours. The sample was confined at 10 MPa with an axial stress of 29.5 MPa. The complete 2500 hour creep strain curve to failure is shown in Fig.4.

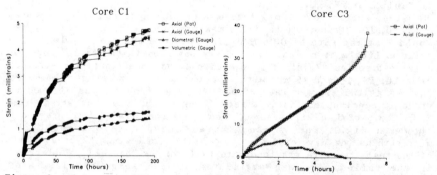

Figure 2 : Creep curve for core C1   Figure 3 :Creep curve for core C3
      from PCS Cory.   from PCS Cory.

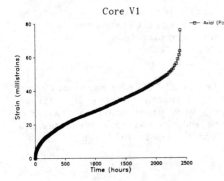

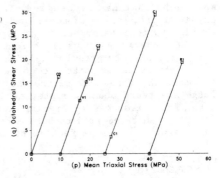

Figure 4 : Creep curve for core V1
from Cominco Vanscoy.

Figure 5 : Summary of evaporite
test results.

9. ROCK MECHANICS DISCUSSION

Although the work reported is primarily intended to establish the
credentials of the LSTTF as a testing laboratory, some unique
mechanical property data for large evaporite samples has been
accumulated. These data are summarized in Fig.5.

Of the five failures, three (samples R1,C1,C2) were induced by
loading and two (samples C3,V1) were induced by creep. However, the
loading rates were relatively slow for samples R1,C1 and C2 and when
expressed as strain rates at failure all are about 10 -5 /sec.

Core R1, which proved to be substantially weaker than the other
cores, was an extremely coarse-grained, halite-rich sample from the
PCS Rocanville mine (with a typical halite crystal size of 50 mm). All
other cores were finer-textured, sylvite-halite cores (crystal sizes
from 10 to 20 mm diameter) and were obtained from the PCS Cory and
Cominco Vanscoy mines close to Saskatoon.

Cores C1 and C2 show the expected increase in "strength" with
increasing confinement when failed under similar strain rate
conditions. Core C0, from the same mine was tested uniaxially at GELUS
at a comparable strain rate, failed at 28.2 MPa.

Cores C2, C3 and V1 show the expected fall in "strength" with
reducing strain rates for similar confining pressures. The strain at
failure for these samples increases as the strain rate falls.

The isolated point for core C1 is for creep at low deviator stress.
Since the period of creep was only 192 hours, this value (240
microstrains per day) is probably an overestimate of the long-term
creep rate.

The application of these and similar data to the design of mine
openings are discussed by Serata (1968), Mraz (1980) and Reeves (In
press).

10. RESEARCH APPLICATIONS

The Large Sample Triaxial Test Facility (LSTTF) is very versatile. The
unique feature of the laboratory is the very large size of the test

specimens that can be handled. The scale dependence of many of the physical properties of rocks and soils is well established and the ability to test large specimens is very important in :
  (a) coarsely crystalline rocks,
  (b) coarsely granular tailings and fills and
  (c) fractured rocks and soils
A second major feature of the LSTTF is the ability to carry out very long-term tests under computer control so that virtually any "stress path" for a test may be specified. With very minor modifications, the facility can be adapted to both measure and control pore-pressures and temperatures so that effective stress paths may be followed.

11. CONCLUSIONS

The test facility at the Saskatchewan Research Council is viable and one of the ten cells is fully operational.

The data so far obtained on halite and halite-sylvite cores appears to be internally consistent and in agreement with earlier (sparse) laboratory studies and in-situ measurements. Complete creep curves to failure have been obtained for secondary (linear) creep rates between 1×10^{-6} and 4×10^{-9} /sec (95 to 0.35 microstrains/day). Failures under load have been satisfactorily recorded at confining stresses between 10 and 40 MPa with axial stresses from 36 to 76 MPa.

Further hardware adaptations and software development are necessary to allow controlled tests of greater sophistication to be undertaken. In particular, to permit the use effective stresses and volumetric strains and temperature as control parameters. These enhancements to the system are the subject of on-going research at LSTTF and GELUS.

ACKNOWLEDGEMENTS

Funding for the work described in this paper was provided by CANMET as part of their START program. The laboratory work was carried out by Z.Szczepanik (U of S) and J.Jones (SRC) under the supervision of the author. Advice and assistance in obtaining suitable material for testing was provided by PCS and Cominco.

REFERENCES

Chudobiak, J.M. & Williams, K. 1977. A report on an experimental study of a triaxial test cylinder. Dept. Mech. Eng., University of Saskatchewan.

Mraz, D. 1980. Plastic behaviour of salt rock utilized in designing a mining method. CIM Bulletin, 73, 815, 115-123.

Reeves, M.J. 1984. Creep cell evaluation and laboratory testing of large evaporite samples. Saskatchewan Research Council Report, 130pp.

Reeves, M.J. In press. Dynamic brittle-rupture and stable-creep criteria in the design of evaporite mines. Inst. Min. Metallog. Lond., K.C.Dunham volume.

Serata, S. 1968. Application of continuum mechanics to design of deep potash mines in Canada. Int. J. Rock Mech. Min. Sci. & Geomech. Abstr., 5, 293-314.

21. Instrumentation

Chair: JEAN-CLAUDE ROEGIERS
Dowell Schlumberger Inc., Tulsa, Oklahoma, USA

Cochair: FRANÇOIS E. HEUZE
Lawrence Livermore National Laboratory, California, USA

Some recent developments in vibrating wire rock mechanics instrumentation

PIYUSH K.DUTTA
US Army Cold Regions Research & Engineering Laboratory, Hanover, New Hampshire, USA

1 INTRODUCTION

Long-term field measurement instrumentation must have high reliability, remote monitoring capability, the ability to withstand adverse
environmental conditions, and simplicity of operation. Accuracy and
precision of measurement are primarily determined by instrument capability and testing techniques and methods. The purpose of this paper
is to review some recent developments in vibrating wire technology for
rock mechanics instrumentation, and to discuss how the measurement
requirements cited above can be met to a great extent by judicious use
of vibrating wire instruments.

2 BACKGROUND

The major categories of instruments in which vibrating wire technology
has been successfully used are: rock stressmeters, strain gages, pore
pressure measuring piezometers (pressure transducers) and load cells.
Some lesser known new instruments are roof bolt gages and joint
meters. The general advantages of the use of vibrating wire instruments in field measurements have been summarized by Moore (1981),
Sherad (1981), and Bordes and Debreville (1985).

The basic principle of vibrating wire measurement technology is that
when a strain is applied to a stretched wire the frequency of vibration changes to a new value. By monitoring the change in frequency
one can calculate the strain in the wire. Then, by computation, the
strain change in the wire can be related to stress in rock, change in
load, pressure, displacement, temperature, or any other parameter
responsible for the strain change in the wire. The sole exception to
this principle is the measurement technique used with a vibrating wire
joint meter or displacement meter. In this method the frequency of
vibration of a wire under constant strain is changed by changing its
span with a traveling wiper connected to the moving part.

The major advantage of a vibrating wire sensor system over the more
conventional electrical resistance or piezoelectric transducers lies
mainly in the use of frequency, rather than voltage, as the output
signal from the sensors. In field instrumentation it is very important that signals be transmitted over long cables without appreciable

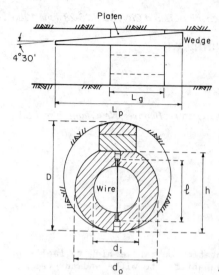

Figure 1. Vibrating wire stressmeter
(Irad Gage design) (after Hawkes
and Bailey 1973).

degradation caused by variations in cable resistance, contact resistance, or ground leakage. Compared to frequency signals, voltage
signals are more likely to degrade over long transmission lines.
Therefore, for remote geotechnical monitoring vibrating wire sensors
are preferable. However, the vibrating wire sensor system is not
suitable for dynamic (> 5 Hz) measurements, as the electromagnetic
plucking frequency of the wire itself is of the order of 1 to 2 Hz.

3 VIBRATING WIRE STRESSMETER

Since its development by Hawkes (1973), the vibrating wire rock
stressmeter (Figure 1) has been in common use for rock and coal pillar
stress measurements in this country and abroad. In using the stressmeter, the uniaxial rock stress change from σ_{r_1} to σ_{r_2} is related
to the vibrating wire frequency change as follows:

$$\sigma_{r_1} - \sigma_{r_2} = 4\left[f_1^2 - f_2^2\right]\ell_w^2 \frac{\rho_w}{g}\,\alpha \tag{1}$$

where

f_1 = natural frequency of vibrating wire at σ_{r_1} rock stress level
f_2 = natural frequency of wire at σ_{r_2} rock stress level
ℓ_w = wire length
ρ_w = density of wire material
g = acceleration due to gravity
α = calibration constant

The manufacturer supplies an electronic readout box, which, instead
of reading the frequency of the wire vibration, reads the period
(i.e. $1/f$) of one vibration and displays this reading after multiply-
ing it by 10^7. Hence, a reading of 2500 on the display is equivalent
to a period of 250 microseconds or a frequency of 4000 Hz.

Equation (1) shows that if the length of the wire, ℓ_w, and density, ρ_w, are maintained constant in the manufacturing process, the change of rock stress will be proportional to the difference of the squares of the initial and final frequencies; that is, α will be a constant. This is what is expected from a rigid inclusion stressmeter. However, some controversy has arisen in recent years concerning the calibration characteristics of the stressmeter (Fossum et al. 1976, Dutta et al. 1981, Jaworski et al. 1982, Lingle and Nelson 1982). Critics have stated that the calibration depended upon the initial setting pressure of the stressmeter in the hole, the initial factory-set tension in the wire, the temperature, and the stress level.

The author's own investigation, reported in 1981, showed that at very low stress levels (< 6.9 MPa) α in eq. (1) was not constant when the initial setting load of the gage was below a certain threshold value. The initial factory-set wire tension had negligible influence on α, but greatly affected the range and resolution of the meter. The influence of temperature on the calibration factor was not negligible, and system calibration is desirable for accurate measurements in a high-temperature environment.

Another important source of error is the assumption that α is independent of host rock modulus. While this assumption may be valid for softer rocks (Young's modulus < 14 GPa, for example coal), for high-modulus rock the error may be of the order of 25 to 30%. Again, laboratory calibration is desirable if the stressmeter is to be used in any high-modulus rock.

During setting of the stressmeter, misalignment of the wedge and platen assembly, as well as unevenness of the hole surface, can cause nonuniform stress distribution in the stressmeter body. Erroneous readings may be obtained under these circumstances. In an improperly manufactured stressmeter, clamping of the ends of the wire may introduce a residual torsional strain in the wire, resulting in double frequency or erroneous frequency readings.

The response of the stressmeter in biaxial and triaxial stress fields has been investigated by several authors (Jaworski et al. 1982, Dutta et al. 1981). It should be noted that, whatever the stress field may be, it is the deformation (strain) of the wire, ε_w, along its own axis that causes the frequency readings to change. The relationship of the wire stress, σ_w ($\sigma_w = \varepsilon_w \times E_w$), to the three modes of applied stress (uniaxial σ_r, biaxial p_o, and triaxial p_2) is shown in Figure 2.

In recent years the most severe criticism of the stressmeter has been that corrosion of the meter body and wire results in failure of the instrument in installations (Lingle and Nelson 1982, Gregory and Kim 1981, Rogue 1983, Carlson et al. 1980). The majority of these failures have happened in moist, hot environments when experiments were being conducted to simulate conditions around nuclear waste isolation canister holes. However, despite the above-mentioned problems the vibrating wire stressmeter has been widely accepted as a device for measuring stress change in rock (Leighton 1982, Clark 1979, Witherspoon et al. 1981), and improvements in its design have been made to make it more durable.

1045

Mode of Loading	Uniaxial	Biaxial	Triaxial
Model	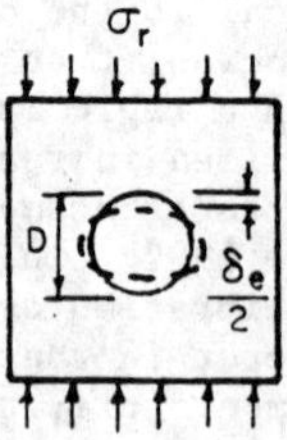	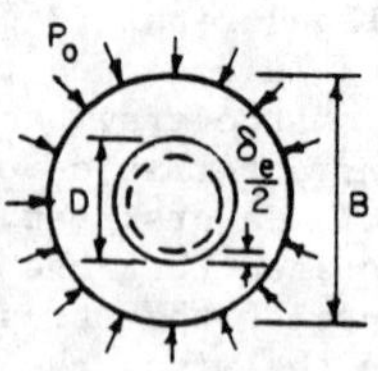	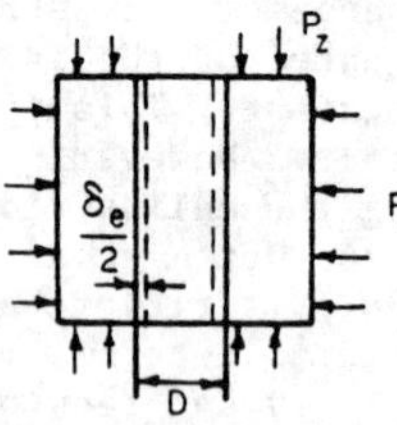
Hole deformation in line with the stress-meter wire	$\delta e = \dfrac{3D \sigma_r}{E_r}$	$\delta e = \dfrac{2D B^2 P_0}{E_r \left(B^2 - \frac{D^2}{4}\right)}$	$\delta e = \dfrac{2D B^2 P_0}{E_r \left(B^2 - \frac{D^2}{4}\right)} - \dfrac{\upsilon D P_z}{E_r}$
Equivalent uniaxial rock stress σ_r	σ_r	$\sigma_r - \dfrac{2P_0 B^2}{3\left(B^2 - \frac{D^2}{4}\right)}$	$\sigma_r = \dfrac{1}{3}\left[\dfrac{2P_0 B^2}{B^2 - \frac{D^2}{4}} - \upsilon P_z\right]$
For B = 5.50 in. and D = 1.5 in. σ_r	σ_r	$\sigma_r = 0.72\, P_0$	$\sigma_r = 0.72 P_0 - 0.07 P_z$
Equivalent uniaxial stress sensitivity $\dfrac{\sigma_w}{\sigma_r}$	$\dfrac{\sigma_w}{\sigma_r}$	$\dfrac{\sigma_w}{0.72\, P_0}$	$\dfrac{\sigma_w}{0.72\, P_0 - 0.07\, P_z}$

Figure 2. Hole closure and equivalent uniaxial stress sensitivity under uniaxial, biaxial and triaxial loading (after Dutta et al. 1981).

In recent design of vibrating wire stressmeters (Simmonds 1985) the wire cavity is evacuated and completely sealed from the environment by two stainless steel cups welded to the body. The electromagnetic coil potted in epoxy plucks the wire through the thin stainless steel barrier. A number of these stressmeters were installed in the Lawrence Livermore Laboratory's Spent Fuel Test - Climax facility in 1981. Since then these stressmeters have worked satisfactorily (Patrick, 1985).

In another vibrating wire stressmeter design the vibrating wire has been oriented at a right angle to the direction of uniaxial stress measurement (McRae 1985). As opposed to the design mentioned earlier, an increasing compression stress on this stressmeter body causes wire vibration period readings to go down, indicating that the wire tension becomes tighter. This feature allows the stressmeter to be wedged into the hole at a very high preload and to have a very high stress range.

Another variation of the stressmeter has been developed and used by Cox and Johnson at CRREL (1983) to measure stresses in a biaxial

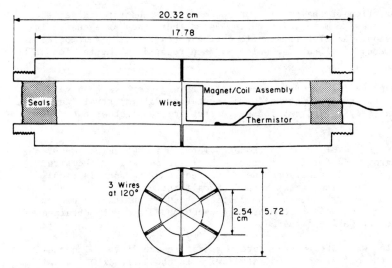

Figure 3. Three-wire embedment type stressmeter used for ice
stress measurement.

stress field in ice. Figure 3 shows a schematic of this stressmeter.
The sensor consists of a stiff cylinder made of steel, about 20.3 cm
long, 5.7 cm in diameter, and with a wall thickness of 1.6 cm. Three
tensioned wires are set 120° from each other across the cylinder
diameter. Under the applied stress field the diametral deformations
of the meter in these three directions are sensed by the three wires.
The device can measure radial displacements as small as 10^{-3} μm, which
corresponds to a sensor resolution of about 20 kPa stress when
embedded in ice.

4 OTHER VIBRATING WIRE INSTRUMENTS

4.1 Vibrating wire strain gages

Vibrating wire strain gages are excellent devices for long-term strain
measurements in rock, concrete and steel structures. The strain gage
consists of a length of steel wire which is tensioned between two end
blocks (Figure 4). The end blocks are either arc-welded to the steel
surface being studied, or anchored to the rock surface using groutable
end blocks. In concrete the strain gages are generally embedded.

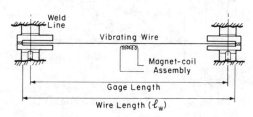

Figure 4. Principle of vibrating wire strain gage.

A deformation of the steel, rock or concrete substrate causes the two end blocks to move relative to one another, causing a change in wire tension. An electromagnetic coil excites the wire and monitors the frequency of vibration, which is then related to the tension of the wire.

Long base ($\simeq$ 152 mm) vibrating wire strain gages have been very common in the past. Spot-weldable short base (51 mm) strain gages are a comparatively recent development. They are less robust but easier to install.

A major source of error in these devices is in determination of the gage length or calibration factor. The relation between the wire length and gage length is not well defined, and the user is required to depend on the analytical method of calibration. As the gage factor depends on the wire length, the distance between the two welded end blocks, and the weld placement, erroneous results may be obtained if these are not well controlled.

Vibrating wire strain gages are temperature-sensitive. The coefficient of thermal expansion of steel wire is about 11.2×10^{-6} m/m/°C If the substrate thermal expansion coefficient is different from this value an apparent strain will result. Therefore, under a varying temperature it is important to monitor the temperature and apply the appropriate correction to the strain readings.

4.2 Vibrating wire piezometers

The advantages of vibrating wire piezometers have been extensively discussed by Sherad (1981). In terms of long-term stability, vibrating wire piezometers have a good record. Figure 5 is a design schematic showing the essential components of a piezometer, including the vibrating wire pressure transducer. The transducer essentially consists of a diaphragm coupled to a pretensioned vibrating wire. Changing pressure causes deflection of the diaphragm, thereby altering the tension of the wire and its resonant frequency of vibration. Some manufacturers hermetically seal the vibrating wire cavity by welding all leak paths. The transducer body as well as the piezometer body are made of stainless steel to reduce corrosion during prolonged use. Recent developments in transducer construction include matching the thermal expansion coefficient of the meter body with that of the wire,

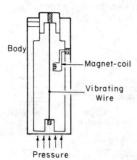

Figure 5. Design schematic of vibrating wire piezometer.

so that the device is less temperature-sensitive. Some piezometers have two nylon tubes which extend into the transducer housing cavity to permit in situ checking of the sensitivity (calibration). Others have a sealed and evacuated cavity which monitors absolute pressure rather than gage pressure.

Vibrating wire pressure transducers are used in a number of configurations to build pressure cells, stress cells, settlement gages, profile gages, etc. Variation of fluid pressure on the transducer diaphragm because of rock or soil stress or change of static head of fluid is monitored by these devices.

4.3 Vibrating wire load cells

Unlike the most commonly used resistance strain gage load cells, vibrating wire load cells are suitable for remote monitoring. They are manufactured in both solid and hollow versions. The sensing strain gage elements can be hermetically sealed for long-term application. In hollow load cells, three or four strain gages are used, and the electronic readout devices can automatically sense the load in each element and display the average load.

Vibrating wire load cells are also being made using sensing elements constructed similar to the pressure transducer discussed earlier. In this case the diaphragm is deflected by the applied load, either directly or through fluid pressure.

Runstadler et al. (1983) have recently reported the development of a unique sensor for remote monitoring of coal dust deposition rate in mines. Figure 6 shows the schematic of this sensor. Again the principle of monitoring the dust load here is by diaphragm deflection.

4.4 Rock bolt gage

Recently a unique cable-free instrumented rock bolt (with cable mounting option for remote monitoring) for measuring load on the bolts has been developed for tunnel and mine applications. A schematic of this instrument is shown in Figure 7. A vibrating wire strain gage is

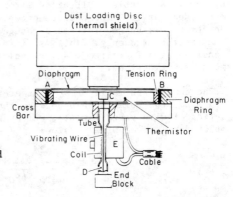

Figure 6. Vibrating wire dust load monitoring sensor (after Runstadler et al. 1983).

1049

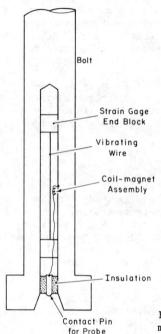

Bolt

Strain Gage
End Block

Vibrating
Wire

Coil-magnet
Assembly

Insulation

Contact Pin
for Probe

Figure 7. Schematic of vibrating wire instrumented rock/roof bolt.

encapsulated in the bolt. The electrical connection to the electromagnetic sensing coil is terminated at the bolt head. A carry-around
probe provides electrical contact at the bolt head to read the bolt
tension.

4.5 Vibrating wire jointmeter

In rock mechanics measurements, jointmeters meet the need for field
measurement of cracks, fractures and joints. For progressive expansion and/or contraction of joints a continuous remote monitoring
system is desirable. Vibrating wire jointmeters meet that need. As
mentioned earlier, the measurement principle of the vibrating wire
jointmeter is unique in that a change in the vibrating wire's span
changes the frequency. This is different from the change of wire
tension which forms the basic principle of other vibrating wire
measurement devices.

The design schematic of a jointmeter is shown in Figure 8. Equation
(2) shows the relationship between the wire length (span) ℓ_w and the
period of wire vibration (T), which are directly proportional to each
other for a given wire tension:

$$T = \frac{2\ell_w}{\sqrt{\varepsilon_w E_w \, g/\rho_w}} \tag{2}$$

1050

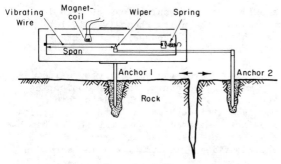

Figure 8. Schematic of vibrating wire instrumented jointmeter.

where

ε_w = wire strain under a given tension
E_w = Young's modulus of wire material
ρ_w = density of the wire material

Like other vibrating wire instruments the jointmeter also provides
long-term stability and a remote monitoring capability.

4.6 Vibrating wire temperature sensors

Vibrating wire temperature sensors are not very popular in the USA,
possibly because of higher costs compared to thermistors. As the
sensor element has to be built on a strain-free substrate, the response time is likely to be higher than for thermistor or thermocouple
type sensors.

5 DISCUSSION - ROCK MECHANICS INSTRUMENTATION PROBLEMS

Traditionally, rock mechanics instrumentation measurement results have
been viewed with skepticism because of several deficiencies in the
field measurement systems. These are: (1) scale of measurement, (2)
instrument reliability, and (3) uncertainties about analytical
models. Any rock mechanics instrumentation program should address
these problems and select an instrumentation system that will minimize
the adverse effects of these factors.

5.1 Scale of measurement

The immediate question in any field measurement program is whether the
population of measurement points is high enough to represent the character of the total mass of the rock. In other words, within cost
limits, we need a large number of measurement points, and therefore
more units so that the data can be acquired from them cost effectively. In recent years, the availability of automatic data acquisition
systems (data loggers) and low-cost computers has greatly reduced the
cost of expensive manual methods of reading instruments and reducing

the data. This condition should greatly encourage use of more instrument units provided that the cost of the units themselves is low enough to permit their large-scale use. Of course, the instrument design should be such that the installation cost is also low.

As an example, the recent development of the vibrating wire instrumented rock bolt may possibly meet these requirements in monitoring strata load distribution over a wide area. If available within a price range of $30 to $50 per gage, this device can find wide application in mine roof load monitoring. Isolated measurement points can be avoided and a suitable grid system for instrumentation can be developed; as a result, higher confidence in strata loading data can be obtained.

5.2 Instrument reliability

Vibrating wire instruments have a history of years of reliable operation. Bordes and Debreville (1985) recently reviewed their 50 years of experience with the durability and stability of vibrating wire instruments, including statistics on survival rates. They have concluded that with proper care and skill in installation and maintenance, 80% of the installations can be expected to be operating after 50 years.

However, adverse conditions, for example corrosive water and/or steam (as in the nuclear waste repository research program), have damaged many instruments in the past. The latest improvement in the construction of the gage, in which a hermetically sealed wire cavity and high-temperature-resistant materials are used, has mitigated the problem partially. Cable wire corrosion, insulation degradation, and meter body corrosion are other problems.

5.3 Uncertainties of analytical models

Because most in situ rock is inhomogeneous, anisotropic, fractured or jointed, with variable mineralogical and moisture content, application of even the most sophisticated analytical model, which takes into account these variables, is never perfect. Thus, when the instrument data do not conform to the model predictions on occasion, the question arises as to whether the instrumentation performed poorly or the data are really correct. In order to reduce these uncertainties, not only should the instrument performance reliability be established prior to field installation, but also predictive models should be verified through systematic investigation.

In vibrating wire instrumentation one should note that what we actually measure is the wire vibration frequency, but what we infer is stress, pressure, load or strain, depending on the type of instrument in use. The analytical models enable us to predict these parameters from the frequency readings. Development of confidence in these models is therefore as important as instrument reliability.

We have earlier mentioned the problems of inferring rock stress from the frequency (period) data of the stressmeter. Whether similar problems can occur with other vibrating wire instruments in field applications should be an important consideration prior to installation of these gages.

6 SUMMARY

Vibrating wire instruments offer some unique advantages in remote and long-term geotechnical monitoring. Since frequency of vibration rather than voltage or current is measured, the devices are insensitive to resistance changes. The long-term stability of the device results from the fact that measurements of the tensioned wire are of its mechanical rather than electrical properties. However, the design should be adequate to prevent moisture ingression and resist corrosion.

Before installation, the adequacy of the instrument should be properly understood, both in terms of accuracy as well as its response characteristics in the installation environment. The existence of any drift in the instrument should be noted. Calibration in a simulated environment may be necessary for critical measurements. The algorithm used for calculating the geotechnical parameter should be verified. Only then can proper confidence be developed in the data obtained by the instrument.

REFERENCES

Bordes, J.L. & P.J. Debreville 1985. Some facts about long-term reliability of vibrating wire instruments. National Research Council/ Transportation Research Board Symposium on Reliability of Geotechnical Instrumentation, Washington, D.C.

Carlson, R.C. et al. 1980. "Spent Fuel Test – Climax" technical measurements interim report, FY80. Lawrence Livermore Laboratory Report UCRL-53064. Livermore, California.

Clark, B.R. 1981. Stress anomaly accompanying the 1979 Lytle Creek earthquake: Implications for earthquake prediction. Science 211: 51-53.

Clark, B.R. 1979. Continued monitoring of stress changes near active faults. Leighton and Associates Final Technical Report; USGS Contract #14-08-0001-16746.

Cox, G.F.N. & J.B. Johnson 1983. Stress measurements in ice. U.S. Army Cold Regions Research and Engineering Laboratory, CRREL Report 83-23.

Dutta, P.K., R.W. Hatfield & P.W. Runstadler 1981. Calibration characteristics of Irad Gage vibrating wire stressmeter at normal and high temperature. UCRL-15426, Lawrence Livermore National Laboratory, Livermore, California.

Fossum, A.F. et al. 1976. Calibration analysis for the in situ response of a vibrating-wire stress gauge in soft rock. SESA Spring

Meeting, Silver Springs, MD, 9-14 May, SESA, 21 Bridge Square, Westport, CT 06880.

Gregory, E.C. & K. Kim 1981. Preliminary results from the full-scale heater tests at the Near Surface Test Facility. 22nd Symposium on Rock Mechanics, Mass. Inst. of Technology, 28 June - 2 July.

Hawkes, I. & W.V. Bailey 1973. Design, develop, fabricate, test and demonstrate permissible low cost cylindrical stress gages and associated components capable of measuring change of stress as a function of time in underground coal mines. U.S. Bureau of Mines Contract Report (HO 220050)

Jaworski, G.W., B.C. Dorwart, W.F. White & W.R. Beloff 1982. Behavior of a rigid inclusion stressmeter in an anisotropic stress field. Issues in Rock Mechanics - Proc. 23rd Symposium on Rock Mechanics, Edited by R.E. Goodman and F.E. Henze. Society of Mining Engineers, New York.

Leighton, F. 1982. A case history of a major rock burst. U.S. Bureau of Mines Report of Investigation.

Lingle, R. & P.H. Nelson 1982. In situ measurements of stress change induced by thermal load: A case history in granitic block. Proc. 23rd Symposium on Rock Mechanics, Edited by R.E. Goodman and F.E. Henze, Society of Mining Engineers, New York.

McRae, J. 1985. Geokon Inc., Personal Communication.

Moore, D.R. 1981. The vibrating wire gauge: One answer to the hostile environment. B.S.S.M.-S.E.S.A. International Conference, "Measurements in Hostile Environments," University of Edinburg.

Patrick, W.C. 1985. Lawrence Livermore Laboratory, University of California, Personal Communication.

Rogue, F. 1983. Reliability of geotechnical, environmental and radiological instrumentation in nuclear waste repository studies. Lawrence Livermore Laboratory. NUREG/CR-3494.

Runstadler, P.W., P.K. Dutta, R.W. Hatfield & R. Tenenbaum 1983. Development of a remote coal dust deposition rate monitor. USBM Contract No. J0188058, USBM Office of Assistant Director, Mining, Washington, DC.

Sherad, J.L. 1981. Piezometers in earth dam impervious sections. Symposium on Instrumentation Reliability and Long-Term Performance Monitoring of Embankment Dams - ASCE Annual Meeting, New York, 11 May.

Simmonds, T. 1985. Irad Gage, Personal Communication.

Witherspoon, P.A., N.G.W. Cook & J.E. Gale 1981. Geologic storage of radioactive waste: Field studies in Sweden. Science, February.

Application of holographic interferometry
to in-situ stress measurement

DOUGLAS R.SCHMITT
Seismological Laboratory, California Institute of Technology, Pasadena, USA

JAY D.BASS
Department of Geology, University of Illinois, Urbana, USA

THOMAS J.AHRENS
Seismological Laboratory, California Institute of Technology, Pasadena, USA

A borehole stressmeter which records stress-relief displacements via double exposure holography is under development. For a detailed description of the stressmeter and its theory of operation the reader is referred to Bass et al,1985. Briefly, the stressmeter records a three-dimensional displacement field resulting from the drilling of a small stress-relieving hole is the borehole wall. Data is stored in the form of a fringe pattern superimposed on the image of the borehole wall and the stress-relief hole.

The hologram photographs centered on the stress-relief holes in figures A,B, and C are three examples of stress-relief experiments conducted in a horizontal North-South borehole in an oil shale mine pillar. All three stress-relief holes were drilled at a depth of 127 cm from the pillar face and at clock azimuths of 10:30, 1:30, and 4:30 as seen by an observer facing North into the borehole and shown schematically in the respective borehole line drawings in the figures. The stress-relief holes are of radii 4.76 mm and depths of 1.27 cm in oil shale of Young's modulus of 8.3 GPa and Poisson's ratio of 0.345. The numbers (1-4) at the corners of the photographs correspond to the numbers in the borehole line drawings and show the orientation of each stress-relief experiment.

Beneath, and in the same orientation as, each photograph is its corresponding calculated stress-relief fringe pattern. The stress-relief calculations have the input parameters of the three non-trivial borehole wall stresses: the hoop stress around the borehole, the normal stress parallel to the borehole axis, and the borehole wall shear stress. These stresses are varied until the calculated and observed fringe patterns match. The borehole wall stress magnitudes in MPa and directions are shown around the calculated fringe pattern for each case. Tensile stresses are displayed by opposing arrows pointing away from each other, compressive stresses are displayed by opposing arrows pointing towards each other, and the rotation direction of the shear stresses are shown by arrows at the corners.

Consider a non-principal stress reference frame with the normal axii coincident with the North-South, the East-West, and the vertical (-Z-+Z) axii as shown in the borehole line drawings. Then with the present data set shown in the figures, and by the method of Leeman and Hayes (1966), the farfield calculated North-South normal stress at the measrurement depth in the borehole is a tensile stress of 2.2 MPa. Since the stress-relief experiments of figures A and C are 180 degrees from each other the data set is not independent and only the sum of the vertical and East-West normal stresses may be calculated as a compressive stress of 1.9 MPa. If the vertical stress is assumed to be that of the estimate of the average vertical compressive stress in the pillar of 11.2 MPa; then the East-West normal stress would be a tensile stress of 9.3 MPa. Analysis of further stress-relief holograms at an independent azimuth from the present three in figures A,B and C will allow for calculation of all six components of the stress tensor.

REFERENCES

Bass, J.D., D.R.Schmitt, & T.J.Ahrens 1985. Holographic in-situ stress measurements. Geoph. Journ. R. Astr. Soc.. in press.
Leeman, E.R. & D.J.Hayes 1966. A technique for determining the complete state of stress in rock using a single borehole. Proc. 1st Congr. Int. Rock Mech. Lisbon. 2:17-24.

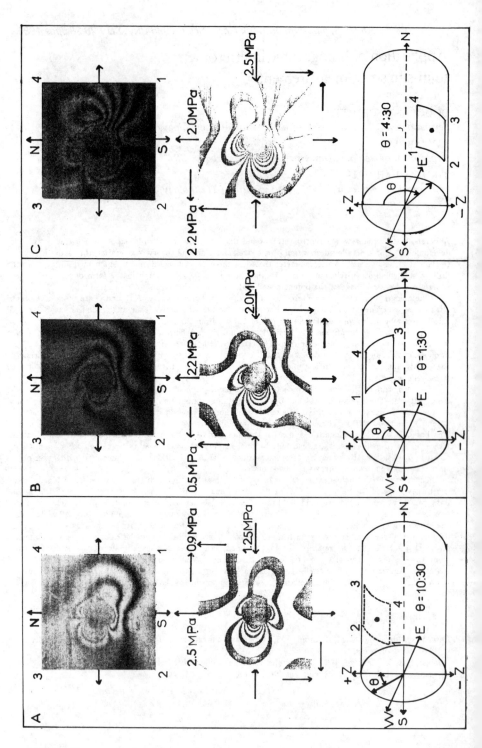

An apparatus for the study of the behavior of rocks under three dimensional loading

AKHTAR S.KHAN & FERSHEED K.IRANI
School of Aerospace, Mechanical & Nuclear Engineering, University of Oklahoma, Norman, USA

ABSTRACT

An experimental apparatus has been constructed to carry out an in depth study of the plastic behavior of rocks until fialure under truly three-dimensional loading conditions. This will facilitate in developing constitutive relations for rock-like materials. In this apparatus thin walled hollow cores (0.2" or 5.1 mm) are subjected to complex tension-torsion and compression-torsion loading conditions in the presence of hydrostatic pressure.

1. INTRODUCTION

The studies on behaviors and failure of rocks has been of interest to several investigators since the turn of the century (Admas 1901-Kin et al. 1984). The most widely used method of loading rock samples is the "three dimensional compression" and "three dimensional tension" technique where the solid cylindrical cores are loaded in uniaxial compression in the presence of hydrostatic pressure; if this compression is less than the hydrostatic pressure then it is assumed to give a "three dimensional tensile" loading. Thus in both these situations all three principal stresses are actually compressive in nature. Therefore due to the limitations of the loading, the scope of these studies have been very limited. Also in this type of tests on solid cores as well as torsion of solid cores, the stresses are not uniform through the thickness; they are function of the radius at any point on the core. Thus although the technique us very widely used, it definitely has limitations.

Robertson (1955) carried out triaxial compression tests on solenhofen limestone in the presence of a hydrostatic pressure of 2,000 atmosphers. He investigated the elastic limit as a function of strain rate, and reported the effects of hydrostatic pressure and temperature on the plastic deformation of rocks. He also examined the experimental data with respect to various failure criterias. Similar "triaxial" studies were later carried out by other investigators (Serdengecti et al. 1961, Smith et al. 1969, Rutter 1972, Green 1972 and Price et al. 1980) at different temperatures and strain rates on a variety of rocks. The specimens used in these tests were either solid and/or hollow cores. The study by Handin et al. (1967) is among few investigations where the effect of intermediate principal stress on the failure of rocks is considered. In their experiments the loading consisted of torsion in the presence of triaxial compression on solid and hollow cylindrical cores. Also, in most of the studies mentioned above, the strains are calculated by measuring displacements of the ends of the cores in the axial and radial directions. This technique is not accurate especially for small strains.

The experimental apparatus that has been designed and developed we are capable of carrying out truly three-dimensional experiments on hollow rock cores, and also the strains are monitored accurately by bonding strain gage rosettes on the surface of the core. The hollow cores are subjected to tension-torsion or compression-torsion in the presence of hydrostatic pressure to obtain any combination of three-dimensional loading. In hollow cores, the assumption of uniform shear stress or stresses due to pressure is much better than similar assumption for the case of solid cores.

2. EXPERIMENTAL PROCEDURE

Hollow cylindrical rock specimens are obtained by coring twice, first with a core drill of 1.25" diameter and then with a core drill of 1.875" diameter. This results into a hollow specimen with outer diameter of 1.68" and inner diameter of 1.25". The thin walled hollow core is assembled in the experimental apparatus, where it is subjected to axial and torsional loads in the presence of hydrostatic pressure. This will produce a loading with three non-equal principal stresses. Further, since the rock sample is a thin hollow core, therefore, the stresses would be almost constant through the thickness.

A dead weight type tension-torsion machine as shown in Figure 1 is used so that the loading, unloading and reloading is applied at a constant stress rate. The test specimen is bonded in two grips, G_u at the upper end, and G_l at the lower end in a specially designed assembly fixture by means of high strength epoxy, which ensures the specimen axis to coincide with the axis of the grips, which in turn is the loading axis. This sub-assembly of the specimen and the two end grips is then assembled with the high pressure cylinder and the cylinder end caps using proper size o-rings and rubber gaskets between end caps and the cylinder (see Figure 2). The complete pressure vessel assembly is then mounted on the testing machine.

The upper grip is attached to a 4.5" (114.3 mm) diameter drum 'D' and forces tangential to the drum apply torque to the specimen. The upper grip is free to rotate about its axis while such rotation of the lower grip is prevented. The lower grip is free to rotate about the other two axis perpendicular to the axial direction at G_l. Its alignment in the vertical plane is ensured by universal joints J_u and J_l at the upper and the lower ends respectively. Tangential forces on the drum which is connected to the upper grip is achieved by means of aircraft steel cable connected to the loading bucket L_s through symmetrically located low friction pulleys. Unloading is achieved through an unloading bucket U_s, which causes tangential forces in the opposite direction.

The specimen is subjected to tensile or compressive loading through barrel L_t or U_t respectively, lever arm 'L', dual knife edge cam 'C' and universal joint J_u. The universal joint J_u is connected to the drum through thrust bearings B_1 and B_2 so that the two combinations of loads (tension-torsion or compression-torsion) can be applied independently of each other. In case of both tension/compression and torsion, the loading

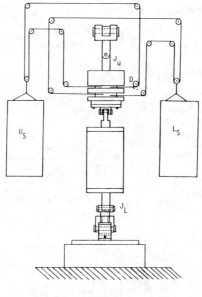

Front view

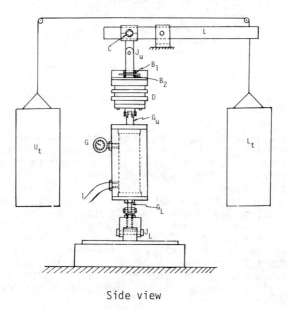

Side view

Figure 1. Schematic diagram of tension-torsion machine with pressure chamber.

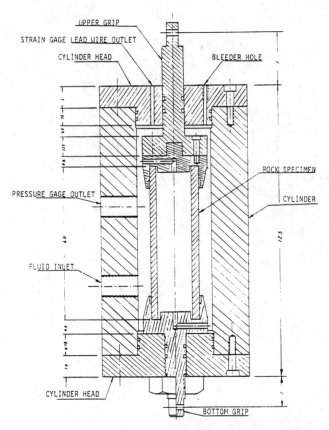

Figure 2. High pressure vessel cylinder assembly (sectional view).

as well as the unloading is achieved by water flowing under a constant head from an overhead tank. The rate of loading and unloading can be controlled by changing the outlet nozzle, a larger inside diameter of the outlet nozzle results into a higher stress rate.

Hydrostatic pressure in the range of 0-15,000 psi can be developed surrounding the core using HASKEL AW-150 air amplifier pump and 10W-40 oil as the fluid media. The specimen is insulated from both inside and outside by coating it with a thin layer of commercially available silicone rubber paste and allowing it to cure for 24 hours. The pressure gage 'G' measures the fluid pressure inside the pressure chamber. The desired pressure in the pressure chamber is controlled by regulating the inlet air pressure to the air amplifier pump. A constant inlet air pressure of 'p' maintains a constant fluid pressure of "150 p" in the pressure chamber.

The strains in the rock sample are measured by bonding electrical resistance strain gages on the outside and inside surfaces of the core. Micro-measurements glue type M-Bond 200 (or Eastman 910) is used to mount the strain gages on the rock sample. Two different kinds of gages, manufactured by Kyowa will be used. The first type (KDF-5-C1-11) is a general purpose constantan alloy foil gage with polyimide backing of gage length 5 mm and a resistance of 120 Ω. The other type (KFC-10-D17-11) is specially designed for concrete. The strains are measured and recorded using Vishay switch and balance unit (Model #SD-1) and strain indicator (Model #P-3500) manufactured by Measurements Group.

3. THEORETICAL ANALYSIS

The experimental investigation failure results are compared with following existing criteria.

Tresca and Coulomb-Mohr Criteria: It is generally assumed that plastic flow or failure occurs when, on any plane at any point in the rock mass, the maximum shear stress τ reaches an amount that depends linearly upon the cohesive stress C, and the normal stress σ on the failure plane, and is given by:

$$\tau = C + \sigma \tan\phi \tag{1}$$

This equation was first suggested by Coulomb in 1773. The angle ϕ is known as the angle of internal friction of rock. If ϕ is zero, then equation (1) represents Tresca's yield criterion. The constants C and ϕ can be looked upon simply as parameters which characterize the total resistance of the rock media to shear. In order to express (1) in terms of principal stress components σ_1, σ_2 and σ_3, appropriate for general treatment of three-dimensional problems, we use the graphical representation of stress due to Mohr. In the Mohr diagram (Fig. 3) the normal stress σ and the shearing stress τ are used as co-ordinates.

The values of σ, τ satisfying the Coulomb yield criterion (1) are represented in Fig. 3 by two straight lines OE and EF, the latter inclined at angles ϕ to the positive σ axis. If a state of stress σ_1, σ_2, σ_3 is such that the Mohr circles lie within the wedge-shaped region (OEF), the rock remains in the linear elastic range. Plastic flow or fracture of rocks occurs for any stress state at or outside this boundary. In terms of principal stresses, the criterion is given by equation (2)

$$(\sigma_1 - \sigma_3)/2 = \{(\sigma_1 + \sigma_2)/2\} \sin \phi + C \cos \phi \tag{2}$$

4. EXPERIMENTAL RESULTS AND DISCUSSION

Uniaxial Tension Test: The average uniaxial tensile strength for granite was measured as 1068 psi, Young's modulus of 6.68×10^6 psi and the poissions ratio of 0.178.

Pure Torsion Test: The average shear strength for this rock was 960 psi with an average shear modulus of 3.07×10^6 psi.

Two-Dimensional Test: Several experiments were carried out under two dimensional loading. These include tension followed by torsion (Test #6, 30, 35, 37), torsion followed by tension (test #18, 28, 29, 34), combined tension-torsion loading (test #23,36) and compression followed by torsion (test #42, 43, 44). The values of the stresses at failure are given in Table 1.

Three-Dimensional Test: Experiments carried out under this category include external pressure loading (Test #47, 48) internal pressure test (Test #49, 50), confining pressure followed by axial tension (Test #51, 52), axial tension followed by confining pressure (#55), equal internal

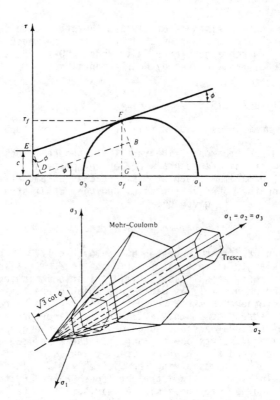

Figure 3. Coulomb-Mohr criterion.

and external pressure (Test #54, 63), axial compression followed by confining pressure (Test #56, 58, 59, 60), torsion followed by confining pressure (Test #57, 64), confining pressure followed by torsion (Test #65), and axial compression followed by confining pressure and then by torsion (Test #61, 62). Stresses at failure for the above test were measured and are given in Tables 1.

Determination of Parameters: The two parameters associated with Coulomb-Mohr failure criterion (angle of internal friction ϕ and cohesion C) can be determined from the laboratory test on the material conducted up to failure conditions. The values of ϕ and C can be determined using eq. 2 and a plot of

$$\frac{\sigma_1 + \sigma_3}{2} \text{ and } \frac{\sigma_1 - \sigma_3}{2} \text{ (see Fig. 4).}$$

In order to establish the failure envelope several laboratory tests under different loading conditions are carried out and the stresses at failure are calculated as listed in Table 1 from which principal stresses are calculated.

Fig. 4 shows plot of $\frac{\sigma_1 + \sigma_3}{2}$ versus $\frac{\sigma_1 - \sigma_3}{2}$.

Table No. 1   Normal and shear stresses at failure for various tests ($\tau_{r\theta} = \tau_{rz} = 0$ for all tests).

Exp. No.	Exp. Type	σ_r psi	σ_θ psi	σ_z psi	$\tau_{z\theta}$ psi
12,24,25 27,31,32,33	Tension	--	--	1068*	--
13,26,45,46	Torsion	--	--	--	960
6	Ten→Tor	--	--	581*	405
18	Tor→Ten Comb	--	--	710	525
23	Ten→tor	--	--	599	663
28	Tor→Ten	--	--	1045	216
29	Tor→Ten	--	--	948	327
30	Ten→Tor	--	--	499	770
34	Tor→Ten	--	--	517	779
35	Ten→Tor→Ten Comb	--	--	407	814
36	Ten→Tor	--	--	1082	177
37	Ten→Tor	--	--	271	778
42	Comp→Tor	--	--	-854	1155
43	Comp→Tor	--	--	-546	1188
44	Comp→Tor	--	--	-1245	1331
49,50	Int. Pr	-125*	841*	-357	--
51	Hyd Pr→Ten	-1000	-1000	-553	--
52	Hyd Pr→Ten	-1000	-1000	880	--
54	Equal Int- Ext Pr	-2500	-2500	--	--
55	Ten→Hyd Pr	-1200	-1200	614	--
56	Comp→Hyd Pr	-3300	-3300	-1422	--
57	Tor→Hyd Pr	-2800	-2800	--	643
58	Comp→Hyd Pr	-4500	-4500	-1610	--
59	Comp→Hyd Pr	-3600	-3600	-1626	--
60	Comp→Hyd Pr	-6000	-6000	-2779	--
61	Comp→Hyd Pr→Tor	-4300	-4300	-3042	445
62	Comp→Hyd Pr→Tor	-3000	-3000	-3756	889
63	Equal Int- Ext Pr	-2800	-2800	--	--
64	Tor→Hyd Pr	-1440	-1440	--	472
65	Hyd Pr→Tor	-2000	-2000	--	425

*Average value

5.   SUMMARY AND CONCLUSIONS

An experimental apparatus has been designed and developed to study the behavior of rocks until failure under truly three-dimensional loading. In these experiments, stress components are prescribed and the resulting strains are accurately measured by bonding strain gage rosettes on both the inner and outer surface of the core. The two loads, tension or compression, and torsion are applied independent of each other and also the corresponding strains are measured independently of each other.

Since all of the experiments were carried out on thin hollow cores, the assumption of uniform shear stress or stresses due to pressure through the thickness is a better assumption than in the case of solid cores.

The following average mechanical properties of granite were measured from various experiments:

Young's Modulus: $E = 6.68 \times 10^6$ psi
Shear Modulus: $G = 307 \times 10^6$ psi
Poission's Ratio: $\nu = 0.178$
Tensile strength $= 1055$ psi
Shear strength $= 935$ psi

The parameters required for the two failure criteria are evaluated and are as follows:

Tresca: $K = 936$ psi
Coulomb Mohr $C = 931.5$, $\phi = 24.142°$

Figures 4 demonstrates that at lower values of $\frac{\sigma_1 + \sigma_3}{2}$ the Coulomb-Mohr criterion predict reasonably well the failure strength of this granite under three-dimensional loading. However, at higher values of $\frac{\sigma_1 + \sigma_3}{2}$ the experimental results deviate considerably from the Coulomb-Mohr envelope. In the latter range, the failure strength in granite seems to be a lot less sensitive to the hydrostatic part of the stress tensor, and these results are thus more consistent with Tresca criterion.

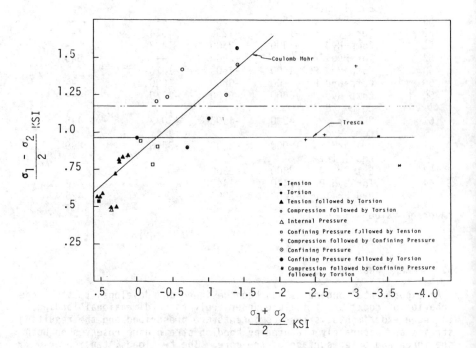

Figure 4. Envelopes for Tresca and Coulomb-Mohr models.

ACKNOWLEDGEMENTS

The authors gratefully acknowledge the financial support of the Energy Resources Institute, the expert design of the apparatus by K. Y. Liu, the accurate machining by William Petre, and the skillful typing of this report by Fran O'Bryan. We are also appreciative of the help and the discussions with Professors Charles W. Bert and John S. Wickham.

REFERENCES

Adams, F. D. and J. T. Nicholson 1901. "An experimental investigation into the flow of marble," Phil. Trans. Ray. Soc. London, Ser. A, Vol. CXCV pp. 363-401.

Adams, F. D. and J. A. Bancroft 1917. "Internal Frictior during Deformation and the Relative Plasticity of Different Types of Rocks," Jour. Geol. Vol. XXV pp. 597-637.

Bordia, S.K. 1972. "Complete Stress-Volumetric Strain Equation for Brittle Rock up to Strength Failure." Int. Jr. of Rock Mech. and Min. Sci., 9,1, pp. 17-24.

Burton, P. 1961. A Modification of the Coulomb Mohr Theory of Fracture." Jr. of Appl. Mech., pp. 259-268.

Ely, R. E. 1965. "Strength of Graphite Tube Specimens Under Combined Stresses." J. of American Ceramic Society, vol. 48, No. 10, pp. 505-508.

Goldsmith, W., J.L. Sachman, and C. Ewerts 1976. "Static and Dynamic Fracture Strength of Barre Granite." Int. J. of Rock Mech. Min. Sci. and Geomech. Abstr. vol. 13, pp. 303-309.

Green, S.J., et al. 1972. "Triaxial Behavior of Solenhofen Limestone and Westerly Granite at High Strain Rates." Jr. of Geophysical Research 77, 20, 3711-3724.

Griggs, D. T. 1936. "Deformation of Rocks Under High Confining Pressures. I. Experiments at Room Temperature," The Jr. of Geol., Vol. XLIV #5, pp. 541-577.

Griggs, D. T. and W. B. Miller 1951. "Deformation of Yule Marble: Part I: Compression and Extension Experiments on Dry Yule Marble at 10,000 Atmosphere Confining pr, Room Temp," Bull. of the Geol. Soc. of America, vol. 62, pp. 853-862.

Handin, J., H.C. Heard, and J.N. Magourik 1967. "Effect of the Intermediate Principal Stress on the Failure of Limestone, Dolomite and Glass at Different Temperatures and Strain Rate." Jr. of Geophysical Research, vol. 72, No. 2, pp. 611-640.

Hudson, J. A., E. T. Brown, and C. Fairhurst 1971. "Shape of the Complete Stress-Strain Curve for Rock" Proceedings Thirteenth Symposium on Rock Mechanics, pp. 773-795.

Khair, A. W. and H.R. Hardy Jr. 1977. "Failure of Indiana Limestone Under a Tension-Tension Compression Stress State." Energy Resources and Excavation Technology Proceedings Eighteenth U.S. Symposium on Rock Mechanics, pp. 3B1-1-3B1-9.

Kim, M. K., and P.V. Lade 1984. "Modelling Rock Strength in Three Dimensions." Int. J. of Rock Mech. and Min. Sci. and Geomech. Abstr., Vol. 21, No. 1, pp. 21-33.

Kumar, A. 1968. "The Effect of Stress Rate and Temperature on the Strength of Basalt and Granite." Geophysics 33, 501.

Miller, T.W., and Cheatham, J.B., Jr. 1972. "A New Yield Condition and Hardening Rule for Rocks." Int. Jr. of Rock Mech. and Min. Sci., 9,4, 453-474.

Price, A. M. and I.W. Farmer 1980. "A General Failure Criterion for Rocks." Proceedings of the 21st U.S. Symp. on Rock Mechanics, pp. 256-263.

Ramez, M.R.H. 1967. "Fracture and the Strength of Sandstone Under Triaxial Compression." Int. J. of Rock Mech. and Min. Sci., vol. 4, pp. 257-268.

Robertson, E. C. 1955. "Experimental Study of the Strength of Rocks", Bull. of the Geo. Soc. of Am., Vol. 66, pp. 1275-1314.

Rutter, E.H. 1972. "The Effects of Strain-Rate Changes on the Strength and Ductility of Solenhofen Limestone at Low Temperatures and Confining Pressures." Int. Jr. of Rock Mec. and Min. Sci. 9,2, 183-189.

Serdengecti, S., and G.D. Bozer 1961. The Effects of Strain Rate and Temperature on the Behavior of Rocks Subjected to Triaxial Compression, in Fourth Symposium on Rock Mechanics, pp 83-97, Pennsylvania State University, University Park.

Smith, J. L., K.L. DeVries, D.J. Bushnell & W.S. Brown 1969. "Fracture Data & Stress-Strain Behavior of Rocks in Triaxial Compression." Experimental Mechanics, pp. 348-355.

Swanson, S.R. and Brown, W.S. 1972. "The Influence of State of Stress on the Stress-Strain Behavior of Rocks." Jr. of Basic Engineering, Transactions of the ASME Series D, 94, 1, pp. 238-242.

Turner, F.J., Griggs, D.T., Clark, R.H., and Dixon, R.H., 1956, Deformation of Yule Marble. Part Vii: Development of Oriented Fabrics at 300°C-500°C, Bull. Geol. Soc. Amer., v. 67, p. 1259-1294.

Von Karman, T. 1921. "Festigkeitversuche unter allseitigem druck," Zeitschr. des Vereers deutscher Ingerieure, Vol. LV (1911) 1749-57. For a discussion of this paper see W. H. Bucher, "The Mechanical Interpretation of Joints", Jour. Geol., Vol. XXIX p. 13.

The use of the pressuremeter to evaluate
the strength-deformation characteristics of soft rocks

ROBERT C.BACHUS
Georgia Institute of Technology, Atlanta, USA

1 INTRODUCTION

Soft rocks, particularly soft sandstones, are often characterized by extreme difficulties in obtaining intact and competent samples for laboratory testing. Due to the particulate nature of these materials and the potentially sensitive bond between particles, sampling is extremely difficult. In many cases the samples which are recovered from the field and returned to the laboratory for properties testing may bear little resemblance to the undisturbed subsurface mass in the field. In the absence of quality laboratory test results, empirical relationships may be employed to estimate properties. As a companion approach and in many cases as an alternative to a lab testing program, in-situ testing techniques may prove valuable in evaluating reliable engineering properties. For the soft sandstones reported in this paper, a self-boring pressuremeter, an in-situ testing instrument developed for use in soft clays, was modified to allow drilling in soft rocks. The stress-deformation characteristics of the in-situ rock mass as determined by the interpretation of the pressuremeter test results compared extremely well to similar laboratory-determined properties obtained from high quality block samples recovered in the field and carefully trimmed in the lab. Conventionally obtained samples of the material were disturbed and often crumbled upon extrusion from the sampling tube.

2 CONVENTIONAL SAMPLING AND TESTING DIFFICULTIES

The material studied during this investigation was found just south of San Francisco in an elevated marine terrace of Middle Pleistocene age overlain by loose dune sands of Holocene age. These materials have been described as weakly consolidated moderately cemented sands (Crosby and Associates 1978) and are typical of the material found in numerous exposures in the San Francisco Bay area generically referred to as soft sandstones and lightly or weakly cemented sands (Sitar, et al. 1980). The bonding agents for this material are often calcium carbonate and iron oxide. In both natural cuts and man-made excavations, near vertical slopes of approximately 30m remain stable for extended period of time under static loading yet can be easily carved by hand. However, instability of these soils during earthquakes has been recorded by the USGS (Youd and Hoose 1978).

The difficulty of sampling the particular cemented sands were documented earlier (Bachus 1982; Clough and Bachus 1982). Conventional soil sampling techniques of driving thick walled split spoons and pushing thin walled Shelby tubes generally recovered fragments of intact sandstone intermixed within a matrix of uncemented sand. This contradicted the appearance of the intact block samples obtained from bluff faces and trench sidewalls. Pitcher barrel coring and sampling proved equally unsuccessful in providing representative samples. Further evidence of sampling disturbance was noted by comparing the densities of the specimens extruded from the sampling tubes in the lab. Consistently, the sample densities and the quantity of the remolded sand matrix ranked as follows: split spoon > Shelby tube > Pitcher barrel > block samples. Although the variations were often <5%, the consistency of both appearance and density seems to indicate that due to the disturbance induced by the sampling process many of the interparticle bonds were broken thus allowing the remolding and densification of the now uncemented sand within the sampler. Furthermore, there is strong evidence that the degree of remolding is a function of natural water content. Regardless of the sampling technique, specimens drier than ~14% water content disintegrated upon extrusion from the sampler and could not be tested. This is apparently due to insufficient capillary water to bond the particles together (Clough and Bachus 1981). Clearly, the sandstones found at this site are sensitive to disturbances induced by the drilling and sampling operation and require extreme care in order to obtain specimens representative of the remaining subsurface material.

Potentially the most bothersome aspect of these materials is that even though many of the samples recovered during the conventional drilling/sampling process were disturbed, they remained intact, possibly by the capillary moisture, and could be tested. To quantify the effects of disturbance, conventional laboratory triaxial compression tests were conducted on the recovered samples. The results of this laboratory investigation has been previously presented by Clough and Bachus (1982) and Clough, et al. (1981). For purposes of this report the effects of sampling technique, and thus sample disturbance, on the dry density, strain to failure, strength and stiffness are summarized in Table 1. The effect of initial tangent modulus, E_i, variation to confining pressure, σ_3, is normalized with respect to atmospheric pressure, p_a, by the following equation:

$$E_i = K p_a \left(\frac{\sigma_3}{p_a}\right)$$

The coefficients K and n are reported in Table 1. Clearly, the disturbance induced during the sampling operation results in a denser, more ductile and generally weaker sample, for samples able to be recovered and trimmed in the lab. Nearly 50% of the field recovered specimens crumbled upon extrusion or were so severely disturbed that they could not be tested.

At the Pacifica test site chosen for the reported study, bluffs of the weakly cemented sands afforded access for block sampling. During conventional site investigation this capability is seldom a feasible option. Simply based on visual appearance these samples were the least disturbed of all the specimens tested. In the absence of block samples for testing an obvious question of evaluation and reliability of laboratory test results is posed the engineer. Neither split spoon nor Shelby tube sampling techniques provided samples which truly represented the in-place material and thus results of tests using these samples are of questionable reliability.

Table 1. Summary of the effects of sampling techniques on the results
of conventional laboratory testing.

Sampling Technique	Dry Density (kN/m³)	Strain to Failure (%)	Strength Parameters		Modulus Parameters	
			C (kN/m²)	ϕ	K	N
Block sample	16.7	2	25	40	770	0.65
Pitcher barrel	17.7	4.8	46	21	Not available	
Shelby tube	17.8	4.8	42	30	225	0.62
Split spoon	18.3	10.9	28	36	30	0.13

3 IN-SITU TESTING TECHNIQUES IN WEAKLY CEMENTED SANDS

It appears that when dealing with soft sandstones or weakly cemented
sands, the driving/pushing/coring action of the sampler is sufficient
to break the sensitive interparticle bonds between adjacent grains.
To reduce the dependence on the disturbed samples for evaluation of
engineering properties, in-situ testing techniques for use in soft
rocks were sought. Due to the weakly cemented nature of the material,
in-situ tests useful in rock mechanics were considered to have little
chance of success. NX borehole jack tests were previously conducted
at a nearby site on similar subsurface materials. Results of tests
conducted on poorly cemented sandstone were extremely erractic and
difficult to interpret (Dames and Moore 1977) due possibly to the
softening of the borehole sidewalls during the coring operation. As
a result, intimate contact between the rigid borehole jack plates and
weak sandstone is unlikely.
    Conventional in-situ tests useful in the evaluation of the proper-
ties of soils were considered and attempted. Test considerations and
results were reported previously by Bachus (1982). Unfortunately,
both the Standard Penetration Test (SPT) and the Dutch cone penetrometer (CPT) tests yielded inconclusive results. The corrected blow
counts from the SPT test to a depth of 17m indicated medium to very
dense sand. In many cases the blow counts exceeded 100. As mentioned
previously, the samples obtained from the split spoon sampler at the
conclusion of the SPT test were also generally classified as uncemented
sands. Therefore, although the blow counts indicate reasonably
competent material, they do not offer a clue as to the true cemented
nature of the material. The high tip bearing pressure and relatively
low friction ratio resulting from the CPT test are indicative of dense
or cemented sands (Sanglerat 1972). For material encountered at the
Pacifica site the test depth was limited to only 3m as the tip bearing
pressure was sufficient enough to lift the rear of the drilling rig
from its leveling pads. The particular cone system used at Pacifica
was not designed for greater reaction forces and thus anchoring the
rig for deeper penetration was not considered. Although the penetrometer offers some potential in characterizing the material, a more
rugged design would be required.

The pressuremeter was considered for testing at the site. In its simplest form the instrument is comprised of a long cylindrical membrane over an inner steel mandril which is lowered down the borehole and hydraulically inflated to contact and test the sidewalls of the borehole. The pressuremeter has been used previously to study the behavior of soft rocks (Dixon and Jones 1968) but results and utility have been limited. Using carefully prepared hand and machine augered boreholes, conventional pressuremeter tests were conducted on cemented sands at an adjacent site. These tests were moderately successful due primarily to over-inflation and puncture of the membrane. Owing to this condition, none of the early prototype tests could be carried above the elastic limit of the tested soil. Additionally, the limited test results clearly indicate the importance of borehole preparation technique. All holes advanced using water or drilling mud were eroded to a diameter unsuitable for testing. The drilling fluid in contact with the borehole sidewalls also noticeably weakened the material, yielding a softer stress-strain pressuremeter response than anticipated. Therefore, conventional pressuremeter testing of the weakly cemented sands, while feasible, must address the issue of borehole preparation as well as the interaction effects of drilling fluid on in-situ properties.

To assess the in-situ characteristics of the weak sandstones at Pacifica and yet overcome the drawbacks of the conventional pressuremeter test, modification of a self-boring pressuremeter to resist the rugged drilling environment of soft rock was initiated. The self-boring pressuremeter, shown schematically in Figure 1, was developed primarily for the testing of soft clays (Wroth and Hughes 1974), but has proven a valuable tool for testing soils characterized by sampling difficulties. The instrument was constructed by Cambridge Insitu and is similar to the conventional pressuremeter in that it consists of a long cylindrical flexible membrane attached to a stainless steel mandril. Unlike a pre-bored pressuremeter the center of the probe is hollow and allows the use of drilling rods which are activated at the ground surface and which rotate a cutter at the bottom of the probe. Drilling fluid is supplied through the center of the drill rod and cuttings are flushed to the ground surface via the annular space between the drill rod and the probe body. In this manner the probe is drilled into place with a minimum of borehole sidewall disturbance. Once at the selected test depth the membrane is inflated via bottled nitrogen gas and radial deformation is recorded by 3 spring-actuated feelers, located at 120° intervals around the middle of the instrument, which track the inside movement of the membrane during expansion. Data generated during the test are sensed via the strain gages on the 3 feeler springs and 2 diaphram strain gages within the probe. In this way radial deformation, total lateral pressure and pore water pressures can be monitored continuously during a test.

Prior to deployment at the Pacifica site and based on trial testing at an adjacent site, the pressuremeter protection system and self-boring drilling system had to be modified for testing soft rocks. Specific modifications to the instrument and to the operation included a) incorporation of reusable ground anchors to the ground frame for adequate vertical reaction, b) development of a high speed drill bit for use in homogeneous weak sandstone, c) modification of the Chinese lantern which protects the rubber membrane during both insertion and inflation, and d) development of a drilling technique using air pressure to flush the cuttings from the freshly drilled borehole.

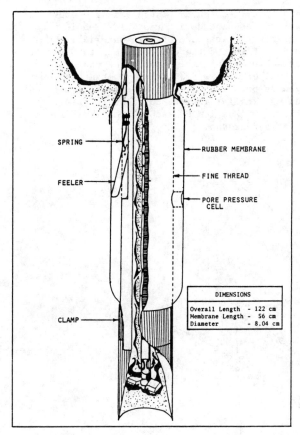

Figure 1. Schematic of the self-boring pressuremeter (after Wroth and Hughes 1974).

Details of these modifications were presented by Bachus (1982) and are beyond the scope of this paper. Using these techniques, however, allowed successful completion of the self-boring pressuremeter test program. Drilling rates of 25 mm/min and using bottled compressed air for flushing in these tests potentially preclude its consideration as a production tool at this time, but as a research device the difficulties posed by the isolated site location and abrasive drilling conditions were overcome and a total of 5 tests were conducted.

4 SELF-BORING PRESSUREMETER TEST RESULTS

At the Pacifica test site the self-boring pressuremeter was successfully used to conduct 5 high quality tests in the weak sandstone. The results of these tests are shown in Figure 2 as a plot of applied total lateral pressure, corrected for the stiffness of the membrane/Chinese lantern system, versus the strain, defined as the change in radius relative to the initial radius of the borehole sidewall. The data shown in Figure 2 indicate a apparently linear initial relationship gradually tending

1071

towards a concave downward, i.e., softened, response as the pressure
increases. The unload-reload response during test PAC-PM-5 is also
shown to depict the actual elastic response of this material. Due to
the scale selection chosen in Figure 2 the curves appear to start at the
origin. Expansion of the scale in the early reaches of the test reveal
that there was a finite level of stress required to initiate movement
of the membrane. The results presented in Table 2 summarize the test
depth, initial shear modulus, initial in-situ horizontal stress, and
derived strength properties. Discussion of each of these results is
presented in the subsequent paragraphs.

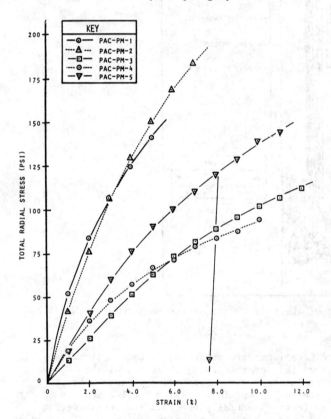

Figure 2. Self-boring pressuremeter curves for tests conducted at
Pacifica.

One of the unique features of the self-boring pressuremeter is the
theoretical ability to insert the probe into the ground without admitt-
ing any lateral relaxation of the in-situ lateral stresses. The value
of horizontal stress is recorded in Table 2. The relatively low magnitude of these stresses is attributed to the shallow test depths and
relative position to the exposed bluff face. In fact, the data is
generally consistent with respect to both depth and horizontal distance
to the bluff. In cases where knowledge of the in-situ lateral stresses
in soft rocks is required, the self-boring pressuremeter appears a
viable tool.

Table 2. Results of the self-boring pressuremeter tests at Pacifica.

Test No.	Hole No.	Depth (m)	G (kPa)	σ_h (kPa)	Strength Parameter*	
					c (kPa) $\phi = 40°$	ϕ c = 35 kPa
PAC-PM-1	1	3.1	16540	26.9	76	45
PAC-PM-2	1	4.2	12540	12.4	83	44
PAC-PM-3	2	1.8	4610	4.8	69	45
PAC-PM-4	3	1.8	5650	6.2	21	37
PAC-PM-5	3	2.8	7430	6.9	96	48

* Strength parameters c and ϕ are not independent based on the authors interpretation scheme. Evaluation of the parameters shown utilized the assumption of either c = 35 kPa or ϕ = 40°.

Pressuremeter loading of subsurface soils can be approximated as the expansion of a thick walled cylindrical cavity. If the initial loading conditions are considered elastic, then solution of the Lame equation for initial shear modulus, G, is shown to be equivalent to one half the initial slope of the radial pressure-strain curve shown in Figure 2. Like the lateral stress results, the calculated values of G are generally consistent with both depth and position relative the bluff face. When appropriate values of Poisson's ratio are chosen and Youngs Modulus, E, is backcalculated and compared to the laboratory test results, the results are encouraging. In all cases the moduli derived from the field studies is generally within $\pm$ 30% of the lab results for block samples. Direct comparison of results is difficult due to the rotation of principal stresses and potential anisotropic effects during the pressure-meter test. It is, however, most encouraging that these results are considerably higher than results from the conventionally obtained samples.

Interpretation techniques for evaluating the strength characteristics of pressuremeter tests in soft rocks, cemented sands or other materials which exhibit both cohesion and friction are not well developed and verified. Techniques developed by Ladanyi (1976) and a modification of the technique developed by Hughes, et al. (1977) for sands appear to offer significant potential in the interpretation of pressuremeter test results. The details of the various techniques are far too extensive for presentation in this format. The reader is directed towards the previously referenced work of Bachus (1982) or Bachus, et al. (1981) for additional discussion. The latter technique which is based on an assumed linear c - ϕ Mohr-Coulomb failure envelope and on the validity of the stress-dilatancy concept for a continuum developed by Rowe (1962) was shown to be reasonably insensitive to small variations in the test data, a problem attributed the Ladanyi (1976) procedure. Use of the modification as proposed by the author depends on the solution of the following equation:

$$c = \sigma'_r \left(\frac{1 + \sin\phi'}{2 \cos\phi'} \right) \left(\frac{1 - \sin\phi'}{1 + \sin\phi'} - \frac{1-s}{Ks+1} \right)$$

in which s is the slope of the log-log plot of the data shown in Figure 2 at the specified value of σ'_r. The parameter K is defined as the maximum principal stress ratio of the material shearing at constant volume. Obviously the solution to this equation in terms of c and ϕ is

1073

not unique. Either prior knowledge of one of the values for a trial and error solution for one in terms of the other is necessary. In many cases it is easier to estimate the value of ϕ rather than c. Therefore this equation can be used to determine the cohesion. For the results shown in Table 2, solutions based on assumed values of c = 35 kPa and $\phi = 40°$ are presented as these values are reasonably close to the block sample test results. The calculated values are consistently slightly greater than the lab obtained values but are realistic.

SUMMARY

To allow the in-situ testing of soft rocks, modification of a self-boring pressuremeter, a device generally developed to study soft clays, was made. Development of a test interpretation scheme was reported. Tests were successfully conducted and the interpreted results are realistic and encouraging.

REFERENCES

Crosby and Associates 1978. Soil and geologic investigation, Palmetto Ave. near Westline Dr., Pacifica, Ca.
Sitar, N., G.W. Clough, and R.C. Bachus 1980. Behavior of weakly cemented soil slopes under static and seismic loading conditions. Report No. 44, The John A. Blume Center, Stanford University.
Youd, T.L. and S.N. Hoose 1978. Historic ground failures in northern California triggered by earthquakes. United States Geological Survey. Professional paper No. 993.
Bachus, R.C. 1982. An investigation of the strength deformation response of naturally occurring lightly cemented sands. PhD Thesis. Stanford University.
Clough, G.W. and R.C. Bachus 1982. An investigation of sampling disturbance in weakly cemented sand. Engineering Foundation Conf. on Updating Subsurface Sampling and In-Situ Testing, Santa Barbara, Ca.
Clough, G.W., N. Sitar, R.C. Bachus, and N. Shafii-Rad 1981. Cemented sands under static loading. Journal of the Geotechnical Engineering Division, ASCE, Vol. 107, No. GT6.
Dames and Moore 1977. Geotechnical investigation, proposed positron-electron project. Stanford Linear Accelerator Center, Stanford, Ca.
Wroth, C.P. and Hughes, J.M.O. 1974. The development of a special instrument for the in-situ measurement of the strength and stiffness of soils. Engineering Foundation Conf. on Subsurface Exploration for Underground Excavation and Heavy Construction, Henniker, N.H.
Sanglerat, G. 1972. The penetrometer and soil exploration. Elsevier Publishing Co., 1st ed.
Dixon, S.J. and Jones, V.W. 1968. Soft rock exploration with pressure equipment. Civil Engineering, Vol. 38, No. 10.
Ladanyi, B. 1976. Quasi-static expansion of a cylindrical cavity in rock. Proceedings of 3rd Symposium on Engineering Applications of Solid Mechanics, Vol. 2, University of Toronto.
Hughes, J.M.O., C.P. Wroth, and D. Windle 1977. Pressuremeter tests in sands. Geotechnique, Vol. 27, No. 4.
Rowe, P.W. 1962. The stress-dilatancy relation for static equilibrium of an assembly of particles in contact. Proceedings of the Royal Society of London, Series A, Vol. 269.

A borehole instrument for measuring mining-induced pressure changes in underground coal mines

ERIC R.BAUER, GREGORY J.CHEKAN & JOHN L.HILL III
US Department of the Interior, Bureau of Mines, Pittsburgh Research Center, Pennsylvania, USA

ABSTRACT

The U.S. Bureau of Mines, Pittsburgh Research Center, has been using a simple and inexpensive instrument for measuring mining-induced pressure changes in coal pillars and mine roof. The instrument, referred to as the Borehole Platened Flatjack (BPF), is a copper flatjack (bladder) positioned between aluminum platens. It is calibrated in a simulated coal or coal measure rock medium prior to in-mine installation. Laboratory tests have shown the BPF to be repeatable and reliable, and that the relationship between gage pressure and strata pressure is dependent on the initial setting pressure. Field tests have shown that the BPF is easily installed, and that it effectively indicates mine areas experiencing increasing or decreasing pressures.

INTRODUCTION

Current Bureau of Mines ground control research indicates the need for an instrument which can be quickly and easily fabricated and installed using a minimum of equipment and personnel, can adequately determine the magnitude and direction of mining-induced pressure changes, and can be used near face operations with a minimum of production delays. The BPF is an adaptation of existing instrumentation (Miller and Sporcic, 1964; Gilley, Sporcic and Zona, 1964; Curth, 1967; Lu, 1984); the primary modification being the substitution of aluminum platens for the various encapsulation materials. This allows the instrument to be calibrated prior to in-mine installation. Calibration of each BPF enables the relationship between gage pressure and strata pressure (K factor) to be established, and allows for correction of the slight differences between individually fabricated bladders which can create different responses to pressure changes.

Once each BPF has been calibrated in the laboratory, the instrument is ready for installation. Installation time is minimal when compared to other pressure measuring instruments, which make the BPF very advantageous for use near face operations. The BPF is designed to allow up to three BPFs to be installed in a single borehole, thus permitting pressure change measurements in more than one direction from a single borehole.

Two field investigations (described later in the paper) have been conducted using the BPF. Both investigations were conducted near face operations where initial magnitude and direction of pressure changes were unknown.

Both laboratory tests and underground investigations with the BPF have demonstrated the usefulness of this instrument, especially near face operations. The results of the work show that the BPF is an effective instrument for measuring the magnitude of mining-induced pressure changes in a known direction in underground coal mines.

DESCRIPTION OF BOREHOLE PLATENED FLATJACK

Figure 1 shows the BPF, with the major parts listed in the insert. The copper bladder is constructed from 2.54 cm (1 in) diam Type K copper tubing, which has been worked to a final dimension of 15.24 cm (6 in) long by 3.49 cm (1.375 in) wide by 0.64 cm (0.25 in) thick. Copper refrigeration tubing is used to connect the bladder to the gage; its length dependent on the depth of installation. The system is filled with hydraulic oil while simultaneously bleeding all trapped air. The platens are machined from 5.08 cm (2 in) diam aluminum stock to a finished size of 17.78 cm (7 in) long by 4.13 cm (1.625 in) wide by 2.06 cm (0.8125 in) high. Aluminum was selected for the platens because it is lightweight, easy to machine, and its creep effect within the expected loading range is considered negligible. Grooves are cut to accommodate two rubber o-rings which keep the bladder positioned between the platens. Finally, holes are drilled through the length of both platens to accommodate leads from other BPFs installed in the same borehole.

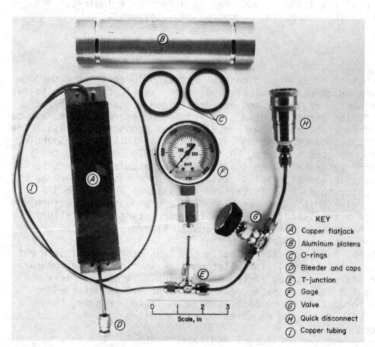

Figure 1. Borehole platened flatjack.

The basic steps of in-house fabrication of the BPF are (1) construction of the copper bladder, (2) attachment of copper leads to bladder, (3) connection of gage, T-junction, valve, bleeder, and quick disconnect, (4) filling system with oil, and (5) machining of platens. This fabrication process takes approximately 2 man-h per BPF.

The BPF was designed for installation in a 5.08 cm (2 in) diam borehole. Successful installations have been achieved using a pneumatic, hand-held drill with 4.76 cm (1.875 in) auger drill steel and 5.08 cm (2 in) bit. In several field investigations, two BPFs have been installed in the same borehole in a coal pillar at a maximum depth of 15.24 m (50 ft). The BPFs are set in the borehole by inflating the bladder with hydraulic oil using a hand-operated pump. Installation pressure is calculated on the estimated pressure exerted by the overburden and the percent recovery after first mining. The closer the setting pressure is to the actual strata pressure, the less time needed for the instrument to reach equilibrium. Although the BPF can be installed to measure pressure changes in any direction, it is most commonly installed in either a vertical or horizontal attitude. Detailed fabrication and installation procedures can be obtained from the authors and will be available in a Bureau of Mines publication in the near future.

CALIBRATION

The primary reason for modifying existing instrumentation was to obtain an instrument that could be calibrated prior to in-mine installation. As stated earlier, calibration was necessary so that the relationship between gage pressure and strata pressure could be determined and to eliminate differences between individual bladders. This results in a more accurate determination of actual pressure changes.

Reliable calibration was dependent upon selection of an appropriate medium. Lucite (Reference to specific trade names or products does not imply endorsement by the Bureau of Mines) was chosen to simulate coal because it has a compressive modulus of elasticity [25.51 to 31.72 x 10^5 kPa (3.7 to 4.6 x 10^5 psi)] (Commercial Plastics and Supply Corp., 1978) in the range of most coals [10.34 to 37.92 x 10^5 kPa (1.5 to 5.5 x 10^5 psi)] (Moebs, 1984) and thus similar deformational response to compressive loading. Calibration could also be conducted in blocks of coal or coal measure rocks where the BPFs are to be installed. This becomes impractical for various reasons including cost and problems of obtaining the blocks, and because the material would experience extensive fracturing due to repetitive loading during calibration. For calibration of BPFs for use in coal measure rocks, Lucite type mediums which have compressive properties similar to the rocks in question are available. To select and design the calibration medium, several simplified assumptions were made regarding the physical properties of the Lucite, coal, and state of stress around a circular opening in massive rock (Obert, Duvall, Merrill, 1960). These include:

1. Massive rock and Lucite medium obey Hooke's Law and are isotropic and homogenous with respect to their linear elastic properties.
2. The opening is in an infinite medium. This condition is satisfied if the distance from the opening to an adjacent boundary is greater than three times the dimension of the opening.
3. Coal strata will behave like a massive rock when subject to loading.

To satisfy assumption 2 and to insure that an infinite boundary condition exists, the Lucite block was cut to a final dimension of 38.1 cm (15 in) high by 38.1 cm (15 in) wide by 17.8 cm (7 in) thick. A 5.08 cm (2 in) diam hole is drilled perpendicular to the larger sides at the center of the block, and the uniaxial loads are applied on a pair of the smaller sides parallel to each other.

The BPFs are calibrated in a standard compression testing machine. The calibration load ranges from the cell setting pressure to the machine maximum, of 47,627 kg (105,000 lbs). The upper limit results in a cell pressure of 6895 kPag (1000 psig). For example, if the desired setting pressure is 3450 kPag (500 psig), the following procedure is used. First, the Lucite block is pre-loaded to the cell setting pressure. Next, a BPF is inserted in the hole at the center of the block with the flatjack oriented perpendicular to the loading on the block, then pressurized to the setting pressure using the hand-operated pump. The block is then loaded from the setting pressure to the machine maximum and back to the setting pressure. No readings are recorded during this initial loading and unloading because it is used to enable the BPF to reach equilibrium with the block. Finally, several loading and unloading cycles are run while recording gage pressure versus machine load, both as the load is increasing and decreasing. Based on the above assumptions and repetitive loading data recorded, a K factor is determined and a calibration curve is generated for each BPF. A typical calibration curve is shown in figure 2 where a straight line fit to the data gives a K of 0.713576 for a loading range of 2000 kPag (290 psig) to 440 kPag (640 psig).

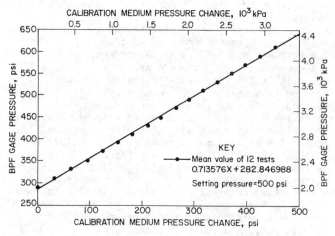

Figure 2. Typical calibration curve for a BPF.

BPF CHARACTERIZATION

Additional lab tests were conducted to characterize the use and limitations of the BPF. The specific items investigated were repeatability, precision of fabrication, K factor, and effect of borehole size variations.

Repeatability was demonstrated through successive loadings during calibration of each BPF (fig. 3). The close proximity of the upper and lower 99.7% limits to the mean value indicates that the values obtained during successive loadings vary little, thus acceptable repeatability has been obtained for the cell pressure range expected. Precision of fabrication was determined by comparing the K factors of several BPFs, calibrated at the same setting pressure. The absence of variation in the K factors (a measure of the ability to fabricate nearly identical bladders) is shown in table 1. Although this comparison is based on a small sample, the K factors vary no more than ± 0.023, indicating consistent fabrication. K factor tests showed that the K factor varied depending on the initial setting pressure of the BPF. Figure 4 is a group of K factors for one particular BPF and illustrates that the BPF is more sensitive to pressure changes as the setting pressure increases. As yet, no testing has been conducted to determine the K factors for setting pressures of 10,340 kPag (1500 psig) and greater. The graph indicates the K factors should remain about 1.4. This trend can only be verified by additional testing.

TABLE 1. - Precision of fabrication

BPF No.	K factor 2760 kPag (400 psig)	K factor 3450 kPag (500 psig)
0	0.54	0.68
3	0.52	----
4	----	0.71
6	----	0.67
Mean	0.53	0.687
Precision	± 0.01	± 0.023

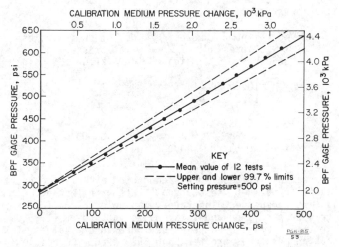

Figure 3. BPF repeatability from twelve successive tests.

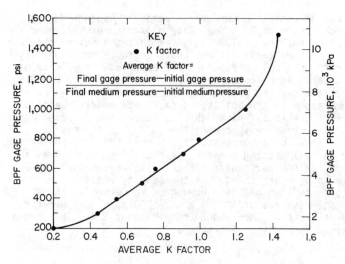

Figure 4. Variation of K factor as setting pressure increases.

The effect of oversized holes on BPF performance was determined by reducing the size of the platens (to simulate larger diameter holes) while running standard calibration tests. Figure 5 illustrates the reduction of the K factor as the effective diameter of the hole increases. This graph stresses the importance of drilling a 5.08 cm (2 in) diam borehole, if accurate and reliable pressure monitoring based on laboratory calibration is to be obtained. Diameter of the borehole can be estimated by the number of pump strokes required to inflate the bladder to the desired setting pressure. Table 2 lists the number of pump strokes required to set a typical BPF in a borehole of different diameters.

TABLE 2. - Required number of pump strokes for various borehole diameters and installation pressure

Hole diameter cm (in)	No. of pump strokes* at pressure of 3450 kPag (500 psig)	No. of pump strokes at pressure of 6895 kPag (1000psig)
5.08 (2.000)	10.00	11.74
5.40 (2.125)	16.21	19.85
5.72 (2.250)	22.14	27.10
6.03 (2.375)	26.38	32.77
6.35 (2.500)	30.48	38.00

* Volume of oil per stroke is 0.557 cm^3 (0.034 in^3)

Calibration and repeatability testing was conducted by an independent testing firm, in addition to in-house testing (Pittsburgh Testing Laboratory, 1984). The independent laboratory was able to duplicate our testing with greater precision and to a load of just over 111,580 kg (246,000 lb), or 16,150 kPag (2340 psig) cell pressure. Values of K factors for BPF setting pressures greater than 5520 kPag (800 psig) obtained from the independent testing were combined with the Bureau's

1080

obtained from the independent testing were combined with the Bureau's
in-house test results to produce the curve of K factors in figure 4.

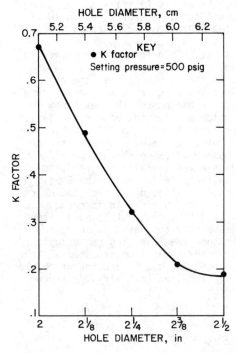

Figure 5. Reduction of K factor as diameter of borehole increases.

In summary, a series of laboratory tests are necessary at each
setting pressure to characterize BPF performance. The tests should
include (1) K factor, (2) K factor versus borehole size, (3) required
number of pump strokes versus borehole size, (4) repeatability, and (5)
calibration in simulated coal or coal measure rock medium.

FIELD INVESTIGATIONS

The BPF has been used in many field studies including (1) investigation
of cutter roof failure, (2) effects of multiple seam mining, (3) coal
mine bump investigations, and (4) investigation of roof problems
associated with geologic anomalies. Of these, the investigation of the
causes of cutter roof failure and the effects of multiple seam mining
will be addressed in this paper.
    The first case study was conducted to determine the mechanism behind
cutter roof failure. Initial research revealed a correlation between
the occurrence of clastic dikes and the formation of cutter roof
failure (Hill and Bauer, 1984). This suggested that the disruption of
roof integrity, due to the presence of clastic dikes, was contributing
to the formation of cutters. The natural beam of the roof rock,
spanning from pillar to pillar, is severed when a clastic dike is
present, and this causes the roof to behave as a cantilever beam.

In an attempt to measure and quantify the roof beam effect, BPFs were placed in the roof strata to measure pressure horizontal changes parallel and perpendicular to the entries as mining advanced. The BPFs were set in the roof strata to a height of 1 m (3 ft) from the mine roof surface at the center of the roof span. The BPFs had an initial setting pressure of approximately 1800 kPag (260 psig) to ensure a solid contact with the strata.

The following is a typical example of BPF performance in measuring the roof beam effect. Two BPFs (No. 1 and 2) were installed in an entry, approximately 3m (10 ft) outby the face. At the time of installation, no cutters or clastic dikes were present. Approximately three days after installation, the face had passed the next inby crosscut, exposing a clastic dike which was located approximately 1.5 m (5 ft) from the cells, when loading began to occur on BPF 1 which was measuring pressure changes perpendicular to the direction of the entry (fig. 6). BPF 2 was oriented to measure pressure changes parallel to the direction of the entry. Six days after installation, a cutter began to develop adjacent to the clastic dike just inby the BPFs. As the cutter progressed to the next outby clastic dike, the loading on BPF No. 1 continued to increase. Loading continued to increase on both BPFs and roof conditions continued to deteriorate until the entire entry had to be cribbed to control the roof (by day 30). Loading eventually leveled off as the cribs took the load, and the entry finally stabilized. Both BPFs responded as would be expected if the immediate roof was under lateral compression due to bending of the roof span. Thus, the use of this instrument helped to verify the ground movement in the roof near clastic dikes.

BEHAVIOR OF LOAD CELLS 1 AND 2

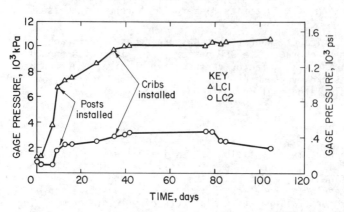

Figure 6. Behavior of BPFs 1 and 3 (Hill and Bauer, 1984).

In the second case study, BPFs are being used to study ground inter-actions associated with the mining of multiple coal seams. Two multiple seam sites are currently under investigation to monitor in-mine subsidence and pillar load transfer (Haycocks, Ehgartner, Topuz, 1982).

To investigate subsidence, within the mines, BPFs were used to measure pressure changes in the pillars and roof of a mine section where ground conditions are severely affected by previous extractions in an underlying mine. The seam in this particular section had subsided creating strata flexure, or bending. BPFs were installed in pillars to measure vertical pressure changes during advance and retreat mining. No significant pressure changes were noted during first mining, but during retreat mining, the BPFs indicated pillar pressure increases averaging 3450 kPag (500 psig). This increased pressure did not affect the general stability of the pillars but caused minor rib sloughage. The mine roof posed the more significant ground control problem, both during advance and retreat mining. Several large roof falls occurred ranging from 3 to 12.2 m (10 to 40 ft) in length and 3 to 4.6 m (10 to 15 ft) high. One BPF installed in the roof to measure horizontal pressure changes continuously lost pressure, possibly indicating that the roof was in tension. Initial investigations with the BPF in subsidence zones show that roof tension may be the major ground interaction.

Pillar load transfer, the transfer of load from pillars in an overlying coal seam to pillars in an underlying coal seam, is another multiple seam interaction currently under investigation. In this particular study, the simultaneous mining of two seams has resulted in a slow but steady transfer of load to the lower mine. In several areas of the lower mine, already affected by this interaction, pillar crushing and roof cutters are the major modes of ground failure. To further study this problem, BPFs were installed in three selected pillars in the lower mine to measure vertical pressure changes (fig. 7).

Figure 7. Two BPFs installed in a single borehole of a coal pillar to measure pillar load transfer.

The BPFs were set at depths of 3 to 7.5 m (10 to 25 ft). At the time of installation, overmining operations were just commencing. During the time (approximately 2 weeks) when mining was directly superjacent to the location of the BPFs, no increases in pillar pressure was recorded. Approximately 4 months after superjacent mining, the BPFs began to show a slow but continuous increase in pressure. Two BPFs installed at the 7.5 m (25 ft) depth have recorded a 690 kPag (100 psig) increase. This observation indicates that the pillar load transfer is not immediate but gradual. Monitoring of the BPFs is continuing in an attempt to determine the long term interaction of mining multiple seams.

CONCLUSIONS

Actual field use of the Borehole Platened Flatjack, coupled with information obtained from extensive laboratory testing, has shown the BPF to be an effective instrument for monitoring mining induced pressure changes in the range of 1380 to 13,800 kPag (200 to 2000 psig). Its ability to be quickly and easily fabricated and installed, and the ability to calibrate the instrument prior to in-mine installation, has provided the mining industry with an instrument for use in many in-mine pressure monitoring situations. Continued use of this instrument in Bureau of Mines ground control research projects will provide a working knowledge of the pressure monitoring conditions where the BPF is applicable, and should reveal any additional limitations to its use. Additional laboratory tests are being conducted to increase the data base for statistical validity of its measurement capability and to establish its reliability for practical applications.

REFERENCES

Commercial Plastics and Supply Corp. (Richmond Hill, NY). 1978. Plastics Properties Chart, 14 pp.

Curth, E.A.. 1967. Relative Pressure Changes in Coal Pillars During Extraction: A Progress Report. BuMines RI 6980, 20 pp.

Gilley, J.L., R. Sporcic and A. Zona. 1964. Progress in the Application of Encapsulated Cells in Coal Mines Subject to Coal Bursts. Proc. 6th Symp. Rock Mechanics, Univ. of Missouri, Rolla, MO, pp. 649-667.

Haycocks, C., B. Ehgartner, M. Karmis and E. Topuz. 1982. Pillar Load Transfer Mechanisms in Multi-Seam Mining. Pres. at Soc. Min. Eng. AIME Annual Meeting, Dallas, TX, Soc. Min. Eng. AIME preprint 82-69, 7 pp.

Hill, J.L. III and E.R. Bauer. 1984. An Investigation of the Causes of Cutter Roof Failure in a Central Pennsylvania Coal Mine: A Case Study. Proc. 25th Symp. Rock Mechanics, Northwestern Univ., Evanston, IL, pp. 603-614.

Lu, P.H. 1984. Mining-Induced Stress Measurements with Hydraulic Borehole Pressure Cells. Proc. 25th Symp. Rock Mechanics, Northwestern Univ., Evanston, IL, pp. 204-211.

Miller, T.C. and R. Sporcic. 1964. Development of a Hydraulic Device for Measuring Relative Pressure Changes in Coal During Mining: A Progress Report. BuMines RI 6571, 13 pp.

Moebs, N.N. (USBM). 1984. Private communication; available upon request from N.N. Moebs, BuMines, Pittsburgh, PA.

Obert, L., W.I. Duvall and R.H. Merrill. 1960. Design of Underground Openings in Competent Rock. BuMines Bulletin 587, 36 pp.

Pittsburgh Testing Laboratory (Pittsburgh, PA). 1984. Calibration of Pressure Cell. Report of Testing Results PPS-662, 4 pp.; available upon request from E.R. Bauer, BuMines, Pittsburgh, PA.

22. In situ case histories

Chair: MARK ZOBACK
          Stanford University, Palo Alto, California, USA
Cochair: BEZALEL C.HAIMSON
          University of Wisconsin-Madison, USA

Pore pressure effects on the minimum principal stress direction in shallow tar sands

DANIEL D.BUSH
Terra Tek Inc., Salt Lake City, Utah, USA

NICK BARTON
Terra Tek Inc., Salt Lake City, Utah, USA
Presently: NGI, Taasen, Norway

ABSTRACT

Shallow tar sands for the most part are located in unconsolidated media. Data interpretation must consider these units as basically a soil where pore pressure will greatly affect the minor principal stress direction. If the tar sands are considered analogous to a confined aquifer, the role of pore (tar) pressure to total stress is more clearly defined. The magnitude and direction of the minimum principal stress will be dependent on the tar pore pressure. Test data show that under fully tar saturated conditions at shallow depth, less than 442 m (1450 ft) the minimum principal stress is vertical, while in undersaturated unconsolidated formations at similar depth, the minimum principal stress is horizontal. Under fully tar-saturated conditions, intragranular pressure would decrease due to dilatancy and the media would become almost cohesionless. Under these conditions the formation stresses would be nearly isotropic with the minimum principal stress equal to the overburden (vertical). At greater depth or where the formation is not fully saturated, a smaller fraction of the overburden load will be carried by the tar due to closer sand grain packing. This increased effective normal stress will reduce Poisson's ratio, resulting in a horizontal minimum principal stress.
  A vertical minimum principal stress direction will be indicated when the stress gradient would approximately equal 1 [stress (psi)/depth (ft)].

INTRODUCTION

In-situ stress determinations in elastic media by small scale hydraulic fracturing is well known and has been frequently demonstrated for both cased and open hole operations. However, the application of this technique to non-elastic media is not well documented. Unlike other methods of in situ stress determination, hydraulic fracturing does not require precise knowledge of the mechanical properties of the "rock mass" under investigation. Published data pertaining to the stresses within shallow tar sands is limited and indicate diverse opinions.
  Several investigators have suggested that the minor principal stress direction in the lithology overlying the Alberta Tar Sand formations changes from vertical to horizontal probably between 790

and 1765 feet (240-540 m). Conversely, horizontal stresses have been calculated to be three times the vertical stress at relatively shallow depths in an open pit mining operation.

Shallow tar sands for the most part are located in unconsolidated media. The stratigraphic complexity of these unconsolidated tar sands, pore pressure within the various zones, and the viscous property of the hydrocarbon deposits all contribute to complicate the interpretation of in situ stress measurements via small scale hydraulic fracturing.

Data interpretation must consider these units as basically a soil where pore pressure will greatly affect the magnitude and direction of the minimum principal stress. If the tar sands are considered analogous to a confined aquifer, the role of pore (tar) pressure to total stress is more clearly defined. Under fully tar-saturated conditions, the tar sands would become almost cohesionless, and the principal stress differences could not exceed the limiting shear strength of these frictional (C = 0) materials.

THEORY

In rock, a change in the direction of the minimum principal stress occurs at depth due, in effect, to the intersection of the vertical stress gradient and the minimum horizontal stress gradient. In saturated shallow tar sands, it is possible that the change of stress direction (vertical to horizontal) is affected by the tar pore pressure. If the overburden load is born chiefly by the tar at shallow depth, the effective vertical stress (between grain contacts) will be low with the tar (pore pressure) transmitting pressure equally in all directions. Therefore, the minimum principal stress will be equal to the overburden (vertical) and shown as a high total stress in analysis of the test data. Though the overlying strata to the tar sands are frequently considered unconsolidated, early stage diagenesis of this lithology must be considered as having altered the media. At greater depth or in unsaturated conditions, a smaller fraction of the overburden will tend to be carried by the tar, increasing the effective stress due to closer sand grain packing. The increased shear resistance caused by this increased effective normal stress between grains will have reduced Poisson's ratio, resulting in a horizontal minimum principal stress, and shown as a low total stress by the data.

By definition, the total vertical pressure sensed by a formation is:

$$P_t = P_i + P_h \qquad (1)$$

where: P_t = total pressure

P_i = intragranular pressure

P_h = hydraulic (pore) pressure

The intragranular pressure or "effective" pressure is that pressure transmitted by the individual grains of the unconsolidated formation at their contact points (Lambe and Whitman, 1969). An increase in hydraulic pressure due to complete saturation by a viscous fluid would result in a decrease in P_i (intragranular pressure) due to dilatancy.

The formation would essentially be cohesionless. The formation stresses would be nearly isotropic, with only a small component of differential stress, limited by the available shear resistance as defined by:

$$t = \frac{\sigma_1' + \sigma_3'}{2} \tan \phi \qquad (2)$$

$$\sigma_1' - \sigma_3' < t$$

where: t = shear resistance

σ_1' = maximum effective stress

σ_3' = minimum effective stress

ϕ = effective angle of internal friction (drained)

In situ stress measurement data acquired via small scale hydraulic fracturing have been shown by several investigators (Gronseth and Detourney, 1979; Doe, T., et al., 1981; Haimson, 1981; and Teufel, 1983) to be in good accord with rock overcoring data analysis. Nolte and Smith (1979), and Gronseth and Kry (1981) have provided a procedure for the estimation of the minimum in situ stress from pressure decline analysis after shut-in. Gronseth (1981, 1982) found that the instantaneous shut-in pressure (ISIP), based upon analysis of the minimum reopening and instantaneous shut-in pressures after several cycles, was a reliable estimate of the minimum total stress. A typical hydraulic fracturing pressure-time sequence is depicted in Figure 1. The ISIP has been equated to the inflection point in the pressure decline curve and is defined by:

$$P_{ISIP} = \sigma_{min} \qquad (3)$$

where P_{ISIP}, the instantaneous shut-in pressure (ISIP), is the quasi-static equilibrium pressure required to just keep the hydraulic fracture open without further propagation or closure. McLennan and Roegiers (1981) note that the general procedure of repeated repressurizations ensures that the major influence of wellbore proximity is overcome. This procedure also removes the remaining rock tensile strength and provides a representative instantaneous shut-in pressure.

APPLICATION

Hydraulic fracturing pressure-decline profiles in tar sands do not present the classic elastic media breakdown-extension profiles. This non-elastic behavior is shown in Figure 2. As the tar sand is not a competent rock mass, the tar sand "yields" to the applied in situ stress measurement fracturing pressure. This is evidenced by the continued high pressure profile which does not indicate a formation breakdown prior to shutting-in the well (Figure 3).

The usual experience of reducing ISIP (or σ_{min}) values with increasing number of pressurization cycles has been experienced in the great majority of small scale hydraulic fracturing tests in rock. Signifi-

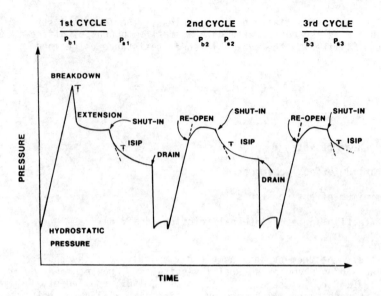

Figure 1. Schematic of typical elastic breakdown (re-opening), extension, shut-in, drain cycles. Generally, three or more cycles are performed at each test interval.

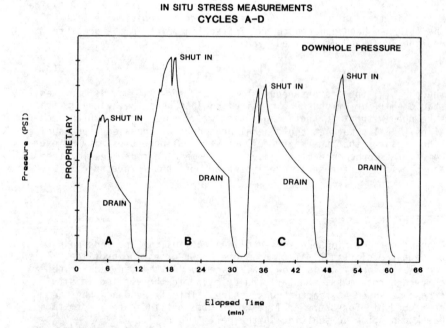

Figure 2. Stress measurements in a tar saturated lithology, showing increased minimum principal stress due to test injection fluid.

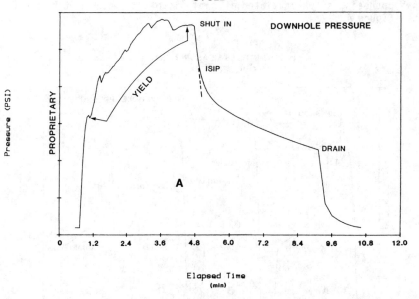

IN SITU STRESS MEASUREMENTS
CYCLE A

Figure 3. First pressurization cycle (A) showing formation "yield" to test injection fluid.

cantly, the present investigation in tar sand, and tar sand work reported by Holzhausen, et al. (1980) and Bawden (1982), all produced opposite effects, namely increasing ISIP (or σ_{min}) with increasing numbers of cycles.

The reasons for this phenomenon are obviously important in the interpretation of the data, but do not appear to have been adequately explained to date. The authors believe that the explanation lies with the viscous second phase present in tar sands. During fracture extension, with a less viscous injection fluid flowing through the fracture (network) the tar coated sand is held open. Immediately after the well is shut-in, flow stops, and the fluid pressure falls rapidly close to the well. The stress concentration around the wellbore is sufficient locally to close and tar-seal the fracture (or portions of the fracture network) such that the injection fluid is partially trapped within the formation and would result in incomplete drainage.

After the first pressurization cycle and following shut-in, the overpressured pockets of injection fluid trapped within the tar would locally increase the total stress, resulting in a higher ISIP to be registered on the next cycle. As the total stress is increased, the tar-sealing mechanism envisioned above would be made more efficient, so that the trend could continue on subsequent cycles. Obviously the early ISIP values will be most representative of the undisturbed σ_{min} value.

In unconsolidated media at shallow depths, the minimum principal stress direction in tar sands is dependent on pore pressure as related to fluid saturation. This stress direction dependency on pore pressure presents the possibility that unsaturated lithology adjacent to the tar sands could have a minimum horizontal principal stress direction. This hypothesis is substantiated in analysis of data acquired in field tests (Figure 4).

IN SITU STRESS MEASUREMENTS
CYCLES A–D

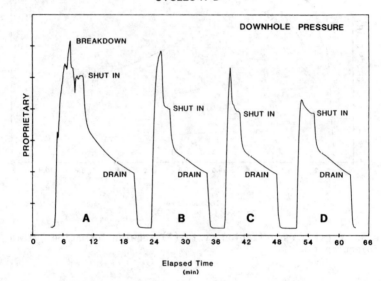

Figure 4. Stress measurements in an unsaturated bounding lithology showing a more classic breakdown behavior. The minimum stress is 20% less than tar sands.

CONCLUSIONS

In tectonically relaxed areas under saturated conditions, the stress measurements would reflect the overburden (vertical) stress as expressed by a stress gradient near or equal to one [ISIP (psi)/depth (ft)]. Small scale hydraulic fracturing test data shows that in a fully tar-saturated lithology at shallow depths [<442 m (1450 feet)] the minimum principal stress is vertical, indicating a pore pressure relationship. In saturated tar sands, the change from a vertical to a horizontal minimum stress direction does not occur due to the reduction of the effective stress by the tar pore pressure. The pressure-decline curve of the initial test cycles can give a reliable estimate of the minimum principal stress as this is in response to the in situ stress regime. However, increased pore pressure induced through the test procedures in subsequent cycles can produce erroneous data.

In unconsolidated lithology where the formations are not fully tar-saturated and higher intragranular pressures are present, the minimum principal stress can be horizontal. Evidence suggests that in unsaturated poorly consolidated lithology the change in the minimum principal stress direction occurs at a depth less than 1225 feet (371 meters). Small scale hydraulic fracturing data for non-saturated lithology adjacent to the tar sands shows a stress gradient [stress (psi)/ depth (ft)] of less than 1, most generally in the range of 0.9 to 0.7. This low stress gradient indicates the minimum principal stress direction is horizontal.

It should be noted that if the state of stress in a formation is nearly isotropic as would be the case in a saturated homogeneous lithology, any induced fracture would most likely have no preferred orientation. In strongly bedded unconsolidated lithology of dissimilar composition (gravel/ sand) the potential exists that the injection fluid would follow the path of least resistance, i.e., follow bedding planes or lithology with the greatest permeability.

Changes in the tar sand pore pressure through extraction, leakoff, etc., could increase the effective stress of the formation to where the minimum principal stress becomes horizontal.

The maximum principal stress is not determinable through standard elastic theory calculations as the tar sands are essentially cohesionless without true elastic properties.

ACKNOWLEDGEMENTS

The support of Husky Oil Ltd. of Canada is gratefully acknowledged without which these findings could not have been made.

REFERENCES

Bawden, W.F., 1982, Hydraulic Fracturing in Alberta Tar Sand Formation - A Unique Material for In-Situ Stress Measurments, U.S.G.S. Workshop XVII, Dept. of the Int. Open File Rpt 82-1075, pp. 237-276.
Doe, T., Ingevald, K., Strindell, B., Haimson, B., and Carleson, H., Hydraulic Fracturing and Overcoring Stress Measurements in a Deep Borehole at the Stripa Test Mine, Sweden, 22nd U.S. Symp. on Rock Mechanics, MIT, MA.
Dusseault, M.B., 1977, Stress State and Hydraulic Fracturing in Athabasca Oil Sands, Journal of Canadian Petroleum Technology, V. 16, pp. 19-27.
Gronseth, J.M. and Detourney, 1979, Improved Stress Determination Procedures by Hydraulic Fracturing, Final Rpt for the U.S.G.S. Menlo Park, CA, Contract No. 14-08-0001-16768.
Gronseth, J.M. and Kry, P.R., 1981, Instantaneous Shut-In Pressure and Its Relationship to the Minimum In Situ Stress, U.S.G.S. Menlo Park, CA, Open-File Rpt 82-1075, Vol. I.
Gronseth, J.M., 1982, Determination of the Instantaneous Shut-In Pressure from Hydraulic Fracturing Data and its Reliability as a Measure of the Minimum Principal Stress, 23rd Symp. on Rock Mech., Berkeley, CA, Soc. of Mining Eng., New York, N.Y.
Haimson, B.C., 1981, A Comparative Study of Deep Hydrofracturing and Overcoring Stress Measurements at Six Locations with Particular Interest to the Nevada Test Site, USGS Menlo Park, CA, Open-File Rpt 82-1075, Vol. I.
Holzhausen, G.R., Wood, M.D., Raisabeck, J.M., Card, C.C., 1980, Results of Deformation Monitoring During Steam Stimulation in a Single-Well Test, Applied Oil Sands, Geoscience Conf., Edmonton, Alberta, June.

Lambe, W.T., Whitman, R.V., 1969, Soil Mechanics, John Wiley & Sons, Inc., New York, 553 p.

McLennan, J.D. and Roegiers, J.C., 1981, Do Instantaneous Shut-In Pressures Accurately Represent the Minimum Principal Stress, USGS Workshop on Hydraulic Fracturing Stress Measurements, Monterey, CA.

Nolte, K.G. and Smith, M.B., 1979, Interpretation of Fracture Pressure, SPE 8297, presented at SPE-AIME 54th Annual Fall Technical Conference and Exhibition, Las Vegas, NV.

Teufel, L.W., 1983, Determination of In Situ Stress from Anelastic Strain Recovery Measurements of Oriented Core, SPE/DOE 11649, SPE/DOE Symposium on Low Permeability, Denver, CO, March.

Problems associated with near surface in-situ stress measurements by the overcoring method

P.GARRITTY & R.A.IRVIN
University of Newcastle upon Tyne, UK

IAN W.FARMER
University of Arizona, Tucson, USA

I INTRODUCTION

In-situ stress measurement using the overcoring method is sound in principle. There are however a number of factors and effects which may invalidate the results from these tests and in some cases lead to an incorrect derivation of the in-situ geostatic stress tensor. These fall into two broad categories; environmental and instrument design. Those associated with the former category include the magnitude of in-situ stress; the ambient temperature of the rock and its effect on interfacial adhesion; the rock type and rock anistropy. Amadei (1983) has discussed the effect rock type and anistropy. Factors associated with the instrument include design of circuits; compensation for changes in temperature; resistance of connections and leadwires and gauge/crystal interaction. Some of these have been discussed by Fossom (1983). Instrument design and in particular the design of strain gauge circuits were found to have a critical effect on stress derivation during a test program at Troon Mine in Cornwall, U.K. (see Hudson et al, 1984). The discussion which follows is based on observations made during this program.

2 IN-SITU STRESS MEASUREMENTS BY THE OVERCORING METHOD

The overcoring method involves placement of a cylindrical cell containing an array of strain gauges in a small diameter hole. This hole is positioned to minimize the effect of random stress redistributions around existing openings, joints and other discontinuities on the in-situ stress tensor. The small diameter hole containing the cell bonded to its surface with adhesive is 'overcored' by a large diameter coring bit which allows the resulting annulus of rock, once restrained by the in-situ stresses, to freely deform. By determining the relaxation of the annulus through strains induced in gauges in the cell the in-situ stress may be calculated. In theory strain gauge rosettes can be arranged in the cell so that one overcoring operation, or several in one hole, will yield sufficient information to enable the calculation of the complete in-situ stress tensor. However, complicating factors and experimental errors require that a number of measurements are made in different directions.

In the test program, four different types of overcoring system were tested. Of the four systems used, the three which enable the complete stress tensor to be calculated from one measurement are bonded to the wall of the pilot hole by the extrusion of epoxy glue into the annulus between cell, and the sidewall rock. These included the CSIRO hollow inclusion gauge (see Worotniki and Walton, 1976; Duncan Fama and Pender, 1980), a solid inclusion cell (see Rocha and Silverio, 1969; Blackwood, 1982) and a modified Leeman cell (Leeman and Hayes, 1966). The fourth, the USBM gauge (Merrill, 1967 Panek, 1966), which gives a two dimensional measurement is held in place by friction. As with most modern instruments, strain gauges are continuously monitored during the overcoring process, giving evolution curves which provide valuable information and help to validate the data.

3 MAGNITUDE OF IN-SITU STRESS

In environments where the magnitude of the geostatic stress tensor is low difficulties may be encountered using conventional overcoring measuring systems and analysis techniques. Where experimental errors exist, such as those associated with the design of the instrument or temperature changes within the overcore, these errors are generally of fixed magnitude. In measurements made in moderately deep to deep mines they comprise such a small proportion of the total stress measured that they are often either undetectable or insignificant. In shallow mines where the geostatic stress may be low these errors can cause strains in excess of those due to the relief of the geostatic stress within the overcore. Those errors associated with the design of the instruments are generally unaccountable, those associated with thermal stresses within the overcore can usually be corrected.

The errors introduced by the thermal response of the overcore annulus itself were measured during the second phase of the instrumentation program. Each of the inclusion cells were fitted with thermistors to monitor the temperature at the gauged section. These thermistors were monitored before, during and after the overcoring operation along with the nine or more ers gauges. Figure 1 illustrates an overcore evolution curve for one gauge together with a temperature curve, illustrating the inverse correlation between the temperature of the gauged section and the response of the strain gauges. In this case the reduction in strain beyond 55 minutes must be attributed to the increase in temperature and the related relaxation of the core. It is probable that the preceding increase in strain was also affected by expansion of the core during temperature rise. The effects are difficult to define but it appears that they have been monitored by other workers including Doe et al (1983) and Gregory et al (1983). By monitoring these thermal effects and correlating them with the temperature rise at the gauged section corrections are possible.

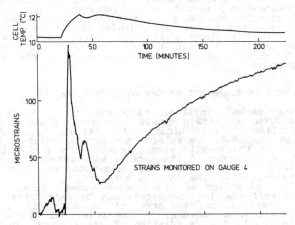

Figure 1. Effect of temperature variation during overcoring on the reading of a single gauge (No 4) on a CSIRO cell.

4 AMBIENT TEMPERATURE OF THE ROCK

The ambient temperature of the rock in which stress measurements are to be made has been shown (Irvin et al, 1985) to affect indirectly measurement of the geostatic stress tensor through its action on the interfacial adhesive. The majority of adhesives supplied by gauge manufacturers appear to be sensitive to temperature and humidity. This increases the likelihood of adhesive bond failure in certain environments. During the first phase of the test program problems were encountered with the use of CSIRO hollow inclusion cells. The adhesives supplied with the cells were found to cure in approximately

10 hours, forming a strong brittle material. However, when the sample was warmed in the palm of the hand, the once hard brittle glue softened and became malleable.

To test whether the rise in temperature generated by the overcoring operation was sufficient to cause post cure glue yield, a CSIRO hollow inclusion cell was installed and overcored. The strain evolution curve derived from this experiment is illustrated in Figure 2. As can be seen it appears to have a correct form. The overcored cell was removed and split to examine the glue bond which was found to be in a malleable state.

The results are clearly in error since the near vertical minor principal stress calculated from the measured strains was three times the magnitude of that estimated from the weight of the overburden. In addition, the major principal stress was almost parallel to the borehole axis. The same observations were made when a second borehole experiment using a similar glue was carried out in a hole drilled orthogonally to the first.

It was apparent from these two experiments that when a cell is installed with a glue which softens with temperature rise during overcoring the calculated major principal stress invariably appears parallel to the borehole axis. This can be explained if the thermal behaviour of an unrestrained CSIRO cell is examined. In the experiments described above the strains associated with the major principal stress which was calculated to act parallel to the borehole axis were the results of (a) thermal expansion of the almost unrestrained cell in the longitudinal direction, and (b) some degree of movement associated with the actual deformation of the overcore annulus.

The strains associated with the minor and intermediate stresses, which are essentially radial to the borehole axis and were similar in magnitude and are a result of (c) the partially restrained expansion of the cell into the deformed annulus of the overcore and (d) the expansion of the cell and the displacement of the malleable adhesive.

Examination of published data by other authors (see for instance Doe et al, 1983; Gregory et al, 1983) indicates that the problem of post cure glue yield is not uncommon. In weak rocks a similar problem may occur due to the actual wall rock of the pilot hole yielding. Examination of results presented by Blackwood et al (1976) appear to suggest some form of rock yield.

The problems caused by glue yield can manifest themselves in a number of ways. A number of different strain evolution curves have been identified and are described below. One of the most disturbing factors discovered during the experimental program was the apparently perfect evolution curve produced (Irvin et al, 1985) when glue yield occurred.

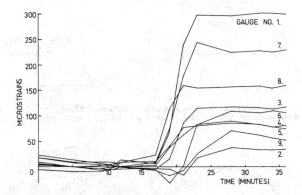

Figure 2. Strain evolution curves from an overcoring test on a CSIRO cell. Computed stress tensor:

σ 1	14.03 MN/m*2	289.5 deg Azimuth	−8.9 deg Dip
σ 2	3.68	198.6	−5.5
σ 3	2.88	257.4	79.5
Borehole direction:		300.0	−7.0
Depth from surface 35m.			

5. OVERCORE EVOLUTION CURVES

Analysis of overcoring data produces results in two forms: the overcore strain evolution curve and the calculated stress tensor. The combined use of these data is required for an appreciation of the validity of an individual test. During the second phase of the test program and during subsequent research, four different forms of overcore evolution curve have been identified and are described below.

Figure 3a illustrates a classic grouping of overcore evolution curves. The two axial gauge strain curves are generally similar and the individual radial and 45 degree curves, whilst differing in magnitude are generally grouped together. Readings are stable both prior to, and after overcoring. The rise in strain as the overcore bit passes the gauged area is rapid and constant, with the readings remaining constant after the bit passes. If glue yield occurs, the immediately noticeable difference will be the somewhat higher axial strain values (Figure 3b) resulting from longitudinal expansion.

Analysis of such data will indicate a high principal stress parallel to the borehole axis and low and approximately equal principal stresses in the radial direction. Although, radial expansion is usually restrained by the filled annulus, and is thus generally restricted to that of the overcore expansion, some increase will occur due to longitudinal expansion.

Figure 4a illustrates grouping of overcore evolution curves found during the first phase of the program. The curves have a form different to those of Figure 3. They may be divided into four broad sections. Section I is similar to the classic curves having stable plateau prior to the overcoring of the gauged area. Section II of the curve is also similar, with a rapid linear increase in tensile strain to an apparent stable level associated with the overcoring of the gauged area. The non-linear rise in section III is thought to be associated with debonding of the cells from the wall rock and the type of thermal straining found in an unrestrained C.S.I.R.O. cell. The fall of Section IV, is probably due to thermal stress in the rock itself, (see Figure 1) causing a net reduction in the radius of the pilot hole due to an inner fiber temperature rise. This form of curve is clearly anomalous and would normally be disregarded. If however, the test were important, some useful information may be obtained from the strains measured at the end of section II. The strain magnitude at this point would probably be of a somewhat lower magnitude than the actual rock strains but may provide some useful information on stress directions.

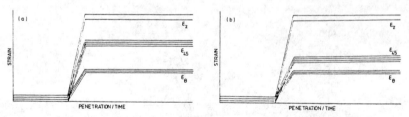

Figure 3 Typical overcore evolution curves showing (a) a perfect grouping (b) a grouping where boundary yield has occurred.

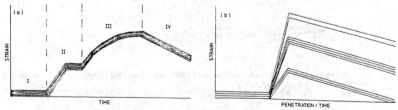

Figure 4 Grouping of overcore evolution curves illustrating (a) combined effects of boundary yield and heating (b) effects of temperature rise without yield.

Figure 4b illustrates the type of evolution curve found during phase II of the insitu stress measurement program. In many respects the form of the curve is similar to that in Figure 3. The curves are characterized by stable readings prior to overcoring, a rapid, almost linear change in strain as the overcore bit passes the strain gauges area, and an almost linear compressional trend after the bit passes the gauged area. Examination of the temperature at the gauged area (see Figure 1) indicates that the fall in strain is directly related to the rise in temperature of the gauged area.

A series of experiments were conducted on CSIRO cells in a laboratory granite core to study thermal relaxation effects. As the temperature rose through 1 degree Celsius it was accompanied by a fall in strain reading of about 60 microstrains, which is sufficiently consistant for correction:

Strain Gauge No. (Strains in microstrains)

	1	2	3	4	5	6	7	8	9
13.0	-5	-25	-110	218	-87	141	5	-182	-138
13.2	-18	-43	-127	201	-104	122	-9	-196	-151
13.4	-28	-57	-138	189	-116	108	-20	-207	-161
13.6	-38	-70	-150	173	-129	92	-30	-220	-174
13.8	-49	-86	-165	161	-143	76	-43	-232	-185
14.0	-59	-99	-175	147	-156	62	-52	-243	-197

6. ELECTRICAL RESISTANCE STRAIN GAUGE MEASUREMENTS

The final errors examined were those associated with the wiring configurations and the use of ers gauge circuits . The four cells evaluated in the program utilize ers gauges in bridge circuits to record data from which the geostatic stress tensor can be calculated. Users of strain gauges must be aware of their inherent limitations in this type of application. Errors are introduced into measurements as the effects of factors other than the straining of the cell are monitored during testing. Ideally a strain gauge bonded to a rock specimen would respond only to straining of the rock and remain unaffected by the other environmental variables. In practice errors occur from temperature change, poor connections, lead capacitance, inadequate bonding, surface irregularities, gauge misalignment, stresses applied directly to the gauge itself (as opposed to the body to which it is attached), creep and lead wire resistance.

The changes in the resistance of ers gauges which occur as a result of straining of the guage are very small. Conventional ohmmeters are incapable of measuring this change in resistance with sufficient precision. However, resistances can be measured with a very high degree of precision using a Wheatstone bridge circuit.

Circuits are widely described as 1/4 bridge, 1/2 bridge or full bridge. This nonemclature describes the fraction of the Wheatstone bridge which is attached to the instrument and is basically self explanatory. These terms do not, however, specify the number of (active) gauges in the strain measurement bridge which are strained as a result of the phenonmenon being investigated. Various arrangements of active strain gauges are possible within the external fraction of the Wheatstone bridge circuit.

Generally speaking the greater the number of gauges, suitably arranged, the greater the sensitivity of the system and the greater the degree of error compensation attained. Thus while a single two wire external strain gauge is the simplest circuit possible, it is the least sensitive to strain and subject to the greatest number of potential errors. If at least 2 gauges are subjected to compressive strain and an equal number subjected to tensile strain, as might for example occur if they are arranged in 90 degree rosettes, they can be connected to form a full bridge giving maximum sensitivity and the greatest degree of error compensation. A half bridge circuit might consist of one active gauge and one unloaded gauge mounted so as to be subjected to the same temperature changes, thereby forming a temperature compensated system since both gauges are subject to identical temperature effects.

Temperature induced strains are caused by two concurrent and algebraically additive effects in the strain gauge installation. First, the electrical resistance of the gauge conductor is temperature dependent and any resistance change with temperature due to this effect appears as a strain to the strain indicator. Secondly, differential thermal expansion between the gauge conductor and the test part results in mechanical straining of the gauge as it conforms to the apparent expansion or contraction of the test part. The resultant resistance change is recorded as a real strain by the strain indicator.

Alloys used in electrical resistance strain gauges are now manufactured with thermal expansion coefficients matched to some test materials (usually metals). In this way apparent strains due to differential thermal expansion are minimized when gauges are applied to the materials for which they are intended.

Apparent strains which result from electrical resistance changes due to changes in temperature can, in theory, be completely eliminated by employing some type of temperature compensating system. Since the compensating gauge is only subjected to the temperature which affects the active gauge, the thermal strains manifest within the two gauges should be identical. Identical resistance changes in adjacent arms of the Wheatstone Bridge do not unbalance the circuit and the apparent strains in the active and compensating gauge should cancel exactly, leaving only the stress induced strain to be registered. However, for this to be precisely true the leadwires should be of equal length and preferably short.

The resistance of the leadwires also varies with temperature. Experiments have shown that the resistance of a 10m length of 7/0.2 cable changes it resistance by 0.003 ohms per degree Celcius. Although this is a small value it still represents about 12.5 microstrains per degree Celcius change in cable temperature with a temperature compensating 1/2 bridge circuit. A two wire 1/4 bridge circuit is subject to the greatest errors due to lead resistance changes, since the entire resistance change appears in the same arm of the bridge as the active gauge. Leadwire resistance itself may be significant if small diameter wire cables are used in the simple bridge arrangements. The resistance of the leadwires in these circumstances may not be negligible, the effect being to reduce the effective gauge factor. A full bridge circuit will tend to compensate for these basic effects.

The cells and leadwires used in the measurement of geostatic stress are subject to an increase in temperature due to the heat generated at the bit during overcoring. Gauges and leadwires will respond to these effects. However, both the cells and the rock will also tend to expand because of the increase in temperature, and since they have different coefficients of thermal expansion a strain will be recorded due to differential thermal expansion of the cell and host rock. This is the type of temperature effect commonly recorded in in-situ stress measurements using hollow or solid inclusion cells. Characteristically, the gauges in an installed cell show a compression with increasing temperature as the cell has a higher coefficient of thermal expanison than that of the rock. Gauges in a cell in free air go into tension with increasing temperature as the cell is then free to expand.

Connection effects arise primarily from the effective resistance of connectors or couplings made in the circuit. This happens when cell cables are coupled to a switch box or data logger connector. Such errors are particularly significant where the continuity of the bridge is broken, as for example when individual leads are connected in turn to a device designed for one connection only, even when switches are used for the purpose. In all such cases there is a risk of differences in contact resistances which show as apparent strains on the strain indicator. Experiments have shown that when a 250mm length of standard cable wire is subjected to a difference in contact pressure apparent errors in measured strains of between 20 microstrains and several times this amount may result. It is therefore better to make permanent lead connections. Standard methods of connection in ascending preference would therefore be: screw clamping; switch/plug and socket; heavy gauge spade clips, and soldered joints.

Terminal connection errors are most significant when the simpler bridge configurations are used. With full bridge circuits significant errors due to contact resistances are largely avoided.

Although leads connections and generally have a small capacitance, the effects of this capacitance may be significant in some circumstances. Lead capacitance can give rise to additional voltages and currents within the bridge circuit. As with all the sources of error discussed above the effects of lead capacitance are most significant with 1/4 bridge circuits and of progressively less important with 1/2 and full bridge circuits.

7. SYSTEMS CIRCUITS

The solid inclusion cell (Blackwood 1977) uses a simple two wire 1/4 bridge circuit. This is the simplest configuration possible and as such is subject to all the errors associated with strain gauge circuits. It represents therefore the least accurate system used and in practice this limits its applicability. Because of the errors discussed above leadwire lengths in particular must be restricted to approximately 15m. In practice readings from this cell proved to be unstable, requiring upwards of one minute for a stable meter reading, and longer with a data logger. It is also worth pointing out that the stress/gauge reading response of this type of cell is actually non-linear.

The CSIRO hollow inclusion cell (Worotnicki and Walton, 1976) uses a three wire 1/4 bridge circuit which provides some compensation for leadwire effects. The stress/strain reading response of this type of gauge is also non-linear.

The Interfels triaxial cell uses a single dummy gauge 1/2 bridge circuit to provide (Leeman & Hayes, 1966) some temperature and leadwire compensation. The necessity for using a plug connector forms a potential source of error as it is necessary to uncouple and recouple the cell to take the 2 sets of readings required. In biaxial testing this cell gave stable readings showing minimal hysteresis.

The USBM diametal deformation gauge (Merrill, 1967) uses a full bridge circuit which is compensated for the most significant sources of gauge reading error. In practice it gave some of the most stable readings but is affected by water entering the probe and vibration caused by the drill. The stress/gauge reading response of this particular wiring configuration is linear.

Electrical resistance strain gauges were originally intended for use in the measurement of the strains in metal objects (primarily steel and aluminium) in response to imposed stress fields. In such applications many of the potential sources of error can be minimized and considerable confidence placed in the data obtained. Their use in systems designed to measure geostatic stress fields, generally in a hostile environment, make them prone to many sources of error and a much lower confidence is therefore placed upon the geostatic stress tensor calculated from their response to overcoring. For overcoring measurements made at shallow depth using systems based on 1/4 or 1/2 bridge circuits, apparent stresses due to the effect of all sources of gauge reading error are significant. However, continuous monitoring of measurement cells during overcoring does allow some assessment of the degree to which readings are affected by error. Since the core dilates rapidly in response to the stress relief, errors which accumulate during this short time period will be considerably less significant then the net total of the apparent strains due to error effects which acrue during the entire overcoring operation. The hollow inclusion, solid inclusion, and USBM cells allow continuous recording of the strain evolution curve. The Interfels probe does not lend itself to ready modification to permit continuous recording of its strain gauges. A comparatively low confidence level would therefore be expected in the stress tensor calculated from the results of the Interfels Leeman-type cells.

An additional source of gauge error is the interaction between tthe strain gauges themselves and the rock. This effect would be expected to be particularly prevalent in cells such as the Interfels triaxial probe where the strain gauges are in intimate contact with the borehole wall. Experiments have shown that in coarsely crystalline, multi-mineral rocks, consistent strain readings are usually obtained when individual strain gauges are of a length greater than or equal to ten times the average crystal dimensions. This figure is supported by CSIRO who suggest that crystal/gauge interaction commences with the hollow inclusion cell at grain sizes above 2mm. At the Troon test site the average crystal dimensions are of the order of 15mm. Crystal/gauge interaction is caused by a number of factors which include; crystal size, moduli differences between minerals in a multi minerallic rock, crystal boundary effects, residual rock stresses, strain gauge size and the distance of the strain gauges from the wall rock.

CONCLUSIONS

The measurement of in-situ stress by overcoring in cool near surface environments is difficult. Measurements in all environments are affected by errors associated with the design of the instrument, the logging equipment and environment in which the measurement is being made. The errors associated with these are generally of small magnitude, and as such do not constitute a problem when measuring in-situ stress at depth. In measurements made at shallow depths, or in low stress environments, the magnitude of these errors may well exceed the magnitude of the strains due to the relief of stress within the overcore annulus. In these cases account must be taken of these errors and an attempt made to remove them. A method of measuring these errors has been developed by the authors and used with success.

The problem of post overcore yield can occur irrespective of the depth of measurement. The detection of glue yield may be difficult unless two or more differently oriented holes are used. The causes of glue yield and the suggested methods and precautions for avoiding glue yield have been presented. The majority of errors encountered tend to affect all the strain gauges within the respective cells and as such do not effect the calculation of the directions of the stress components. This has been found throughout the measurement program carried out by the authors. This applies to all errors except for glue yield, where both the direction and magnitude of the stress components are radically changed.

ACKNOWLEDGEMENTS

The work was carried out with the aid of grants from the Building Research Establishment of the Department of the Environment. The contributions of Miss C. Cooling, Dr. J. H. Hudson, now of the Royal School of Mines, L. W. Tunbridge of Golder Associates, J. Borden of Orebit Exploration, and B. Watkins of Elcon Electrical (Western) are acknowledged with thanks.

REFERENCES

Amadei, B., (1983). Rock anisotropy and the theory of stress measurements. Berlin: Springer- Verlag.
Blackwood, R.L. Hargraves, A.J. and McKay, J. (1976). Absolute stress investigation in coal at Appin Colliery, N.S.W., Proc. Int. Soc. Rock. Mech. Symp. "Investigation of Stress in Rock - Advances in Stress Measurement", Sydney. pp. 17-22.
CSIRO Handbook, Rock Instruments Pty, Windsor, Prahran, Vic. Australia.
Doe, T.W., Ingevald, K., Stindell, L., Leijon, B., Hustrulid, W., Majer, E., and Carlson, H. (1983) In-situ stress measurements at the Stripa Mine, Sweden., Lawrence Berkeley Laboratory, University of California, Berkeley, California.
Duncan Fama M.E. and Pender M.J. (1980) Analysis of the hollow inclusion technique for measuring in-situ rock stress., Int. Jl. Rock Mech. Min. Sci. and Geomech. Abstr., Vol. 17, pp. 137-146 (1980).
Fossom, A.F. (1983). Room stability in salt repositories., Rpt. to Office of Nuclear Waste Isolation, Battelle Memorial Institute, 505 King Avenue, Columbus, OH 43201-2693.
Gregory, E.C., Rundle, T.A., McCabe, W.M., Kim, K., (1983). In-situ stress measurement in a jointed basalt: The suitability of five overcoring techniques., Proc. 5th R.E.T.C., Chicago, Vol. 1, pp. 42-61.
Hudson, J.A., Cooling C.J. and Tunbridge L.W. (1984), Paper presented to Cambridge ISRM conference.
Irvin, R.A., Garritty, P., Farmer, I.W., (1985). The effect of boundary yield on in-situ stresses measurements using the overcoring technique. Paper in press.
Leeman E.R. and Hayes D.J. (1966) A technique for determining the complete state of stress in rock using a single borehole., Proc. 1st Cong. ISRM, Lisbon (1969) Vol 2, pp. 17-24.
Rocha M. and Silverio A., (1969) A new method for the complete determination of state of stress in rock masses, Geotechnique, Vol. 19, pp. 116-132.
Panek L.A. (1966) Calculation of the average ground stress components from measurement of the diametrical deformation of a drill hole. U.S. Bureau of Mines, Rept. Invest. 6732.
Merrill R.H., (1967) Three component borehole deformation gauge for determining the stress in rock, U.S. Bureau of Mines, Rept. Invest. 7015.
Tunbridge L.W. (1984), Some studies of rock mass structure and in-situ stress. Proc. Symp. Design & performance of underground structures, Cambridge, pp. 199-206, Brit. Geotech. Soc., London.
Worotnicki, G. and Walton, R.J. (1976). Triaxial "hollow inclusion" gauges for the determination of rock stresses in-situ. Proc. Symp. on Investigation of stress in rock and advances in stress measurement. I.S.R.M., Sydeny, supplement, pp. 108.

In situ rock stress measurements in French coal mines:
Relation between virgin stresses and rock bursts

R.REVALOR, J.ARCAMONE & JP.JOSIEN
Mining Techniques Division, Cerchar, France
JP.PIGUET
Strata Control Laboratory, Nancy School of Mines, France

The "Lorraine" collieries are mining in the North East of France a deposit which contributes 55 % to the French coal production. The deposit which is of Carboniferous age is relatively dense with about 30 mineable seams separated by conglomeratic sandstones more or less shaly.

Two major tectonic foldings have affected the basin ie the anticlines of Merlebach and Simon ; these disturbances have resulted in the existence of highly contrasted conditions of deposit, ie flat to vertical strata. The method of mining by longwall faces has been adapted, with constant stress on increased mechanisation, so as to suit the variety of conditions encoutered ; the annual production of the coal field is approximately 10,5 Mt of clean coal and the output per man shift is about 4100 kg.

One of the sub-vertical seam areas of the deposit which is situated on the south eastern limit of the anticline of Merlebach, is exploited by the Vouters mine with a method of mining by ascending slices and stowing. In this zone, the mineable coal seams are divided in two series, designated as "Flambants inférieurs" (lower flame coals) and "Flambants supérieurs" (upper flame coals) separated by the barren conglomerate of Merlebach.

During the development of a new level of mining, at a depth of 1250m, a roadway being driven in the lower flame coals was subject to intense and violent breakages of the rock mass. The description of these breakages, which were of rock-burst type, is given in the first part of this paper together with a presentation of the environment in which the occurrences took place. With a view to investigating the effect of the structure of the deposit and of the virgin stresses in the strata on the occurrences that were observed, stress measurements were carried out on the site using various methods. The results obtained, and the understanding that can be derived for the prevention of such occurrences, are presented in the second and third part of the paper.

1 THE OCCURRENCES OBSERVED AND THEIR ENVIRONMENT
1.1 - Description

The mine working concerned by the occurrences is an arched roadway of 20 m2 cross-section, excavated by blasting. The blasts were made with a load of 120 kg of explosive of type Minex ; there are 46 holes of 3,2m drilled parallel and blasted with 11 delays (half a second each).

The observed occurrences were in the form of violent breakages of the rock mass which affected a volume much greater than that which was produced by the blasting (figure 1).

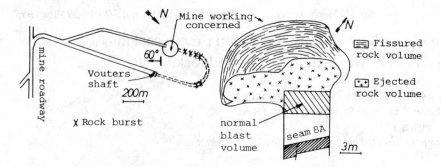

Figure 1. Lorraine Coalfield - Vouters shaft receipt at 1250m
level - Sketch of the first rockburst.

The fracturation occured around and ahead cf the face of the roadway
on a distance cf approximately 10 m ; the volume of fragmented rock was
1500 to 3000 m3, of which about 500 m3 were ejected into Lhe roadway.
The occurrence was accompanied by the release of 6 to 8000 m3 of
firedamp (Josien, 1983).

The fragmentations are characterized by the following features : the
massif is broken up into small platy pieces of several centimeters
thickness and the fragmentation is intragranular.

Up to now, 6 rock-bursts, all of which correspond roughly to the
above description, have been observed. All the cccurrences took place
in the straight segments of the roadway which were being driven in a
cross-drivage configuration (figure 1).

All the occurrences took place after a blasting and were precisely
coincidental with the explosion of the last delay as evidenced by a
seismoacoustical hearing which was conducted during the drivage of the
roadway.

1.2 Review of the natural and mining factors of influence

In addition to the identification of zones of hazard based on the analysis of disc corings for which norms of danger have been established
(Chemaou, 1984), more fundamental investigations have been undertaken
with a wiew to understanding the causes and processes which are
controlling these occurrences.

A number of characteristic features of the area that was concerned by
the occurrences are to be mentioned in this respect.

All the occurrences took place in the lower flame coal measures ; no
occurrences of similar nature was reported in roadways that were driven
in the upper flame coal measures on the same level, or in the upper
levels whatever the coal measures.

A structural survey of the site (Thomas and Piquet, 1983) indicated
that the sandstone beds present, in the area concerned by the occurrences, a major flexure ie their dip changes suddenly from 65 to 50°
with wide local variations.

An extensive geotechnical characterisation of the strata was carried
out in the laboratory using a total of 1000 rock specimens (Chemaou,
1984). These investigations have indicated that the mechanical characteristics of the beds of lower the flame coal measures (Rc = 89 MPa - E =

20700 MPa) are lower than those of the upper flame coal measures and of the upper levels (Rc = 123 MPa - E = 25500 MPa).

The flexure of the strata and the variation of mechanical characteristics appear to be related to the same tectonical disturbance.

Methane gas is mainly contained in the porosity of the sandstones. The pressure of the gas could not be measured in situ ; it was estimated and ranges between 3 to 10 MPa which is consistent with the values that were measured in other sites (USSR - FRG) where similar occurrences have been reported (Josien, 1983).

The type of breakages observed in rock-bursts leads to assume that such fracturation is caused by in situ mechanical stresses ; the free gas contained in the sandstones and the decrease of their mechanical strenght are aggravating factors.

According to practical experience that has been obtained in this particular deposit about the volume of influence of mine workings, (Dejean, 1977), it can be considered that the zone concerned is out of the area of influence of mining operations that are conducted in the upper levels of the mine. Hence, in the investigations that were carried out for discovering possible causes of the occurrences, emphasis was placed on the influence of virgin stresses in the area ; the evaluation of these stresses required to undertake several measurement campaigns.

2 EVALUATION OF THE STATE OF VIRGIN STRESSES
2.1 The methods of measurement

During the last decade, rock engineering has given increasing importance on the knowledge of virgin stresses in the strata and their influence on the behaviour of engineering workings. This is evidenced by the number of sites in which investigations are going on in various countries ; the results that have been obtained have led to new perspectives on the distribution of virgin stresses in situ. In this context, Cerchar (French Coal Mines Research Center) has developed and applied in various sites, several technologies for measuring in situ stresses ie the flat jack, the overcoring and hydrofracturing methods.

The principles of these methods, which are known all over the world, are not reminded here ; it is suggested that the reader refer to various articles concerned with this aspect (Bertrand, 1983 ; Cornet, 1981 ; Haimson, 1978 ; Helal, 1983). The adaptation of these methods to our mining conditions has resulted in the development of original methods, both in their implementation in the field and in the process of the data obtained.

Hence, the interpretation of test results obtained with the flat jack method uses a data processing software package which applies finite element calculations according to the flow-sheet of figure 2. This software package enables to estimate the state of virgin stresses which explains best (in a least squares approach) the pressures measured in a number of cuts made all along the periphery of the roadway section (Tinchon and Piquet, 1982).

The equipment for measuring stresses by overcoring is characterized by a measuring cell, which is specially designed to estimate at the same place the modulus of elasticity of the strata by mean of a pressiometric test, and the deformation of the sides of the hole during overcore drilling (Helal, 1983).

In addition, a system for obtaining test results automatically has

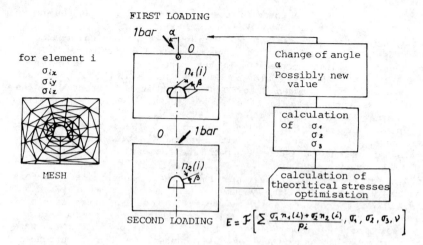

Figure 2. Determination of the stresses by a serie of tests using the flat jack method - Flow-sheet of the method of data processing.

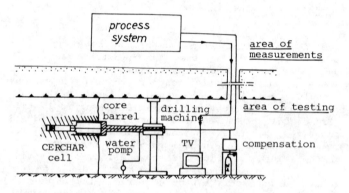

Figure 3. Equipment for measuring stresses by overcoring method.

been developed using a micro-computer. This enables to obtain continuous record of test data during the process of drilling (figure 3).

The equipment for measuring stresses by hydrofracturing was developed with a view to having an equipment suited to a working situated at great depth ; therefore the equipment has to be strong and sufficiently powerful to measure high stresses. The method of measurement is applied in two steps ie a first estimation of the state of stresses by mean of the conventional method using a vertical hole (Haimson, 1978) ; then verification from tests made on natural isolated fractures (Cornet, 1981).

The application of these three methods in different sites (including level 1250 m of Vouters mine) has enabled to understand their relative pros and cons and also their respective domains of application (table 1).

Table 1 : Advantages and disadvantages of the 3 methods of measuring stresses

	Advantages	Disadvantages	Best conditions of application
Flat jack	Direct measurement (pressure). Evalua tion of the modulus of elasticity of the rock. Tough and Robust	Measurements limited to the side walls of the working. high cost	Measurement of stres ses in concrete linings or pillar rib – sides etc...
Overcoring	Measurements out of the influence of the working. Eva luation of the modu lus of elasticity. High accuracy	Indirect measure- ment (= deforma- tion) high cost	In sites where stres ses are moderate (shallow depth) or great depth in high strength rock
Hydrofrac- turing	Direct measurement (pressure) out of the influence of the working. Easy to utilize low cost Tough. Applicable in sites of vary ing characteristics	Orientation of the fracture is unknown far away from the drill-hole. Problems are encountered in permeable rocks	In fractured rock with high stresses (great depth).

2.2 State of natural stresses at Vouters Coal Mine

The first measurements of virgin stresses were carried out with the flat jack method at different depths. The results enabled to show that the state of virgin stresses was strongly dependent on the tectonical structure of the deposit (Tinchon and Piquet, 1982). Due to the disadvantages of this method of measurement, particularly the fact that measurement is made on the skin of the roadway, another campaign of measurements was undertaken at level 1250 m, near the roadway that had been affected by the rock-bursts ; the three methods of measurement were applied at the same location.

The results are presented on table 2.

The flat jack method leads to a state of stresses which appears to be almost hydrostatic ; the values are very lower than those obtained with the two other methods. The highest differences concern the major principal stress which, in the site investigated, is horizontal and transverse to the test roadway (figure 4).

With the flat jack method, this stress is evaluated from cuts made at the crown, parallel to the axis of the roadway ; these cuts are therefore located in a zone which is most likely to be unconsolidated and unstressed. This observation which points out the main disadvantage of the flat jack method, has been reported by other authors (Bertrand, 1983).

Table 2 : Comparison of the results of the 3 methods of measurement on the same site (Lorraine coalfield. Vouters Mine. 1250 m level)

	Major principal stress $\sigma 1$		Mean principal stress $\sigma 2$		Minor principal stress $\sigma 3$	
	Modulus (MPa)	Orientation	Modulus (MPa)	Orientation	Modulus (MPa)	Orientation
Flat jack	18,1	isotropic	18	isotropic	16,1	parallel to the structure by assumption
Overcoring	36,0	N 110 E sub.horiz.	26	sub.vertical	17	N 20 E sub-horizont.
Hydrofracturing	37,3	N 120 E sub. horiz.	29	sub.vertical	17,7	N 30 E sub.horizont.

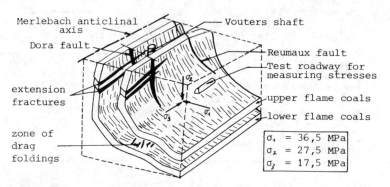

Figure 4. Principle diagram of strains at Vouters coal Mine.

Conversely, the consistency between the overcoring and the hydrofracturing method is excellent ; the two methods lead to the same test result within 10 %. The state of stresses is characterized by a high anisotropy of stresses in the horizontal plane ie

* a major principal stress of 36,5 MPa roughly transverse to the axis of the anticline of Merlebach.

* a minor principal stress of 17,5 MPa roughly parallel to this same axis.

The ratio of anisotropy of the stresses in this plane is maximum and has a value of approximately 2. The mean principal stress is 27,5 MPa and vertical ; it corresponds to approximately to 10 % of the weight of the overlying strata (figure 4).

The structural analysis of the area (Thomas and Piquet, 1983) that was conducted prior to this investigation, leads to expect high horizontal stresses, transverse to the axis of the structure, in the central block delimited by the faults of Dora and Reumaux (figure 4). The state of stresses which has been measured precisely in this block, confirms that this expectaction was correct. The structural approach, which comes in supplement, is systematically carried out prior to any campaign for the measurement of natural stresses.

3 PRACTICAL CONSEQUENCES FOR THE BEHAVIOUR OF MINE WORKINGS
3.1 Distribution of stresses around the roadway

A similar degree of anisotropy in the virgin state of stresses has been reported in other sites where rock-bursts have occurred ; this applies both in France for other type of mine workings (Josien, 1980) and in other countries in similar type of workings (Broch, 1979 ; Carlsson 1982 ; Broch, 1984). The effect of stress anisotropy, on the breakages observed at level 1250 should be examined in greater depth in view of the fact that this roadway concerned by the occurrences was being driven parallel to the major principal stress and in a plane where the anisotropy of the stresses is maximum.

So, the distribution of stresses around the roadway concerned by the rock-bursts was investigated by assimilating the roadway to a circular gallery of 2,5 m radius. The stresses were calculated as a function of virgin stresses ie

* on the side of the gallery, considering a section behind the face of the drivage, by using the solution of Hiramatsu (1968).

* in the central zone of the face of the drivage on the basis of research work conducted by Bonnechere (1971), which gives an approximate solution to the problem.

In each zone, the calculation was carried out for different orientations of the gallery, relative to the major principal stress ; the case $\alpha = 0$ corresponds to the actual orientation of the working. The results are represented on figure 5.

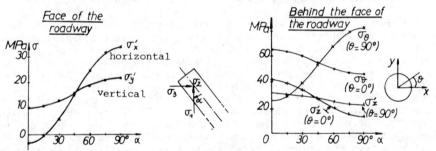

Figure 5. Stresses around a circular hole. Variation according to hole orientation relative to the state of virgin stresses.

3.2 Hypothesis on the processes of breakage

At the face of the gallery ie where the occurrences were concentrated, it is of course the horizontal stress (in the plane of maximum anisotropy) which is the most sensitive to the orientation of the gallery (figure 5). This stress is even a tensile stress (- 3,5 MPa) when the gallery is parallel to the major principal stress. In this case, the solution shows that these tensile stresses appear in front of the face, when the ratio of anisotropy $\sigma 1/ \sigma 3$ is greater than 1.8. The face of the gallery was typically in such conditions when it was affected by the rock-bursts.

Several observations should be mentioned in support of this result
* All the rock-bursts that have been observed took place in straight sections of the roadway. They disappear when the gallery changes its direction, particularly when driving rounded contour section (figure 1).

The results indicate that the tensile stresses disappear ahead of the face once the gallery makes an angle of more than 15° with the major principal stress (figure 5).

* The tensile stresses show a type of breakages which occur violently as they are well known for their brittleness. The rock-bursts of Vouters Mine differ from the more usual breakages that are normally observed around mine workings in the fact that they are most sudden and violent. It can further be supposed that the occurrences are all the more violent as the tensile stresses are suddenly established by the blast.

* The tensile stresses appear in so far as high axial stresses tend to curve the face of the roadway towards the void created by the excavation.In this respect, it should be mentioned that a method applied in Russia in order to avoid similar occurrences, is to drive the roadway with a concave face which precisely aims at suppressing these stresses.

The above observations lead to substantiate the hypothesis that the rock bursts of Vouters mine were caused by mechanical stresses (ie tensile stresses) in direct relation with the sudden disconfinement brought by the blast. This state of stresses was aggravated by the gas contained in the rock which permitted the propagation of the breakage. This situation may have been aggravated by local conditions (higher natural stresses or gas pressure, lower strenght of rocks) due to local heterogeneities noted by the structural and the geological analysis.

3.3 Orientation of roadways and state of natural stresses

More generally, the question of the orientation of a gallery driven in a rock mass which is characterized by a high degree of anisotropy of stresses can be posed. Figure 5 shows that behind the face of the gallery, the tangential stress at the side of the gallery appears to be the most sensitive to the orientation of the roadway. For the two extreme situation (ie α = O and α = 90°), the tangential stress attains respectively 65 MPa at the sidewall and 82 MPa at the crown for a compressive strength of 89 MPa. A calculation by finite elements, which modelizes the geometry of the gallery, confirms these results in a more exact way including the fact that the crown and the sidewal of the gallery attain the point of breakage for these two orientations (figure 6).

In the field, the breakages of these two zones were less important than the breakages of the face.

Moreover, figure 5 shows that in the cas of Vouters mine, there is

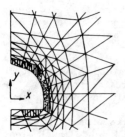

▦breakage elements
σ_y=26,5MPa σ_x=36,5MPa α=90°

▦breakage elements
σ_y=26,5MPa σ_x=17,5MPa α=0°

Figure 6. Breakage zones around the roadway investigated by finite element calculations.

a preferential orientation (α = 45°) for which the risk of rock breakage is minimal both at the face and on the sides of the gallery ie along the crown or the ribs.

In the case of a roadway driven in the plane of maximum anisotropy of the stresses, the calculations that were made in the general case, show that this orientation is given by the following equation ;

$$\alpha = Arcsin \left[\frac{\sigma_2 - \sigma_3}{\sigma_1 - \sigma_3}\right]^{\frac{1}{2}} \quad avec \quad \sigma_1 > \sigma_2 > \sigma_3$$

In such conditions which are characterized by an anisotropic and high state of virgin stresses - ie conditions which may be met more and more frequently due to the increased depth of mining -, the approach proposed, despite its simplicity as regards the calculations, can provide data which enable to better orient mine workings taking into account these natural conditions of stresses.

4 Conclusion

In its investigations on mine geotechnical aspects, Cerchar has developed and practically applied methods of measurement of the in situ stresses. Among the 3 methods available - ie the flat jack method, overcoring and hydrofracturing -, the two latter methods are more particularly reliable for measuring high stress levels in rock and give concordant results. Indeed the sidewalls of galleries subject to high stresses are often fractured which is a disadvantage for the flat jack method, which leads to under estimating the in situ stresses.

The case that has been presented in this paper - ie the occurrence of rock-burst in a roadway driven in sandstones at a depth of 1250m in the "Lorraine" coalfield in France -, has enabled to relate these phenomena to the existence of high natural stresses presenting a high degree of anisotropy. The state of stresses measured is perfectly consistent with the structural survey conducted in the area.

A simple model of calculation has been applied in order to assess the consequences of such conditions on the stress distribution around the roadway.

The results confirm that the orientation of the roadway was such that tensile stresses could exist at the face of the gallery and that these are likely to have initiated the breakage. Moreover, the results indicate that in such an environment, there is a preferential orientation of the gallery which minimizes the risk of breakage at all points of its geometry.

Although the approach does not claim to have accounted for the full complexity of the environment, it provides some understanding of the processes which control certain brutal breakages in rocks. It can also be used as a guide for preventing these breakages - ie localisation of suspect areas and better orientation of mine working in such an environment.

REFERENCES

Bertrand L., E. Durand, 1983. In situ stress measurements : comparison of different methods Proc. Int. Symp. Soil and Rock Investigations by in situ testing 2 : 431-470

Bonnechere F., 1971. Contribution à la détermination de l'état de contraintes des massifs rocheux. Thèse Université de Liège.

Broch E., B. Nilsen, 1979. Comparaison of calculated, measured and observed stresses at the Ortfjell open pit (Norvay). Proc. 4th Int. Congr. Rock Mechanics, Montreux, 2 : 49-56. Rotterdam : Balkema

Broch E., S. Sorheim, 1984. Experiences from the planning, construction and supporting of a road tunnel subjected to heavy rock-bursting. Rock Mechanics and Rock Engineering. 17 : 15-35

Carlsson A., T. Olsson, 1982. Rock bursting phenomena in a superficial rock mass in Southern Central Sweden. Rock Mechanics. 15 : 99-110

Chemaou O., 1984. Etude des phénomènes dynamiques dans les creusements au rocher et recherche de méthodes de prévision. Application au cas des surtirs de Merlebach (HBL). Thèse Docteur-Ingénieur. Institut National Polytechnique de Lorraine. Ecole des Mines de Nancy.

Cornet F.H., 1981. La mesure in situ des contraintes dans un massif rocheux. Tunnels et ouvrages souterrains. 48 : 262-273

Dejean M., B. Enchayan, 1977. Volume d'influence d'une exploitation en gisement penté. Proc. 6th Conf. Int. sur les pressions de terrains, Banff, Thème 4 n° 29

Haimson C. 1978. The hydrofracturing stress measuring method and recent field results. Int. J. Rock Mech. Min. Sci. Geomech. Abstr. 15 : 167
178

Helal H., R. Schwartzmann, 1983. In situ stress measurements with the Cerchar dilatometric cell. Proc. Symp. "Field measurements in geomechanics". Zürich, 1 : 127-136

Hiramatsu Y., Y. Oka, 1968. Determination of the stress in rock unaffected by boreholes or drifts, from measured strains or deformations. Int. J. Rock Mech. Min. Sci. 5 : 337-353

Josien JP., R. Revalor, 1983. Prévision et maitrise des phénomènes dynamiques (coups de terrain). Rapport final convention n° 7220 AC/1309. Communauté Européenne du Charbon et de l'Acier

Josien JP., 1980. Le comportement des terrains autour de l'exploitation. Les coups de terrain du bassin de Provence. Revue de l'Industrie Minérale. Suppl. n° de Juin 80 : 100-110

Thomas A., L. George, JP. Piguet, 1983. Interprétation des mesures de contraintes en site minier à partir d'un modèle tectonique. Revue de l'Industrie Minérale. Avril 83. : 169-178

Tinchon L., C. Daumalin, L. George, JP. Piguet 1982. Evolution des contraintes en fonction de la profondeur et des facteurs naturels. Proc.
7th Conf. Int. sur les pressions de terrains, Liège, : 587-606

Implications about in situ stress at Yucca Mountain[1]

S.J.BAUER
Sandia National Laboratories[2], Albuquerque, New Mexico, USA

J.F.HOLLAND
Technadyne, Albuquerque, New Mexico, USA

D.K.PARRISH
RE/SPEC Inc., Albuquerque, New Mexico, USA

1 Abstract

Volcanic tuffs under Yucca Mountain on the Nevada Test Site (NTS) are being
considered as potential media for geologic disposal of radioactive waste. Calculations in support of site evaluation, repository design, and performance assessment require accurate estimates of the *in situ* stresses and the variability in the
stress state within Yucca Mountain. This paper uses the regional geologic studies that pertain to the stress state at the NTS, stress measurements in Yucca
Mountain, and stress measurements in nearby Rainier Mesa, in conjunction with
finite element calculations to estimate the *in situ* stresses at Yucca Mountain.
Based on these data, values of lateral earth-stress coefficients (K_o) in the range
$0.3 < K_o < 0.8$ are reasonable for repository depths in thermomechanical analyses.

2 Introduction

The Nevada Nuclear Waste Storage Investigations (NNWSI) Project, administered by the Nevada Operations Office of the U.S. Department of Energy is considering the volcanic tuffs under Yucca Mountain on the Nevada Test Site as potential media for geologic disposal of radioactive waste. Calculations in support
of site evaluation, repository design, and performance assessment require accurate estimates of the *in situ* stresses and the variability in the stress state within
Yucca Mountain. For example, the *in situ* stresses define the initial conditions for
analyses of the thermomechanical response of the tuffs when subjected to stresses
caused by excavation of a geologic repository and by temperature rises during
the containment period of the repository. This paper uses the regional geologic
studies that pertain to the stress state at the NTS, stress measurements in Yucca
Mountain, and stress measurements in nearby Rainier Mesa, in conjunction with
finite element calculations to estimate the *in situ* stresses at Yucca Mountain.

[1] This work was supported by the U.S. Department of Energy (DOE) under contract
E-AC04-DP00789.

[2] A U.S. DOE facility

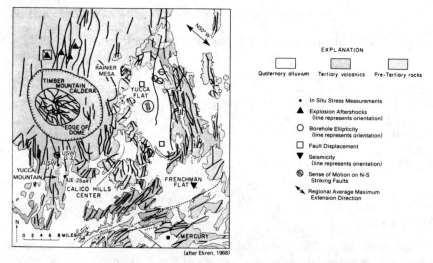

Figure 1: Map of Nevada Test Site and Vicinity Showing Basin and Range Faults, and Indicators of Maximum Extension Direction.

The state of stress existing prior to disturbance by excavation is the virgin *in situ* state of stress. Three main components contribute to that state of stress in these shallowly-buried tuffs. One component, gravitational stress, is induced by the weight of the overburden. A second component, residual stress, is contributed by strain energy stored in the rock during the geologic past. The third component, tectonic stress, is caused by current tectonic forces affecting the region. Stress measurements sense the combined effects of all three components.

Analysis of the regional geologic structures indicates that the stress state within the Basin and Range tectonic province, which includes the NTS, has changed from crustal shortening to crustal extension within the last 20 to 30 million years [Eaton, 1979]. The regional extension has resulted in a series of faults and joints that strike approximately north northeast (Figure 1). The direction of maximum extension is approximately N50°W, based on regional structures [Carr, 1974], orientations of fractures in the playa of Yucca Flat [Carr, 1974], seismicity studies [Hamilton and Healy, 1969; Fischer, *et al.*, 1972], analyses of borehole ellipticities [Carr, 1974; Stock, *et al.*, 1984], stress measurements [*e. g.*, Haimson, *et al.*, 1974; Obert, 1964; and Lindh, *et al.*, 1973], and strain measurements [Smith and Kind, 1972].

3 Finite Element Approximations and Analyses

In this study, finite element calculations based on simple assumptions about the stress field and material properties were used to estimate the *in situ* stress field at two locations, Rainier Mesa and Yucca Mountain. Gravitational stress was the only loading mechanism modeled. Other assumptions used in the calculations were plane strain conditions and linear elastic material responses. The mechanical effects of pore pressure were not included except as pore water modifies the effective mass that induces gravitational loads. Inclusion of pore pressures will not change the results of the calculated stresses in the modeled regions that are of primary interest for repository design calculations. Those regions are above the water table. The validity of these approximations for estimating the *in situ* stress field were examined by comparing the calculated stresses with carefully measured stresses at Rainier Mesa [Warpinski, *et al.*, 1981]. The same assumptions were then used for calculations that were compared with measured stresses at Yucca Mountain.

Two potential effects upon the gravitationally-induced component of horizontal stress are studied: topography and mechanical stratigraphy. These separate effects are analyzed by comparing calculations that assigned one set of homogeneous elastic properties to the entire modeled region to identify topography effects with calculations that included the vertical variation of mechanical properties for Rainier Mesa [Teufel, pers. comm., 1984] and Yucca Mountain [Nimick, *et al.*, 1984].

The calculations that used homogeneous elastic properties resulted in stress magnitudes that varied smoothly from the surface to the deepest portions of the modeled regions of Rainier Mesa and Yucca Mountain (Figure 2). The stress contours from the Yucca Mountain model are somewhat horizontal at elevations between 500 and 600 m (Figure 3a). At this elevation, the topographic effects are minimal.

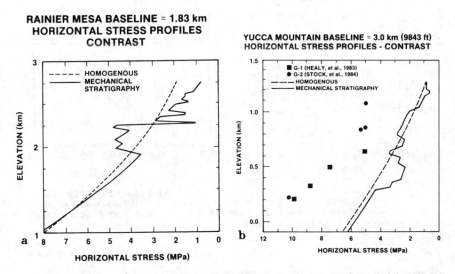

Figure 2: Variation of Calculated Horizontal Stress with Depth at (a) Rainier Mesa and (b) Yucca Mountain. Measured *in situ* stresses are projected to the cross sectional plane used for the calculation.

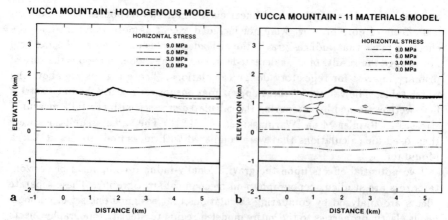

Figure 3: Contoured Horizontal Stress Magnitudes at Yucca Mountain. (a) Homogeneous Material Properties. (b) Mechanical Stratigraphy.

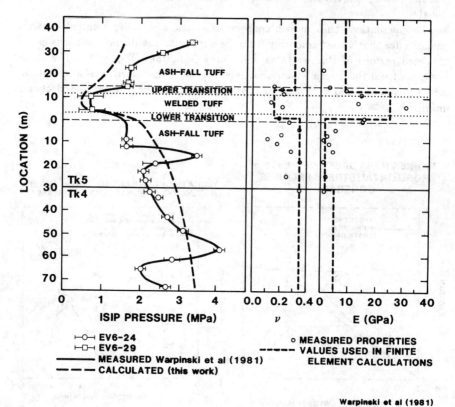

Figure 4: Comparison of Calculated Horizontal Stresses with Instantaneous Shut In Pressures (ISIP) Measured at Rainier Mesa. Variation of elastic properties are also shown.

A separate set of calculations included appropriate elastic properties for selected mechanical units representative of the mechanical stratigraphy. The stress magnitudes resulting from these calculations deviated from the magnitudes calculated using homogeneous elastic properties (Figure 2a). The deviations are consistent with trends in measurements of *in situ* stress in Rainier Mesa (Figure 4) [Warpinski, *et al.*, 1981]. The calculated minimum horizontal stresses are within the range of measured *in situ* stresses in Rainier Mesa (Figure 4). The stress magnitudes are generally higher in the units characterized by high values of Poisson's ratio and low Young's modulus and the stress magnitudes were lower in units characterized by low Poisson's ratios and high Young's modulus (Figure 4). This agreement between calculated and measured values is expected because Rainier Mesa stands high in relief ($\sim$ 400 m) above the surrounding terrain. Consequently, stress magnitudes in Rainier Mesa apparently are not influenced significantly by the regional tectonics even though the stress orientations align with the directions of regional extension.

In situ stresses at Yucca Mountain have been measured by hydrofracturing rock in three core holes (Healy, *et al.*, 1983a; Healy, *et al.*, 1983b; Stock, *et al.*, 1984). The orientation of the minimum principal compressive stress was inferred from fractures observed using a televiewer in the core hole (Stock, *et al.*, 1984). The orientations of the fractures imply that the direction of minimum compressive stress at Yucca Mountain (N60°W to N65°W) is aligned with the direction of maximum extension at the NTS as interpreted from regional tectonics. The calculated vertical stresses ($\sigma_v = \rho g h$) and the estimates of the minimum horizontal stresses (σ_h) derived from the instantaneous shut-in pressures indicate that the minimum coefficient of lateral earth-stress ($K_o = \sigma_h/\sigma_v$) ranges between 0.4 and 0.8 (Figure 5) at the potential repository horizon depths (cf. Stock, *et al.*, 1984).

The *in situ* stress measurements at both Rainier Mesa and Yucca Mountain are consistent with the extensional tectonics of the region. Normal faulting that characterizes the region is usually developed in regions where the coefficient of lateral earth-stress, K_o, is much less than 1.0. Values of $K_o = 0.5$ are frequently associated with normal-fault terrain [Jamison and Cook, 1980].

Tectonic extension is not likely to reduce the horizontal compressive stresses to values less than those induced by gravity because the faults continuously position material to laterally restrain fault-bounded blocks. If the regional extension had completely relieved any tectonic or residual components of horizontal compression on the modeled region, the only component of *in situ* stress is likely to be the gravitational component.

Our finite element calculations that neglect tectonic and residual stresses, and include the effects of gravitational stresses, topography, and stratigraphy, predict minimum horizontal stress magnitudes that are lower than those measured at Yucca Mountain. The lateral earth-stress coefficients that are calculated using the calculated minimum horizontal stress magnitudes are approximately $K_o = 0.3$ at potential repository depths. The higher values of K_o that are calculated using the *in situ* stress measurements suggest that (1) tectonic or residual stresses

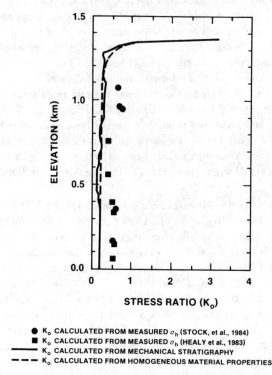

YUCCA MOUNTAIN BASELINE = 3.0 km (9843 ft)
STRESS RATIO PROFILES

● K_o CALCULATED FROM MEASURED σ_h (STOCK, et al., 1984)
■ K_o CALCULATED FROM MEASURED σ_h (HEALY et al., 1983)
—— K_o CALCULATED FROM MECHANICAL STRATIGRAPHY
– – – K_o CALCULATED FROM HOMOGENEOUS MATERIAL PROPERTIES

Figure 5: Variation of Lateral Earth-Stress Coefficients (K_o) with Depth at Yucca Mountain.

contribute a horizontal compressive component to the measured stress field at Yucca Mountain, or (2) the rock-mass elastic properties assigned to the tuff units were not representative, or (3) inelastic responses and anisotropic material responses affected the measurements but were not included in the calculations, or (4) the measured horizontal stress values were high (see discussion by Stock, *et al.*, [1984]). Inclusion of pore pressures in the finite element calculations would have resulted in higher stress values for the modeled region below the water table.

4 Discussion and Conclusions

Finite element analyses using a gravity-loading model allowed for assessment of the potential effects of topography and mechanical stratigraphy upon the calculated horizontal stress at Yucca Mountain. Topographic effects vary as a function of position beneath the mountain but are present everywhere at elevations greater than 500 to 600 meters. Therefore, this work indicates that topographic effects may result in spatial variations in the horizontal stress field at the elevations of the proposed repository. Also, by considering the vertical variation in mechanical properties (mechanical stratigraphy), deviations from a smooth increase in horizontal stress with depth are predicted. Location and interpretation of future stress measurements should, therefore, be made with observation in mind; locating measurements well within mechanical boundaries should provide a means to limit some ambiguity.

The combination of tectonic setting, measured values of *in situ* stress, and finite element approximations of the stress state at Yucca Mountain provide a basis for estimating the lateral earth-stress coefficient (K_o) that should be used in design and performance assessment calculations for a radioactive waste repository at Yucca Mountain. A working range of values of K_o which is consistent with regional tectonics, measurements, and finite element calculations is $0.3 < K_o < 0.8$. Further evaluation of this range of values and the calculational approach will require data from *in situ* measurements in the exploratory shaft at Yucca Mountain.

References

Carr, W. J., 1974. *Summary of Tectonic and Structural Evidence for Stress Orientation at the Nevada Test Site,* Open File Report 74-176, U.S. Geol. Surv., 53 pp.

Eaton, G. P., 1979. "A Plate-Tectonic Model for Late Cenozoic Spreading in the Western United States," in *Rio Grande Rift: Tectonics and Magmatism,* R. E. Riecker, ed., pp.7–32.

Ekren, E. B., 1968. "Geologic Setting of Nevada Test Site and Nellis Air Force Range", in *Nevada Test Site, Geological Society of America Memoir 110,* E. B. Eckel, ed., Geol. Soc. of Am., Boulder, CO, pp. 11–20.

Fischer, F. G., Papanek, P. J., and Hamilton, R. M., 1972. *The Massachusetts Mountain Earthquake of 5 August 1971 and Its Aftershocks, Nevada Test Site,* Report USGS-474-149, U.S. Geol. Surv., 16 pp.

Haimson, B. C., J. Lacomb, A. H. Jones and S. J. Green, 1974. "Deep Stress Measurements in Tuff at the Nevada Test Site," *Advances in Rock Mechanics,* National Academy of Science, Washington, D.C., pp. 557–561.

Hamilton, R. M. and J. H. Healy, 1969. "Aftershocks of the BENHAM Nuclear Explosion," *Bull. Seis. Soc. Am.,* v. 59, pp. 2271–2281.

Healy, J. H., S. H. Hickman, M. D. Zoback, and W. L. Ellis, in preparation. *Report on Televiewer Log and Stress Measurements in Core Hole USW-G1, Nevada Test Site,* Open-File Report, U.S. Geol. Surv.

Healy, J. H., J. Stock, J. Svitek, and S. Hickman, 1983. "Hydrofrac Stress Measurements on Yucca Mountain, Nevada," (ABS.) *EOS, Trans. Am. Geophys. Union,* v. 64, p. 320.

Lindh, A. G., F. G. Fischer, and A. M. Pitt, 1973. "Nevada Focal Mechanisms and Regional Stress Fields," (ABS.) *EOS, Trans. Am. Geophys. Union,* vol. 54, p. 1133.

Jamison, D. B. and N. G. W. Cook, 1980. "Note on Measured Values for the State of Stress in the Earth's Crust," *J. Geophys. Res.,* v. 85, pp. 1833–1838.

Nimick, F. B., S. J. Bauer, and J. R. Tillerson, 1984. *Recommended Matrix and Rock-mass Bulk, Mechanical and Thermal Properties for Thermomechanical Stratigraphy of Yucca Mountain,* Keystone Doc. 6310-85-1, Sandia National Laboratories, Albuquerque, NM.

Obert, L., 1964. *In Situ Stresses in Rock, Rainier Mesa, Nevada Test Site,* Report WT-1869, Applied Physics Laboratory, U. S. Bureau of Mines, 27 pp.

Smith, C., W. C. Vollendorf, and W. E. Warren, 1981. *In Situ Stress from Hydraulic Fracture Measurements in G-Tunnel, Nevada Test Site,* Report SAND80-1138, Sandia National Laboratories, Albuquerque, NM.

Smith, S. W., and R. Kind, 1972. "Observations of regional strain variations," *Jour. Geophys. Research,* v. 77, No. 26, p. 4976-4980.

Stock, J. M., J. H. Healy, and S. H. Hickman, 1984. *Report on Televiewer Log and Stress Measurements in Core Hole USW G-2, Nevada Test Site, October-November, 1982,* Open File Report USGS-OFR-84-172, U.S. Geol. Surv., 29 pp.

Warpinski, N. R., D. A. Northrup, R. A. Schmidt, W. C. Vollendorf, and S. L. Finley, 1981. *The Formation Interface Fracturing Experiment: An In Situ Investigation of Hydraulic Fracture Behavior near a Material Property Interface,* Report SAND81-0938, Sandia National Laboratories, Albuquerque, NM.

Topography, stresses, and stability at Yucca Mountain, Nevada

HENRI S.SWOLFS & WILLIAM Z.SAVAGE
US Geological Survey, Denver Federal Center, Colorado, USA

1 ABSTRACT

Plane-strain solutions are used to analyze the influence of topography
on the state of stress at Yucca Mountain, Nye County, Nevada. The
results are in good agreement with the measured stress components
obtained in drill holes by the hydraulic-fracturing technique,
particularly those measured directly beneath the crest of the ridge,
and indicate that these stresses are gravitationally induced. A
separate analysis takes advantage of the fact that a well-developed
set of vertical faults and fractures, subparallel to the ridge trend,
imparts a vertical transverse isotropy to the rock and that, as a
consequence of gravitational loading, unequal horizontal stresses are
induced in directions perpendicular and parallel to the anisotropy.

2 INTRODUCTION

Yucca Mountain, located on the western boundary of the Nevada Test
Site (fig. 1), is a north-south-trending ridge of moderate relief that
projects southward from the higher terrain near Timber Mountain into
the lower, broad plains of Crater Flat, the Amargosa Desert, and
Jackass Flats. Regional gravity and seismic-refraction surveys
(Snyder & Carr 1984; Mooney et al. 1982), as well as extensive
drilling in the area, reveal that Yucca Mountain and Crater Flat are
underlain by a thick (3-4 km) section of ash-flow tuffs and related
rocks that fill a steep-sided north-south-trending depression in the
pre-volcanic rocks. The eastern edge of this depression rises to
within 1.5-km depth from the surface just east of Yucca Mountain where
Silurian and Ordovician carbonate rocks have been penetrated by the
drill.
    According to Scott et al. (1983), Scott & Castellanos (1984), and
Scott & Bonk (1984), Yucca Mountain is cut by major north- to north-
east-striking and generally westward-dipping normal faults, forming
blocks of Miocene ash-flow tuffs tilted gently eastward (fig. 2). In
general, the density of these faults decreases toward the north, where
northwest-striking strike-slip faults with apparent right-lateral
offset become prevalent. The rock types contained within these blocks
include densely welded devitrified and vitric ash-flow tuffs,
nonwelded vitric ash-flow tuffs, vitric bedded tuffs, nonwelded

1121

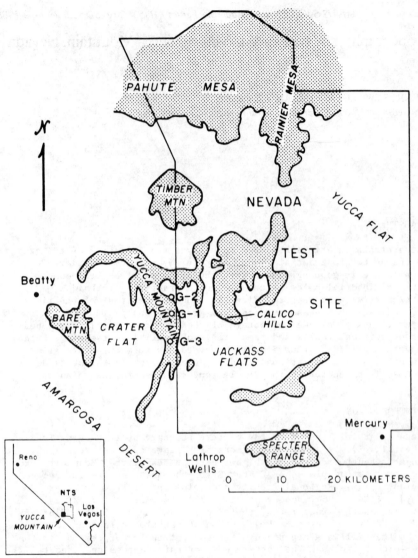

Figure 1. Map showing the location of Yucca Mountain and drill holes
USW G-1, G-2, and G-3. Areas of positive relief are shaded.

zeolitic and argillaceous ash-flow tuffs, and zeolitic and
argillaceous bedded tuffs.

As revealed by structural mapping of the surface of Yucca Mountain
and analyses of oriented cores (Scott et al. 1983), fractures and
minor faults are abundant and pervasively distributed throughout the
ridge (fig. 2). The dominant fractures have steep to near-vertical
westward dips and nearly constant north to northwest strikes. The
frequency of these fractures is several times greater in the welded
tuffs than in the nonwelded tuffs. The orientation and attitude of

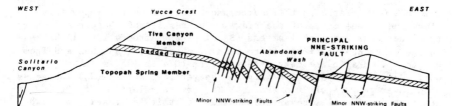

WEST   Yucca Crest   EAST

NO VERTICAL EXAGGERATION

Figure 2. Structure section across Yucca Mountain in the vicinity of
drill hole USW G-3 showing the overall cross sectional shape of the
ridge and the disposition of normal faults and tilt blocks in the
ridge. (From Scott et al. 1983.)

these fractures impart a mechanical anisotropy to the rocks; in fact,
Scott et al. (1983) attribute the observed deviation from vertical of
several deep drill holes, as well as the directions of deviation to
this anisotropy.

Because the static water table at Yucca Mountain is 500 to 800 m
below the surface, the unsaturated zone above the water table is being
considered as a possible location for a nuclear-waste repository
(Winograd 1981; Roseboom 1983). The study and characterization of the
constraints on the design and construction of the repository imposed
by the geological environment include the investigation of the state
of regional stress. To this end, measurements of stress by the
hydraulic-fracturing technique (cf., Haimson & Fairhurst 1967) have
been made in several drill holes by the U.S. Geological Survey (Healy
et al. 1984; Stock et al. 1984; J.M. Stock, written commun. 1984).
The majority of these measurements, however, were made in the
saturated zone below the water table to a depth of 1.4 km. Upward
extrapolation of the results of stress measurement into the
unsaturated zone is difficult and, perhaps, unwarranted without some
theoretical guidance.

The aim of this paper is, therefore, to describe two aspects that
may exert some influence on the local state of stress in Yucca
Mountain. First, we shall consider the stresses induced at repository
depths by topography using solutions obtained by Savage et al. (1985)
and, second, we shall consider the effect of fracture anisotropy on
the horizontal-stress distribution following the procedures outlined
by B. Amadei (oral commun. 1985). Both theoretical approaches deal
only with the gravitational component of the regional stress field;
implicit in the analyses is the assumption of lateral restraint
(Jaeger & Cook 1979), which seems reasonable considering the geologic
setting of Yucca Mountain.

3 OBSERVATIONS

To date, 11 hydraulic-fracturing tests have been conducted to estimate
the stresses in the saturated zone at Yucca Mountain (Healy et al.
1984; Stock et al. 1984; J.M. Stock, written commun. 1984) at depths
from 646 to 1356 m. Of these tests, eight were done in drill holes
USW G-1 and USW G-2 located north of the proposed repository block and
east of the ridge crest. The three remaining tests were done in drill

hole USW G-3 located in the southernmost portion of the repository block and on the crest of the ridge. The results of these tests show that the least horizontal stress (S_h) increases from 4.2 to 14.8 MPa in the test interval from 646 to 1288 m in holes G-1 and G-2 and from 6.8 to 11.5 MPa in the test interval from 1074 to 1356 m in hole G-3. Due to the overburden weight, the vertical stress (S_V) increases at an average rate of 20.6 MPa/km. The few calculations of the greatest horizontal stress (S_H) indicate that it increases from 16.8 to 17.9 MPa in holes G-1 and G-2 and from 10.6 to 17.9 MPa in hole G-3.

The measured stresses at Yucca Mountain are indicative of a normal faulting or extensional stress regime where $S_V > S_H > S_h$. This is consistent with the fault orientations shown in figure 2. However, the stresses obtained in hole G-3 are consistently smaller than those obtained at equal depths in either hole G-1 or G-2. For instance, comparing the ratios of measured least-horizontal to vertical stresses, we find that S_h/S_V is 0.49 in hole G-1 and 0.5 in hole G-2, whereas the same ratio is 0.37 in hole G-3. Similarly, the greatest horizontal- to vertical-stress ratio (S_H/S_V) averages 0.73 in holes G-1 and G-2 and is only 0.57 in hole G-3. The lower stress ratios obtained in hole G-3 may, in part, be due to the fact that the determination of S_V by borehole gravimetry has not been corrected for topographic effects.

Depths to the water table also vary with position relative to the ridge crest, because the static water levels are found at depths of 575 m in hole G-1, 526 m in hole G-2, and 752 m in hole G-3 (Scott et al. 1982).

Horizontal-stress orientations have been inferred from features observed in the drill holes by means of televiewer surveys (Healy et al. 1984; Stock et al. 1984; J.M. Stock, written commun. 1984). This evidence consists of drilling-induced hydraulic fractures and sidewall spalling (breakouts) along section of the drill holes. Hydraulic fractures are likely to be propagated when the bottom-hole pressures of the drilling fluid exceed the value of S_h, the least horizontal stress. At Yucca Mountain, this criterion is readily satisfied by filling the holes to the surface with drilling fluid (Ellis & Swolfs 1983). The drilling-induced fractures are parallel to the drill holes for long vertical distances and strike north to northeast. In near-vertical holes, breakouts are zones of limited failure that are oriented in directions normal to the greatest horizontal stress or at right angles to the hydraulic-fracture planes. The azimuths of the observed breakouts in holes G-1 and G-2 are west to west-northwest; no breakouts were recognized in hole G-3. For the purposes of this paper, we take the orientation of the least-horizontal stress (S_h) to be normal to the ridge, and the orientation of the greatest-horizontal stress (S_H) to be parallel to the ridge and the vertical fracture-anisotropy. The vertical stress (S_V) is assumed equal to the weight of the overburden.

4 ANALYSIS

4.1 Topography

In this section, we shall attempt to explain the observation that the least-horizontal stresses measured beneath the crest of Yucca Mountain in hole G-3 are smaller than those measured at comparable depths under the eastern flank of the ridge in holes G-1 and G-2. To do this, we make use of the results of Savage et al. (1985) who derived an exact solution for topographically induced stresses by the Kolosov-Muskhelishvili method of complex potentials for plane elasticity. They use a conformal mapping function to transform an isolated symmetric ridge (cf., fig. 2) into a half-plane in which expressions are obtained for the gravity-induced stresses in the symmetric ridge. Stresses given by the solution satisfy all conditions of the problem; i.e., shear stresses vanish on the ridge surface and on the axial plane of the ridge, stresses normal to the ridge surface vanish, and at great depth and distance from the ridge all stresses are compressive and approach the state of stress given by the assumption of lateral restraint (Jaeger & Cook 1979).

East-west cross sections through Yucca Mountain incorporating holes G-1, G-2, and G-3 are approximated by the conformal mapping function for a symmetric ridge that is 250 m high and 750 m wide at mid-height. Assuming the ridge materials to be isotropic, homogeneous and elastic, the topographically induced stresses are calculated for Poisson's ratio of $\nu = 0.32$ (Ellis & Swolfs 1983) and an average density of $\rho = 2.14$ gm/cm^3. Figures 3A, 3B, and 3C show the calculated variations of the least-horizontal and vertical stresses (S_h and S_v) with depth as solid curves in the vicinity of holes G-1, G-2, and G-3, respectively. Also shown are the least-horizontal stress gradients (dashed lines) calculated in the absence of topography which, at depth, are the asymptotic bounds to the topographically induced components of S_h.

The least-horizontal stresses (shut-in pressures) measured by the hydraulic-fracturing technique are shown as open symbols for each hole in figures 3A, 3B, and 3C. Although the agreement between the calculated least-horizontal stresses and the measured components appears to be good, it is clear that topography has little effect on the stresses measured in holes G-1 and G-2 lower on the flanks of the ridge (figs. 3A and 3B). However, the effect of topography on the stress measurements in hole G-3 under the crest of the ridge is obvious and significant (fig. 3C). Here, the calculated topographic component S_h shows little tendency to increase with depth for the first 200 m, whereas S_v increases steadily with depth, albeit at a slightly lower rate than shown in figures 3A and 3B. Below about 800 m, both stress components increase linearly with depth but, at comparable depths, the magnitudes of these stresses are lower than the calculated and measured stresses shown in figures 3A and 3B. Although not shown in figures 3A, 3B, and 3C, this discrepancy finally dissolves at a depth of about 2 km.

The construction shown in figure 3D is obtained by superposing figures 3A, 3B, and 3C such that the dashed lines in these figures coincide. In effect, the measured stresses (S_h) in the saturated zone are corrected for topography by referencing them to a common datum or flat surface. The distribution obtained in this way reinforces the conclusion that these stresses share a common gravitational origin.

The calculated topographically induced stresses are affected by the relative position of the measurement holes with respect to the crest of the ridge. Near the crest, the least-horizontal stress is greater than the vertical stress to a depth of about 100 m (fig. 3C). Away from the crest, these horizontal stresses are diminished (figs. 3A and 3B). Calculations of maximum shear stresses induced by topography

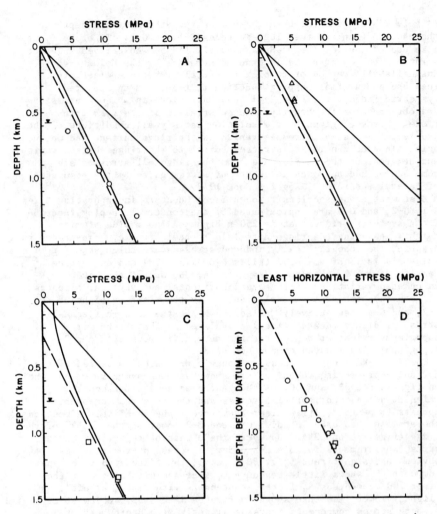

Figure 3. Comparison between the calculated (solid lines, S_h & S_V) and measured stresses (open symbols, S_h) in drill holes USW G-1 (A), USW G-2 (B), and USW G-3 (C). Depths to the static water table are indicated by solid, inverted triangles (A, B, & C). Composite plot of all measurements of S_h in the saturated zone corrected for topography (D).

show that the stress differences are minimized at a depth of about 100 m under the crest of the ridge. This is shown in figure 3C, where $S_h = S_V$. If the plane-strain assumption holds at this depth, S_H will be close in value to S_h and S_V, and the greatest structural stability would be expected here.

In hole G-2, three attempts were made to estimate the shut-in pressures in sections of the hole in the unsaturated zone above the static water table (Stock et al. 1984). These estimates of the shut-in pressures at which the fractures close are obtained from pumping

rate versus pressure plots; the results are shown in figure 3B at
depths of 295 m, 418 m, and 432 m. Because it is not known whether
these fractures are freshly formed or already present, and what their
attitudes are, some uncertainty exists about the interpretation of the
shut-in pressures in terms of the least-horizontal stress (S_h). What
is clear, however, is that the normal stress across the fracture
tending to close it should vary with fracture attitude or dip and
range between the local calculated values of S_h and S_V, as indicated
in figure 3B.

Finally, because of the plane-strain assumption in the analytical
model of Savage et al. (1985), the calculated values of the greatest-
horizontal stress (S_H) are only slightly greater than S_h, a result
that is not in accord with the observations. To find an explanation
for the observation that the ratio of horizontal stress is
$S_h/S_H \simeq 2/3$, we shall proceed by characterizing the fractured rock
material at depth under Yucca Mountain as transversely isotropic in
vertical planes parallel to the ridge.

4.2 Fracture anisotropy

The problem to be considered here is the determination of the stress
distribution in anisotropic rock induced by gravitational loading at
depths beyond the effect of topography. Solutions are given by B.
Amadei (oral commun. 1985) for the case where the planes of transverse
isotropy are vertical. Horizontal stresses parallel and perpendicular
to the anisotropy are S_H and S_h, respectively. The governing
equations are

$$S_h/S_V = \nu'(1+\nu)/(1-\nu'^2 E/E') \tag{1}$$

and

$$S_H/S_V = (\nu+\nu'^2 E/E')/(1-\nu'^2 E/E') \tag{2}$$

where $S_V = \rho g h$, and E, E', ν, and ν' are the elastic constants. The
Poisson's ratios, defined in terms of strain ratios and directions,
are $\nu = -\varepsilon_H/\varepsilon_V = -\varepsilon_V/\varepsilon_H$ and $\nu' = -\varepsilon_H/\varepsilon_h = -\varepsilon_V/\varepsilon_h$. The Young's moduli
parallel and perpendicular to the anisotropy are E and E',
respectively.

Table 1. Transversely isotropic material properties.

S_H/S_V	ν'	E/E'
0.75	0.29	3.0
0.70	0.29	2.6
0.65	0.30	2.2
0.60	0.31	1.8
0.55	0.32	1.4

At depths sufficiently removed from the effects of topography, the
stresses at Yucca Mountain are such that $S_H/S_V \simeq 3/4$ and $S_h/S_V =$
1/2. If we assume, as before, that $\nu = 0.32$ (Ellis & Swolfs 1983),
then equations 1 and 2 may be solved simultaneously for the two
unknowns, ν' and E/E'. Because of the uncertainty in the magnitude

of S_H, the results are given in table 1 for a range of S_H/S_V ratios.
The results show a weak dependence on ν', but a strong dependence on
the modulus ratio. For the extreme case where $S_H/S_V = 3/4$, the
modulus contrast is a factor of three, although it decreases rapidly
as the stress ratio is diminished. In a fractured medium, such as
that found in Yucca Mountain, the range of modulus contrast listed in
table 1 is not altogether unrealistic.

5 CONCLUDING REMARKS

We have attempted to explain the measured stresses at Yucca Mountain
using two separate theoretical models. From the results, it is
apparent that the measured stresses in the saturated zone are of
gravitational origin and are affected by fracture-induced anisotropy
and selectively by topography. Stress states above the saturated zone
at repository depths remain enigmatic. However, the model for
topographically induced stresses provides a basis for predicting the
stress magnitudes and degree of structural stability at these depths.
   Neither of the two theoretical models is alone sufficient to predict
the stresses at Yucca Mountain. A more refined model combining both
anisotropic and topographic effects is required. An exact solution of
this type would be exceedingly difficult to obtain, however, and
recourse to numerical methods becomes essential.

REFERENCES

Ellis, W.L. & H.S. Swolfs 1983. Preliminary assessment of in-situ
   geomechanical characteristics in drill hole USW G-1, Yucca Mountain,
   Nevada. U.S. Geol. Survey Open-File Rept. 83-401.
Haimson, B.C. & C. Fairhurst 1967. Initiation and extension of
   hydraulic fractures in rock. J. Soc. Petr. Engrs. 7:310-318.
Healy, J.H., S.H. Hickman, M.D. Zoback & W.L. Ellis 1984. Report on
   televiewer log and stress measurements in core hole USW-G1, Nevada
   Test Site, U.S. Geol. Survey Open File Rept. 84-15.
Jaeger, J.C. & N.G.W. Cook 1979. Fundamentals of rock mechanics. New
   York, Chapman Hall.
Mooney, W.D., D.B. Snyder & L.R. Hoffman 1982. Seismic refraction and
   gravity modeling of Yucca Mountain, Nevada Test Site, southern
   Nevada [abs.]. EOS [Trans Am. Geophys. Union] 63:1100.
Roseboom, E.H. 1983. Disposal of high-level nuclear waste above the
   water table in arid regions. U.S. Geol. Survey Circ. 903.
Savage, W.Z., H.S. Swolfs & P.S. Powers 1985. Gravitational stresses
   in long symmetric ridges and valleys. Int. J. Rock Mech. Min. Sci.
   & Geomech. Abstr. (in press).
Scott, R.B., R.W. Spengler, S. Diehl, A.R. Lappin & M.P. Chornack
   1983. Geologic character of tuffs in the unsaturated zone at Yucca
   Mountain, southern Nevada, in J.W. Mercer, P.S.C. Rao & I.W. Marine
   (eds.), Role of the unsaturated zone in radioactive and hazardous
   waste disposal. Ann Arbor Sci, Ann Arbor, Mich.:289-335.
Scott, R.B. & M. Castellanos 1984. Stratigraphic and structural
   relations of volcanic rocks in drill holes USW GU-3 and USW G-3,
   Yucca Mountain, Nye County, Nevada. U.S. Geol. Survey Open-File
   Rept. 84-491.

Scott, R.B. & J. Bonk 1984. Preliminary geologic map of Yucca
    Mountain with geologic sections, Nye County, Nevada. U.S. Geol.
    Survey Open—File Rept. 84—494.
Snyder, D.B. & W.J. Carr 1984. Interpretation of gravity data in a
    complex volcano—tectonic setting, southwestern Nevada. J. Geophys.
    Res. 89:10193—10206.
Stock, J.M., J.H. Healy & S.H. Hickman 1984. Report on televiewer log
    and stress measurements in core hole USW G—2, Nevada Test Site.
    U.S. Geol. Survey Open—File Rept. 84—172.
Winograd, I.J. 1981. Radioactive waste disposal in thick unsaturated
    zones: Science 212:1457—1464.

23. Rock blasting (Organized by SEE)

Chair: ROBERT G.LUNDQUIST
The Ohio State University, Columbus, USA

Cochair: CATHERINE T.AIMONE
New Mexico Institute of Mining & Technology, Socorro, USA

Insitu measurement of blast damage underground by seismic refraction surveys

PAUL N.WORSEY
Rock Mechanics & Explosives Research Center, University of Missouri-Rolla, USA

1 INTRODUCTION

Disturbed zones of rock adjacent to blasted highway final perimeter walls have been documented in detail by Matheson and Swindells of the Transport and Road Research Laboratory (TRRL) of Great Britain. These zones have been shown to be directly attributable to the blasting process and accordingly vary in depth depending on blasting technique. Perimeter blasting such as smooth-walling and pre-splitting has been shown to be effective in reducing the depth of disturbed rock. Although extensive work has been carried out on surface excavations for medium diameter (100mm) blast holes, none has been undertaken in underground excavations.

The purpose of this research is to continue the work for underground excavation using small diameter boreholes. The results and conclusions of the TRRL work may not necessarily be directly transferred to underground excavation due to the following reasons:

1. The 90° degree difference in blast hole orientation.
2. The confined nature of tunnel excavation.
3. The vastly different principle stress orientation.

2 BLAST DAMAGE AND DISTURBANCE

2.1 Mechanics of blast damage and disturbance formation.

Blast damage/disturbance in final excavation limits is directly attributable to many of the same processes involved in the fragmentation of the rock excavated in forming the final opening profile. As described by Holmberg (1983), "When an explosive charge detonates in a borehole, the expansion of the high pressure gaseous reaction products sets the borehole walls in an outward motion, creating a dynamic stress field in the surrounding rock. The initial effect in the nearby rock is a high intensity, short duration shock wave which quickly decays. The gas expansion leads to further motion and sets up an expanding stress field in the rock mass." At the same time radial fracturing is initiated from the blast hole and the rapidly expanding shock wave induces the elongation of favorably oriented micro-fractures and loosening of discontinuities. Radial fracturing in efficient blasting can be expected to extend a minimum of half the blast hole spacing around each blast hole (Worsey, 1981b).

Therefore damage could be expected to a comparable depth, measured from the last row of bulk holes in homogeneous rock. However, in discontinuous rock the extending radial fractures will be halted prematurely by optimally oriented discontinuities which act like individual pre-split planes (Worsey et al, 1981a). These discontinuities are weakened and/or opened by the preceding shock wave and are subsequently further opened by penetrating explosive gases which originate from the blast-hole. In this case it is more apt to use the term "disturbed". Such zones up to 8m deep have been documented by Matheson (1981) and Swindells (1981).

2.2 Effect of damage and disturbance

In both cases of damage and disturbance, thin voids are introduced into the rock mass which significantly reduce its sonic velocity. Therefore a two layer situation exists where the surface layer has the lower sonic velocity, a configuration ideal for both detection and measurement using the two layer seismic refraction technique.
   The affect of blast damage and disturbance on final excavation perimeters is multi-fold, and undesirable. Deleterious effects include over-break, reduced natural support capacity, access for weathering, increased instability, increased support requirements and a potential dramatic increase in permeability. It can be argued that the pre-determination of perimeter disturbance is of high importance for the design of most rock excavations. In addition post excavation disturbance surveys can be highly beneficial.

3 SEISMIC REFRACTIVE TECHNIQUE

The seismic refractive technique applied to blast damage/disturbance measurement, after Matheson (1979), is as follows:
   A single geophone can be used in conjunction with an enhancement seismograph. Seismic impulses are provided by a hammer at increasing distances from the geophone. First arrival times for each hammer

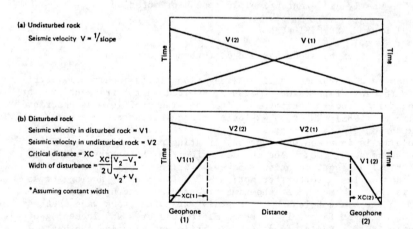

Figure 1. Seismic profile plot and equation for determination of depth of disturbance using the refractive seismic technique, after Matheson, 1979.

location are plotted with distance from the geophone, as shown in
Figure 1. The seismic velocities of each layer are calculated and along
with the critical distance are substituted into the given equation to
give the depth of the velocity boundary/disturbance. It is normal to
perform an additional reverse traverse for check purposes. A straight
line with no inflection point indicates undisturbed rock with the
proviso that a sufficient geophone separation is used.

4 EXPERIMENTAL PROGRAM

The depth of disturbed rock created by excavation through the use of
various explosive techniques including; fracture control, pre-splitting,
smooth-walling and bulk blasting was investigated for small diameter
underground tunnels. Both pre-existing documented underground excavations and a tunnel purposely excavated during the course of research
were used. Data were augmented by surface quarry measurements at the
same site including natural bedding planes.

4.1 Excavation of experimental tunnel

An experimental heading was driven 7 rounds, approximately 15m. The
heading nominally 2.5m (8ft.) wide by 2.15m (7ft.) high was driven
using small diameter holes (38-45mm). Each round was drilled to a
depth of 2m (6ft.) using a jack leg drill. Round design is illustrated
in Figure 2. In the center a 9 hole box burn cut with 4 relievers

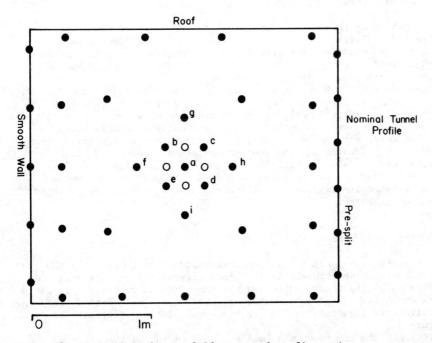

Figure 2. Experimental tunnel blast round configuration.

spaced at 6in. centers was surrounded by a diamond of 4 holes spaced
9in. out from the burn. The burn and surrounding diamond, excluding
the 4 relievers, were loaded with 5 (0.3mx32mm) (1ft.x1.25in.) sticks
of Atlas Powermax 140X explosive and stemmed with 0.3m of bagged muck.
The burn was delayed in a spiral manner as illustrated.

The main round holes were loaded with 4 sticks of Powermax 140X. In
the roof a lighter loading of 3 sticks per hole was used and in the
floor a heavier loading of 5 sticks per hole was utilized. Main
round holes were not generally stemmed.

On the left hand side of the tunnel 5 smooth-wall holes were drilled
per round at 0.46m centers. These holes were loaded with 1.22m (4ft.)
of Kleenkut "U" perimeter explosive and stemmed at the collar with
0.3m of bagged stemming. All smooth-wall holes in each round were
fired on the same delay.
On the right hand side of each round 6 pre-split holes were drilled
at 0.36m centers, loaded as above, and fired on zero delays.

From previous experience the smooth-wall was located 0.23m from the
edge of the main round whereas the pre-split was located 0.15m out on
the right from the round. 38mm holes were used in the main round.
45mm holes were used for the perimeter to provide greater decoupling
for the Atlas Kleenkut charges which were the smallest diameter charges
readily available.

Initiation was provided by both Atlas Rockmaster ms. delay electric
blasting caps and Nonel non-electric blasting caps. A total of 7
rounds were completed out of the 9 targeted, giving sufficient lengths
of smooth-wall and pre-split for the seismic refractive surveys.

4.2 Seismic Survey Technique.

The depth of disturbed rock for each face was measured using the
refractive seismic technique, as developed by TRRL. The equipment
used comprised of; a Bison enhancement seismograph - multi-trace Model
1580, shielded co-axial cables and MB electronics vibration pickup
Type 24 geophones. Seismic impulses were provided by a 3kg hammer.
Triggering for the Bison unit was provided by a fabricated make switch
located next to the hammer head and connected to the trigger input of
the Bison via suitable cabling and an electronic de-bouncing circuit.

The geophones were connected to the seismograph channels 1 and 2
via 30m co-axial shielded cables. Non-ferrous spikes were driven into
convenient fractures and the geophone attached. However, suitable
cracks were not always available. To solve this problem 0.3m, 38mm
diameter boreholes were drilled to afford both easy emplacement and
good acoustic coupling. A detailed account of the technique employed
is given by Worsey (1984).

4.3 Site Descriptions

The research was conducted at the University of Missouri-Rolla (UMR)
experimental mine property in Jefferson City Dolomite. All perimeter
control blasting faces, including the experimental tunnel are in the
Rock Mechanics and Explosives Research Center research drift. Geophone
and traverse locations within the research drift are displayed in
Figure 3.

The bulk blasted faces examined are located in the Experimental
(teaching) Mine as displayed in Figure 4. The overburden for both

1136

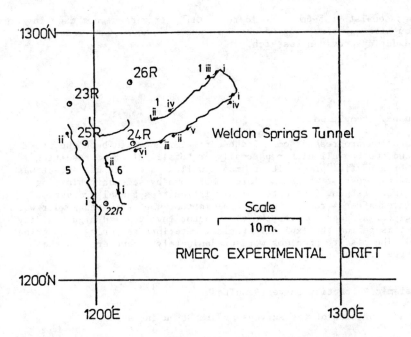

Figure 3. Geophone and traverse locations within research drift.
    Geophone location and
    Traverse direction

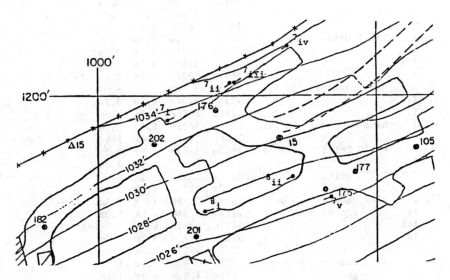

Figure 4. Geophone and traverse locations in experimental mine.

workings consist of 5-8m of solid rock. Other traverses were made in small on site quarries, one of which is known to have been crater blasted during previous research.

5 RESULTS

5.1 Tunnel Excavation

As excavation progressed some of the perimeter-holes in both the pre-split and smooth-wall either partially or totally misfired resulting in either a partial pre-split or smooth-walled face. The net effect was under-break, most of which was later shot down by secondary blasting using light charges. Due to technical difficulties tunnel excavation was delayed after 4 rounds for several months. The perimeter powder was nitro-glycerin based. Due to the time factor involved and high humidity during this period the explosive rapidly deteriorated during the spring of 1984. The misfire problems were predominately encountered in the last three rounds.

5.2 Seismic Refraction Survey Results

The results of each of the surveys are reported in Table 1.

Table 1. Seismic refraction survey results.

Ref.NO.		Location	Surface		V1	V2	XC	WD
1	i	RMERC Drift	SM/W	1	2366m	5898m	2.7m	0.9m
	ii				2917m	5917m	2.8m	0.8m
	iii				1432m	4504m	4.1m	1.5m
	iv				1433m	5828m	4.1m	1.6m
2	i	RMERC Drift	P/S	3	1612m	6831m	1.3m	0.5m
	ii				2123m	5471m	2.7m	0.9m
	iii				2622m	4163m	3.8m	0.9m
	iv				1689m	5329m	1.4m	0.5m min
3	i	RMERC Quarry	Bd pln		4483m	----	---	---
	ii				3234m	5394m	2.5m	0.7m
	iii				3185m	5486m	3.7m	1.0m
4	i	Mine Quarry 1	Bd pln		2006m	5431m	6.1m	2.1m
	ii				1846m	5462m	4.6m	1.6m
5	i	RMERC Drift	P/S	1	2840m	3385m	1.8m	0.3m
	ii				3732m	----	?m	0.0m
6	i	RMERC Drift	P/S	2	2037m	6022m	1.5m	0.6m
	ii				1622m	4175m	1.6m	0.5m
7	i	Mine Under-	B wall		1695m	5348m	4.1m	1.5m
	ii	ground			2114m	5095m	4.8m	1.5m
	iii				3148m	5385m	6.2m	1.6m min
	iv				3618m	5723m	5.2m	1.2m
	v				2191m	4957m	8.3m	2.6m
8	i	Mine Under-	B pillar		1951m	5245m	5.6m	1.9m
	ii	ground			2151m	4782m	4.8m	1.5m

F/C = Fracture Control, P/S = Pre-split, S/W = Smooth Wall

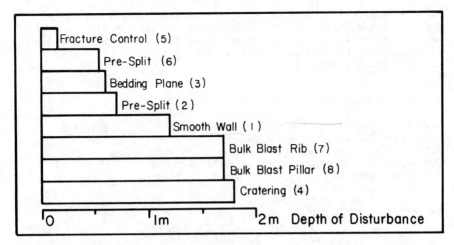

Figure 5. Average disturbance depths for technique and location.

Average blast damage values for each location and perimeter blasting technique are illustrated in Figure 5. These results indicate the fracture control technique to be most effective for minimizing blast damage, with pre-splitting following a close second. Smooth-walling perimeter technique results indicate that it produces slightly shallower disturbed zones than with traditional bulk blasting which gave disturbed zone depths up to and above 2.5m (8ft.). Most importantly, it was discovered that non-optimum pre-splitting still produces smaller disturbance zone depths than smooth-walling.

Seismic refractive data were compared for both fracture control and pre-split locations with core analysis results derived by McGroarty (1984), and were found to correlate closely.

The results at location 4 verify that this area had been blasted during past research. Location 3 indicated that heavy toe charges right up to the present surface may have been used during excavation.

6 CONCLUSIONS

1. Disturbed zones of rock exist around explosively excavated under-ground openings similar to those documented for surface excavations.
2. The seismic refractive technique can be successfully applied under-ground to accurately determine blast induced damage/disturbance depth.
3. The degree of disturbance within the disturbed zone is a measure of the velocity ratios between disturbed and intact rock.
4. For ideal blasting conditions and configurations, the minimum depth of disturbed rib rock is achieved by the use of fracture control blasting. This is followed closely by pre-splitting, then by smooth-walling and the worst technique is standard bulk blasting. The use of fracture control in small diameter tunnels can reduce blast disturbance to less than 0.3m, whereas no perimeter protection can result in disturbance depths in excess of 2.5m (8ft.) for only 38mm ANFO loaded holes.
5. There appears to be no difference in disturbance depth for rib or pillar rock, using the same excavation technique.

6. Finally poorly performing pre-splits increased blast disturbance depth. However, this disturbance is less than for bulk blasted perimeters. Therefore the use of any perimeter blasting technique whether or not successful from an excavation stand point will still reduce the depth of blast disturbance.

7 ACKNOWLEDGMENTS

I wish to acknowledge the following who have contributed to this research: The faculty, staff and graduate students of the Rock Mechanics and Explosives Research Center, UMR Experimental Mine staff, UMR Dept. of Geology and Geophysics, Atlas Powder Company and finally the Weldon Springs Research Foundation for funding this research.

REFERENCES

Holmberg, R. 1983. Hard Rock Excavation at the CSM/OCRO Test Site Using Swedish Blast Design Techniques. Report BMI/OCRO-4(3), 103 pages.
Matheson, G.D. 1979. Enhancement Seismic Refraction in Highway Site Investigation. TRRL Leaflet LF898.
Matheson, G.D. and C. Swindells 1981. Seismic Detection and Measurement of Blast Disturbance. TRRL LF928.
McGroarty, S. 1984. An Evaluation of the Fracture Control Blasting Technique for Drift Round Blasts in Dolomitic Rock, University of Missouri-Rolla: Unpublished M.S. Thesis.
Swindells, C. 1981. Seismic Inspection of Excavated Rock Slope. University of Dundee: Unpublished and Restricted Ph.D. Thesis.
Worsey, P.N. et al. 1981a. The Mechanics of Pre-splitting in Discontinuous Rocks. Proc 22nd U.S. Symp. on Rock Mech., M.I.T., pp. 205-210.
Worsey, P.N. 1981b. Geotechnical Factors Affecting the Application of Pre-split Blasting to Rock Slopes. Univ. Newcastle-upon-Tyne: Unpublished Ph.D. Thesis.
Worsey, P.N., 1984. A Comparison of Blast Damage for Different Perimeter Blasting Techniques Underground. Final report to Weldon Springs Research Foundation, 50 pages.

Statistics – A key to better blast vibration predictions

AMITAVA GHOSH & JAAK J.K.DAEMEN
Department of Mining & Geological Engineering, University of Arizona, Tucson, USA

ABSTRACT

Several predictors are available in the literature to predict the level
of ground vibration at any point from the detonation of a specified
quantity of charge. The choice of one predictor over others is generally left to the choice of the engineer. In this study several statistical techniques were used to decide the best prediction technique.
Twenty-three data sets of actual mine blasts were used for analysis.
These statistical techniques can not only compare quantitatively the
relative merits of each predictor for predicting the amplitude of
ground vibration from similar blasts at a particular site, but also can
bring out the presence of some extraneous variables in the data set
which may be the controlling factor in wave propagation.

1 INTRODUCTION

Ground vibration produced during blasting is an undesirable side-
effect. This ground vibration can cause annoyance to the public or
even structural damage if it has sufficient magnitude. It is very
important for a field engineer to predict the maximum level of ground
vibration that may be produced by a blast at a given site, knowing the
amount of explosive to be detonated at any particular delay interval
and the distance of the point of interest from the blasting site. The
design of the blast may be modified if the predicted level exceeds the
maximum allowable limit at that point. Several predictors or prediction techniques are available (e.g. Ambraseys and Hendron, 1968;
Nicholls et al., 1971; Ghosh and Daemen, 1983; Holmberg and Persson,
1979). The choice of one predictor over the others becomes a difficult task, and generally is left to the preference of the engineer.
   The blast prediction technique should be determined for each specific case based on how well it predicts the level of ground vibration to
be observed from a blast using the known quantity of charge per delay
interval. Although it is undesirable, extrapolation beyond a range of
measured data occasionally becomes necessary in practical situations.
Therefore, the chosen predictor should be able to conform to the trend
of the data very well. Statistics can be of immense help in choosing
the best predictor as the discriminative power of the statistics not
only can be used to evaluate quantitatively the strength of each

prediction technique in modelling the wave propagation characteristics, but also can be used to bring out any presence of some extraneous variables which may be the controlling factors in wave propagation.

In this study, twenty-three data sets of actual mine blasts were used to compare different prediction equations using various statistical parameters. Plots of peak particle velocity vs. either square-root or cube-root scaled distances were also produced to get a visual picture of the decay of amplitude of ground vibration.

2 GENERAL CHARACTERISTICS OF THE PREDICTORS

Ground vibration from blasting, after generation, propagates away from the drillhole. The amplitude of the vibration at any point depends on:
1) distance of the point of measurement from the point of origin;
2) weight of the charge detonated at a time or more specifically, the amount of energy delivered by the explosive;
3) the propagation characteristics of the medium, especially the propagation velocities of different types of waves and their attenuation parameters, and the presence of geological discontinuities having different reflection and refraction characteristics; and
4) interaction of the waves from one hole with those from other holes detonating at different instants in time.

It is generally impossible for any one predictor to account for all these effects into one elasto-dynamic equation. Therefore, every prediction equation simplifies the generation and propagation characteristics of the ground vibration in some manner. These simplified equations have few empirical constants whose numerical values may differ from site to site, and, probably, from one type of blasting pattern to another.

3 PREDICTORS CONSIDERED

The predictors can be broadly classified into three groups depending on the basic assumption involved in modelling the source:
1) those using cube-root scaling of charge weight/delay,
2) those using square-root scaling of charge weight/delay, and
3) those using site-specific scaling of charge weight/delay.

In each group two types of predictors were considered in this study:
a) an improved predictor which separates the geometrical spreading effect from inelastic attenuation (Ghosh and Daemen, 1983), and
b) the conventional predictor, which does not separate these two effects and inherently assumes a straight-line decay on a log-log scale.

The specific prediction equations are given below:

$$V = k_{ci} \, [D/W^{1/3}]^{-n_{ci}} \, e^{-\alpha_c D} \qquad (1)$$

$$V = k_c \, [D/W^{1/3}]^{-n_c} \qquad (2)$$

$$V = k_{si} \, [D/W^{1/2}]^{-n_{si}} \, e^{-\alpha_s D} \qquad (3)$$

$$V = k_s \, [D/W^{1/2}]^{-n_s} \qquad (4)$$

$$V = k_{ssi} \, D^{-ai} \, W^{bi} \, e^{-\alpha_{ss} D} \qquad (5)$$

$$V = k_{ss} \ D^{-a} \ W^b \qquad\qquad (6)$$

where V = peak particle velocity in any of the three mutually perpendicular directions,
D = distance from the blasting site to the point of measurement,
W = maximum charge weight in any delay of more than 9 msec,
e = base of natural logarithm, and
k_{ci}, k_c, k_{si}, k_s, k_{ssi}, k_{ss}, n_{ci}, n_c, n_{si}, n_s, ai, a, bi, b,
α_c, α_s, α_{ss} are empirical constants, subscript i indicating
the improved predictor of Ghosh and Daemen (1983).

All these equations are basically non-linear, but intrinsically
linear, which means that each prediction equation can be expressed in a
linear form by suitable transformation of variables - both dependent and
independent (Draper and Smith, 1966).
Logarithm transformation of both sides of equations (1 - 6) will make
these equations linear. For example, equation (1) becomes

$$\ln V = \ln(k_{ci}) - n_{ci} \ln[D/W^{1/3}] - \alpha_c D \qquad (7)$$

or, $\quad Y_i = \beta_0 + \beta_1 x_1 + \beta_2 x_2 + \epsilon_i \ , \quad i = 1,2,\ldots,n \qquad (8)$

where n = number of observations
$\quad$ Y = lnV
$\quad$ $x_1 = \ln[D/W^{1/3}]$
$\quad$ $x_2 = D$
$\quad$ $\beta_0 = \ln(k_{ci})$
$\quad$ β_1 = population n_{ci} which is the value of n_{ci} if all the possible
$\qquad$ occurrences of V, $[D/W^{1/3}]$ and D are analyzed
$\quad$ β_2 = population α_c
$\quad$ ϵ = logarithm of error.

The model implies that Y_i are normal random variables or V has log-
normal distribution so that lnV has a normal distribution. Lucole and
Dowding (1979) conclude that V is lognormally distributed. Other equations can be modelled similarly.
β_0, β_1, β_2 (or β_i, i = 0,1,2) and ϵ are unknowns in equation (8).
It will be difficult to discover ϵ as its value changes with every
observed Y. Though β_0, β_1, and β_2 remain fixed, we cannot find their
exact values without examining all possible occurrences of Y, x_1 and
x_2. However, we can use the information from observed values to
estimate b_0, b_1 and b_2 for β_0, β_1, and β_2, respectively, by multiple
regression analysis, using the least-square method. Therefore, the
predicted value of Y, $\hat{Y}$, for given values of x_1 and x_2 will be

$$\hat{Y} = b_0 + b_1 x_1 + b_2 x_2 \qquad (9)$$

1143

where b_0, b_1 and b_2 are determined by regression analysis. Once b_0, b_1 and b_2 are determined, exponential transformations of both sides will bring back the original form of the model and can be used for prediction.

4 STATISTICAL COMPARISON

The performance of any prediction technique to predict the peak ampli-tude of ground vibration at a particular site from a particular blast depends on how closely the actual geological characteristics of the ground and blasting parameters are modeled by the prediction equation having some inherent simplifying assumptions. The differences among different predictors can be quantified by various statistical parameters or statistics such as coefficient of determination, R^2, standard error of estimate SEE, adjusted coefficient of determination, Ra^2, etc. R^2 is a popular measure for determination of goodness of fit in the regression analysis and is used extensively in the literature (Draper and Smith, 1966; Seber, 1977; Siskind et al., 1980; Shoop and Daemen, 1983; etc.). Standard error of estimate SEE is also used extensviely (Draper and Smith, 1966; Seber, 1977; Wiss and Linehan, 1978; etc.). The coefficient of variability gives the standard error of estimate as a percentage of the mean of the dependent variable. It is not a totally new statistic and was not included in the analysis. Other statistics, such as Mallows' Cp, MSEP criterion and Rothman's Jp (Seber, 1977), are available to compare different models. They are difficult to calculate and are not standard outputs from the SPSS program. Therefore, they were not used in this study.

The definitions of R^2 and SEE are available in Draper and Smith (1966) and Seber (1977). R^2 does not recognize the number of indepen- dent variables in the model. It can be proven that addition of more independent variables to the model can only increase the value of R^2 (Seber, 1977). It has been suggested by statisticians (e.g. Seber, 1977) to use a modified measure which recognizes the number of indepen-dent variables in the model. This statistic is called 'adjusted coef-ficient of determination' Ra^2, which is defined as

$$Ra^2 = R^2 - [\frac{k}{N - k - 1}] (1 - R^2) \qquad (10)$$

where k = number of independent varaibles in the prediction equation,
      N = number of observations.

The value of Ra^2 may actually become smaller when another independent variable is introduced in the model. As the predictors considered have different numbers of variables, Ra^2 was preferred over R^2 in this study.

The overall F test uses statistical inference procedures to test the null hypothesis that multiple correlation is zero in the population from which the sample is drawn and any observed correlation is due to sampling fluctuation or error in measurement (Nie et al., 1975).

The F ratio is defined as

$$F = \frac{R^2/k}{(1 - R^2)/(N - k - 1)} \qquad (11)$$

The degrees of freedom for F are k and $(N - k - 1)$. If the computed value of F is larger than the critical value from the statistical table for a given significance level, the null hypothesis β_i, i.e. $\beta_1 = \beta_2 = \beta_k = 0$ will be rejected. Otherwise, the observed β_i are not significant at the given significance level.

Residual value is defined as the difference between the actual and predicted value. If the residual values are plotted in time sequence, i.e. in the same order as the data were gathered in the field, any deviation from normality can be observed if data points show some specific trend. Data points drawn from a normal population will give a totally random scatter.

5 RESULTS OF ACTUAL CASE STUDIES

Twenty-three data sets reported by Wiss and Linehan (1978), Nicholls et al. (1971), and Shoop and Daemen (1983) were used in this study. Separate equations were derived for each velocity component (radial, vertical and transverse) using the multiple regression analysis subprogram of the SPSS program (Version 8.3.0 - May 1982) (Nie et al., 1975). As the entire analysis was performed using logarithmic transformation, all the data pertaining to a particular point of measurement, where at least one value of particle velocity was reported 0.0, was omitted. The values of R^2, SEE, Ra^2 and overall F statistics were calculated for each of the orthogonal components for each data set using each of the six prediction techniques. The time sequence residual plot was also made for each case.

The regression equation given by the method proposed by Ghosh and Daemen (1983) is best represented by a three-dimensional logarithmic plot where the third axis is the distance. The regression equation is actually a surface in three dimensions, and every point on this surface gives the predicted value for a particular distance and charge weight. The three-dimensional plot becomes very complicated. Therefore, the best-fit line given by the method proposed by Ghosh and Daemen (1983) for a fixed charge weight was plotted. Generally, the most frequently encountered value of charge weight was taken for plotting the best-fit line. Similar curves can be drawn for other charge weights to get a family of curves. As both the site-specific equations require multidimensional plotting in logarithmic scale, no attempt was made to plot them.

Table 1 gives the equations for best-fit lines using all six prediction techniques of ground vibration data in radial directions from Tebo mine (Wiss and Linehan, 1978). The value of Ra^2 for each predictor shows that equation (3) models the wave propagation best - the largest value of Ra^2. SEE gives a reverse trend which comes from its definition. The differences among equations (1), (3) and (5) are very little, less than 0.1%, whereas these equations fair better than equations (2), (4) and (6). The particle velocity vs. cube-root scaled distance plot (Figure 1) confirms this. The best-fit line of equation (1),

Table 1. Results of statistical analysis of Tebo Mine data. Blast no. T1A-T1D; 20 cases; radial direction.

Equation	Ra^2	SEE
1. $V = 19.2 \, [D/W^{1/3}]^{-0.64} \, e^{-50E-5D}$	0.97685	0.16738
2. $V = 199.6 \, [D/W^{1/3}]^{-1.24}$	0.95155	0.24214
3. $V = 10.4 \, [D/W^{1/2}]^{-0.64} \, e^{-50E-5D}$	0.97721	0.16607
4. $V = 59.3 \, [D/W^{1/2}]^{-1.24}$	0.95198	0.24105
5. $V = 1.5 \, D^{-0.64} \, W^{0.65} \, e^{-50E-5D}$	0.97629	0.16939
6. $V = 25.3 \, D^{-1.34} \, W^{0.77}$	0.94925	0.24781

using W = 302 lb, conforms to the trend of the data very well, especially at large distances. Therefore, using either equations (1), (3) or (5), a better prediction can be made. The time-sequence residual plots show random distribution. Figure 2, using the data of Fabius mine – series 2 in the transverse direction, shows that equation (3) works better than equation (2). The value of Ra^2 confirms this. Table 2 gives the results of data from the Fabius mine – series 4 in the vertical direction. Ra^2 values show that there is very little difference

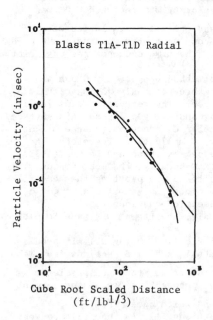

Figure 1. – – – : Eq. (2)
           ––––– : Eq. (1)
                  for W = 302 lb.

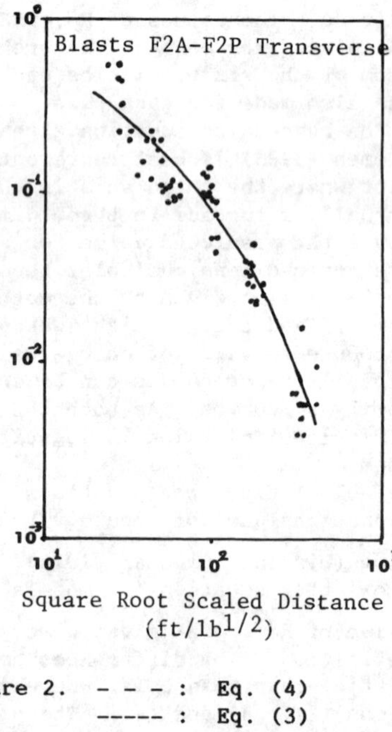

Figure 2. – – – : Eq. (4)
           ––––– : Eq. (3)
                  for W = 200 lb.

1146

Table 2. Results of statistical analysis of Fabius Mine data. Blast no. F4B–F4M; 49 cases; radial direction.

Equation	R_a^2	SEE
1. $V = 116.8 \ [D/W^{1/3}]^{-1.32} \ e^{-7E-5D}$	0.95744	0.37626
2. $V = 313.0 \ [D/W^{1/3}]^{-1.55}$	0.95304	0.39524
3. $V = 21.7 \ [D/W^{1/2}]^{-1.25} \ e^{-9E-5D}$	0.97235	0.30329
4. $V = 50.9 \ [D/W^{1/2}]^{-1.52}$	0.96356	0.34814
5. $V = 2.4 \ D^{-1.09} \ W^{0.80} \ e^{-13E-5D}$	0.97744	0.27396
6. $V = 38.3 \ D^{-1.50} \ W^{0.80}$	0.96295	0.35103

among the six predictors. Figure 3 confirms this conclusion. Figure 4 shows the time sequence residual plot. It shows a curvilinear trend of the residuals – not a random one. Both linear and quadratic terms in time should have been included in the model (Draper and Smith, 1966). The reason for this behavior could not be explained. Systematic drift of the response of the instrument or peculiar geology are possible reasons. A linear trend was observed in the radial direction. Again, the reason for this behavior could not be explained. These specific trends in the data show that the variations in the data are not entirely due to some random process. There is some other effect which is intro- ducing this systematic error. Special care should be taken to gather

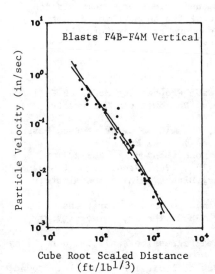

Cube Root Scaled Distance
(ft/lb$^{1/3}$)

Figure 3.   – – – : Eq. (2)
            ––––– : Eq. (1)
            for W = 500 lb.

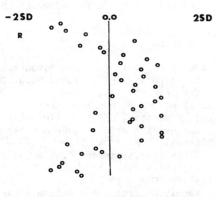

R indicates out of 2SD limit.

Figure 4.   Time–sequence residual plot from Tebo Mine – Series 2 (Wiss and Linehan, 1978) in transverse direction using equation (3). The plot shows a curved trend of the residuals.

1147

future data at that particular site. F statistics for all these data
show that β_i's are significant at 99% confidence interval. Detailed
results of statistical analysis for each component of vibration from the
twenty-three data sets are given elsewhere along with the particle
velocity vs. scaled distance plots (Ghosh and Daemen, 1983).

   As geology and blasting practices varied widely from one data set to
another, the characteristics of wave propagation were also different.
Therefore, no single prediction technique was best in all cases. In
general, the methods proposed by Ghosh and Daemen (1983) faired better
than the conventional techniques. Results do not show significant differences among the three scaling techniques. Cube-root scaling was
better in a few isolated cases where the charge per delay was very high
(1000 to 2700 lb). Similarly, in a few cases where charge per delay was
small, the square-root scaling technique faired well.

6 CONCLUSIONS

Various statistical techniques were used very successfully to determine
the best prediction technique of ground vibration from blasting for each
situation in a quantitative way. Discriminative power of statistics
also brought out some specific trends in a few data sets. Use of these
simple statistical techniques will enable better prediction of ground
vibration from blasting.

ACKNOWLEDGEMENT

This material is based upon work partially supported by the Office of
Surface Mining and U.S. Bureau of Mines under Grants No. G5105010 and
G51115041. Any opinions, findings and conclusions or recommendations
expressed in this publication are those of the authors and do not
necessarily reflect the views of the sponsors of the grants.

REFERENCES

Aimone, C.T., 1982, Three-Dimensional Wave Propagation Model of Full-
   Scale Rock Fragmentation, Ph.D. Thesis, Northwestern University,
   Evanston, Illinois, 194 p.
Ambraseys, N.R. and A.H. Hendron, 1968, Dynamic Behavior of Rock Masses.
   In K.G. Stagg and O.C. Zienkiewicz (eds.), Rock Mechanics in
   Engineering Practice, John Wiley and Sons, London, p. 203-207.
Attewell, P.B., I.W. Farmer, and D. Haslam, 1965, Prediction of Ground
   Vibration Parameters from Major Quarry Blasts, Mining and Minerals
   Engineering, December, p. 621-626.
Dowding, C.H., 1971, Response of Buildings to Ground Vibrations
   Resulting from Construction Blasting, Ph.D. Thesis, University of
   Illinois at Urbana-Champaign, 204 p.
Draper, N.R. and H. Smith, 1966, Applied Regression Analysis, John Wiley
   and Sons, Inc., New York, 407 p.
Ghosh, A. and J.J.K. Daemen, 1983, A New Analytical Predictor of Ground
   Vibrations Induced by Blasting, Report to U.S. Bureau of Mines, OFR
   105(4)-84, NTIS No. PB 84-191964, 315 p.
Holmberg, R. and P.A. Persson, 1979, Design of Tunnel Perimeter
   Blasthole Patterns to Prevent Rock Damage, Tunneling '79, Proceedings

of the 2nd International Symposium, London, March, Institute of Mining and Metallurgy, p. 280-283.

Lucole, S.W. and C.H. Dowding, 1979, Statistical Analysis of Blast Emission Records from Quarrying, Mining and Construction Operations in the State of Illinois, Illinois Institute of Natural Resources, Division of Environment Management, IINR Document No. 79/02, 200 pp.

Nicholls, H.R., C.F. Johnson, and W.I. Duvall, 1971, Blasting Vibrations and Their Effects on Structures, U.S. Bureau of Mines Bulletin 656, 105 p.

Nie, N.H., C.H. Hull, J.G. Jenkins, K. Steinbrenner, and D.H. Bent, 1975, Statistical Package for the Social Sciences, McGraw Hill, Inc., U.S.A., 675 p.

Olson, J.J., R.A. Dick, D.E. Fogelson, and L.R. Fletcher, 1970, Mine Roof Vibrations from Production Blasts, Shullsburg Mine, Shullsburg, Wis., U.S. Bureau of Mines Report of Investigations, 7462, 35 p.

Olson, J.J., D.E. Fogelson, R.A. Dick, and A.D. Hendrickson, 1972, Ground Vibrations from Tunnel Blasting in Granite - Cheyenne Mountain (NORAD), Colorado, U.S. Bureau of Mines Report of Investigations 7653, 25 p.

Seber, G.A.F., 1977, Linear Regression Analysis, John Wiley and Sons, New York, 465 pp.

Shoop, S.A. and J.J.K. Daemen, 1983, Ground Vibration Monitoring and Assessment of Conventional Predictors, Report to U.S. Bureau of Mines OFR 105(2)-84, NTIS No. PB 84-191949, 193 p.

Siskind, D.E., M.S. Stagg, J.W. Kopp, and C.H. Dowding, 1980, Structure Response and Damage Produced by Ground Vibration from Surface Mine Blasting, U.S. Bureau of Mines Report of Investigation 8507, 74 p.

Wiss, J.F. and P.W. Linehan, 1978, Control of Vibration and Blast Noise from Surface Coal Mining, Volumes I-IV, Report to U.S. Bureau of Mines OFR(1-4)-76, December.

Seismic characterisation of rock masses before and after mine blasting

R.P.YOUNG
Department of Geological Sciences, Queen's University, Kingston, Canada
J.J.HILL
Department of Electronic Engineering, University of Hull, UK

1 INTRODUCTION

The excavation of overburden rock at most mine sites is aided by the use of explosives. The preparation, distribution, amount and detonation sequence of explosive (or blast design) within the overburden has a major effect on the products of a blast and often determines the level of ground vibration and fragmentation. Too much explosive is costly and inefficient and will provide over fragmentation and can cause unnecessary ground vibration. Insufficient explosive, although reducing ground vibration levels, often causes machine damage and therefore loss of production time due to poor fragmentation. The aim of this work was to seismically characterise the fragmentation efficiency of a mine blast.

Previous research based on seismic velocity has not provided a unique interpretation of rock quality for this particular application (Bamford and Nunn 1979, Sjogren et al., 1979). For this reason, additional information regarding the rock mass is required and some of this becomes available when seismic attenuation is taken into consideration (King et al 1978). Previous work by the authors has shown that spectral analysis of seismic signals, after they have been used to interrogate the rock, can be used to characterize rock mass quality. Seismic attenuation spectral signatures have been shown to correlate to selected discontinuity parameters, using multivariate statistical analysis techniques (Young and Hill 1982, 1984). This work has shown that certain frequencies within seismic signals are attenuated dependent upon the ratio of the seismic wavelength to the size characteristics of rock fractures. Hence, the seismic attenuation spectra can be viewed as a rock signature, where the shape of the spectral signature is directly related to selected discontinuity characteristics within the rock mass. This wavelength dependent preferential filtering of seismic signals by rock discontinuities is not apparent within rock masses which appear seismically isotropic and homogeneous. In this case, the more normal mechanism of spherical divergence and absorption of seismic energy with distance results in linear attenuation spectral gradients and a simple low pass filter model is observed.

This technique of using seismic attenuation spectra to characterise rock masses has been used in this study to evaluate the fragmentation efficiency of a mine blast. The results show that the fragmentation efficiency of an explosion and the fracture anisotropy of the rock mass can be quantified in terms of 3D attenuation spectra and polar seismic anisotropy diagrams.

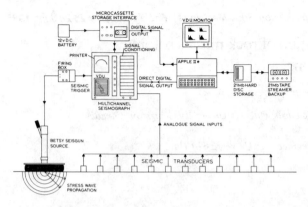

Fig. 1 Microcomputer controlled seismograph system

2 SEISMIC INSTRUMENTATION AND PROCESSING

The instrumentation and processing system used is shown in Fig. 1 and consists of a microcomputer enhanced Geometrics ES-1210F digital engineering seismograph, calibrated transducers, signal conditioning and a microcassette data logger (Hill et al., 1983). The data logger, designed and constructed at the University of Hull, is able to store 12 channels of seismic data on one side of a microcassette and therefore a normal two way, 12 channel refraction survey can be stored on one microcassette. The Apple microcomputer can be interfaced to the logger or the seismograph directly by a specially designed parallel interface card. Data can be transferred either from the seismograph memory or the microcassette tape to the microcomputer. A Betsy seismic gun was used as the energy source for all seismic experiments. This gun fires a 25gm lead slug into the ground to generate approximately 12kJ of impact energy. The frequency content of the signal on solid rock was useful to 500Hz (with a 10bit dynamic range) with a peak in the energy spectrum at 150Hz. The Betsy gun was also used in conjunction with a shear wave tube attachment to generate horizontally polarised shear waves.

The software of the Apple system is written in Pascal and a wide variety of processing options are available on an interactive basis through using a multi-level menu driven system. The processing options include: storage and retrieval of data, power spectral computation, spectral smoothing, display of power and attenuation spectra, seismic refraction analysis, digital filtering of waveforms and particle motion analysis for triaxial geophone arrays. Markers can be used to select the first arrival times of the seismic signals for velocity determination, and can also be used when compting power spectra by selecting a time window over which the machine code FFT is computed. This facility, in conjunction with particle motion analysis, is used to calculate spectra for a predominant wave type. When displaying spectra, the marker can be used to select a line in the power or attenuation spectra. The frequency and value in dB of this line is continually updated on the display. Zoom facilities are also provided for expanding portions of the display to the resolution limit of the system. The system software is compatible with a research database facility which

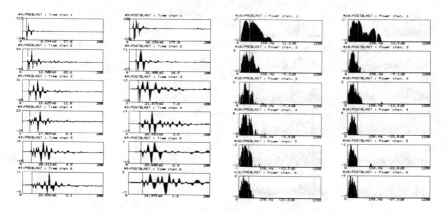

Fig. 2 Pre and post blast seismic time signals and power spectra

allows more advanced statistical processing of the data. The seismic
signals shown in this paper, have been processed on this system and
graphical output has been obtained from a standard dot matrix printer.
This system has now been repackaged as a portable apple unit with bubble
memory, twin disk drives and 5" Hi-Res monitor. The unit includes an 8
channel, 25usec, 12bit A/D converter, internal battery power supply,
programmable gain amplifiers and menu driven seismic software, including
a pretrigger memory facility for blast monitoring. The system can be
used in the field as a self contained seismic processing system or as an
interface to a standard engineering seismograph, so as to provide the
enhanced processing facilities described above.

3 PRE AND POST BLAST SEISMIC EXPERIMENTS

The pre and post blast seismic surveys consist of two major experiment
types. The first is carried out to measure near surface seismic rock
mass anisotropy and the second, to determine attenuation as a function
of depth of penetration of the seismic waves. From experiment 2, the
data for two seismic lines are described, seismic line 8, 10m away from
and parallel to the high wall (previous excavation edge) and seismic
line 4, 20m away from and parallel to the high wall. These have been
chosen because they have been blasted using different quantities of
explosive (see Fig. 3). The rock mass studied in this investigation
exhibited a gradual increase in seismic velocity with depth prior to
blasting and in general, showed curved or two layer seismic refraction
profiles. Up to 25m of unblasted overburden rock was removed from the
rock mass several months prior to the tests and it is probable that the
subsequent stress release contributed to the opening up of existing
fractures in the rock mass near to the surface and resulted in higher
than normal near surface attenuation, prior to blasting.

Identical seismic experiments were carried out prior to and after
blasting. A comparison of these two data sets for experiment 2 can be
seen from Figs. 2-4, which represent the results from a single
component seismic survey. Fig. 2 shows the expanded seismic time
signals from sensors, as a function of source to transducer spacing, for

1153

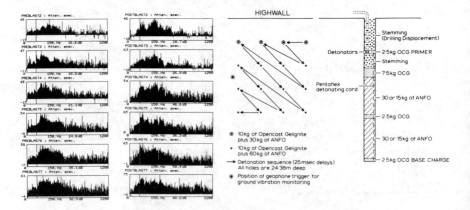

Fig. 3 Pre and post blast attenuation spectra and blast design

seismic line 4 prior to and after blasting. Fig. 2 also shows the
effect of blasting on power spectra for the same seismic line. Visual
analysis of the time data shows that the arrival times of the seismic
signals, as indicated by the cursors, is much later and the signals much
broader (generally lower frequency content) for postblast results. From
the power spectra on Fig. 2, it can be seen that the power for a given
frequency and bandwidth of the seismic spectra are in general lower for
postblast data. The total power shown, however, is a function of the
magnitude of the particular preblast or postblast shot and this is
corrected for before further analysis. It is interesting to compare
identical channels for preblast and postblast results as it is these
differences, after corrections for source magnitude, which are used to
seismically characterise the effectivness of the blasting process. in
order to filter out the effects of variations in the shape of the
preblast and postblast input energy spectra, attenuation spectra are
calculated using the source power spectrum (channel 1) for each survey
as input and the other channels as output. The resulting attenuation
spectra are shown in Fig. 3 for pre and postblast data from seismic line
4 for six source to transducer offset spacings (4-24m in 4m increments).
After correction for source magnitude effects, the attenuation spectra
in Fig. 3 conform to what would be expected, that is higher attenuation
values for the postblast rock mass. From Fig. 3, it can be seen that
attenuation results for a given frequency (for example as shown by the
cursors at 150Hz) are considerably higher for the postblast condition
for all source to transducer spacings. It can also be seen that, up to
the effective bandwidth of the signal (300Hz.), the gradient of the
attenuation spectra, in general, is much steeper for the postblast rock
mass.
   From these corrected spectra, it is then possible to compute preblast
and postblast seismic attenuation pseudo-depth profiles (attenuation
spectra as a function of source to transducer spacing) and attenuation
difference profiles (the arithmetic difference in dB of the postblast
and preblast attenuation spectra). This reduction of data is carried
out by utilising a 3D graphics package resident in the database system.
The 3D attenuation spectra are then corrected for distance and
geometrical spreading and attenuation is given in dB/m. Fig. 4 shows

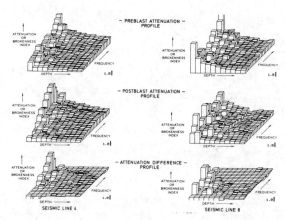

Fig. 4 Effect of blasting on the seismic attenuation and brokeness of rock masses

typical 3D seismic spectral pseudo-depth profiles (3D seismic attenuation spectra) for seismic lines 4 and 8 before and after blasting. The lower diagrams show the difference between preblast and postblast results. These diagrams show attenuation ratio as a function of pseudo-depth and frequency. Cross-sections taken parallel to the "depth" axis, represent attenuation as a function of source to transducer offset spacing for different frequencies of seismic energy (15-300Hz in 15Hz increments). The diagram represents the ratio of the seismic attenuation calculated after blasting to that calculated before blasting, expressed in dB/m. An attenuation ratio of one (0dB/m) on this diagram, or the base plane on the 3D image, represents zero change in the seismic characteristics due to blasting.

It is possible to make a number of general statements in relation to Fig. 4 which are also true for all of the "difference" profiles obtained. The shape of this 3D surface is characteristic of the performance of the blasting process. Height in the diagram is attenuation ratio and is proportional to the increase in brokenness and openness of fractures in the rock mass caused by blasting. It can be seen that the highest values are obtained from shallow depths (small source to transducer offset spacings). Attenuation as a function of frequency is more irregular for shallow depths than for spectra at depth. This is a result of large fractures opening due to lack of confinement near the surface and these large fractures cause frequency dependent scattering of the seismic waves. At depth, there is less increase in seismic attenuation as a function of frequency and it becomes more linear. Although fractures have been propagated by the blast, at depth, they are closed due to confinement.

It has also been noted that for the effective bandwidth of the seismic signals, seismic line 8 shows, for higher frequencies, less attenuation due to blasting than seismic line 4. This could be a result of several phenomena, including poor signal to noise ratio and the different quantities of explosive used. However, it has been observed that in general, seismic lines parallel and close to the highwall often exhibit low attenuation due to blasting and some cases display apparent amplifications due to blasting, which is not the case for seismic lines

1155

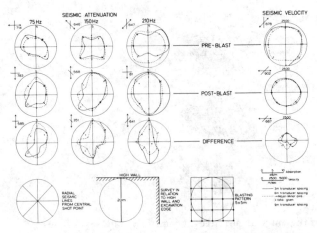

Fig. 5 Effect of blasting on seismic anisotropy

perpendicular to the highwall (see experiment 1 data, Fig. 5). This is
a result of high frequencies of seismic energy being trapped between
major discontinuities which act as wave guides. Prior to blasting, if
normal spherical divergence and absorption of energy with distance takes
place, this process can be hindered at higher frequencies after
blasting, by blast induced fissures which are oriented parallel to the
seismic line and trap the seismic energy. This feature has been
particularly useful for characterising blast induced fissures by
comparing "difference profiles" for different orientations of seismic
lines. This is highlighted in the discussion of experiment 1 data shown
in Fig. 5.

The associated compressional wave velocities, computed from the line 4
seismic signals prior to blasting, are 1100 m/sec for the near surface
rock mass increasing to 1750 m/sec at depth. After blasting, the near
surface velocity is reduced to 600 m/sec, with the velocity increasing
to 1050 m/sec with depth. The near surface velocity for seismic line 8
(nearer the previous excavation edge) prior to blasting, is 950 m/sec,
increasing to 1700 m/sec with depth. After blasting, the near surface
velocity for seismic line 8 was reduced to 700 m/sec, with a velocity at
depth approaching 1200 m/sec. In general, the results show a lowering
of the seismic velocity, together with a marked increase in attenuation
of the seismic energy, due to the blasting process.

Similar trends are obtained for the triaxial experiments and therefore
the spectra have not been given for brevity. However, reduced velocity
and attenuation data plotted on polar diagrams provide additional
information. These polar diagrams are used to display anisotropic
effects in the seismic data and hence, the rock mass. Fig. 5 shows, for
selected frequencies, how attenuation and velocity vary as a function of
orientation. The high wall and the dragline excavation edge is shown on
the key in order to orientate the data. Pre and post blast results are
given, together with a difference diagram for this radial set of seismic
lines. Each diagram contains 3 curves which represent the different
source to transducer spacings. The values given at the side of each of
the polar diagrams are the direction and ratio of the minor to major
attenuation and velocity axes. The curves are constructed for eight
points obtained from a star pattern of seismic lines. The values are

corrected for distance and geometrical spreading and displayed in dB/m
for the selected frequencies.

Many attenuation parameters can be expressed in this way but the
selection given in Fig. 5 shows many of the features observed. The
radius of the seismic lines was limited by the blast bench to 10m and
therefore the results can only be used to describe the directional
variability (anisotropic effects) for near surface rock material.
However, other results indicate that at increasing depths, the effects
are similar but less pronounced, due to the closure of fractures with
depth. Several interesting features can be observed for the diagrams
given in Fig. 5 and these are:

1. Preblast results show an increase in attenuation with frequency (as
would be expected), but the relationship with transducer spacing or
depth of penetration of the seismic waves is confused. This is possibly
because the values given are all affected by near surface features and
therefore the differences are not really significant and could be
averaged.

2. Preblast attenuation show maxima at approximately 45 degrees to the
high wall and minima parallel to the high wall. This correlates quite
well with maximum attenuation at right angles to orthogonal joint sets
within the preblasted rock mass. Preblast seismic velocity as a
function of direction is less well defined than the attenuation results.

3. Postblast results show attenuation maxima at right angles to the
highwall. This correlates with the opening of fractures, due to
blasting, parallel to the highwall

4. Postblast velocity diagrams show velocity minima in the same
direction as the attenuation maxima (as would be expected).

5. Postblast attenuation results parallel to the highwall show, in
selected cases, a decrease in attenuation after blasting. This
phenomenon is probably associated with parallel blast induced fissures
acting as a wave guide and trapping the seismic energy between major
discontinuities within the rock mass.

6. Difference polar diagrams, which characterise the efficiency of the
blast, show that the maximum attenuation effects are perpendicular to
the highwall, although attenuation/brokenness increases due to blasting
in all directions. These results are substantiated by the velocity
results.

7. Difference results indicate that the effects of the blast are more
pronounced for rock nearer the highwall (values in the northern half of
the diagrams: fractures parallel to experiment 2 - seismic line 8) than
rock away from the highwall (values in the southern half of the
diagrams: fractures parallel to experiment 2 - seismic line 4).

At present, pattern recognition techniques, including cluster and
principal component analysis, are being utilised to isolate significant
trends in the 3D and polar diagrams.

4 CONCLUSIONS

It has been shown that seismic attenuation can give additional
information about the quality of rock masses, which is not available
from velocity parameters alone, although in many practical situations,
the advantages of attenuation are outweighed by the relative simplicity
and more fully understood physical laws involved with velocity
techniques. It has been highlighted in this study that fractures within
rock masses before and after blasting, have a marked effect on the

propagation of seismic waves. Although the experiments carried out were identical before and after the blast, resultant changes within the rock mass itself caused anisotropic frequency dependent seismic wave guide phenomena, which did not predominate prior to blasting. This phenomenon by itself does not change the seismic velocity, but has a marked effect on the attenuation of seismic signals parallel to blast induced fissures. In consequence, the mechanisms of attenuation of seismic waves change in selected directions and can result in apparent amplification, with respect to preblast propagation, of the seismic signals parallel to major blast induced fissures. This anisotropic effect occurs because the normal spherical divergence and absorption of energy with distance, has been restricted by open, parallel fissures. The results for more than 25 rock masses show that this mechanism is not predominant prior to blasting. This is because fractures/joints are more closed and are relatively "seismically invisable" because the size characteristics are small compared to the wavelength, whereas this is radically changed by the introduction of major blast induced open fissures parallel and close to an unconfined rock face. It has been shown that the combination of 3D attenuation profiles, seismic velocity and polar seismic anisotropy diagrams provides useful information about the character of discontinuities within a rock mass. The results, in general, show that selected characteristics of rock discontinuities within a rock mass can be seismically determined and this in turn can be used to define the fragmentation efficiency and anisotropic effects of the blasting process, for the design and optimisation of mine blasts.

ACKNOWLEDGEMENTS

The authors would like to thank the Opencast Executive of the British National Coal Board and the University of Hull for their support and guidance. R. Middleton, I. Bryan, R. Haigh and T. White are thanked for their contributions to the project.

REFERENCES

Bamford, D. and Nunn, K.R., 1979. In-situ seismic measurements of crack anisotropy in the carboniferous limestone of Northwest England. Geophys. Prosp. 27:322-338.
Hill, J.J., Young, R.P. and Haigh, R.N., 1983. A low cost microcomputer-based seismic processing system. J. Software and Microsystems 2:19-25.
King, M.S., Stauffer, M.R. and Pandit, B.I., 1978. Quality of rock masses by acoustic borehole logging. Proc. Symp. III Int. Congress I.A.E.G. 1:156-164.
Sjogren, B., Ofsthus, A. and Sandberg, J., 1979. Seismic classification of rock mass qualities. Geophys. Prosp. 27:409-442.
Young, R.P. and Hill, J.J., 1982. Statistical analysis of seismic spect-tral signatures for rock quality assessment. Geoexploration 20:75-91.
Young, R.P. and Hill, J.J., 1984. Seismic remote sensing of rock masses for the optimisation of excavation efficiency. IEEE Trans. Geoscience and Remote Sensing 22:704-711.

Predicting grain size distribution of blast material based on rock fabric information

DIRK VAN ZYL
Department of Civil Engineering, Colorado State University, Fort Collins, USA

ABSTRACT

Rock fabric information is gathered on a routine basis at most mining and rock excavation projects. Such information can include Rock Quality Designation (RQD) and smallest piece from cores as well as pit wall surveys. These data are used to obtain discontinuity spacing and length information. A statistical analysis of the data is typically made and the information used for slope stability or excavation evaluations (D'Andrea, et al 1974; White 1979; Einstein and Baecher 1983; Call and Nicholas 1978). Rock fabric information has also been used to estimate block volume distributions (Hudson and Priest 1979; Dinis Da Gama 1977; Beyer and Rolofs 1981).

This study was performed as part of an NSF project to investigate the spatial variation of geotechnical parameters in rockfill. The work was performed at a large open pit copper mine in Arizona.

The most important assumption made in this study is that blasting only separates the blocks along pre-existing fractures and that rock breakage due to blasting can be neglected.

Three rock types were investigated: dacite, schist and porphyry. The following information available from the mineral exploration drilling program was used in the prediction analysis of grain size distribution: largest piece, percent particles larger than 25mm, and RQD. Color slides were available for the most recently collected cores. Grain size distributions were estimated per core run (1.3 to 2 m). "Mean" bench grain size distrtibutions were obtained by using weighted averages.

Line surveys on a pit wall are often conducted to evaluate slope stability. Surveys of discontinuities for the purpose of identifying major structures for subsequent stability analyses are not detailed enough for the prediction of grain size distributions. Photographs of the pit wall were used to estimate the grain size distribution. Fracture spacings were evaluated along a series of parallel lines on the photograph. It was assumed that each particle was cubical. This assumption was based on measurements made on particles in the field. Another approach, assuming that the third dimension into the bench is controlled by a joint set parallel to a face, was also investigated. In this approach most of the particles will be parallelepipeds instead of cubes.

Photographic techniques were used to obtain grain size distributions of blasted material. Comparisons were made between the grain size distributions obtained from the borehole data, the pit wall photographs and the blasted material.

REFERENCES

Beyer, F. and F. Rolofs 1981. Size distributions of rock blocks from measurements on rock faces (in German), Rock Mechanics, 14:105-113.
Call, R.D. and D.E. Nicholas 1978. Prediction of step path failure geometry for slope stability analysis, 19th U.S. Symp. on Rock Mech.
D'Andrea, D.V., R.A. Dick, R.C. Steckley and W.C. Larson 1974. A fragmentation experiment for in situ extraction, in Solution Mining Symp. 1974, AIME, Chapter 10, p.148-161.
Dinis Da Gama, C. 1977. Computer model for block size analysis of jointed rock masses, 15th APCOM symp., Brisbane, Australia, p.305-315.
Einstein, H.H. and G.B. Baecher 1983. Probabilistic and statistical methods in engineering geology, specific methods and examples, Part I: Exploration, Rock Mechanics and Rock Engineering, 16:39-72.
Hudson, J.A. and S.D. Priest 1979. Discontinuities and rock mass geometry, Int. J. Rock Mech. Min. Sci. & Geomech. Abstr. 16:339-362.
White, D.H. 1979. Analysis of rock mass properties for the design of block caving mines, Preprint 79-309, SME-AIME Fall Mtg. & Exhibit, Tucson, AZ, 17pp.

24. Underground excavation

Chair: V.RAJARAM
Engineers International Inc., Westmont, Illinois, USA

Cochair: IAN W.FARMER
University of Arizona, Tucson, USA

Field measurements of rock displacement in deep shafts in quartzite with high in situ stress

M.J.BEUS & J.K.WHYATT
US Bureau of Mines, Spokane Research Center, Washington, USA

ABSTRACT

The Bureau of Mines, under cooperative agreements with Hecla Mining Co. and Callahan Mining Co., is measuring rock displacement during sinking of circular and rectangular shafts in deep mines in northern Idaho. The objective of the project is to evaluate support behavior and rock deformation when deep shafts are constructed in high, in situ stress fields and anisotropic rock masses. Rock displacement data and preliminary analysis show the effect of shaft sinking, rock mass anisotropy, and yielding.

INTRODUCTION

For many years, the Bureau of Mines has conducted research to determine the in situ stress field and to develop structural guidelines for designing shafts in deep vein-type mines. Much of this work has centered on determining the in situ conditions that affect the structural stability of shafts in the Coeur d'Alene district of northern Idaho. Currently, work is concentrated on field monitoring of actual rock and support behavior under these in situ conditions during shaft sinking.

Hecla Mining Co. is further developing its Lucky Friday Mine near Mullan, Idaho, with completion of a 2,000 m deep, circular, concrete-lined production shaft (McKinstry, 1983). Callahan Mining Corp. is sinking a 1,600 m deep, rectangular, timber-supported exploration shaft near Wallace, Idaho. Figure 1 shows the location of these two shafts. Cooperative agreements were established between the Bureau and Hecla early in 1980 and Callahan early in 1984 to instrument and evaluate the structural response of these new shafts during and after construction.

Hecla's Silver Shaft was the first to be monitored followed by Callahan's Caladay Shaft. These deep shaft projects in highly stressed mines of northern Idaho provided an ideal opportunity for the Bureau to conduct deep mine research. This report presents results and a preliminary analysis of data from instruments installed at the 1,800 m level of the Silver Shaft and the 1,450 m level of the Caladay Shaft. Subsequent reports will present data from four

test levels in the Silver Shaft, long-term displacement and timber
support performance data from the Caladay, and more detailed numerical
analyses. Previous reports have shown Silver Shaft liner response to
nearby excavation and shaft advance (Board, 1984).

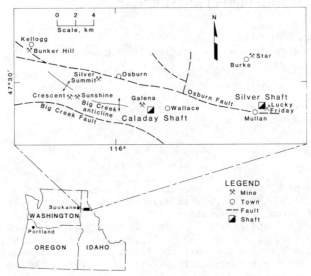

Figure 1. Location of the Silver Shaft and Caladay Shaft in the
Coeur d'Alene Mining District.

INSTRUMENTATION

Design of the shaft measurement system, including orientation and
location of the instruments, is based on the projected in situ stress
conditions, shaft geometry, and geologic environment. The basic
instrumentation approach is to obtain the maximum amount of information with minimal interference with shaft sinking activities. The goal
is to produce a totally sealed, remotely accessed, environmentally
secure package with no exposure of electronic components once the
system leaves the shaft collar. Installation was scheduled during
downtime and holidays to minimize interference with shaft sinking.

The in-shaft instrument package for monitoring displacement includes
multiple position borehole extensometers (MPBX's), connecting signal
cable, and a junction box (J-box). Surface equipment consists of a
data receiver and microcomputer. Figure 2 shows an artist's concept of
the overall instrumentation and data acquisition plan for the shafts.

SITE DESCRIPTION AND INSTALLATION

The Silver Shaft lies near the Osburn Fault, which is the most
dominant structural feature of the district, striking west-northwest,
with several miles of lateral displacement.

Conventional drill-and-blast sinking practices were followed using
handheld sinkers, bench blasting, and a cactus grab rotary-boom mucker
mounted on the bottom deck of the Galloway stage. Shaft steel and

services were advanced concurrent with sinking. Initial support at the face consisted of 152 cm split sets over wire mesh. The 30 cm nominal thickness lining was maintained about 10 m above the shaft bottom in 5 m advances.

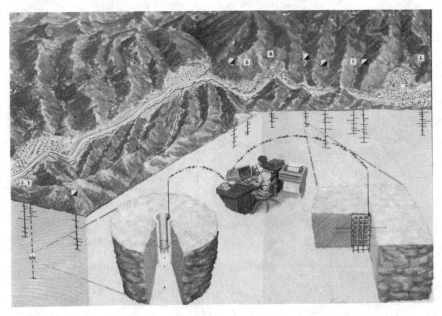

Figure 2. Conceptual drawing of the instrumentation scheme for deep shafts.

The rock around the 1,800 m level of the shaft is mainly argillitic quartzite, with medium to massive clean beds and varying amounts of interbedded argillaceous material. Most rocks belong to the St. Regis and Revett Formations of Precambrian Age. The strata strikes at about N 70° W and dips about 50° to the southwest. There are several visible shear zones and a well defined joint system. Figure 3 shows a plan view of this test site with bedding and instrument locations.

The Caladay Shaft is located at the east end of the southern extension of the district on the south side of the Osburn Fault. Existing development at the project site includes a main adit, several short crosscuts, a shaft station, and related service excavations. The shaft collar station is located 1,600 m inside the portal of the main adit, under 400 m of overburden, but still 100 m above the adjacent valley floor.

The shaft is roughly 7 m by 4 m with 30 cm x 30 cm timber sets installed on 2 m centers. Conventional drill-and-blast sinking with handheld sinkers, bench blasting, and a Cryderman mucker mounted in the center compartment is used. Shaft timber and services are advanced concurrent with sinking. Timber support is carried 6 to 8 m above the bottom, and extended in three set intervals. Initial support at the face consists of 150 cm split sets and 180 cm grouted rebar with wire mesh and matting.

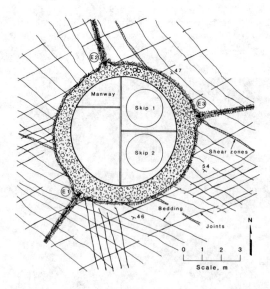

Figure 3. Plan view of the Silver Shaft test site showing orientation of the bedding and instrument locations.

The test level is at a depth of 1,450 m, between the 1,400 m and 1,500 m stations. The rock at this depth is thinly bedded argillitic quartzite with interbedded argilliceous material of the Revet Formation. The shaft end walls are parallel to the strata, which strikes at N 35° W and dips 65° to 75° northeast. There are numerous gouge-filled joints, partings, and minor faults. Figure 4 shows the overall plan with orientation of the shaft, bedding, and instrument locations.

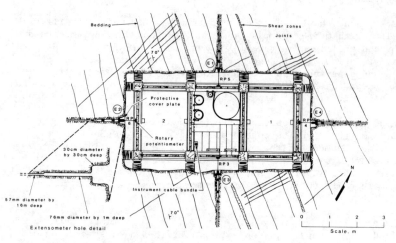

Figure 4. Plan view of the Caladay Shaft test sith with bedding, instrumentation, and extensometer hole detail.

The installation sequence followed a similar procedure for both shafts and required about 2 days. Geologic mapping was followed by locating and drilling the MPBX holes within 120 cm of the shaft bottom. The horizontal holes were oriented normal, parallel, and 45° to the bedding in the Silver Shaft and at the midpoint of the four walls in the Caladay (see figures 3 and 4). Hole depth was 16 to 20 m to provide a "zero displacement" reference. Small "dogholes" were blasted at each hole location so that the MPBX head could be recessed flush with the shaft walls. Figure 4 shows the extensometer hole detail.

After completion of the installation holes at the selected depth and orientation, the MPBX bundle was carried from the assembly site to the shaft collar, slung below the sinking bucket, and lowered down the shaft. This assembly was then guided into the hole as the bucket was slowly lowered.

The anchors were then pressurized, starting with the deepest and working inward to the shaft collar standpipe. Prior to setting the standpipe anchors, the extensometer head was adjusted to allow approximately 75 mm closure over the 100 mm range of each transducer. The flex conduit housing the MPBX signal cable was tied to the wire mesh on the shaft walls and routed to the J-box. Exposed conduit was covered with 35 mm bull hose and steel channel, and the MPBX head covered with 3/8-in aluminum plate bolted to the shaft walls for protection from blasting. Sinking began as soon as connection was made to the J-box.

RESULTS

Net displacement at each extensometer anchor location is relative to the deepest anchor, which was assumed to be stable with zero displacement. Initial data processing at the mine site provided plots of displacement versus time. This provides an immediate evaluation of the effect of shaft sinking and support at the face. Final plots are completed at the Bureau's Spokane Research Center for detailed analysis and long-term trends.

Silver Shaft

All of the MPBX's in the Silver Shaft were installed in relatively competent quartzite. Subsequent bench excavations affect corresponding MPBX's to a greater or lesser degree, depending on the proximity of the bench being excavated. By pulling 2 m rounds on alternating north and south benches, the average full-face shaft advance was about 1 m per blast.

Figures 5A, 5B, and 5C show 30-day displacements for MPBX's E1, E2, and E3, with arrows indicating blast times. Several channels were lost when flyrock from the initial blast damaged the signal cable, as can be seen on the plots. Thirty days after the installation, 5 of the original 15 MPBX channels continued to operate. From figure 5, the following observations can be made:

o Instantaneous displacements are in response to the initial blasts, decreasing as the shaft advances.

o Maximum displacement occurs at the shaft walls and decreases rapidly with depth.

o   Displacement of E2 and E3, parallel and 45° to the bedding,
    respectively, are similar.

o   Displacement of E1, normal to the bedding, is almost 6 times
    that of E2.

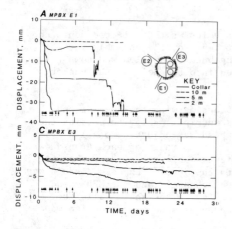

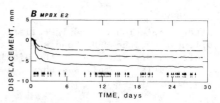

Figure 5. Thirty day
displacements for MPBX's:
(A) E1, (B) E2, and (C) E3.

Caladay Shaft

Figures 6A, 6B, 6C, and 6D show 30-day displacements for MPBX's E1,
E3, E2 and E4, respectively, including the first four excavation-
and-timber cycles, representing 23 m of shaft advance. Individual
bench rounds are discernable, with alternating large and small
jogs reflecting blasts on alternating benches directly below the
extensometers. The data gaps around the 6th and 7th blasts were DAS
malfunctions caused by overheating. The response was somewhat
similar to that seen at the Silver Shaft. Additional observations
are as follows:

o   There is significant time-dependent deformation between blasts,
    persisting throughout the period.

o   The displacement of the end walls, which are parallel to the
    bedding, are 2 to 6 times greater than the front and back wall
    extensometers.

o   While E2 and E4 have similar deformations, E1 and E3 differ
    significantly.

DATA INTERPRETATION

Observation of the shaft wall displacements indicate that movement
is a function of shaft sinking, rock mass anisotropy, and a high
stress level. The extensometers are installed 120 to 180 cm above
the shaft bottom. At a face distance of 150 cm, about 70 pct of the
displacement has already occurred, according to a recent study showing
the effects of face advance on elastic displacement (Schwartz, 1979).
Therefore, the measured component represents only about 30 pct of
the total displacement.

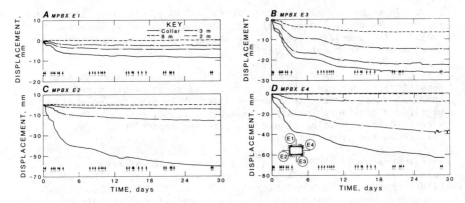

Figure 6. Thirty day displacements for MPBX's: (A) E1, (B) E3, (C) E2, and (D) E4.

Figures 7A and 7B show the displacement of the shaft wall for the first 5 days in the Silver and Caladay Shafts, respectively. In the Silver Shaft, this represents 10 drill-and-blast cycles and almost 9 m of shaft advance. Note in figure 7A that instantaneous response has amost disappeared after the first four blasts, prior to instal- lation of the liner. By the end of the 5-day period, displacement has almost stopped, with the shaft bottom about 1-1/2 diameters away.

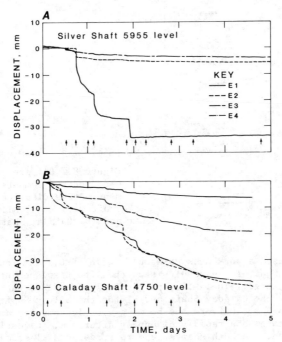

Figure 7. Five day displacements of the shaft wall - (A) Silver Shaft and (B) Caladay Shaft.

Figure 7B shows a similar trend for the Caladay, with the first 5 days representing about 7 m of shaft advance and eight drill-and-blast cycles. In contrast to the Silver Shaft, the instantaneous response is apparent throughout the period.

The stress field and rock mass anisotropy are the primary in situ conditions determining shaft response. Based on previous research, the horizontal stress field in the district is high and unequal, with magnitudes considerably larger than the vertical stress. In addition, steeply dipping bedding planes and jointing impact considerable anisotropy into the rock mass.

To illustrate the effect of in situ stress field and rock mass anisotropy, simple 2-D elastic analyses were conducted. For the Silver Shaft, a Kirsch solution was used, and for the Caladay Shaft, a boundary element solution. Figures 8A and 8B show the difference between displacements computed with elastic solutions and those actually measured for both shafts, as a function of distance into the shaft wall. The measured values are those observed after about 7 m of shaft advance, immediately before installation of internal shaft support, thus reducing the influence of differences in shaft support systems.

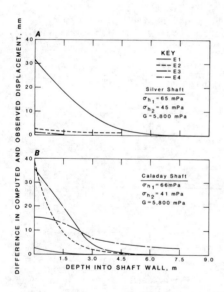

Figure 8. Difference between measured and computed displacement versus distance into the shaft wall – (A) Silver Shaft and (B) Caladay Shaft.

The analysis used a rock mass Poisson's ratio of 0.2 and Young's modulus of 14 Gpa. These results show that the displacement of the shaft wall is largely inelastic, particularly normal to the bedding (E2 and E4 for the Caladay Shaft and E1 for the Silver Shaft) and in the outer 3 to 5 m. Differences between elastic computed and actual measured displacements rapidly disappear after 5 m, suggesting that beyond this depth in both shafts, the rock responds elastically regardless of orientation. Furthermore, a zone of yielded rock is evident around both shafts.

CONCLUSIONS

The measured field data from both shafts indicates both elastic and inelastic responses, evidenced by instantaneous displacements following blasting and creep between blasts. Also, measured displacements are strongly dependent on anisotropy due to bedding. Elastic analysis shows that displacements in both shafts may be adequately predicted parallel and 45° to the bedding while displacements normal to the beds exhibit inelastic behavior.

The in situ stress field also has a significant impact on displacements and the extent of the yield zone. Rock beyond this zone behaves very much like an elastic model, regardless of orientation to the bedding. In conclusion, deformation, especially at deeper levels, is controlled by rock anisotropy at the surface of the shaft wall, and exhibits elastic behavior deeper into the shaft wall.

ACKNOWLEDGMENTS

The authors express their gratitude to officials and personnel of Hecla Mining Co. and Callahan Mining Co., particularly P. Boyko and D. England, respective project managers, and J. S. Redpath Co. and Fausett International, shaft sinking contractors, for assistance with installation of the instruments.

Further thanks goes to R. Muhs, mining engineer; B. Hand, electronic technician; G. Stone, computer specialist; J. R. McVey, supervisory electronic technician, of the Bureau's Spokane Research Center; and T. Stephenson, mining technician, of Hecla Mining Co.; for computer hardware and software development, data processing, and assistance with instrument preparation and installation.

REFERENCES

McKinstry, B. A., 1983, Sinking the Silver Shaft, Proc. 1983 RETC, Vol. 1, Chicago, IL, June 12-16, 1983, pp. 493-512.

Board, M. P., and M. J. Beus, 1984, Instrumentation and Preliminary Analysis of a 6,200-Ft Deep Circular Shaft in Northern Idaho, Proc. Geomechanics Applications in Underground Hardrock Mining Symposium SME-AIME Fall Mtg., Denver, CO, September 23-26, 1984, pp. 127-140.

Schwartz, C. W., and H. H. Einstein, 1979, Simplified Analysis for Ground Structure Interaction in Tunneling, MIT Technical Report R79-27, prepared for U.S. Department of Transportation.

Development of a geo-numerical model as an aid in stope design

R.PAKALNIS & H.D.S.MILLER
University of British Columbia, Vancouver, Canada
T.MADILL
Ruttan Mine, Sherritt Gordon Mines Ltd, Leaf Rapids, Manitoba, Canada

1. ABSTRACT

Rock mass classification is a widely used tool in the field of Civil Geo-Technical Engineering. It is only recently that it is being applied in the design of mining structures. This paper describes recent studies that empirically attempt to relate optimum stope geometries to the rock quality and the stress configuration that surrounds individual stopes. The dominant dilution sensitive factors were evaluated and incorporated into guidelines enabling preliminary estimates of stope dimensions to be made. The empirical data base, at this stage, is composed of eighteen (18) stopes yielding dilution figures (200) at various stages of extraction. This study is presently confined to the Ruttan Mine, Sherritt Gordon Mines Ltd., a 6,000 T.P.D. underground operation located in Northern Manitoba, Canada.

The mining method employed is transverse open stoping with delayed backfill and extends from surface to 860m below surface. Approximately sixty stopes (1,000 dilution records) will ultimately form the data base that will reinforce and confirm the concepts initially presented in this paper.

Optimum stope configuration is defined by the authors as that yielding a minimal acceptable stope dilution. The following relationships are discussed with respect to the Ruttan Deposit:
.Dilution versus rock mass rating
.Dilution versus excavation rate
.Dilution versus shape of individual stopes
.Dilution versus stope volume excavated.

2. INTRODUCTION

There exists no accepted design methods for predicting optimum stope dimensions in jointed materials. Beam theories, numerical methods and empirical criteria have been employed in the past to some degree of success. The major drawback is that many of our classical approaches to opening design have been based on assuming that homogeneous, isotropic, elastic conditions exist.

The elastic beam and plate solutions (Evans 1940) are based on concepts derived from solid mechanics. They assume that the rock above the excavation behaves as a series of elastic beams or plates loaded by self-weight. The roof span is designed based on, not exceeding, the tensile strength of the beam. A further modification is the voussoir beam which recognizes that cross joints may exist within the beam and consequently, may not allow tensile stresses to develop. The voussoir beam is assumed to be supported by an arching action which results in a lateral thrust being applied to the individual blocks forming the beam. Overall stability is controlled by ensuring that the individual blocks are under a sufficiently high state of confinement and therefore are prevented from falling out. Numerical codes (Mathews 1981), such as finite and boundary element methods, would delineate critical stress areas surrounding an excavation. Tensile stresses in the back would be analogous to a zone of relaxation enabling structural blocks to fall out. High compressive stresses in the back may result in buckling or shear failure.

The above use of analytical methods in stope design is best summarized by Mathews (1981) whereby "in general the number of variables to be considered is too high to permit other than empirical approaches to stope design. However, analytical methods are often used to identify excessive stress conditions or excessive deformations".

Empirical design methods relate practical experience gained on past projects to the conditions anticipated at a proposed site. Rock mass classifications (Bieniawski 1983) have been successfully employed in the overall design of civil engineering structures since the late 1940's. They are based on empirical methods of design and have been derived from numerous field measurements and observations. Rock mass classification systems have evolved from the need to relate rock substance properties to those of the jointed rock mass.

This paper will expand on the use of an integrated approach to the design of optimum stope dimensions based on the rock quality and the resultant stress configuration surrounding an individual stope. Optimum is defined as that stope configuration that would result in a minimal acceptable dilution. Dilution sensitive parameters, such as blasting, excavation rate, among others, will be assessed in terms of arriving at optimum stope design guidelines. This approach relies heavily on geological and numerical modelling and subsequently, the term "Geo-Numerical Modelling" will be employed to identify the relationship between the two. The study will be confined to the Ruttan operation of Sherritt Gordon Mines Ltd. The mine provides a large data base encompassing sixty stopes with approximately 1,000 dilution measurements recorded at various stages of stope excavation.

3. BACKGROUND

The Ruttan Mine of Sherritt Gordon Mines Ltd., a 6,000 T.P.D. undergound operation is located in Northern Manitoba, Canada. The Ruttan copper-zinc orebody is a multi-lensed, steeply dipping (70°) en echelon deposit (fig. 1). Individual lenses have a maximum strike length of 350m with widths varying from 7 to 61m. The mining method is open stoping with delayed backfilling and extends from surface to the 860m below surface.

This mining research is a result of a joint effort between the University of British Columbia and Sherritt Gordon Mines Ltd. with the objective of better understanding the mechanisms involved in the design of large open stopes.

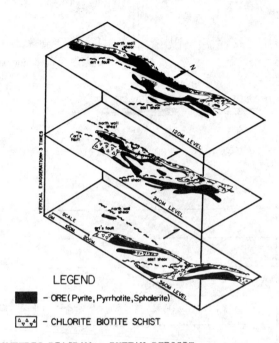

FIGURE 1 ISOMETRIC DIAGRAM - RUTTAN DEPOSIT

Stope spans at the Ruttan Mine were designed initially employing classical beam theory. Failures at the mine were found to be controlled primarily by structure, and could not be explained by the previous homogeneous model. Figure 2 is a plot of stress trajectories surrounding the mined out stopes on the 320m level. It is evident from this figure that the hanging and footwall of most stopes is in a state of relaxation and consequently, allowing structural blocks to fall out.

The absence of a confining stress, coupled with a foliated wall contact, enabled one to arrive at a relationship which showed that a higher dilution resulted when stopes having poorer rock mass rating were mined (fig. 3).

4. INTERGRATED APPROACH TO DESIGN

A rock mass rating patterned after the CSIR system (Bieniawski 1983) has been applied to the footwall, ore and hangingwall of each

1175

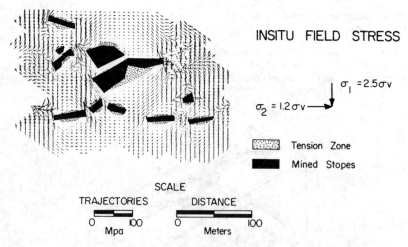

INSITU FIELD STRESS

$\sigma_1 = 2.5\sigma v$

$\sigma_2 = 1.2\sigma v$

░ Tension Zone

■ Mined Stopes

SCALE

TRAJECTORIES   DISTANCE

0   100   0   100
Mpa   Meters

FIGURE 2 STRESS TRAJECTORIES SURROUNDING STOPES ON 320M LEVEL,
PLAN VIEW

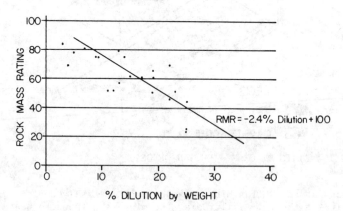

$RMR = -2.4\% \text{ Dilution} + 100$

% DILUTION by WEIGHT

FIGURE 3 PLOT OF ROCK MASS RATING VS HANGINGWALL DILUTION - RUTTAN
MINE - 30 STOPES

individual stope at the Ruttan Mine. Figure 4 shows a typical stope
layout which is complicated by the en echelon nature of the deposit.

Dilution measurements were subsequently compiled for all stopes at
various stages of extraction. Dilution is defined as the weight per
cent of tons slough to the reserves mined. It is this value that is
correlated to the stope volume excavated in evaluating the most
dilution sensitive parameters. Due to the complex stope interaction,
one has to further analyze the following cases individually:

.Isolated Stope - No other stopes in vicinity
.Rib Stope - Other stopes exist along strike
.Echelon Stope - Other stopes exist along strike and dip

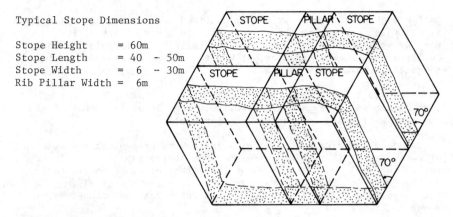

Typical Stope Dimensions

Stope Height   = 60m
Stope Length   = 40 – 50m
Stope Width   = 6 – 30m
Rib Pillar Width = 6m

FIGURE 4 TYPICAL EN ECHELON STOPE CONFIGURATION

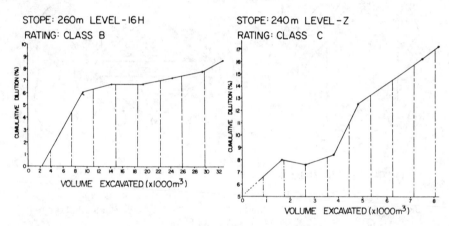

STOPE: 260m LEVEL-16H
RATING: CLASS B

STOPE: 240m LEVEL-Z
RATING: CLASS C

FIGURE 5 CUMULATIVE DILUTION VERSUS VOLUME EXCAVATED

The findings presented in this paper relate solely to the isolated case. Since, at present, only eighteen stopes have been evaluated, it is not possible to determine the effect of mining on rib and echelon configurations.

Figure 5 is a typical plot showing the relationship between cumulative dilution versus the volume excavated for a particular stope. The rock mass rating is further grouped into the following cases:

Class	Rock Mass Rating
A	80 – 100%
B	60 – 80
C	40 – 60
D	20 – 40
E	0 – 20

Wall slough at Ruttan is primarily confined to the hanging wall. It
is for this reason that the rock quality in the vicinity of the
hanging wall will be employed in characterizing an individual stope.
In certain instances, however, it was found that an assessment of the
footwall is more critical when:

.A major fault intercepts the footwall
.The rock mass rating of the footwall is much lower than that of the
 hanging wall (one class or more difference).

It was also found that an initial dilution was present at low volumes
of excavation. This value was higher for stopes exhibiting a lower
rock mass quality. Figure 6 shows the effect of stope configuration
on the extent of the zone of relaxation. A slot is initially
excavated from footwall to hanging wall which has the dimensions
shown in figure 6.

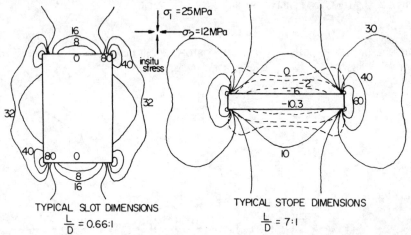

FIGURE 6 MINOR (DASHED) AND MAJOR (SOLID) STRESS CONTOURS SURROUNDING
        INDIVIDUAL STOPES AT RUTTAN - PLAN VIEW

The slot excavated exposes mininal wall contact under the most
favourable confining conditions. It is therefore of the authors'
opinion that the initial dilution is a combination of blast induced
damage and recording error. This initial value was subtracted from
the subsequent dilution figures recorded to result in a corrected
dilution reading.

A strong correlation existed between corrected dilution and the rate
of excavation as shown in figure 7.

It is evident from figure 7 that an accelerated rate of mining would
yield a lower dilution for a particular stope volume. Further, it has
been found that the more competent the rock quality of a given stope,
        the less sensitive dilution is to the excavation rate.

Figure 8 shows that the dilution is not particularly sensitive to the
stope configuration for the isolated case. This is partly explained
by figure 9, whereby for typical stope geometries employed at Ruttan,

the hanging and footwall will always be in a state of relaxation. The extent of the wall slough will always be contained within this tensile zone for stope span/width ratios indicated in figure 8.

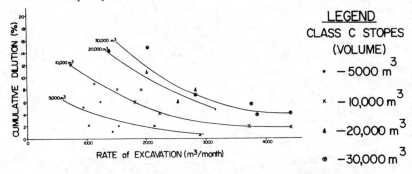

FIGURE 7 CUMULATIVE DILUTION VERSUS RATE OF EXCAVATION

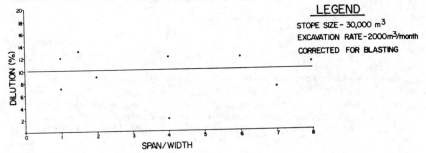

FIGURE 8 CUMULATIVE DILUTION VERSUS STOPE GEOMETRY

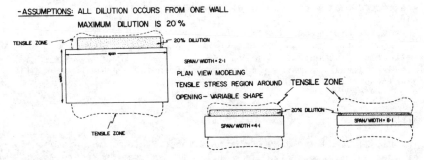

FIGURE 9 EFFECT OF TENSILE ZONE ON RESULTANT DILUTION

Based upon the observations obtained from eighteen stopes (200 dilution records) the authors were able to arrive at the following conceptual relationship, figure 10.

Note that figure 10 was found to be valid for a particular excavation rate only. The design curves have been successfully employed in the prediction of dilutions for future stopes that have subsequently been mined.

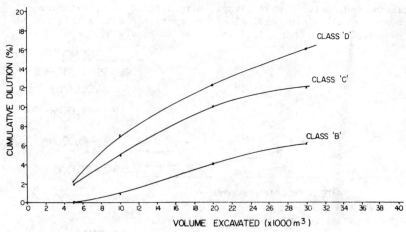

FIGURE 10 DESIGN CURVES - EXCAVATION RATE = $2,000m^3$/MONTH
- CORRECTED FOR BLASTING

5. SUMMARY AND CONCLUSION

The concepts presented were found to better equip the designer to predict resultant dilutions, given a particular stope configuration and characterization. In addition, through the modification of design and mining procedures, one can derive optimum stope dimensions given an acceptable level of dilution. The authors are extending and verifying the above observations through the analysis of a further forty stopes. This data base will be supplemented with data obtained from other large open stoping operations.

It is expected that with the larger data base, the following may be evaluated:
.The effect of mining depth on dilution
.The effect of rib and echelon stope geometries on dilution
.The effect of fill on dilution
.Relate dilution in terms of a stope span dimension rather than an all encompassing volume expression.

6. REFERENCES

Bieniawski, Z. T. 1983. Rock Classifications: State of the Art and and prospects for standardization. U. S. Transportation Record 783.

Evans, W. H. 1940. The Strength of Undermined Strata. Trans. Instn. Min. Metall. 1150:475-532

Mathews, K. 1981. Prediction of Stable Excavation Spans For Mining at Depths Below 1,000m in Hard Rock. Canmet No. 05Q80-00081.

An in situ technique for the assessment of failure in coal pillars

JAMES J.SNODGRASS
Denver Research Center, Bureau of Mines, US Department of the Interior, Colorado, USA
DAVID A.NEWMAN
Department of Mining Engineering, University of Kentucky, Lexington, USA

ABSTRACT

A coal pillar is comprised of two distinct zones, a solid elastic core enclosed and confined by an exterior of failed or yielded coal. Initially the elastic core-yield zone boundary is located immediately adjacent to the pillar edge. As the pillar load increases, the boundary migrates towards the center of the pillar, ultimately culminating in pillar failure. The ability to delineate the elastic core-yield zone boundary in the field is therefore of fundamental importance.

A dry-hole, sonic velocity logging probe previously developed by Bureau of Mines research was used to define the boundary on the basis of sonic velocity profiles. Underground trials were carried out in a coal pillar in a room-and-pillar mine in Utah and in a longwall section in northern West Virginia. The in situ sonic velocity obtained using the probe was demonstrated to be a valid indicator of the extent of pillar failure. The probe enables the routine determination of the boundary between the failed and stable regions of a pillar.

INTRODUCTION

Research on the stability of coal pillars initiated by Bunting (6) (Numbers in parentheses refer to items in the list of references at the end of this report.) has received prominent attention in U.S. coal mining throughout this century. Most of the approaches developed so far are based on strength-and-size or strength-and-shape relationships as summarized by Hustrulid (10), or on Wilson's (20) "confined pillar core" concept.

An alternate method of chain pillar design was implemented by Choi et al. (7), Dahl (8), and Serata et al. (16) to improve the ground conditions through a redistribution of the stresses surrounding the entries. The method, shown in Figure 1, incorporates "stiff" and "yielding" pillars into the panel layout. The yielding pillars are assumed to undergo progressive but controlled failure in which the pillar initially fails at the edge where the stress concentration is highest and failure progresses inward to the center of the pillar. The core of the yielding pillar is confined by the failed material and therefore subjected to a triaxial state of stress as indicated in Figure 2. Since the distribution of pillar stress is nonuniform and the pillar is comprised of both intact and failed coal, the analysis of stability is complicated.

Lu (13) of the Bureau of Mines proposed a novel approach called "regressive integrity factor" as a parameter for evaluating retreating-longwall chain-pillar stability. He defined the integrity factor as the ratio of the integrated total strength to the integrated total load across the pillar profile. However, most of the conventional approaches to the design and analysis of stability for yielding coal pillars are ultimately dependent upon the ability to locate the boundary between the failed or yielded coal and the intact, elastic core. Although the presence of yielded or failed coal adjacent to the pillar edge is readily apparent to the eye, the accurate delineation of the boundary separating the yielded and elastic zones requires "precise instrumentation" (20). Methods used to delineate the yield zone-elastic core boundary in coal

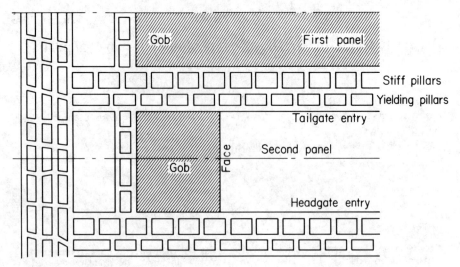

Figure 1. The "Stiff-Yielding" System of Longwall Chain Pillar Design (Dahl and Von Schonfeldt, 1977).

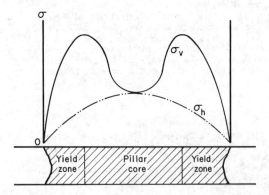

Figure 2. Example of a Theoretical Stress Profile for a Coal Pillar.

pillars have included an air injection technique (2) and the use of a magnetic rod extensometer (11), both of which require substantial time and effort to prepare the field site, install the equipment, and perform the measurements.

Geophysical techniques for rock mass evaluation and failed-zone determination have recently been investigated (1,3,4,12) and proposed for use in evaluating coal pillar stability. In these studies the compressional and shear wave velocities, amplitudes, and frequencies were used to indicate rock mass condition. Hanson et al. (9) measured velocities and attenuation of ultrasonic vibrations in coal samples under different applied loads before and after failure. They determined that attenuation is a sensitive measure of the difference between intact and failed coal, but the velocity data were inconclusive owing to lack of experimental resolution.

This report describes the results of research to verify the sonic velocity measurements as a relatively rapid and practical means to assess coal pillar stability. A dry-hole, full-waveform, sonic logging probe was used to determine the compressional and shear wave velocities as a function of horizontal distance from the rib and as the face approached the instrumented pillar. The sonic measurement data were compared with pillar stress measurements from a field study performed concurrently by the Department of Mineral Engineering, Pennsylvania State University, in a longwall coal mine (14).

DEVELOPMENT OF THE DRY-HOLE SONIC LOGGING PROBE

The dry-hole sonic logging probe was designed and built by Southwest Research Institute under a Bureau of Mines research contract (18). The probe is a hydraulically operated, wall-clamping device with dual-spaced receivers capable of selectively monitoring compressional and shear wave particle motion. The operational specifications of the borehole probe, the control, the receiver, and the transmitter modules are described elsewhere (17,18).

Although the probe may be used in fluid-filled holes, its primary advantage is for use in dry holes. The interpretation of the shear wave velocity is greatly simplified in a dry hole because the tube, Stonely, and fluid waves commonly observed in a fluid-filled borehole are not present to obscure the P and S waveforms. The device was initially devised for downhole sonic velocity measurements; however, it is nonetheless capable of similar measurements in horizontal boreholes.

The initial application of the probe was to determine the height of the caving associated with a longwall panel in New Mexico (17). The criterion for delineating between the caved and intact rock mass was an apparent change in the average elastic wave velocity which could be attributable to the presence of dilated cracks. From the velocity log, a zone of low velocity, high attenuation, and poor quality records was observed to occur approximately 18 m above the coal seam.

The probe has two receiver transducers located 1.8 m and 1.2 m respectively from the transmitter. Velocity measurements were recorded at 0.6-m intervals so that continuity of the log would be assured in the event of poor coupling between the probe and the borehole wall at one location. Using this technique, a rate of 8 m/h was achieved; clamping and unclamping of the probe accounted for the majority of this time.

UNDERGROUND TRIALS OF THE BOREHOLE PROBE

An underground room-and-pillar coal mine in Utah was the site of the first underground trial of the borehole probe. The objective of this trial was to ascertain the depth of failure in a pillar which was visibly spalling into the adjacent entries. A 10-cm-diameter borehole was drilled into the coal pillar to provide access for the probe. The probe was inserted to the bottom of the borehole so that the transmitting transducer was 5.2 m from the collar of the hole. Velocity measurements were recorded at 0.3-m intervals as the probe was pulled out of the borehole.

The shear wave velocities were plotted against depth into the pillar as shown in Figure 3. From the figure it is apparent that a region of reduced velocity occurs to approximately 1.0 m from the edge of the pillar. The velocity tends to increase with depth into the pillar with an anomalous peak at 2.6 m. The factors that affect the propagation velocity of elastic waves in rock are lithology, texture, density, porosity, water content, temperature, anisotropy, and stress. During the time interval of the measurements all of the aforementioned parameters except density and stress can be assumed to have remained constant. As the pillar failure propagates inward from pillar edge, the density of the coal may decrease slightly, but most importantly, the stress distribution across the pillar changes dramatically.

The stress distribution across a coal pillar has been previously investigated (5,19) and was observed to be highly nonuniform because the pillar core was confined by the failed perimeter. The stress distribution generally would be expected to be higher in the stable pillar core.

The effect of stress on elastic wave velocity is directly related to the closure and dilation of pre-existing defects and discontinuities. For coal, three sets of mutually orthogonal discontinuities are present, the face and butt cleats, and horizontal bedding planes. As the load on the coal pillar is increased, the bedding planes should close, increasing the elastic wave velocity in a vertical direction through the pillar. The increase in vertical pressure causes an increase in lateral deformation. The pillar deformation may dilate the coal cleat, resulting in lower velocities in a horizontal direction. However, this is true only if the pillar is unconfined. Since the interior of the pillar remains intact, the elastic wave velocity would be expected to increase toward the center of the pillar.

To further evaluate the capability of the borehole probe in delineating the boundary between the failed and stable regions, a second trial was carried out at a mine in northern West Virginia. The trial was conducted in a chain pillar along the headgate of an active longwall panel.

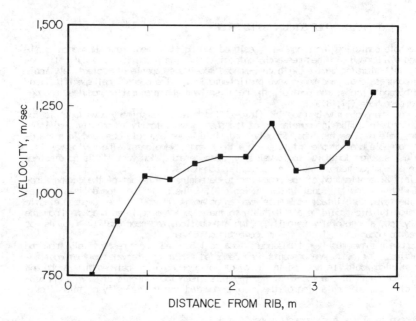

Figure 3. Shear Wave Velocity versus Depth in a Coal Pillar - Utah Mine Site.

The objective of this trial was to correlate the change in pillar stress with the location of the elastic core-yield zone boundary as the longwall face retreated towards an instrumented pillar. The pillar was instrumented with vibrating-wire stress meters (VWS) to record the change in vertical stress at various locations within the pillar. A 10-cm-diameter borehole was drilled 7.0 m into the pillar. The layout of the instrumented pillar is shown in Figure 4. The borehole was drilled and the VWS gages were installed in the pillar when the face was 220 m inby the near pillar edge. An initial velocity profile was constructed along the length of the borehole to establish the extent of failure prior to the influence of the side abutment pressure associated with the presence of the longwall face.

A second velocity profile was constructed when the longwall face was 4.6 m inby the near pillar edge. This profile enabled the determination of the elastic core-yield zone boundary in the pillar. The VWS gages were read throughout the interim period between the first and second profiles. The readings continued as the longwall face passed the instrumented pillar and terminated when rib falls had permanently damaged the lead wires.

A typical set of waveforms are illustrated in Figure 5 where the velocity records for the shear wave channel of the far receiver are shown for the second trial. The velocities were calculated using the following equations:

$$V_{far} = \frac{1.8}{t_1} \text{ m/s}$$

$$V_{near} = \frac{1.2}{t_2} \text{ m/s}$$

$$V_{interval} = \frac{(0.6)}{(t_2 - t_1)} \text{ m/s}$$

where V_{far} is the velocity for the receiver farthest from the transmitter,
   V_{near} is the velocity for the receiver nearest the transmitter,
   $V_{interval}$ is the interval velocity between receivers
   t_1 is the travel time between the transmitter and the near receiver,
   t_2 is the travel time between the transmitter and the far receiver.

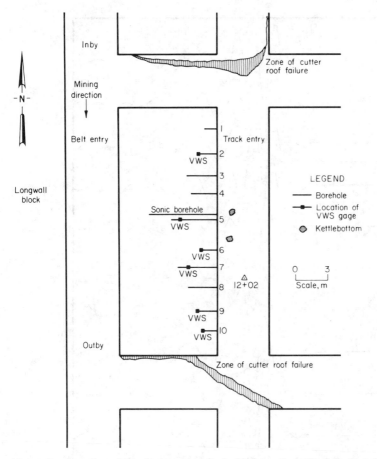

Figure 4. Geometry of the Instrumented Chain Pillar – West Virginia Mine Site.

Figure 6 shows the first and second velocity profiles plotted together to more clearly illustrate changes in velocity with depth into the pillar, and between the different measurement dates.

DISCUSSION

From Figure 6, two observations are immediately apparent. First, shear wave velocity increases to a peak approximately 0.6 m into the pillar for both trials. This suggests that a zone of failure existed in the pillar prior to the influence of the longwall face. The boundary of the elastic core-yield zone did not change as the face retreated towards the instrumented pillar.

Second, in both trials the velocity decreased from the peak at 0.6 m with depth into the pillar, which is opposite to the previous observation in the Utah mine but consistent with the pillar model of stress distribution. The velocity profiles for the two trials in general parallel each other, with the higher values for the second profile indicating the effect of increased pressure due to the proximity of the longwall face.

The change in vertical pillar stress measured using the VWS gages was examined to see whether the stress distribution across the pillar could explain the observed decrease in velocity with depth into the pillar. The stress change for each gage with

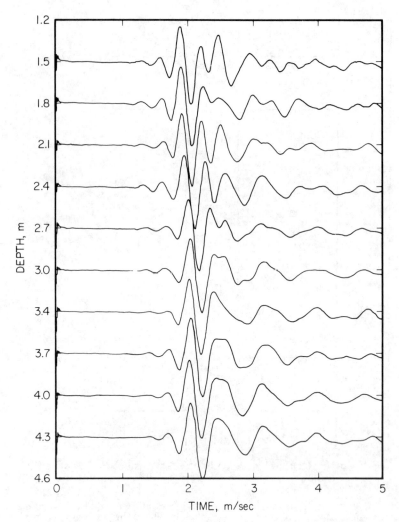

Figure 5. Plot of Full Waveform Recordings versus Depth in the Chain Pillar.

respect to the distance between the gage and the longwall face is plotted in Figure 7. These data and the depths of the WWS gages (Figure 4) suggest higher increases in vertical stress near the pillar perimeter, particularly hole 10, but the data are inconsistent because of the lateral separation of the gages.

During the interval between the two trials, the location of the elastic core-yield zone boundary (region of velocity change) did not migrate toward the pillar interior. The distribution of the in situ velocities and the change in pillar stress suggest that the instrumented pillar did not behave as a true yield pillar since no evidence of progressive failure was observed either visually or through use of the dry-hole probe until the longwall face had retreated outby.

CONCLUSION

The trials of the dry-hole sonic logging probe have demonstrated that the extent of

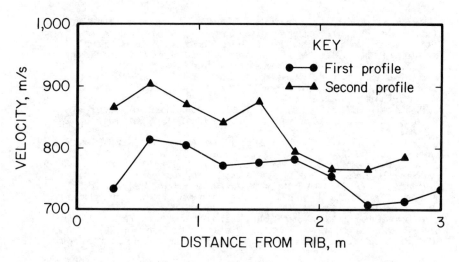

Figure 6. Shear Wave Velocity versus Depth in the Chain Pillar.

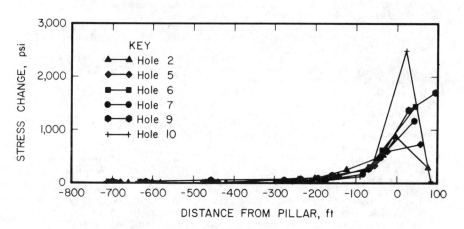

Figure 7. Change in Vertical Pillar Stress as a Function of Distance Between the WWS Gage and the Longwall Face.

pillar failure can be delineated by monitoring changes in elastic wave velocity. The probe provides a relatively rapid means of assessing pillar stability and can be used to monitor progressive failure. During the in-mine trials, elastic wave velocity was found to change with abutment stress as the longwall face approached the pillar. Further research is recommended to establish more specifically correlative relationships between velocity and stress.

REFERENCES

1. Allison, H. and Lama, R.D. (1979). "Low Frequency Sounding Technique for Predicting Failure of Rock", Rock Mech., Vol. 12, pp. 79–97.

2. Barron, K., Wright, P.L., and Smales, T. (1983). "Guidelines for the Design of Coal Pillars in the #7 Seam at McIntyre Mines, LTD., Grande Cache, Alberta," Proc. 1st Conf. on Underground Stability in Mining, Vancouver, AIME, pp. 559-572.

3. Belesky, R.M. (1981). "An In-Situ Assessment of Deformability and Strength of Coal Pillars," M.S. Thesis, The Pennsylvania State University, 275 p.

4. Bieniawski, Z.T. (1978). "The "Petite Sismique" Technique —A Review of Current Developments," Proc. 2nd Conf. on AE/MS Activities in Geologic Structures and Materials, Pennsylvania State University.

5. Bieniawski, Z.T. and Vogler, W.V. (1979). "Load-Deformation Behavior of Coal After Failure," Proc. 2nd Int. Congr. on Rock Mech., ISRM, Belgrade, Vol. 2, Pap. 12, pp. 345-351.

6. Bunting, D. (1911). "Chamber Pillars in Deep Anthracite Mines," Trans. AIME, Vol. 42, pp. 236-245.

7. Choi, D.S., Dahl, H.D., and Von Schonfeldt, H. (1975). "Design of Longwall Development Headings," SME-AIME Trans., Vol. 258, pp. 358-363.

8. Dahl, H.D. (1978). "The State of the Art in Underground Coal Mine Design," Proc. 1st Int. Symp. on Stability in Coal Mining, Vancouver, Brawner and Dorling eds., Miller Freeman, pp. 125-134.

9. Hanson, D.R., Shea, V.R., and Holub, R.F. (1985). "Investigation of Acoustic Wave Propagation and Methane Emission To Determine the Extent of Yielded Material in Coal Pillars," Progress Report No. 10057, Denver Research Center, Bureau of Mines, 35 p.

10. Hustrulid, W.A. (1976). "A Review of Coal Pillar Strength Formulas", Rock Mech., Vol. 8, pp. 115-145.

11. Issac, A.K., Nicholas, P.K. and Smart, B.G.D. (1984). "An Improved Technique of In-Situ Measurement of Fracture Zones Surrounding Coal Mine Gateroads," Proc. 25th U.S. Symp. on Rock Mech., Northwestern Univ., AIME, New York.

12. King, M.S. and Paulsson, B.N.P. (1982). "Acoustic Borehole Logged in a Granitic Rock Mass Subjected to Heating," Proc. 23rd U.S. Symp. on Rock Mech., Berkley, AIME, New York, pp. 39-46.

13. Lu, P.H. (1983). "Stability Evaluation of Retreating-Longwall Chain Pillars With Regressive Integrity Factors", Proc. 5th Congr. on Rock Mech., ISRM, Melbourne, Australia, A.A. Balkema/Netherlands, pp. E37-E40.

14. Newman, D. A. (1985). "The Design of Coal Mine roof Support and Yielding Pillars for Longwall Mining In the Appalachian Coal Field," Ph.D. Dissertation, the Pennsylvania State University, University Park, PA, p. 400.

15. Schneider, B. (1967). "Contribution a l'etude des Massifs de Foundation de Barrages," Travaux du Laboratoire de Geologie de la Faculte de Sciences de Grenoble, Memoires No. 7, Grenoble, 241 p.

16. Serata, S., Carr, F., and Martin, E. (1984). "Stress Control Method Applied to Stabilization of Underground Coal Mine Openings," Proc. 25th U.S. Symp. on Rock Mech., Northwestern University.

17. Snodgrass, J.J. (1982). "A New Sonic Velocity Logging Techniques and Results in Near-Surface Sediments of Northwestern New Mexico," TFR 117, Bureau of Mines, 24 p.

18. Suhler, S.A., Peters, W.R. and Schroeder, E. (1979). "Dry Hole Acoustic Velocity Probe and Control Module," Final Technical Report and Instructional Manual, DOE Contract No. ET-76-C-01-9130, Southwest Research Institute, 130 p.

19. Wagner, H. (1974). "Determination of the Complete Load-Deformation Characteristics of Coal Pillars," Proc. 3rd Int. Congr. on Rock Mech., ISRM, Denver, pp. 1076-1081.

20. Wilson, A.H. (1981). "Stress and Stability in Coal Ribsides and Pillars," Proc. 1st Conf. on Ground Control, West Virginia Univ., pp. 1-12.

ICBM deep basing construction planning study

PATRICK D.LINDSEY
US Army Corps of Engineers, Omaha District, Nebraska, USA

BACKGROUND

In support of the Air Force's ICBM Deep Basing Construction Planning Study, the Omaha District Corps of Engineers has developed a method for analyzing the construction of tunnels, shafts, and chambers rapidly. During the deep basing construction planning studies, three planning documents were developed: a construction methods report, a cost model technical manual, and a cost and schedule model.

CONSTRUCTION METHODS

The construction methods report was developed to allow a planner to rapidly select an excavation method, mucking system and initial support system from decision charts. Tunnels, shafts and chambers were classified by length, type of bends, grade and size as shown in figure 1. The selection charts developed indicate the first, second, and third choice of an excavation method, mucking system, and support system for various generic rock properties. The methods and systems were developed for rock mass properties falling into three categories of rock strengths and rock conditions. The rock strength categories used were moderately soft or weathered 6.9 to 34.5 MPa (1 to 5 ksi), medium hard 34.5 to 96.5 MPa (5 to 14 Ksi), and hard 96.5 to 172.4 MPa (14 to 25 ksi). The rock condition categories used were massive thick bedded; 75 to 100 RQD, foliated thin bedded; 50 to 75 RQD, and weathered, altered or sheared; less than 50 RQD. Plates 1, 2, and 3 are three examples of the 16 selection charts developed for excavation methods, mucking, and support systems.

After the construction methods were selected from the charts fleet combinations were analyzed using several microcomputer BASIC programs for systems consisting of: TBM's and trains, loaders and haulers, hoisting for deep shafts and roadheader advance rates with support installation. These programs are cycle time calculators that allows the analyst or planner to adjust activity durations or resources and fine tune the selected systems.

Another program was developed to analyze the amortization cost for unique pieces of equipment, for which a historical cost is not available. The program output consists of a cost per foot of tunnel based on expected working efficiencies and machine utilizations.

Excavation Categories

Type of Tunnel	Min Length m(ft)	Max Length m(ft)
Very Long	1609(5280)	+
Long	610(2000)	1609(5280)
Medium	152(500)	610(2000)
Short	18(60)	152(500)
Very Short	0	18(60)
Dead End	0	610(2000)

Isolated Systems (groups of connected tunnels)

	Min Grade (%)	Max Grade (%)
Horizontal	0	2
Sloping	2+	32.5
Mild Bends - radius +152m(500 ft)		

Shafts		
Inclined	32.5+	-Vertical
Vertical		±Vertical

Intersections
Right Angle
"Y"

Chambers

Special Openings

Figure 1. Excavation Categories

TUNNEL SUPPORT SELECTION

Plate 3 shows a support selection chart based on a modified combination of the Q and RMR rock mass classification systems. Five support categories are defined by evaluating the rock mass strength, joint spacing, and joint condition. Note that moderately soft rock of good quality has been grouped with hard rock of poor quality and medium hard rock of fair quality. The basis for these groupings is the assumption that a similar amount of rock yield will occur within each rock category. Rock quality is determined by considering joint condition and joint spacing. A good quality rock has been defined as having widely spaced joints that are in good condition; a fair quality rock has been defined as having widely spaced joints that

1190

are in a bad condition; and a poor quality rock has been defined as having closely spaced joints in bad condition.

Joint spacings of 2 feet or greater are considered to be wide, while a joint spacing of 6 inches is close. The joint condition is related to the joint roughness, joint width, continuity of the joint, properties of the gouge materials, and joint weathering. A good joint condition is moderately rough, tight, and unweathered. A bad joint would have slickensided surfaces, be in an open condition filled with weak gouge materals or highly weathered rock that would have low joint shear strength.

Since this method was developed for planning studies when little rock data will be available, it must be realized that actual rock conditions may fall between the extremes sited above, therefore, this method of categorizing rock types is subjective and must be used with judgement.

COST AND SCHEDULE METHODOLOGY

Plate 4 shows the methodology of the costing and scheduling for the project. Cost and advance rate data was developed by modifying data generated by the COSTUN program which duplicates the logic of a tunneling takeoff and provides costs for equipment, labor, and materials. Costs were generated in 1982 dollars using a 30 percent overhead and 10 percent profit, and can be modified by using Engineering News Record Indexes. The data base of costs were graphed in the Cost Model Technical Manual for TBM, Drill/Blast, roadheaders, and raise boring excavation methods; and for conveyor, train, load haul dump, truck and hoisting mucking systems. Support materials such as rockbolts, concrete linings, and backpacking concrete are plotted for various spacings and thicknesses versus tunnel diameter.

Once the underground site layout and geology have been developed, the construction methods report is used to select excavation mucking and support methods. Each underground cavity is costed and provided with a duration by using the cost model technical manual charts, while resources are then developed to match the COSTUN advance rates and applied to the activities scheduled on a CPM network for analysis.

The Project/2 program was selected to develop planning schedules, cash flow analysis, resource scheduling, and restrained schedule analysis. Network analysis was used to find scheduling bottlenecks created by resource availability constraints such as batch plant capacity or maximum muck removal rates. Since resources were applied as quantities or as rates the project end dates could be recalculated based on restrained resource levels. This would force a redistribution of resource usage to activities with the highest criticality (most negative value) and recalculate a project completion date.

The results of this simplified approach have compared favorably to the cost estimates performed by a standard estimating takeoff, and the accuracy of the cost data has been compared to 157 tunneling and shaft projects and consistently yields reasonable results.

CONCLUSIONS

Since the construction methods for this study are based on generic rock properties the decision charts and procedures developed can be applied to any underground construction project. Good results were experienced by the Omaha District when using this method on the Gregory County Underground Powerhouse Study to determine project costs and schedules. While each project may have some unique features the cost data base and construction methods can be used with minor modifications on any underground project. The only item not covered in the manuals on the Gregory County Study was material rippability and ripping costs.

The Omaha District believes that the data developed during the ICBM Deep Basing Construction Planning Study will have applicability to any underground construction project that requires a rapid assessment of project feasibility.

ACKNOWLEDGEMENT

The author would like to acknowledge the sponsorship and direction provided by the Air Force Ballistic Missile Office and the Air Force Regional Civil Engineer for Ballistic Missile Support. Especially Captain John Selstrom for his outstanding efforts in coordinating the Air Force and Corps of Engineers groups.

Basic Rock Properties				Tunnel Cross Section and Dimensions			Excavation Methods
Rock Type	Unconfined Compressive Strength	Rock Condition	Rock Quality Index (RQD)	Shape	Size	Length, Bends	
Medium Hard Rock	(34.5 to 96.5 MPa)	Massive, Thick Bedded	75 or greater	Circular	Greater than 10.7 m	VLG, LG, STR, MD	DB
						MEDIUM, SHORT	DB
						VERY SHORT	DB
					Less than 10.7 m	VLG, LG, STR, MD	TBM
						MEDIUM, SHORT	• SRH, • MBRH, DB
						VERY SHORT	• SRH, DB
				Noncircular	Height greater than 6m Width greater than 8.9 m	VLG, LG, STR, MD	DB, RH2
						MEDIUM, SHORT	DB, RH2
						VERY SHORT	DB, RH2
					Height less than 6 m Width less than 8.9 m	VLG, LG, STR, MD	• RH, DB
						MEDIUM, SHORT	• RH, DB
						VERY SHORT	• RH, DB
		Foliated, Thin Bedded	50 to 75	Circular	Greater than 10.7 m	VLG, LG, STR, MD	DB
						MEDIUM, SHORT	DB
						VERY SHORT	DB
					Less than 10.7 m	VLG, LG, STR, MD	TBM
						MEDIUM, SHORT	• SRH, DB
						VERY SHORT	• SRH, DB
				Noncircular	Height greater than 6 m Width greater than 8.9 m	VLG, LG, STR, MD	DB
						MEDIUM, SHORT	DB
						VERY SHORT	DB
					Height less than 6 m Width less than 8.9 m	VLG, LG, STR, MD	• RH, DB
						MEDIUM, SHORT	• RH, DB
						VERY SHORT	• RH, DB
		Weathered, Altered or Sheared	Less than 50	Circular	Greater than 10.7 m	VLG, LG, STR, MD	DB
						MEDIUM, SHORT	DB
						VERY SHORT	DB
					Less than 10.7 m	VLG, LG, STR, MD	STBM ▲ *
						MEDIUM, SHORT	• SRH, DB
						VERY SHORT	• SRH, DB
				Noncircular	Height greater than 6 m Width greater than 8.9 m	VLG, LG, STR, MD	DB
						MEDIUM, SHORT	DB
						VERY SHORT	DB
					Height less than 6 m Width less than 8.9 m	VLG, LG, STR, MD	• SRH, DB
						MEDIUM, SHORT	• SRH, DB
						VERY SHORT	• SRH, DB

VLG Very Long
LG Long
STR Straight
MD Mild Bend

DB Drill and Blast
TBM Tunnel Boring Machine
SRH Shielded Roadheader-diameters 6.1 m
MBRH Multiple Boom Roadheader Shielded-diameter 6.1 to 11.4 m
CRH Canopy Roadheader
STBM Shielded Tunnel Boring Machine
RH2 Roadheader — 2 passes
RH Roadheader

* Grill bars should be used on the cutter head face when the material is blocky and the face is unstable

▲ Gripper TBM's may become support bound when RQD approaches 50 and may require extra consideration (Shielding, Timber Packing of Grippers or Concrete Reinforcing of Side Walls in soft areas)

• Roadheader should only be used when NCB standard hardness is less than 3

Plate 1.
Proposed Tunneling Method Given Rock Properties and Tunnel Profile (Medium Hard Rock)

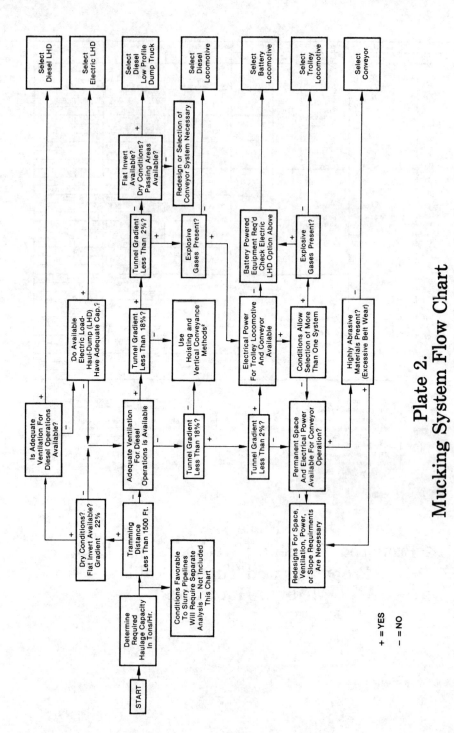

Plate 2.
Mucking System Flow Chart

1194

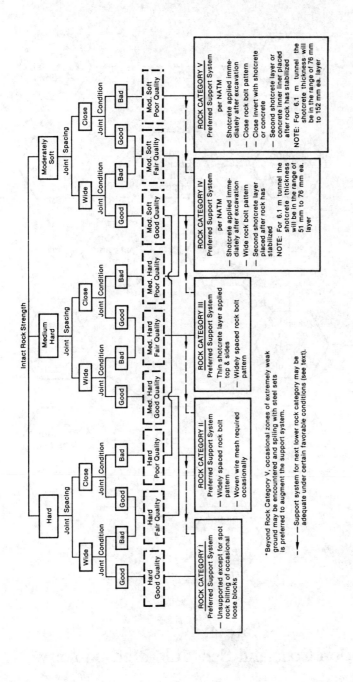

Plate 3.
Support System Selection Flowchart For Tunnels

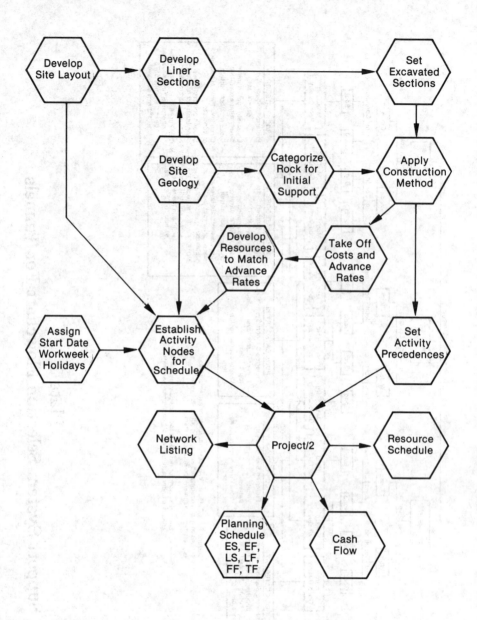

Plate 4.
Construction Cost and Schedule Methodology

25. New stress measurement methods

Chair: EARL R.HOSKINS
           Texas A & M University, College Station, USA
Cochair: LEO VAN SAMBEEK
           RE/SPEC Inc., Rapid City, South Dakota, USA

Insights into the relationship between wellbore breakouts, natural fractures, and in situ stress

LAWRENCE W.TEUFEL
Sandia National Laboratories, Albuquerque, New Mexico, USA

1. ABSTRACT

A direct comparison has been made between the azimuth of wellbore break-outs determined from dipmeter logs with oriented four-arm calipers, the orientation of natural fractures observed in oriented core, and the directions of the principal horizontal in situ stresses determined from hydraulic fracture tests. This comparison shows that the direction of the long axes of breakouts are aligned with the minimum horizontal stress. Breakouts occurred independent of natural fracture occurrence, and are oriented nearly perpendicular to the average strike of near vertical fractures. These observations suggest that analysis of dipmeter logs with oriented four-arm calipers or televiewer logs could provide an inexpensive and reliable method of determining the principal horizontal in situ stress directions.

2. INTRODUCTION

The walls of many boreholes spall so as to produce intervals with non-circular cross sections. Such intervals are defined as breakouts (or borehole elongations) in cases where the shorter diameter of the borehole corresponds to the drill-bit diameter. Breakouts were first documented by Cox (1970) using dipmeter data from western Canada. Cox showed that there was remarkable uniformity in the directions of wellbore breakouts over much of Alberta. Cox's early results have since been observed in other regions (Babcock, 1978; Gough and Bell, 1982).

Two mechanisms have been suggested to explain the origin of wellbore breakouts. Babcock (1978) has attributed breakouts to localized wellbore collapse when the drill-bit encounters prefractured rock. According to this theory the breakouts are aligned with the strike of pre-existing fractures. Another mechanism, proposed by Bell and Gough (1979), is that breakouts are caused by shear fracturing in the zone of stress amplification close to the borehole wall. They proposed that breakouts are a result of two conditions (1) unequal principal horizontal stresses in the rock intersected by the borehole and (2) appreciable initial shear strength in the rock. Their analytical work showed that the long axes of the breakouts have a preferred direction, parallel to the minimum horizontal stress.

There is currently considerable interest by the petroleum and geothermal industry in verifying if one or both mechanisms are responsible for wellbore breakouts. If the breakouts are related only to the horizontal in situ stresses, then analysis of dipmeter logs with oriented four-arm calipers or televiewer logs would provide an inexpensive and reliable method of determining in situ stress directions. Knowledge of stress directions is an important parameter in designing hydraulic fracture treatments for enhanced recovery of low permeability gas reservoirs, enhanced oil recovery, and stimulation of geothermal reservoirs.

To date there has been no published data relating the orientation of breakouts with the direction of the minimum horizontal stress measured by the hydraulic fracture technique at depth in the same or nearby wells or with pre-existing fractures at depth. All evidence in support of the stress induced hypothesis for breakouts has been indirect, coming from inferences of regional stress orientation provided by earthquake fault plane solutions and near surface in situ stress measurements. Data in support of the fracture intersection mechanism is based on studies of surface fractures and very limited observations of fractures in core.

The purpose of this paper is to test the two different theories proposed for the origin of wellbore breakouts. A direct comparison at depth in the same wells has been made between the azimuth of wellbore breakouts determined from dipmeter logs with oriented four-arm calipers, the orientation of natural fractures observed in oriented core, and the directions of the principal horizontal in situ stresses determined from an open-hole hydraulic fracture stress test and the azimuth of three large hydraulic fractures mapped during propagation by a borehole seismic method. The results show that the long axes of wellbore breakouts are aligned with the minimum horizontal stress and are not aligned with pre-existing natural fractures.

3. RESULTS

Three closely spaced wells of the U.S. Department of Energy's multi-well experiment (MWX) were used in this study. The MWX site is located about 6 miles west of Rifle, Colorado in the Piceance Basin. The MWX is a research-oriented field laboratory whose objective is to develop the understanding and technology required for economic production of natural gas in low permeability, lenticular gas sands of the western United States. The three wells are located in a triangular configuration and have an 80 m separation at approximately 2.1 km. Each well was completed to a depth of 2.5 km through the Mesaverde Group. Five stratagraphic zones have been described for the Mesaverde Group at MWX (Lorenz, 1982). The depth intervals and a brief description of these zones are given in Table 1. Each zone is approximately 200 m thick.

3.1 Natural Fractures

Characterization of the natural fractures at MWX involved surface fracture mapping near the MWX site, incorporation of regional fracture and fault maps of the Piceance Basin, and analysis of fractures in the core. Surface fracture studies show an orthogonal pattern of vertical fractures. The orientation of the predominant set of this fracture pattern at the MWX site is $N80°W \pm 15°$, and is consistent with the strike of the major trend of fractures and normal faults in the basin (Smith and Whitney, 1979; Verbeek and Grout, 1984)

An extensive coring program was conducted during the completion of the three MWX wells. Over 1300 m of core was retrieved, with 400 m of this core being oriented. Near vertical calcite-filled fractures were abundant in the core of all three wells. Of the 435 calcite-filled fractures observed in the core, 98 were found in oriented core. The azimuth of these fractures also exhibited an orthogonal pattern, with the predominant set (94% of the total) having an azimuth of $N74°W \pm 11°$ (Figure 1). The azimuth of this predominant set does not change with depth and is in general agreement with the orientation of the major trend of fractures observed at the surface over much of the Piceance Basin. None of the vertical calcite-filled fractures in the core exhibited any indication of shear motion and are therefore considered to be extension fractures. The smaller population of fractures in the orthogonal set were found only in coal beds.

Table 1. Depositional Environments of the Mesaverde Group in the Multi-Well Experiment

Zone	Depth (m)	Description
Upper Fluvial	1330 - 1585	Irregularly-shaped sand lenses with interbedded siltstone and shale
Lower Fluvial	1585 - 1835	Irregularly-shaped sand lenses with interbedded siltstone and shale
Coastal	1835 - 2010	Channel sand lenses with interbedded carbonaceous shale
Paludal	2010 - 2270	Thin channel sand lenses with thinly interbedded shale and coal
Marine	2270 - 2450	Marine blanket-sands, massive marine shales and paralic coals

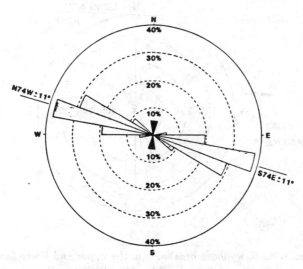

Figure 1. Azimuth of vertical calcite-filled fractures in MWX oriented core.

3.2 Wellbore Breakouts

Wellbore breakouts were observed in all three wells at all depths. However, the quality of the breakouts and consistency of their orientation varied with depth between the different zones of the Mesaverde Group. Results of the upper and lower fluvial zones (1330 m to 1835 m depth) were the best, because of their higher frequency and larger aspect ratio. Differences in the orthogonal caliper readings ranged from 3 to 18 cm. The long axes of 32 breakouts in the upper and lower fluvial zones of the MWX-1 well show a mean azimuth of $N02°E \pm 12°$ (Figure 2). These breakouts occurred only in thick competent sandstone and siltstone layers and not in shale. Breakouts occurred either in zones where no fractures were observed in the oriented core, or if fractures were present, the breakouts were oriented approximately 70° to 90° to the strike of the fractures. Following Bell and Gough (1979), the maximum horizontal stress direction predicted from the breakouts is $N88°W \pm 12°$.

Horizontal stress directions inferred from wellbore breakouts in the three MWX wells as a function of depth for all five zones of the Mesaverde Group are summarized in Figure 3. In all of the zones breakouts were observed only in thick bedded sandstone and siltstone layers and did not occur in shale. Breakouts were not easily identified in the paludal zone (2010 to 2220 m depth) and the range of breakout orientations in this zone is much greater than in the other zones. The increased range and error associated with these breakouts may be a function of lower differential stress in the horizontal stress field (Warpinski et al, 1983) and the less competent, lower strength, and thinner bedded rock units in the paludal zone.

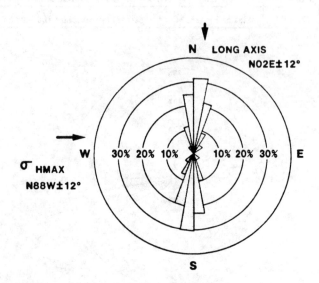

Figure 2. Orientation of wellbore breakouts in the upper and lower fluvial zones (1330 m - 1835 m depth) in the MWX-1 well.

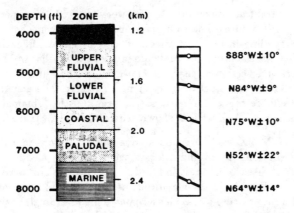

Figure 3. Maximum horizontal stress direction inferred from wellbore breakouts in all three MWX wells as a function of depth and zones of the Mesaverde.

3.3 In Situ Stress Directions

The azimuth of the principal horizontal in situ stress directions have been determined from hydraulic fracture tests in the marine and paludal zones (Figure 4). Two open-hole hydraulic fracture stress tests were conducted in the Rollins sandstone member of the marine zone between 2297 m and 2306 m depth (Teufel and Warpinski, 1984). The ratios of the minimum and maximum horizontal stresses to the overburden was 0.83 and 0.88, respectively. The difference in the magnitude of the principal horizontal stresses was 2.8 MPa. Impression packers were used to determine the trace of the hydraulic fracture (direction of maximum horizontal in situ stress) at the wellbore for each test. Successful impression packer results were obtained only from the lower hydraulic fracture zone and showed that the fracture was not a single plane, but several strands with orientations ranging from $N70°W$ to $N50°W$. The predicted maximum horizontal stress direction from wellbore breakouts in the Rollins sandstone and other sandstone layers in the marine zones was $N64°W \pm 14°$.

Additional observations of the hydraulic fracture azimuth were made at a depth of about 2100 m in the paludal zone using a borehole seismic detection method during hydraulic fracturing in the MWX-1 well, which incorporated an observation well (MWX-3) that was within 80 m of the stimulation well (Hart et al, 1984). The fracture height and azimuth was mapped for 3 different fracture tests and showed a mean azimuth of $N67°W \pm 8°$, compared to a predicted azimuth from wellbore breakouts of $N52°W \pm 22°$.

4. DISCUSSION

The data obtained from the three MWX wells has shown that the long axes of wellbore breakouts are aligned with the minimum principal horizontal stress, as determined by hydraulic fracture tests in two zones. Breakouts occurred independent of natural fracture occurrence and were oriented nearly perpendicular to the strike of the fractures. These observations support the mechanism of shear fracturing and spalling in the zone of compressive stress amplification close to the borehole wall for the origin of breakouts in the MWX wells, and not the pre-existing fracture intersection mechanism. However, these results do not preclude the fracture intersection model from applying elsewhere. The general relationship between wellbore breakouts, natural fractures and the principal horizontal in situ stresses in the MWX wells is shown schematically in Figure 5.

In all three MWX wells breakouts were observed only in thick bedded sandstone and siltstone layers and did not occur in thinly bedded or massive shale layers. The absence of stress induced breakouts in shale may be related to a small or no difference in the magnitude of the principal horizontal stresses in shales. Hydraulic fracture stress measurements made through perforations in in the coastal, paludal, and marine zones show that the minimum horizontal stress in shales is equal to the overburden, and the stress state in most shale layers is probably lithostatic. Whereas in adjacent sandstone and siltstone layers, the ratio of the minimum stress to the overburden ranges from 0.8 to 0.9, and horizontal stress differences are estimated to be greater than 2 MPa. (Warpinski et al, 1983; Warpinski, personal communication).

The orientation of the wellbore breakouts is not constant with depth and suggests a possible clockwise rotation of about 30° of the maximum horizontal in situ stress with depth, from $S88°W \pm 10°$ in the upper fluvial zone starting at 1330 m to $N64°W \pm 14°$ in the marine zone ending at 2450 m. Clark (1983) noted that the MWX site is in a topographic low in the Colorado River Valley, and suggested that gravity loading due to the topography could have a significant effect on the horizontal in situ stresses. At the MWX site mountains rise 1200 m immediately to the north and 1800 m to the south.

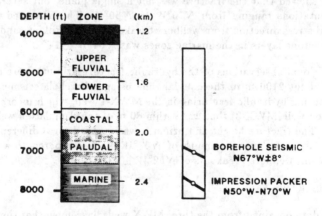

Figure 4. Maximum horizontal stress direction at MWX determined from the azimuth of hydraulic fractures.

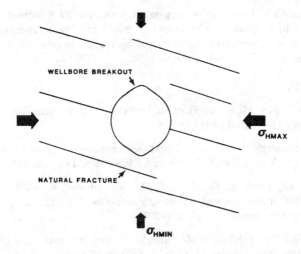

Figure 5. Schematic drawing showing relation between wellbore breakouts, natural fractures, and principal horizontal in situ stresses at the MWX site.

To check the effect of topographic loading Clark made a finite element calculation of the stress state within a homogeneous isotropic elastic medium caused by the three-dimensional surface loading of the topographic relief of the region encompassing the MWX site. Two different cases were considered (1) stress associated only with topography and (2) superimposed tectonic stress (either 1.38 or 2.76 MPa at $N70°W$) on topographic loading. The azimuth of $N70°W$ for the maximum tectonic stress is based on open-hole hydraulic fracture stress tests in a region of low topographic relief in the northern Piceance Basin (Bredehoeft et al, 1976) The results of both cases show a clockwise rotation of the maximum horizontal stress direction with depth. For the first case the maximum horizontal stress rotated from $S74°W$ at 1300 m to $N65°W$ at 2500 m, and for the second case, with a superimposed tectonic stress component of 2.76 MPa at $N70°W$, it showed less rotation: $N87°W$ to $N69°W$ between 1300 m to 2500 m, respectively. The 30° clockwise rotation of the horizontal stresses with depth inferred from the wellbore breakouts is in general agreement with Clark's finite element model, and suggests that the stress state at depth at the MWX site may be due to large, local topographic relief superimposed on the regional stress field of the Piceance Basin.

5. CONCLUSIONS

In the three MWX wells, wellbore breakouts are related to the horizontal in situ stress state and their occurrence is independent of pre-existing natural fractures. For stratigraphic layers which were lithostatic and had no stress anisotropy, such as shale, breakouts did not occur. However, breakouts did occur in sandstone beds in which the difference in principal horizontal stresses was as low as 2.8 MPa. These results suggest that analysis of dipmeter logs with oriented four-arm calipers or televiewer logs could provide an inexpensive and reliable method of determining the principal horizontal in situ stress directions in at least some geological environments.

6. REFERENCES

Babcock, E. A., 1978. Meaurement of subsurface fractures from dipmeter logs. Am. Assoc. Petr. Geol. Bull., 62, 111-126.

Bell, J. S. and Gough, D. I., 1979. Northeast-southwest compressive stress in Alberta: evidence from oil wells. Earth and Planet. Sci. Let., 45, 475-482.

Bredehoeft, J. D., Wolff, R. G., Keys, W. S., and Shuter, E., 1976. Hydraulic fracturing to determine the regional in situ stress field, Piceance Creek Basin, Colorado. Geol. Soc. Am. Bull., 87, 250-258.

Clark, J.A., 1983. The prediction of hydraulic fracture azimuth through geological, core, and analytical studies. SPE 11611, SPE/DOE Symp. on Low Permeability Gas Reservoirs, Denver, CO., March 13-16, 1983.

Cox, J. W., 1970. The high resolution dipmeter reveals dip-related borehole and formation characteristics. 11th Ann. Log. Symp., SPWLA.

Gough, D. I. and Bell, J. S., 1982. Stress orientations from borehole wall fractures with examples from Colorado, East Texas, and Northern Canada. Can. Jour. Earth Sci., 19, 1358-1370.

Hart, C.M., Engi, D., Morris, H.E., and Fleming, R.P., 1984. Fracture diagnostics results for the multi-well paludal zone stimulation. SPE 12852, SPE/DOE Unconventional Gas Recovery Symposium, Pittsburg, PA, May 13-15, 1984.

Lorenz, J. C., 1982. Sedimentology of the Mesaverde Formation of Rifle Gap, Colorado, and Implications for Gas Bearing Intervals in the Subsurface. Sandia National Laboratories Report, SAND82-0249.

Smith, R. S. and Whitney, J. W., 1979. Map of joint sets and airphoto lineaments of Piceance Creek Basin, Northwestern Colorado. U. S. Geol. Surv. Misc. Field Studies Map MF-1128.

Teufel, L.W. and Warpinski, N.R., 1984. Determination of in situ stress from anelastic strain recovery measurements of oriented core: comparison to hydraulic fracture stress measurements in the Rollins sandstone. in Proc. 25th U.S. Symp. Rock Mech. 176-185, C. Dowding and M. Singh (eds), Evanston, IL., June 22-24, 1984.

Verbeek, E. R. and Grout, M. A., 1984. Fracture studies in Cretaceous and Paleocene strata in and around the Piceance Basin, Colorado. U. S. Geol. Surv. Open File Report 84-156.

Warpinski, N. R., Branagan, P. and Wilmer, R., 1983. In Situ stress measurements at DOE's multiwell experiment site, Mesaverde Group, Rifle, Colorado. SPE 12142, 58th Annual SPE Meeting, San Francisco, CA, Oct 5-8, 1983.

In situ stress evaluation from borehole breakouts
Experimental studies

BEZALEL C.HAIMSON & COURTNEY G.HERRICK
Department of Metallurgical & Mineral Engineering, University of Wisconsin-Madison, USA

1 INTRODUCTION

Borehole breakouts (borehole cross-section elongation resulting from preferential rock spalling, see Figure 1) can be important in situ stress indicators because of an unmistakable correlation that appears to exist between breakout orientation and principal stress directions, and because of the theoretical dependence of the spalling process on stress magnitudes. The advantages of using the borehole breakout phenomenon to estimate even roughly the state of in situ stress are quite obvious. The logging of a borehole to detect the existence, the shape and size, and the orientation of breakouts is considerably faster and less expensive than conducting hydrofracturing tests, and can provide independent data when used as a backup technique, or supply the only stress estimate when other methods cannot be employed. In the ultra-deep boreholes that are now being proposed for continental crust studies, breakouts may well be the only source of stress information since their probability of occurrence increases with higher stresses, while the applicability of existing stress measuring methods is drastically reduced.

To date our understanding of the breakout phenomenon, for which there is already extensive field evidence, is based on theoretical analyses correlating spalling to rock strength and in situ stress. Very little experimental verification is available. The objective of the study is to systematically examine in the laboratory the relationship between the most general state of in situ stress and borehole breakouts under simulated realistic field conditions. Some significant results have already been obtained and are reported herein. When completed, the research will provide the experimental information required for the understanding of the phenomenon of borehole breakouts and for its potential use to estimate the in situ state of stress.

2 FIELD EVIDENCE OF BOREHOLE BREAKOUTS

Borehole breakouts were reported as early as twenty years ago (Leeman, 1964). Leeman found that boreholes drilled at great depth in the hard quartzites and conglomerates of the Witwaterstand gold mines in South Africa tend to spall selectively along the borehole wall. He correctly pointed out that spalling is the result of excessive compressive stresses, and that the broken-out segments are perpendicular to the maximum principal stress in the plane of the borehole cross-section. However, were it not for the Schlumberger Four-arm High Resolution Dipmeter well-logging tool, the borehole breakout phenomenon would have probably gone unnoticed. Cox (1970), Babcock (1978) and especially Bell and Gough (1979) and Gough and Bell (1981, 1982) all reported, based on dipmeter logs, the existence and the remarkable directional consistency of borehole breakouts in the Alberta, Canada oil fields. Gough and Bell suggested that the breakouts were aligned with the regional minimum horizontal principal stress (σ_h) and showed that this was true in a number of other oil fields such as in Colorado and Texas. Zoback et al. (1985) have been able to detect borehole breakouts using the Borehole Sonic Televiewer, and discovered that they can occur in almost any rock from sandstone, to tuff and granite. The borehole televiewer can also yield an accurate picture of the spalled borehole cross-section. This, in turn, could be used to estimate stress magnitudes if the mechanism of failure were clearly understood.

3 SUGGESTED MECHANISMS FOR BOREHOLE BREAKOUTS

The most complete analytical model of borehole breakouts to date has been derived by Zoback et al. (1985). In it the breakout shape and size is controlled by the in situ stress magnitudes, rock shear strength parameters, and the pore pressure in the rock. In this model, the stresses around the borehole are compared with the stresses required for failure at every point in the vicinity of the borehole using a linear Mohr-Coulomb envelope, which is characterized by the coefficient of internal friction μ and the cohesion S_o. In terms of S_o, the critical condition for spalling is given by:

$$S_o = (1+\mu^2)^{1/2} \left(\left(\frac{\sigma_\theta - \sigma_r}{2} \right)^2 + \tau_{r\theta}^2 \right)^{1/2} - \mu \left(\frac{\sigma_\theta + \sigma_r}{2} \right) \tag{1}$$

where σ_θ, σ_r and $\tau_{r\theta}$ are the tangential, radial and shear stresses, respectively, at a point around the borehole as obtained by Kirsch's solution and are functions of σ_H and σ_h (largest and least in situ horizontal stresses). If the right hand side of the equation is less than S_o, a stable condition prevails (point a in Figure 1); if it is greater than S_o, spalling will occur (point b in Figure 1). A contour line representing equation (1) can be drawn enclosing the zone within which the stress is sufficient to bring about failure. This line can in turn be characterized by the maximum breakout depth, r_b, and by the breakout angle θ_b, representing breakout width (see Figure 1). The model yields different breakout depths and widths for different in situ stress conditions. This important result suggests that one could estimate the two principal stresses σ_H and σ_h by accurately determining θ_b and r_b.

Mastin (1984) used a boundary element technique to numerically calculate the stress condition around the elongated borehole after the initial spalling. He found that since the in situ stresses remain the same, the stress concentration around the elongated borehole is now even greater than before spalling. This should lead to a new episode of failure. As shown in Figure 2, each new breakout would give rise to

1208

another episode of failure and no stabilization would occur. Mastin suggested that if this model were correct the only reason why breakouts would stabilize in the field is due to incomplete spalling in each of the early episodes. This step by step failure mechanism is problematic in any attempt to correlate breakouts to stress because it would be nearly impossible to determine how many rounds of spalling actually occurred in any given case. Note, however, that the width of breakout remains unchanged throughout this process, and could still provide an important clue as to the range of in situ stresses.

One additional complication in the failure mechanism is based on a suggestion by Freudenthal (1977). Contrary to the premise of the above-mentioned models which predicts that excessive triaxial compressive stresses near the borehole wall bring about shear failure, Freudenthal suggests that extensional or tensile fracturing may actually occur. Based on the high compressibility and low shear modulus of rock, shear dilatancy occurs in a compressive stress field, which is comparable in magnitude to the volume compaction caused by non-deviatoric stresses. In the borehole case, shear dilatancy produces radial tensile stresses. Depending on rock properties, the latter can cause tensile fractures within the zone of high shear stresses unless shear failure occurs first. The zone of critical stress concentration is very similar in shape to that predicted by the Zoback et al model. The difference is that either shear or tensile failure can occur. Field evidence for both tensile rupture and shear fracture as a mechanism of breakout appears to exist (Mastin, 1984).

4 PREVIOUS LABORATORY TEST RESULTS

Prior to our recent study there have been only two known laboratory investigations of borehole breakouts. In both studies, testing conditions simulated only in part real field situations. Haimson and Edl (1972) tested hollow cylindrical specimens of dry Berea sandstone under uniform horizontal stress ($\sigma_H = \sigma_h$) and an independent vertical (σ_v) stress. As expected, the breakouts obtained extended throughout the circumference of the borehole. Their depth showed a clear increase with the rise in confining pressure indicating that a relationship may exist between breakout size and the horizontal in situ stress. The mode of failure appeared to be shear since the displaced rock was completely crushed. The intriguing result was that no failure was observed in or around the borehole until the tangential stress was approximately twice the value of the experimentally determined C_o (the uniaxial compressive strength of the rock). No satisfactory explanation of this phenomenon was presented except for the speculation that the rapid reduction in the ($\sigma_\theta - \sigma_r$) difference away from borehole wall may inhibit the extension of fractures started at the wall when the critical stress (C_o) is reached and thus, higher in situ stress is required to initiate the spall.

A more recent laboratory study was conducted by Mastin (1984). He tested eight specimens of Berea sandstone blocks by subjecting them to uniaxial loading applied perpendicular to the hole axis. This loading condition, while conducive to directional breakouts is an oversimplified simulation of the field situation since stress regimes in which $\sigma_h = 0$ $\sigma_v = 0$ are not typically encountered. Mastin determined that spalling began at $\sigma_H = 36$ MPa, or at a maximum tangential stress at the borehole

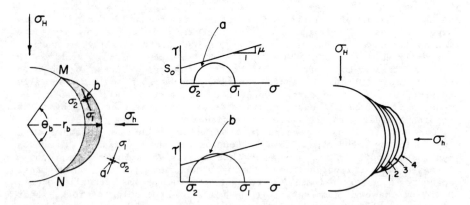

Figure 1. Size and shape of hypothetical breakout zone (shaded area) suggested by Zoback et al (1985) model for a set of principal horizontal stresses. Explanation of stable and breakout zones is given in the form of Mohr circles and Mohr-Coulomb Criterion of failure (after Mastin, 1984).

Figure 2. Breakout shapes at successive episodes of failure under constant in situ stresses using Zoback et al's (1985) model and a numerical technique for calculating the new stress concentrations after each failure occurs (Mastin, 1984).

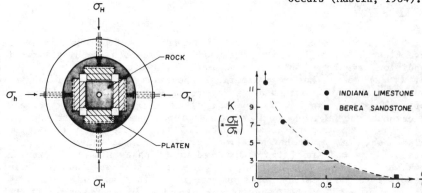

Figure 3. Cross-section of polyaxial stress for the application of non-equal principal horizontal stresses to prismatic rock specimens.

Figure 4. Relationship between horizontal stress ratio and the least horizontal stress at the onset of borehole breakout (Stage 4 in Figure 5). The horizontal stress axis was normalized so that our previous result in Indiana limestone (Haimson and Edl, 1972) could be used to improve the extrapolation of the curve in the shaded zone (where $1 > K > 3$).

wall which was about 1.9 times the uniaxial compressive strength (in accord with Haimson and Edl (1972) results). Mastin noted a substantial variation in the width of breakout within the same sample and between samples which spalled under similar stress conditions. This result would be very significant in that the ability to estimate stress magnitudes hinges on the theoretical correlation between stress and breakout width. Mastin suggested that the inconsistent width may have been the result of uneven loading. It may also have been the consequence of uniaxial loading. Contrary to Mastin's result, the breakout width obtained in our reported tests was surprisingly consistent throughout the borehole (see next section). Mastin concentrated his laboratory effort on observations of the mechanism of failure which in Berea sandstone appears to be a combination of extensional cracking and shear fracturing (supporting in part Freudenthal's (1977) analysis). The important observation was that the width of the breakout remains basically unchanged regardless of the final depth of spalling. Although Mastin's tests were inconclusive regarding the applicability of breakouts to estimating stresses, his detailed study of the spalling process is an important contribution to the understanding of rock failure.

5 PRESENT EXPERIMENTAL PROGRAM - RESULTS AND DISCUSSION

At the University of Wisconsin-Madison we have launched a laboratory experimental program of inducing and examining borehole breakouts under controlled conditions. Rectangular rock blocks 18 cm high x 13 cm x 13 cm are subjected to a general triaxial (or polyaxial) state of stress ($\sigma_v \neq \sigma_H \neq \sigma_H$). While holding the vertical and least horizontal stresses constant, a central vertical borehole (dia. 2.14 cm) is under visual inspection as σ_H is increased in small increments. The apparatus used for these tests is a polyaxial cell (Figure 3) and a 400 ton loading press which allow the application of three independent and mutually perpendicular uniform loads (each up to 100 MPa, simulating any general in situ stress condition to depths of at least 5 km). Each load is servo-controlled, which ensures that constant loads are prevented from drifting and that increasing loads can be programmed to follow certain rates which are repeatable from test to test.

To date we have only tested one rock type, an Indiana limestone, and have only used a low range of σ_h values (1.5 to 13 MPa). The vertical stress was always maintained intermediate to σ_h and σ_H. In this range the corresponding critical σ_H magnitudes leading to borehole breakouts are relatively high (σ_H/σ_h ratios of 18/1 to 4/1). Although the high ratios may seem unrealistic in situ conditions, the breakouts obtained were unaffected by any tensile stress concentrations elsewhere around the borehole. Based on the clearly established trend (Figure 4) σ_H/σ_h ratio will be less than 3/1 in the range of σ_h to be next tested (15-50 MPa).

On the basis of visual monitoring of the borehole wall at different incremental increases of σ_H, we have observed four stages leading to breakouts in Indiana limestone. Typically, the first evidence of failure at the borehole wall is the appearance of short vertical hairline cracks scattered along the general direction of σ_h and spanning a segment of the borehole cross-section that remained unchanged during the entire breakout process (Stage 1 in Figure 5). As σ_H is increased

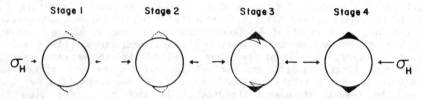

Figure 5. Four distinct stages of breakout formation as observed on the borehole wall.

the hairline cracks tend to link up and eventually form one or more long winding cracks (Stage 2 in Figure 5). At higher σ_H the process of spalling begins and thin chips of rock are detached from the borehole wall, some still hanging on and others falling off (Stage 3 in Figure 5). As the first rock chip spalls off, others are detached behind, with the total depth affected a function of the horizontal stress magnitudes. The last stage is the level of σ_H at which no more rock chips are noticed hanging freely from the borehole wall. At this point the process of breakout appears to be completed (Stage 4 in Figure 5). (Note, however, that we have not tested whether further increases in σ_H would deepen the breakout). We tested the limestone under dry conditions (two sets of simulated in situ stresses), and wet conditions (three sets of stresses). At least two specimens were tested for each of the five conditions. Table 1 summarizes the stress levels at which each of the four breakout stages was obtained. It is apparent that in Indiana limestone all four breakout-forming stages start at a higher σ_H/σ_h ratio in dry rock. Moreover, each stage and in particular the fourth, requires a lower relative value of σ_H as the value of σ_h increases. This significant result and unique relationship between σ_h and σ_H shown for stage 4 in Figure 4 implies that, if σ_h can be estimated from the breakout geometry or otherwise, the value of the critical, breakout-forming σ_H can be readily obtained from the plot. Additional tests are required to complete Figure 4, but the trend is unmistakably there.

Probably the most significant result of the experimental studies to date has been the clear evidence that the size of breakouts with respect to depth (r_b) and lateral extent (θ_b) is directly proportional to the magnitude of σ_H and the corresponding critical σ_H. Figure 6 presents photographs of central vertical cross-sections of four Indiana limestone specimens which were subjected to different constant σ_h and σ_v, and an increasing σ_H until a breakout was obtained. The increase in the width of breakout with σ_H (and the respective critical σ_H) is clearly seen. Figure 7 shows how the breakout depth increases with σ_h and σ_H. These are very encouraging results in that the clear dependence of breakout size on the horizontal stresses implies that mapping of breakout contour in field situations could potentially be used to estimate the corresponding state of in situ stress.

Regarding the observed shapes of the test breakouts, Figure 7 clearly demonstrates that "V" or truncated "V" are predominant. This is contrary to the theoretical shape based on equation (1) (flat and rounded) and shown schematically in Figure 1. The experimental breakout shape approaches that predicted by Mastin (1984) based on episodal failures. However, contrary to Mastin's suggestion that breakouts will continue to grow in depth under unchanging in situ streses, thus

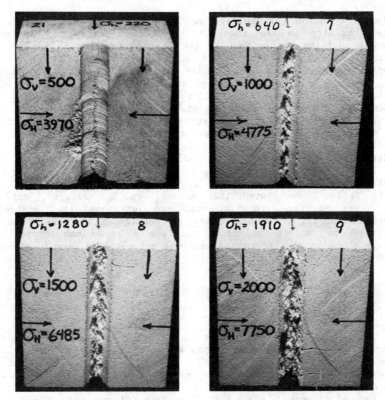

Figure 6. Vertical cross-sections of specimens each loaded wet under a different stress condition (given in psi). Note direct relationship between breakout width and horizontal stresses.

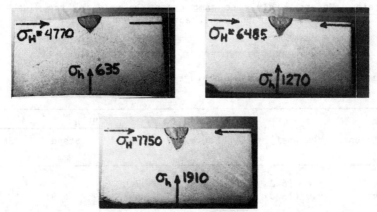

Figure 7. Halves of horizontal cross-sections of three specimens each loaded wet under a different stress condition (given in psi). Note direct relationship between breakout depth and horizontal stress. (Borehole and breakout cavity was filled with cement to prevent further failure during cross-section preparation).

rendering equation (1) useless, we found the experimental r_b to be in close proximity to the theoretical value. Hence, no Mastin type episodal spalling was evident in the tested limestone. The "V" shaped breakouts appear to be the result of Mohr-Coulomb failure predicted by equation (1) near the center (in the σ_h direction), the propagation of which toward the borehole wall (points M and N in Figure 1) is blocked by the initial fractures observed in stages 1 and 2 in Figure 5.

We made twenty measurements of r_b and θ_b in each of the tested specimens (2 to 3 specimens per stress condition) and were surprised by the consistency of breakout size within each specimen and from one specimen to the other. The standard deviation under each stress condition averaged 5% for r_b and 18% for θ_b with the exception of the case $\sigma_h = 1.5$ MPa for which θ_b was so small that the measurement precision was affected (see Table 2).

In Table 2 we listed the mean r_b and θ_b readings ("exp") for each σ_h set magnitude (dry or wet) and juxtaposed them against the expected theoretical values based on Zoback et al. (1985) analysis invoking the Kirsch solution and the Mohr-Coulomb criterion of failure. The latter breakout dimensions are obtained from relationships of the type:

$$\sigma_h = f_1 (S_o, \mu, r_b, \theta_b)$$
$$\sigma_H = f_2 (S_o, \mu, r_b, \theta_b) \tag{2}$$

For the Indiana limestone used in our experiments we conducted a series of triaxial compression tests from which we established the following parameters: Dry rock: $S_o = 8.0$ MPa, $\mu = 0.58$, $C_o = 27.7$ MPa; Wet rock: $S_o = 7.5$ MPa, $\mu = 0.54$, $C_o = 25$ MPa (where C_o is the uniaxial compressive strength).

The experimental r_b values are surprisingly very close to the theoretical ones (within 10% of the latter except for one case). This result suggests that the effect of the in situ stresses on the maximum breakout depth appears to be correctly predicted by the theoretical analysis. Unfortunately, the same cannot be said for the width of the breakout (θ_b). The error between theoretical and experimental θ_b can

Table 1. Stress ratios at each stage of breakout process

Rock Condition	σ_h MPa (psi)	σ_H/σ_h			
		Stage 1	Stage 2	Stage 3	Stage 4
dry	4.4 (640)	6.5	7.0	7.5	9.7
dry	9.0 (1300)	4.4	4.7	4.9	5.5
wet	1.5 (220)	-	-	-	18.0
wet	4.4 (640)	4.1	4.9	6.1	7.5
wet	8.8 (1280)	2.6	2.8	3.6	5.1
wet	13.2 (1910)	2.5	2.7	3.1	4.1

reach 75% (Table 2), and in most cases it is roughly 50%, with the experimental values always the lower. We speculate that the lower than predicted θ_b may be the result of the initial cracks that can be seen on the borehole wall in stage 1 and 2 of the breakout process (Figure 5). As stated above, the horizontal span between these vertical cracks appears to establish the final extent of θ_b. It is possible that these initial cracks form a barrier which block the outward propagation of any shear or tensile fractures developed in the central section of the breakout.

Based on the results listed in Table 2 we attempted to back calculate the stresses σ_h and σ_H from equation (2) and the experimental parameters θ_b (corrected by a factor of 2) and r_b. The values obtained were reasonable approximations in the two wet rock cases for which the r_b errors were small and the θ_b errors were close to 50% (see Table 2). The back calculated values for the applied σ_h = 4.4 MPa and σ_H = 32.9 MPa were: 0 MPa and 30 MPa respectively; for the applied σ_h = 8.8 MPa, and σ_H = 44.7 MPa: 12.4 MPa and 68.2 MPa respectively. In the other two stress cases, for which one or both errors deviated substantially from the rest, the back calculation yielded grossly exaggerated stress values.

We also made an attempt to back calculate the stresses by utilizing the plot given in Figure 4. Since a unique relationship appears to exist between σ_h and the critical breakout forming σ_H, we substituted σ_H with $K\sigma_h$ (K to be picked from Figure 4 depending on σ_h value) and calculated σ_h from equation (1) for shear failure condition at r_b which can be written in the form

$$S_o \text{ (at } r_b) = \frac{1}{2} [c \ \sigma_H + d \ \sigma_h] \tag{3a}$$

or

$$S_o(\text{at } r_b) = \frac{1}{2} [c(K \ \sigma_h) + d \ \sigma_h] \tag{3b}$$

where the factors c and d are functions of μ and r_b only (Zoback et al., 1985). Table 3 gives the results of this back calculation of σ_h (and σ_H) . Except for the largest applied-stress case for which r_b was substantially different from the theoretical value, all estimated stresses were within 50% of the applied values, with four out of five estimates within 25%. This encouraging result could be used in the field to obtain some bounds for σ_h and σ_H . The expected range of in situ stress ratios K at depth is typically between 1 and 3. Provided the extrapolation carried out in Figure 4 for this range is correct (shaded zone), breakouts would occur in situ in Indiana limestone if σ_h > 0.5 Co . For any reliable r_b measured, one could assign K values between 1 and 3 and obtain σ_h from equation (3b) and the corresponding critical (minimum) σ_H . By a process of iteration the most reasonable σ_h and σ_H for the breakout measured depth could be obtained. It should be clear that this does not include the case in which σ_H is substantially higher than the critical value required to obtain complete borehole breakout.

From the laboratory results one learns (1) that the experimental r_b is likely to be closely predicted by the existing theoretical analysis, and (2) that θ_b-exp appears to stay constant throughout all the stages leading to the final breakout at a magnitude controlled only by σ_h (and rock strength parameters). Figure 8 shows that the variation of θ_b-exp with σ_h for the range of σ_h tested in Indiana limestone is

Table 2. Comparison of experimental breakout dimensions with theoretically expected values

Rock Condition	σ_h MPa (psi)	σ_H MPa (psi)	r_b-theory cm	r_b-exp cm (Std. dev.%)	error* %	θ_b-theory degrees	θ_b-exp degrees (Std. dev. %)	error* %
dry	4.4 (640)	42.9 (6215)	1.43	1.37 (4.1)	4	106	45 (21.1)	57
dry	9.0 (1300)	49.5 (7180)	1.53	1.49 (6.6)	3	112	59 (18.6)	48
wet	1.5 (220)	27.4 (3970)	1.21	1.16 (5.6)	4	102	26 (37.0)	75
wet	4.4 (640)	32.9 (4775)	1.41	1.39 (4.2)	2	103	47 (18.8)	54
wet	8.8 (1280)	44.7 (6485)	1.47	1.61 (5.5)	-10	113	60 (16.9)	47
wet	13.2 (1910)	53.4 (7750)	1.50	1.92 (5.7)	-28	121	76 (13.0)	37

*error(%) = [(theory - exp)/theory] x 100 (%).
Note: Initial borehole radius: 1.07 cm.

Table 3. Back calculations of horizontal stresses based on K vs σ_h relationship

Rock	Applied			r_b-exp	Back-Calculated		Error
	σ_h MPa	σ_H MPa	K	cm	σ_h MPa	σ_H MPa	σ_h (and σ_H) %
dry	4.4	42.9	9.7	1.37	3.6	35.1	18
dry	9.0	49.5	5.5	1.49	11.2	61.4	-24
wet	1.5	27.4	18.0	1.16	1.2	20.9	20
wet	4.4	32.9	7.5	1.39	4.3	32.5	2
wet	8.8	44.7	5.1	1.61	13.7	70.0	-56
wet	13.2	53.4	4.1	1.92	41.8	171.6	-217

*Error in σ_h (or σ_H) = [(applied stress-back calculated stress)/applied stress] x 100 (%)

Table 4. Back calculations of horizontal stresses based on θ_b vs. σ_h relationship

Rock Cond.	Applied		θ_b-exp degrees	Back-Calculated		Error*	
	σ_h MPa	σ_H MPa		σ_h MPa	σ_H MPa	σ_h %	σ_H %
dry	4.4	42.9	45	5.1	37.4	-16	13
dry	9.0	49.5	59	8.6	59.2	4	-19
wet	1.5	27.4	26	0.2	12.7	86	54
wet	4.4	32.9	47	5.7	33.2	-30	-1
wet	8.8	44.7	60	8.8	63.8	0	-43
wet	13.2	53.4	76	13.0	97.0	2	-82

*Error (%) = [(Applied stress - Back calculated stress)/applied stress] x 100 (%)

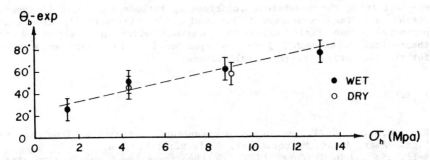

Figure 8. Relationship between breakout width (θ_b) and the least horizontal stress (σ_h) in Indiana limestone for the range of stresses tested.

approximately linear. This suggests another possible technique to solve for the principal horizontal stresses. Provided that the dependence of θ_b-exp on σ_h does not change with borehole diameter, one could conduct a few laboratory tests to obtain a plot such as Figure 8 for any in situ formation under consideration. The mapping of the field drill-hole wall (obtained with a borehole televiewer or other logging tools) will yield a θ_b which can then be used to obtain the corresponding in situ σ_h. The mapped value of r_b together with σ_h and the rock parameters μ and S_o could then be used in equation (3a) to obtain σ_H. In the described tests (Table 2) if we back calculate the principal horizontal stresses, using the straight-line θ_b-exp vs. σ_h relationship in Figure 8, and compare them to the applied σ_h and σ_H we obtain values given in Table 4. The errors between calculated and applied stresses are quite reasonable in view of the fact that the borehole breakout technique should only be expected to yield an estimate or an approximation of the stress field.

Whether or not any of the above techniques will work in the field remains to be seen. The latter method appears to be the most promising for rocks behaving similarly to Indiana limestone. However, the most important finding to date remains that both r_b and θ_b increase with stress. This very encouraging result should lead to a reliable method of estimating the horizontal stresses from borehole breakouts.

6 CONCLUSIONS

Our laboratory tests lead to the following conclusions pertaining to Indiana limestone under the most general state of stress:

a - Breakouts are directly related to the state of stress and occur in two diametrically opposed zones along the borehole wall in the direction of the least horizontal stress.
b - Breakout depth and width do indeed increase with the magnitude of the horizontal stresses as theoretically expected. The depth can be closely predicted by theoretical analysis involving elasticity and Mohr-Coulomb criterion; the width is, however, about one half of the predicted value.

1217

c - Utilizing the consistent relationship between the least horizontal stress and the experimental breakout width (Figure 8), one could potentially use field values of breakout width and depth and the theoretical relationship given by equation (3a) to obtain an estimate for the two horizontal principal stresses.

7 REFERENCES

Babcock, E. A. 1978. Measurement of subsurface fractures from dipmeter logs. Amer. Assoc. Petrol. Geol. Bull. 62: 1111-1126.

Bell, .S. and D. I. Gough 1979. Northeast-southwest compressive stress in Alberta: evidence from oil wells. Earth Planet. Sci. Lett. 45: 475-482.

Cox, J. W. 1970. The high resolution dipmeter reveals dip-related borehole and formation characteristics. Proceedings 11th Annual Logging Symp. Soc. Prof. Well Log Analysts. Los Angeles.

Freudenthal, A. M. 1977. Stresses around spherical and cylindrical cavities in shear dilatant elastic media. Proceedings 18th U.S. Symp. on Rock Mechanics. Keystone.

Gough, D. I. and J. S. Bell 1981. Stress orientations from oil well fractures in Alberta and Texas. Canad. J. of Earth Sci. 18: 638-645.

Gough, D. I. and J. S. Bell 1982. Stress orientations from borehole wall fractures with examples from Colorado, east Texas and northern Canada. Canad. J. of Earth Sci. 19: 1358-1370.

Haimson, B. C. and J. N. Edl 1972. Hydraulic fracturing of deep wells. Soc. of Petrol. Engin. Paper no. SPE 4061.

Leeman, E. R. 1964. The measurement of stress in rock - part 1. J. S. Afr. Inst. Min. and Met., 76-77.

Mastin, L. G. 1984. Development of borehole breakouts in sandstone. M.S. Thesis, Stanford University, Palo Alto.

Zoback, M. D., Moos, D., Mastin, L., and R. N. Anderson 1985. Wellbore breakouts and insitu stress. J. Geophys. Res. (in press).

Determination of in-situ stresses in the floor of a diatomite quarry

RICHARD M.NOLTING
Parsons Brinckerhoff Quade & Douglas, San Francisco, California, USA

GLENN M.BOYCE & RICHARD E.GOODMAN
University of California, Berkeley, USA

INTRODUCTION

The in-situ stress distribution in a rock mass can be significantly influenced by structural discontinuties and by variations in material properties. Point measurements of the stress field such as overcoring are thus functions of inherent rock mass characteristics as well as of tectonic and gravitational forces. An example of the possible effect of such characteristics has been seen in recent field measurements of surface stresses at a diatomite quarry near Lompoc, California.

On April 7, 1981 a magnitude 2.5 earthquake resulted in the occurrence of a 575 meter long surface rupture at the Lompoc quarry (Yerkes, et al, 1983). The faulting was parallel to the diatomite bedding with a maximum reverse dip slip component of 23 cm and a right lateral strike slip component of 9 cm. The study by Yerkes, et al (1983) concludes that the event was triggered by quarrying of the diatomite during the past 30 years in a tectonic setting of north-south compression. Another study, completed just prior to the Lompoc earthquake by Roth, et al (1981), deals with the prediction of potential fault slip in a shale syncline 15 km south of the Lompoc quarry. Slip due to flexural folding is hypothesized as the fault mechanism and a redistribution of the in-situ stresses is a predicted characteristic. The surface fault rupture at the Lompoc quarry and the geologic similarity of the Lompoc situation to that modeled by Roth, et al (1981) provided the impetus for a series of field measurements carried out from 1982 through 1983 at Lompoc. It was hoped that by means of surface measurements the influence of the fault on the existing stress field could be detected.

STRAIN RELIEF MEASUREMENTS

Strain relief measurements were made at 16 sites in an area that included approximately 100 m of the fault rupture and extended 50 m to either side, see Figure 1. Two additional sites 120 m south of the rupture were also established, making a total of 18 measurements. A four component 15 cm diameter rosette of survey points was installed at each site, see Figure 2. The procedure was to measure distances between the points with a Whittemore extensometer gage, overcore the rosette, measure the distances again, and calculate the strain for each component.

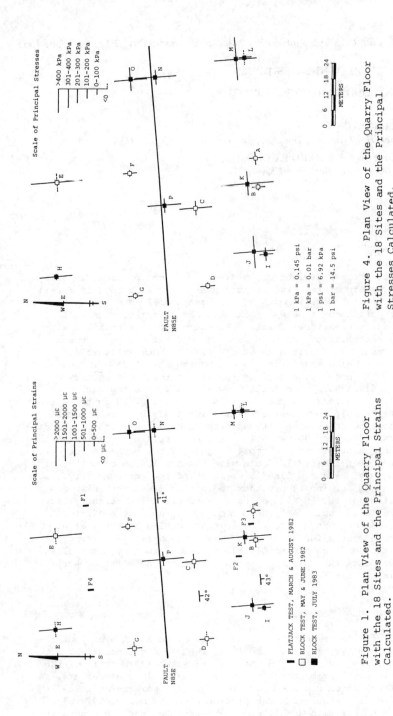

Figure 1. Plan View of the Quarry Floor with the 18 Sites and the Principal Strains Calculated.

Figure 4. Plan View of the Quarry Floor with the 18 Sites and the Principal Stresses Calculated.

The strain measurements were performed with relative ease because of the soft nature of diatomite. The survey points were 60 mm steel nails with seating holes drilled into the ends for the Whittemore gage. The nails were positioned with the aid of a template and hammered into guide holes drilled into the diatomite. "Overcoring" was accomplished using a standard chain saw with a 60 cm bar, see Figure 3. Four overlapping slots were cut around each rosette to form an approximately square block that was left attached at the bottom. Blocks ranged in size from 30 to 60 cm on a side and from 30 to 45 cm deep. During one test the cuts around the block were sawed to increasing depths to determine when major displacement of the survey points had occurred. A depth of 20 cm was found to be the point at which no additional displacement was noted. The effects of temperature on the Whittemore gage and on the diatomite were also examined and found to be insignificant.

Strains in the four rosette directions were reduced to a two dimensional state of strain using a least squares fit and transformed to principal magnitudes and directions. The values for the strains for each site are presented in Table 1 with the average values calculated. The distribution of the strains on the quarry floor is shown in Figure 1. The uniaxial nature of the distribution and the consistent orientation is evident. Remarkable is the uniformity of strain along certain zones parallel to strike; especially in the strata containing sites A, B, I, and L and sites J, K, and M, to be referred to as zones A and J, respectively. However, in contrast to the strain along strike, the strain perpendicular to strike changes abruptly from zone A to zone J. The line of overcored rosettes in zone A is only 4 to 5 m

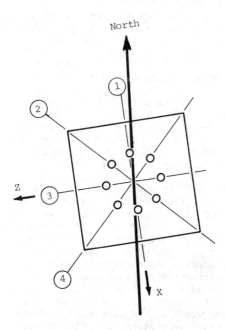

Figure 2. Sketch of the layout of a typical rosette in plan view relative to north.

Figure 3. Photograph of the "overcoring" (or better termed oversawing) of the rosette.

away from that of zone J yet the average change in major principal strain shows a six-fold increase (1670 $\mu\varepsilon$) from zones A to J. The reproducibility of the measurements both in space and with time within the two zones and the number of measurement sites lend confidence to the accuracy of these observations.

IN-SITU STRESS INTERPRETATIONS

A possible explanation for the change in strain between zones A and J is a difference in stress-strain properties. In the presence of a uniform stress field, a sufficient contrast in diatomite properties between the two zones could produce the observed strains. This hypothesis is examined using the moduli values determined in the laboratory as a set of reference elastic constants, see Appendix.

An average stress state for all 18 sites is determined from the average strain by using the reference constants and equation A1. This stress state is assumed to be a uniform stress field that includes zones A and J. Multiples of the reference constants applied to the average strains for zones A and J give stresses close to the average. The ratio between the elastic constants of zones A and J needed to produce the observed strain contrast is 7 to 1. This procedure also demonstrates that a change from the reference constants of 250% for zone A and 50% for zone J is required to produce the assumed state of uniform stress. Poisson's ratio has not been varied in this case, but a similar analysis in which the moduli are held constant and multiples of Poisson's ratio taken shows that unrealistic values of ν and ν' have to be used to produce even minor changes in σ_x.

The five elastic constants have not been determined directly for any zones except those corresponding to the reference constants and these constants apply to strata approximately 13 m to either side of the fault rupture. However, an estimate of the variation in diatomite properties throughout the study area is possible from a series of four flatjack tests located as shown in Figure 1 (Segall, 1982). Back calculations from flatjack tests, see Jaeger and Cook (1976, p. 270), made in slots cut perpendicular to strike gives values for the parameter E, see Table 2. The average E is close to that of the reference case and suggests that the laboratory values are representative of the field and the actual variations are less than 25% of the reference constants. Thus, uniformity in the elastic constants appears to be a general rule for the study area rather than uniformity in stress magnitudes.

The stress distribution at the surface of the quarry, as computed from the measured strains and using the set of reference constants, is shown in Figure 4. The characteristics of the strain distribution described above are reflected in the stress field; that is, the stresses are strongly uniaxial with relatively minor variations from an average N7°W direction and are homogeneous within certain zones parallel to strike. Also, zones A and J clearly demonstrate an abrupt change in magnitude of the stress field in the direction perpendicular to strike.

The original impetus for this investigation as stated in the introduction was to determine whether or not stresses measured in the vicinity of the newly formed fault rupture would show a disturbance of the areal stress field. The problem is not only that the original stress field is unknown but that the present stress field at a distance far from the fault rupture is difficult to measure because of the topographic changes and the lack of convenient sites.

1222

Table 1. Measured Strains and Calculated Principal Stresses for the 18 Sites at the Diatomite Quarry.*

		ε_x	ε_z	Γ_{xz}	σ_1	σ_2	θ
	Units	$\mu\varepsilon$	$\mu\varepsilon$	$\mu\varepsilon$	kpa	kpa	°(ccw)
	A	465	-1	36	94	19	12
	B	413	-36	27	82	1	11
	C	1076	67	-130	222	75	-4
	D	351	-31	22	70	0	5
	E	2894	-755	-52	557	-232	5
	F	146	9	-16	30	10	0
	G	162	-2	10	32	6	9
SITES	H	1388	-82	-388	288	9	-6
	I	251	9	-17	51	15	5
	J	1743	413	-77	370	266	2
	K	2432	50	138	493	125	11
	L	210	-54	-14	40	-17	6
	M	1806	520	124	390	315	22
	N	1504	44	419	321	68	19
	O	1085	201	-38	228	139	1
	P	1189	55	-37	242	76	3
	Q	1546	46	-71	314	86	9
	R	1459	-81	142	292	22	16
	Average	1118	21	4	226	57	7

*Calculations were done for the measured strains using a two dimensional coordinate system with the x direction to the north and the z direction to the west along strike.

Table 2. Elastic Constant E Calculated from Flatjack Tests Perpendicular to Strike.

Flatjack Test #	E (MPa)
1	539
2	346
3	408
4	469
Average	440

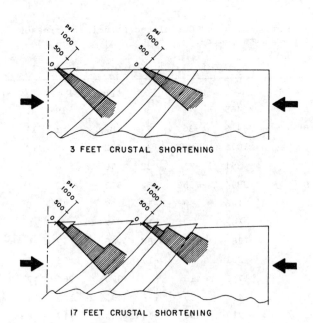

Figure 5. Normal Stresses Parallel to Bedding Planes as Computed by Roth, et al (1982).

The stress discontinuity between zones A and J and the possible stress change across the fault rupture itself suggests that bedding plane displacement is responsible. Apparently no surface rupture occurs between zones A and J, but a small movement of a few centimeters could go undetected in the soft diatomite and may be all that is required to produce a redistribution of the stress field. In the numerical model given by Roth, et al (1981) for flexural folding of strata near Lompoc, a syncline is compressed laterally until failure occurs along certain bedding planes. Figure 5 shows the stress distribution that results following bedding plane slippage. Normal stress distributions show sharp discontinuities across the slip planes of faults. Although additional compression at this stage of deformation produces further slippage, the state of stress does not continue to change. This implies that any amount of initial slip beyond a situation of limiting equilibrium may be sufficient to redistribute stresses.

CONCLUSIONS

The orientations and magnitudes of the surface stresses measured at the Lompoc quarry show strong horizontal compression roughly perpendicular to the bedding with a small right lateral shear along bedding. This result agrees with the regional tectonic style of north-south compression, rather than with local topographic expressions. Thus the mechanics of the faulting is compatible with the regional stress field.

Stress and strain magnitudes are quite uniform along strike within a given stratum, but in places change abruptly from one stratum to the next. These changes could not be attributed to variations in elastic constants; rather they appear to reflect redistribution of in-situ stresses caused by slips along discontinuities parallel to bedding planes. These discontinuities may include not only the known fault that broke the quarry floor but also possible undetected breaks along other bedding planes. It is hypothesized that very small breaks along bedding could be sufficient to redistribute the stresses without exhibiting discernible offset.

The method used to measure the stresses is simple, economical, and effective. It requires a minimum of equipment and instrumentation and can be accomplished rapidly in soft rock with a regular surface. Therefore this method has merit for stress measurements in weak rocks.

ACKNOWLEDGEMENTS

The authors would like to express their appreciation to the Mansville Co. at Lompoc, CA for allowing this study to be undertaken; to Bob Greata and Bob Fullerton, Staff Engineers of the quarry for their assistance, time, and information; to Paul Segall and Paul Okubo of the United States Geological Survey at Menlo Park for providing the use of some of their equipment and data; to Derek Elsworth and Gary Rogers who assisted on the site visits; and to Luis Torres who conducted the laboratory tests.

REFERENCES

Goodman, R.E. 1980. Introduction to Rock Mechanics. New York: Wiley, 478 p.
Jaeger, J.C. and Cook, N.G.W. 1976. Fundamentals of Rock Mechanics, 2nd Ed., London: Chapman and Hall, 585 p.
Roth, W.H., Sweet, J. and Goodman, R.E. 1981. "Numerical and Physical Modeling of Flexural Slip Phenomena and Potential for Fault Movement", 30th Geomechanics Colloquium, Salzburg, Austria.
Roth, W.H., Sweet, J. and Goodman, R.E. 1982. "Numerical and Physical Modeling of Flexural Slip Phenomena and Potential for Fault Movement", Rock Mechanics, Suppl. 12, pp. 27-46.
Segall, P. 1982. Personal communication.
Torres, L.P. 1983. "Determination of Strength and Deformability Properties of Diatomite in the Laboratory". CE299 Paper, University of California at Berkeley, 53 p.
Yerkes, R.F., Ellsworth, W.L. and Tinsley, J.C. 1983. "Triggered Reverse Fault and Earthquake due to Crustal Unloading, Northwest Transverse Ranges, Calif.". Geology, Vol. 11, No. 5, May, pp. 287-291.

APPENDIX - CONSTITUTIVE EQUATION FOR THE DIATOMITE AT THE LOMPOC QUARRY

Field relations and laboratory testing by Torres (1983) show that the diatomite at the Lompoc quarry is essentially homogeneous, transversely isotropic rock. The rock deforms in a linear elastic manner and exhibits brittle failure with unconfined compressive strengths from 1.2 to 2.3 MPa depending on bedding plane orientations (1 MPa = 145 psi = 10 bars).

The following schematic shows the bedded diatomite with a dip angle of α and two coordinate systems: a primed system with axes parallel and perpendicular to the bedding and an unprimed system with axes parallel and perpendicular to the quarry floor.

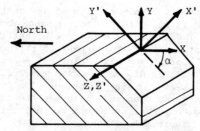

The constitutive relation for transversely isotropic elasticity is derived from the generalized Hooke's law in three dimensions as expressed in the primed coordinate system. See Goodman (1980, p. 174) for an example. Axial transformation by direction cosines (Jaeger and Cook, 1976, p. 49 or Goodman, 1980, p. 350) gives the relation for the unprimed coordinates. Further reduction from three dimensions to the condition of plane stress that exists at the quarry floor gives:

$$\begin{Bmatrix} \varepsilon_x \\ \varepsilon_z \\ \Gamma_{xz} \end{Bmatrix} = \begin{bmatrix} k_{11} & k_{12} & 0 \\ k_{21} & k_{22} & 0 \\ 0 & 0 & k_{33} \end{bmatrix} \begin{Bmatrix} \sigma_x \\ \sigma_z \\ \tau_{xz} \end{Bmatrix} \tag{A1}$$

where for $\alpha = 45°$: $k_{11} = 1/4(1/E + 1/E' + 1/G' - 2\nu'/E')$,

$k_{12} = -1/2(\nu'/E' + \nu/E)$, $k_{21} = k_{12}$, $k_{22} = 1/E$, $k_{33} = 1/2(1/G + 1/G')$.

The values of the elastic constants E, E', G', ν, and ν' are obtained by compression tests on oriented samples. For example, E and E' are determined by loading respectively parallel and perpendicular to the bedding. The value of G is computed from $E/2(1 + \nu)$. The elastic constants and direction cosines for the reference zone are thus:

E = 460 MPa, E' = 100 MPa, G = 202 MPa, G' = 108 MPa, ν = 0.14, ν' = 0.06, and $k_{11} = 5.058 \times 10^{-6}$ MPa^{-1}, $k_{12} = -452 \times 10^{-6}$ MPa^{-1}, $k_{22} = 2174 \times 10^{-6}$ MPa^{-1}, $k_{33} = 7105 \times 10^{-6}$ MPa^{-1}.

In situ stress measurements
in stratified hard rock formations

KRISHNAN SHRINIVASAN & SHOSEI SERATA
Serata Geomechanics Inc., Richmond, California, USA

1 INTRODUCTION

The mechanics of failure of the wall of a borehole in hard rock due to loading by hydraulic pressure via a plastic tube depends both on the material properties of the rock as well as on the initial stress state in the ground. This relationship has been exploited for the purpose of in situ stress and property measurement in a wide variety of geological formations.

The two most commonly used procedures for in situ stress state measurement are overcoring and hydrofracturing. These methods are limited in their applications as a result of the assumptions of ideal conditions that are inherent in them. Overcoring depends on the assumption of ideal elasticity, a condition not often found in actual ground. Overcoring is also limited in the depth of its application.

Hydrofracturing faces problems with loss of fluid pressure in porous media, stratified formations, and other types of complex and non-homogeneous ground. Misalignment of the borehole with the maximum or intermediate principal ground stress direction results in inaccuracies.

The Serata Stressmeter S-100 overcomes these limitations, first by using a plastic tube to contain the fluid while transmitting fluid pressure, and secondly, by measuring diametral deformation in four directions at equal angular intervals of 45°, to determine principal stress orientations. The Stressmeter was originally developed exclusively for ductile rocks such as salt, potash, and coal. Now it is proven equally effective in application to hard rocks.

The Stressmeter can apply a loading pressure up to 70 MPa in a roughly drilled borehole, accepting a large clearance between the borehole wall and the probe, and at the same time allowing large borehole expansion with a high-resolution deformation measurement. Operation of the instrument is described in a later section.

2 THEORY OF BRITTLE FAILURE

Failure of the boundary of a borehole subjected to loading by a dilatometer follows two distinct processes, namely, tensile fracture and shear yield (Serata & Bellman). Failure occurs in a plane perpendicular to the borehole and its process is determined only by the following basic parameters: (1) tensile strength of the rock media, T; (2) shearing

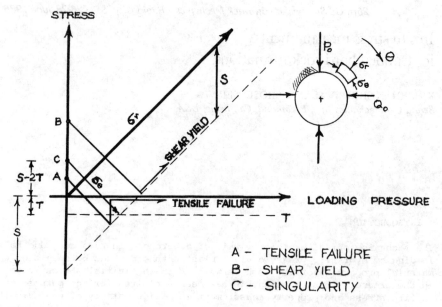

FIG. 1. Graphical Depiction of Borehole Boundary Failure Modes.

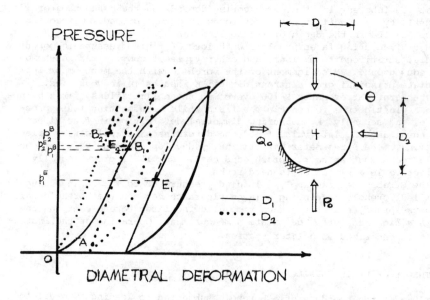

FIG. 2. Load vs. Deformation Curves for Tensile Failure in Two Mutually Perpendicular Directions.

strength of the rock media, S; (3) principal stresses, P_o, Q_o, and orientation thereof, θ.

The interaction between the initial stress state and the properties of the rock media determine the mode of failure when the borehole is subjected to hydraulic pressure. Prior to the application of the hydraulic loading, the stresses concentrated around the borehole boundary are given by the elastic relations:

$$\sigma_\theta = (P_o + Q_o) - 2(P_o - Q_o) \cos 2\theta \tag{1}$$

$$\sigma_r = 0$$

where σ_θ=tangential stress; σ_r=radial stress; P_o=maximum principal stress; Q_o=minimum principal stress; and θ=angle of deviation from the plane direction of P_o.

On application of hydraulic pressure, p, the radial component of the confining stress increases linearly with the loading pressure as shown in Fig. 1. The tangential stress decreases concurrently so that an elastic balance is maintained at all times. The mode of failure of the borehole boundary can be analyzed graphically from Fig. 1 and determined by the following criteria (Serata & Bellman):

1) Failure in the maximum principal stress direction (θ=0): Such failure is dependent upon the quantity $X=\sigma_\theta(0)-S+2T$, which is explained as follows. From Eq. 1, $\sigma_\theta(0)=3Q_o-P_o$. Therefore:

$$X = 3Q_o - P_o - S + 2T \tag{3}$$

If X<0, shear deformation occurs; if X>0, tensile failure occurs; and if X=0, both of the above occur.

2) Failure in the minimum principal stress direction ($\theta=\pi/2$): Such failure is dependent on the quantity, $Y=\sigma_\theta(\pi/2)-S+2T$. From Eq. 1, $\sigma_\theta(\pi/2)=3P_o-Q_o$. Therefore:

$$Y = 3P_o - Q_o - S + 2T \tag{4}$$

If Y>0, shear yield deformation occurs; if Y<0, tensile fracture occurs; and if Y=0, both of the above occur.

From the two expressions in Eqs. 3 and 4, it is apparent that as the hydraulic load on the borehole is increased, tensile failure of the borehole boundary would occur in two mutually perpendicular directions only if $X=3Q_o-P_o-S+2T$ 0, and $Y=3P_o-Q_o-S+2T$ 0. From the two identities expressed above, it can be said that the condition for the occurrence of tensile failure in two mutually perpendicular directions is: P_o < $1/2 \cdot (S-2T)$. Similarly, the condition for the occurrence of shear yield deformation in the two mutually perpendicular directions was derived to be $Q_o > 1/2 \cdot (S-2T)$. The condition described by $Q_o < 1/2(S-2T) < P_o$ represents a point of singularity wherein simultaneous occurrence of tensile failure in one plane and shear yield in the other can be expected.

The case under consideration in this study is the tensile fracture of hard rock subjected to hydraulic loading. The confining stress σ_θ in both the θ=0 and $\theta=\pi/2$ directions would follow a pattern similar to that depicted by Case A in Fig. 1. Fig. 2 depicts the diametral deformation measured perpendicular to the maximum principal stress direction, i.e., $\theta=\pi/2$, as a function of the loading pressure, p. It can be seen that after a large initial deformation (OA) attributed to consolidation of loose dirt at the borehole boundary, the rock behaves in an elastic fashion until Point B, where tensile fracture occurs in the plane of the maximum principal stress, i.e., $\theta=0$. Here the fracture plane does not propagate as in the case of hydrofracturing, but is controlled by an elastic balance between the confining stresses of the ground and the hydraulic loading. On further increase of the loading pressure beyond p_1^B, the initial fracture plane increases in proportion to the loading pressure and a secondary fracture is initiated in a plane perpendicular to that of the primary fracture. The point of initiation of the secondary fracture could be detected by monitoring the diametral deformation in the plane of the maximum principal stress, i.e., $\theta=0$. The dotted line in Fig. 2 represents the diametral deformation in the direction of $\theta=0$ as a function of the loading pressure. Here, the argument is confined to 2-dimensional space, ignoring borehole axis. The pressure at which the secondary failure occurs is denoted by p_2^B.

On releasing the hydraulic loading pressure, the borehole exhibits non-recoverable deformation in both planes, as represented by points D1 and D2. On the second loading cycle, the borehole wall behaves elastically until the points E1 and E2 which represent points of free separation in directions $\theta=0$ and $\theta=\pi/2$, respectively. This means that at the point E1, the loading presure (denoted by p_1^E) has overcome the confining stress $\sigma_\theta(0)$. The same reasoning applies in the direction $\theta=\pi/2$ and to the point E2. Since during the second loading cycle the loading pressure does not have to overcome the tensile strength of the rock media, T, the difference between p_1^B and p_1^E, and p_2^B and p_2^E represents the numerical value of T. Also, from the above reasoning:

$$p_1^E = \sigma_\theta(0) = 3Q_o - P_o \text{ (Eq. 5)}; \quad p_2^E = \sigma_\theta(\pi/2) = 3P_o - Q_o \text{ (Eq. 6)}$$

The solution to the set of simultaneous equations thus derived results in the determination of the values of the principal stresses.

The formation and propagation of the primary failure was simulated using the finite element method code REM. The results indicated that formation of the primary fracture did not affect the confining stress distribution in other planes around the borehole to any appreciable extent.

3 SERATA STRESSMETER

From the discussion of the mode of borehole boundary failure in hard rock, it is apparent that an instrument used to measure stresses applying this principle would be required to monitor diametral deformation in at least two planes, and more if orientation information were also needed. Accordingly, a stressmeter probe was developed at the facilities of Serata Geomechanics, Inc., which involved the use of a polyurethane loading cell and highly sensitive Linear Variable Differential Transducers (LVDTs) to monitor borehole diametral deformations.

The Stressmeter consists, basically, of two sections, a loading cell and an electronics chamber. The loading cell is a polyurethane bag about 0.895 mm long and 99 mm in diameter. Embedded in the polyurethane loading cell are diameter-sensing transducers, which are about 11 cm apart and are circumferentially staggered at intervals of 45°. The 4 LVDTs used in the loading cell have a sensitivity of better than

1 micron (10^{-6}m) of movement. Loading pressure is applied using hydraulic oil which offers unique safety features compared to pneumatic loading. Oil pressure is monitored using a sensitive pressure transducer. Signals from the pressure transducer and LVDTs are communicated to the electronics chamber at the rear of the loading cell wherein they are processed for acquisition. These processed signals are then communicated to a digital data recorder, as shown in the schematic in Fig. 3. The loading pressure vs. diametral deformation information thus obtained is stored in a magnetic tape that is analyzed by a computer via a playback unit.

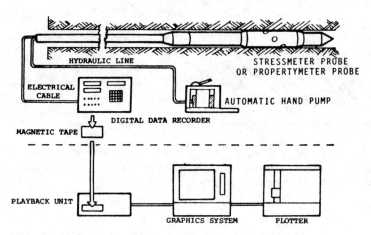

FIG. 3. Schematic of Serata Stressmeter System.

One of the main advantages of this system is the fact that all data processing is totally computerized and self-contained. Also, on-line or real time analysis of the data, invaluable in complex grounds, is possible with a portable computer. This system also does not require a ready source of electric power, as the data recorder can be operated with a bank of storage cells.

4 PRESENTATION OF RESULTS

The principle of stress measurement described in this study, and the Stressmeter probe that was constructed based on this principle, were first tested in a homogeneous and elastic rock formation of known tensile strength and known stress state. The site for this preliminary test was a surface outcropping of competent sandstone near Livermore, California.

Fig. 4 shows the load vs. deformation curve obtained from raw data taken by the stressmeter probe at a vertical depth of 7 m (21 ft). From these curves it was determined that both the primary and secondary tensile failure occurred at a loading presure of 1.4 MPa. In the second cycle of loading, the points of free separation (denoted by E1 and E2 in Fig. 2) were determined to occur simultaneously at a loading pressure of 0 MPa. Hence, from the above observation and Eqs. 5 and 6,

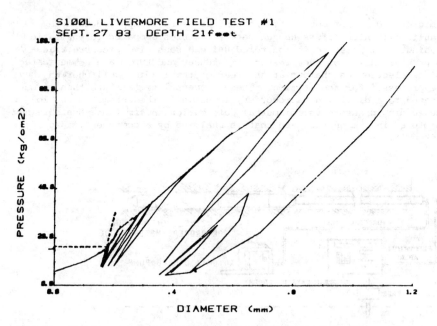

PRESSURE (kg/cm2)

DIAMETER (mm)

FIG. 4. Load vs. Deformation Curve for One Channel in Stress Measurement in Sandstone at Livermore, California.

the initial stress state was determined to be $P_o = Q_o = 0$. This result was in close agreement with the known stress state of the rock formation. The vertical stress P_o calculated from the overburden weight was expected to be less than 0.1 MPa and the lateral stress Q_o non-existent, because of the total lack of lateral confinement.

The tensile strength of the rock was calculated to be around 1.4 MPa, by taking the difference between p_1^B and p_1^E as explained in a preceding section of this study. This result was confirmed by comparison with results from a Brazilian test performed in the laboratory on sandstone. The laboratory test yielded a tensile strength of $1.3 \sim 1.4$ MPa.

The stressmeter probe was then employed to measure stress states in a schist formation near the surface in Shikoku, Japan. This formation of hard rock is characterized by wide variations in strength and the presence of numerous fractures, the latter of which renders conventional methods of stress measurement useless. A test hole 250 m deep was drilled in this formation, and the Serata stressmeter applied at different depths. Fig. 5 shows load vs. deformation curves for one set of measurements taken at a depth of 146 m.

It is obvious from Fig. 5 that after a large initial consolidation, there was tensile failure of the rock in a direction perpendicular to that of the transducer represented by Channel 1, at $p_1^B = 144.0$ kgf/cm^2. From the curve for Channel 2 the secondary fracture was determined to occur at $p_2^B = 188.7$ kgf/cm^2. From the second loading curves, the points

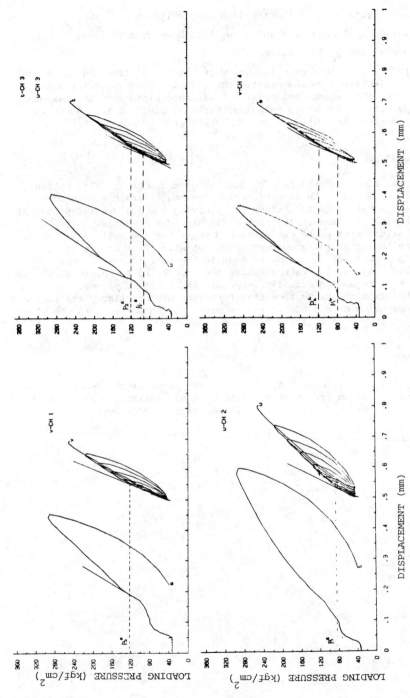

FIG. 5. Load vs. Deformation Curves for Schist Measurements at Depth of 146 m in Shikoku, Japan.

of free separation were determined to be p_1^E=81.5 kgf/cm^2 and p_2^E= 120.8 kgf/cm^2. From Eqs. 5 and 6 and the above observations, P_o = 55.6 kgf/cm^2 and Q_o=45.7 kgf/cm^2.

The principal stress orientations were determined from the magnitude of the deflection from the elastic curve in the load vs. deformation curves from the various channels. It was determined that the maximum principal stress direction coincided with the plane of Transducer #1, and the minimum principal stress direction with Transducer #2.

5 CONCLUSIONS

1) The stressmeter developed for ductile ground such as salt, potash, and coal is found to be also effective for measuring in situ ground stresses in hard rock formations by observing the failure and post-failure behavior patterns of the rock media around a borehole.

2) A stressmeter probe was developed which had the ability to measure not only the principal ground stresses but also their orientation.

3) The results of measurements made in the sandstone outcropping in Livermore, California, help validate the underlying principle of stress measurement regarding mutually perpendicular fracture planes.

4) The REM simulations show that formation of the primary fracture and its propagation do not affect stress distribution patterns in the plane perpendicular to that of the fracture.

REFERENCE

Serata, S., and Bellman, R.A. 1983. Development of the Serata stress measuring system for application to both hard-brittle and soft-ductile grounds. Proceedings, 24th U.S. Symposium on Rock Mechanics.

Predicting the in-situ state of stress
using Differential Wave Velocity Analysis

N.-K.REN & P.J.HUDSON
Dowell Schlumberger, Tulsa, Oklahoma, USA

ABSTRACT

Among the many uncertainties associated with improving the applicability of hydraulic fracturing for enhancing oil and gas production
are the difficulties in predicting azimuth and geometry of the produced fractures. Given the realization that addressing these
technological problems involves a priori knowledge of the in-situ
principal stresses acting in a reservoir, research efforts toward
developing new determination techniques are continuously active.
This paper describes a new approach based on acoustic wave
propagation through an oriented rock sample.

This technique, referred to as Differential Wave Velocity Analysis
(DWVA), is based on the assumed existence of a microcrack density
pattern, a result of stress relief during the coring process.
Evidence exists (Ren and Roegiers 1983; Teufel 1983) that the amount
of expansion a core experiences is related to the preexisting stress
components. In other words, the density of these microcracks may, in
some way, be proportional to the magnitude of the stress
differential. The ultrasonic wave technique is used to evaluate this
microcrack spatial distribution, and statistical analysis is utilized
to compensate for localized inhomogeneities.

Based on documented case studies, it appears likely that a reasonably accurate estimate of the three-dimensional state of stress
(magnitude and direction) can be obtained using the acoustic velocity
method.

INTRODUCTION

One of the consequences of the continuing depletion of oil and gas
reserves is the exploration and development of reservoirs which do
not respond to established stimulation techniques. As more sophisticated approaches become available, it becomes increasingly more
apparent that fracture geometry and selective well spacing ultimately
play a significant role in influencing the overall recovery
efficiency of a field. Among the factors which may be involved in
determining the direction and geometry of an induced fracture, it is
generally agreed upon that the existing stress field exerts the
primary control.

Smith (1979) demonstrated that ultimate recoveries could be increased substantially if conscientious efforts were made to consider the in-situ stress field when planning well spacing. Similarly, Lacy (1984) suggested the importance of determining the optimum well pattern in developing a waterflood program for enhanced recovery.

Numerous techniques already exist for determining the stress tensor at given horizons in the earth's crust. Unfortunately, many of these methods are practically limited to relatively shallow depths, or are subject to economic restrictions. Recently, techniques such as Differential Strain Curve Analysis (DSCA - Strickland and Ren 1979) and Anelastic Strain Recovery (ASR - Teufel 1983) have been used to deal with situations of significant depth. Present research is focused on a potentially faster and possibly more reliable indicator of stress directions and ratio. This technique involves monitoring the spatial variation in acoustic wave travel time.

PRINCIPLE

Following the observation of Adams and Williamson (1923) that the presence of cracks in rocks increases their compressibility, several authors (Richter et al. 1976; Batzel and Simmons 1976) proposed that microcracks in rocks may, in some manner, be related to the preexisting stress field. Based on this premise, it was reasoned that the microcrack signature existing within a rock specimen might somehow reveal its past loading history. Using the concepts proposed by Emery (1962) regarding time-dependent strain in rocks after removal from their preexisting stressed environments, several techniques such as Overcoring (Hooker and Bickell 1974), Differential Strain Curve Analysis (DSCA - Ren and Roegiers 1983) and Anelastic Strain Recovery (ASR - Teufel 1983) have led to procedures for stress prediction. Associated problems with these techniques include depth restriction (overcoring), predominant strain recovery during the coring process itself (ASR), and localized inhomogeneities affecting strain gage application and interpretation (DSCA). These restrictions have served to justify the search for alternatives.

The correlation of compressional wave velocity with applied stress in rocks is not a novel approach. Birch (1960) systematically studied the change in compressional wave velocity during the loading of rocks under hydrostatic compression. Toucher (1957) and Nur and Simmons (1969) also recognized that uniaxial stresses resulted in simultaneous velocity anisotropy with the largest velocity differential taking place in the direction of the applied stress. On the basis of these observations, a simple model representing the relationship between the acoustic behavior at ambient conditions and under confinement has been developed.

Considering viscoelastic, homogeneous rock, a simplified model of stress history can be schematically represented, as in Figure 1a (Robertson 1963; Voight 1967; Blanton 1983). The corresponding strain history, consistent with viscoelastic theory for this ideal case, is illustrated in Figure 1b. Although the crack opening mechanism during strain relaxation is not completely understood for all lithologies (Engelder and Plumb 1984), available evidence suggests that microcracks are frequently induced at the time at which the stress is released (Engelder et al. 1977; Strickland and Ren 1979; Plumb et al. 1984). During this particular research program, it has been observed that crack opening and closing in response to hydrostatic pressure, during load cycling, appeared instantaneous

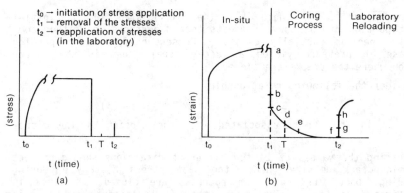

Figure 1. Schematic of stress history (a) and strain response (b).

(msec range) without a significant amount of additional time-dependent strain. In other words, during reloading the majority of the strain associated with crack closure appears to occur instantaneously in response to increasing pressure. This phenomenon suggests the hypothesis that the behavior of opening microcracks is dominantly an elastic process. It seems reasonable, therefore, that the instantaneous strain response corresponding to the removal of the in-situ stresses may be separated into two parts, as shown in Figure 1b.

- A strain segment $\overline{ab}$, resulting from linear relaxation of the rock without microcracks; and
- A strain segment $\overline{bc}$, the result of linear opening of microcracks in the rock.

During the reloading process, the segment $\overline{fg}$ (Figure 1) corresponds to $\overline{ab}$, and segment $\overline{gh}$ to $\overline{bc}$. In this model, the strain measurement segments for the aforementioned techniques are represented as over-coring (a-e), ASR (d-e), DSCA and DWVA (f-h).

DWVA involves measuring acoustic travel times in various directions as a specimen is subjected to hydrostatic reloading. This suggests that DWVA and DSCA are associated with the same strain response and hence should embody the same principles. It is thought that by reversing the expansion of the sample by applying hydrostatic pressure, the contraction of the rock in any specific direction will reflect the original strain induced during unloading (coring) at each specific stress level. A more detailed discussion of this principle and test confirmation can be found elsewhere (Ren and Roegiers 1983; Strickland and Ren 1979; Engelder and Plumb 1984).

DWVA MODEL AND INTERPRETATON

According to the viscoelastic model in Figure 1, and as confirmed by Simmons et al. (1974) and Ren and Roegiers (1983), most rocks, upon reloading, behave in a manner similar to that shown in Figure 2. This is the stress-strain relationship for a single-gage monitoring strain in one particular direction. The curve shown is characterized by two distinct linear segments separated by a transitional zone of continuously changing slope. The second linear portion (defined by the slope β) represents the intrinsic compressibility of the rock matrix after closure of all the microcracks. This corresponds to the segment $\overline{gh}$ or $\overline{ab}$ in Figure 1b. The higher slope of the initial linear portion of the curve suggests that the cracks are either completely open or partially closed. Consequently, a corresponding increase in pressure yields a larger strain than in the latter portion where the cracks are closed.

Consider the following relationship:

$$\beta + \varepsilon' = \theta \qquad (1)$$

where ε' is the strain associated with the closing of the microcracks.

Comparing the values of ε' for different directions should reflect the microcrack density, hence the past stress history. During reloading, once the induced microcracks are closed, the rock is approximated as linear elastic and the wave velocity should remain relatively unchanged with pressure increases . This has been demonstrated by Nur (1971) and Teufel (1983). In a similar manner, prior to crack closure, strain response will be represented by a lower wave velocity or greater corresponding travel time (Figures 3a and 3b, respectively). Comparing curves in Figures 2 and 3b suggests the existence of a possible relationship in which the travel-time curve is analogous to the derivative of the strain curve. The value of the time delay caused by the closing of all of the microcracks may then be defined as:

$$T_\theta - T_\beta = T' \quad . \qquad (2)$$

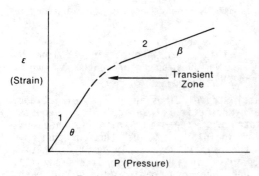

Figure 2. Typical strain curve upon reloading.

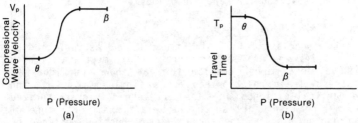

Figure 3. Ideal compressional wave velocity (a) and travel time curve (b) upon reloading.

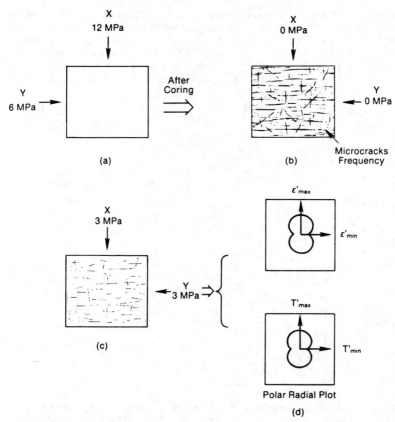

Figure 4. Micorcrack vs pressure schematic: (a) in-situ, (b) after coring, (c) after reloading, and (d) polar plot of strain.

For a two-dimensional case, a simplified example illustrates the basic principles. In Figure 4a, consider a rock under a triaxial state of: 12 MPa in the X-direction and 6 MPa in the Y-direction.

Upon coring, the in-situ stresses are released and the rock is allowed to expand in all directions. Because the X-direction has suffered the greatest stress release, it is hypothesized to expand the most due to crack genesis. Likewise, the Y-direction is least cracked as it has had the least amount of stress release. This is shown schematically in Figure 4b. Upon reloading (Figure 4c), since most cracks are perpendicular to the X-direction, it will be the one most easily compressed and will, therefore, have the highest value of ϵ' and T' at 3 MPa of pressure (refer to Figure 4d).

Applying this simplistic model, the differential values of the wave travel time for different directions can then be used to determine the velocity tensor and to indirectly determine the stress conditions. The detailed formulation of the statistical approach used is similar to that used for DSCA (Ren and Roegiers 1983).

By assuming that the rock is either homogeneous and isotropic, or transversely isotropic, theoretically it may be possible to determine the stress orientation, and approximate the stress ratio by performing tests at atmospheric conditions. In the laboratory, it has been demonstrated that, for isotropic rock, the intrinsic compressibility is essentially equal in all directions. As a result, the intrinsic travel times (T_C) are also basically equivalent, i.e.:

$$T_{\beta 1} \simeq T_{\beta 2} \simeq T_{\beta 3} \simeq T_{\beta 4} = T_C \,. \qquad (3)$$

On this basis:

$$T_{\theta 1} = T_1' + T_C$$
$$T_{\theta 2} = T_2' + T_C$$
$$T_{\theta 3} = T_3' + T_C$$
$$T_{\theta 4} = T_4' + T_C$$

(refer to Figure 5 for relative orientations)

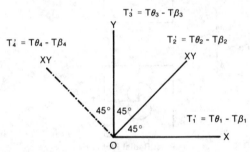

Figure 5. This represents a two-dimensional case, where the differential travel time (T') for each specific direction is defined as the difference between T_θ and T_β (refer to Equation 2).

From these relationships, it can be implied that the principal directions of T' solved for (T_1', T_2', T_3', T_4') and T_θ solved for ($T_{\theta 1}$, $T_{\theta 2}$, $T_{\theta 3}$, $T_{\theta 4}$) produce the same results. Therefore, if assumptions of sample isotropy can be reliably made, then the interpretation of the unconfined data can ultimately be relied upon to provide reasonable predictions of the in-situ stress field. If isotropy or transverse isotropy cannot be assumed, a confined test is required.

PROCEDURE

Benchtop Testing

As mentioned, if mechanical isotropy can be inferred, testing at unconfined conditions may be indicative of stress directionality. This is a relatively quick, nondestructive test which is basically similar to a typical, unconfined, dynamic, mechanical properties testing. The sample configuration consists of a core carefully cut along known orientations to the shape of a dodecahexahedron (Figure 6). Each specimen is ground flat to ensure parallelism to make the angle between any two adjacent faces equal to 225°. Compressional waves are transmitted through the sample in nine directions and velocities are recorded for analysis using an oscilloscope.

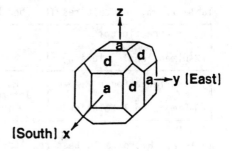

Figure 6.   Dodecahexahedron
specimen.

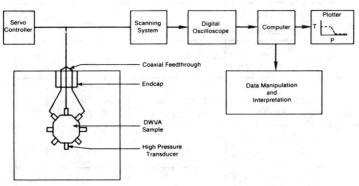

Figure 7.   Schematic of the DWVA apparatus.

Hydrostatic Loading

In a situation where mechanical isotropy cannot be assumed, hydrostatic confining pressure is applied to the same sample configuration.   During loading, the compressional wave travel time is
monitored using specially designed acoustic transducers with an
operating range of up to 150 MPa pressure and 100°C. These transducers are mounted on the sample with silicone rubber and the entire
sample is encapsulated in a plastic jacket to prevent intrusion of
the confining fluid.   In an attempt to minimize the noise level in
the system, coaxial feedthroughs were constructed for transmitting
the signals generated.

The entire assembly is then placed inside a pressure vessel and
subjected incrementally to a hydrostatic load up to approximately 100
to 140 MPa, depending on the depth from which the core was retrieved
(refer to Figure 7).

RESULTS

The results from confined and unconfined tests performed on core
obtained from the Multiwell Experimental Site near Rifle, Colorado,
are summarized in Tables 1 and 2. Both two-dimensional (transducers
in single plane) and three-dimensional (three-dimensional transducer
array) data are included for comparison.   The primary difference
between the two methods is that in two-dimensions one can only
determine the stress orientation based on relative differences in the
acoustic wave travel time.   On the other hand, three-dimensional
measurements also allow the determination of stress ratios and

Table 1. Ambient test results (benchtop).

Direction of σ_{HMAX} (2-Dimensional Solution)		N82°W ($\pm$2°)
Orientation of T_θ (3-Dimensional Solution)	Maximum Intermediate Minimum	Vertical ($\pm$5°) N85°W (+5°) N5°E ($\pm$5°)

Table 2. Hydrostatic test results.

2-Dimensional Solution	Direction of σ_{HMAX}		N83°W ($\pm$3°)
	Ratio of $\sigma_{HMAX}:\sigma_{HMIN}$		1.6 $\pm$ 0.1
3-Dimensional Solution	[†]Orientation of T'	Maximum Intermediate Minimum	Vertical ($\pm$10°) N85°W (+8°) N8°E ($\pm$5°)
	Ratio of $\sigma_V:\sigma_{HMAX}:\sigma_{HMIN}$		1.35:1.24:1.00
	$\sigma_V, \sigma_{HMAX}, \sigma_{HMIN}$ (MPa)		49.6, 46.5, 39.3

[†]The value of T_θ is used for benchtop test calculations, and the value of T' is used for hydrostatic test calculations.

ultimately stress magnitude, provided the overburden is a principal stress component and can be estimated from a field density log or other auxiliary measurement.

In order to evaluate the validity of the DWVA method, Table 3 lists the results from other stress prediction techniques performed on the

Table 3. Data interpretation comparison.

Technique	Maximum Horizontal Stress Orientation
Microhydraulic fracturing	N70°W $\pm$ 5°
Surface fracture mapping	N79°W $\pm$ 10°
Overcoring (surface outcrop)	N90°W $\pm$ 15°
Anelastic Strain Recovery (ASR)	N80°W $\pm$ 10°
Vertical fracture in cores	N75°W
Caliper log	N75°W $\pm$ 15°
Televiewer	N75°W $\pm$ 10°
Differential Strain Curve Analysis (DSCA)	N80°W $\pm$ 10°
Differential Wave Velocity Analysis (DWVA)	N85°W $\pm$ 10°

same well. Laboratory testing similar to this has been performed on several other sedimentary formations (various lithologies) giving results consistent with DSCA, and other measurements when available.

DISCUSSION AND CONCLUSIONS

In many ways, Differential Wave Velocity Analysis may be considered an analog of Differential Strain Curve Analysis, as they both impose the same assumptions. Most of the experimental research done to develop DSCA may be applied to DWVA. This includes conceptual limitations due to the effects of past geologic events, such as erosional offloading or tectonic diversity. Nevertheless, DWVA does have several advantages over DSCA.

- Less localization effect due to measuring deformation under the small area of a strain gage (DSCA). In DWVA, the wave behavior traveling through the entire sample dimension is considered.
- Increased accuracy and reproducibility (evident from experiments performed to date as a consequence of the above advantage).
- Less sample preparation time and less cost.
- A nondestructive benchtop test may be possible.

One of the aspects which remains uncertain involves the crack opening mechanism. The effect of preexisting microcrack fabrics and the apparent preferred crack opening orientation in some igneous and metamorphic textures is still not clear. An ongoing effort is being made to recognize and to separate these effects.

At this stage in the investigation, it appears promising that DWVA can conceivably be used to make a realistic estimate of the three-dimensional stress field at depth, especially for a sedimentary sequence. With additional case studies, comparisons between DWVA and other available techniques will serve to generate a better understanding of the relationship between strain recovery and the in-situ state of stress.

ACKNOWLEDGMENTS

Charles Stevens and Sam Carter assisted in sample preparation and testing design. Nick D'Avirro assisted in transducer design. We wish to thank John McLennan for his review, and thanks are also extended to the management of Dowell Schlumberger for permission to publish this paper.

REFERENCES

Adams, L. N. and E. D. Williamson 1923. The compressibility of minerals and rocks at high pressure. J. Franklin Inst. 195:475-529.
Batzel, M. L. and G. Simmons 1976. Microfractures in rocks from two geothermal areas. Earth Planet. Sci. Lett. 30:71-93.
Birch, F. 1960. The velocity of compressional waves in rocks to 10 kilobars. J. Geophys. Res. 65:1083.
Blanton, T. L. 1983. The relation between recovery deformation and in-situ stress magnitudes. SPE/DOE Symposium on Low Permeability Gas Recovery. SPE 11624.
Engelder, T., M. L. Sbar and R. Kranz 1977. A mechanism for strain relaxation of Barre granite: opening of microfractures. Pure Appl. Geophys. 115:27-40.
Engelder, T. and R. Plumb 1984. Change in in-situ ultrasonic

properties of rock on strain relaxation. Int. J. Rock Mech. Min. Sci. & Geomech. Abstr. 21:(2)75-82.

Emery, C. L. 1962. The measurement of strains in mine rock. Proc. Int. Symp. on Mining Research. Pergamon Press 2:541-554.

Hooker, V. E. and D. L. Bickell 1974. Overcoring equipment and techniques used in rock stress determination. USBMIC 8618:32.

Lacy, L. L. 1984. Comparison of hydraulic fracture orientation techniques. Proc. Annual SPE Tech. Conf. and Exhib. (SPE 13325).

Nur, A. 1971. Effect of stress on velocity anisotropy in rock with cracks. J. Geophys. Res. 76(8).

Nur, A. and G. Simmons 1969. The origin of small cracks in igneous rocks. Int. J. Rock Mech. Min. Sci. 7:307.

Ren, N.-K. and J.-C. Roegiers 1983. Differential Strain Curve Analysis -- a new method for determining the preexisting in-situ stress state from rock core measurements. 5th Congress Int. Soc. Rock Mech. F117-F127.

Richter, D., G. Simmons and R. Siegfried 1976. Microcracks, micropores, and their petrologic interpretation for 72415 and 15418. Proc. 7th Lunar Sci. Conf. 1901-1923.

Robertson, E. C. 1963. Viscoelasticity of rocks: state of stress in the earth crust. Proc. Int. Conf.

Plumb, R., T. Engelder and D. Yale 1984. Near-surface in-situ stress: 3. Correlation with microcrack fabric within the New Hampshire granite. J. Geophys. Res. 89:(B11) 9350-9364.

Simmons, G., and D. A. Richter 1974. Microcracks in rocks. The physics and chemistry of minerals and rocks (R.G.J. Strens, ed.). Interscience, New York. 105-137.

Simmons, G., R. W. Siegfried and M. Feves 1974. Differential Strain Analysis: a new method for examining cracks in rocks. J. Geophys. Res. 79:4383-4385.

Smith, M. B. 1979. Effect of fracture azimuth on production with application to the Watenburg gas field. Proc. Annual SPE Tech. Conf. and Exhib. (SPE 8298).

Strickland, F. G., M. L. Feves and D. Sorrels 1979. Microstructural damage in Cotton Valley cores. Proc. Annual SPE Tech. Conf. and Exhib. (SPE 8303).

Strickland, F. G. and N.-K. Ren 1980. Use of Differential Strain Curve Analysis in predicting in-situ stress state for deep wells. Proc. 21st U.S. Rock Mech. Symp.

Toucher, D. 1957. Anisotropy in rocks under simple compression. Trans. AGU 38111:89.

Tuefel, L. W. 1983. Determination of in-situ stress from anelastic strain recovery measurements of oriented core. SPE/DOE Symposium on Low Permeability. SPE 11649.

Voight, B. 1968. Determination of the virgin state of stress in the vicinity of a borehole from measurements of partial anelastic strain tensor in drill cores. Rock Mech. Eng. Geol. 6:210-215.

26. Physical modeling

Chair: J.B.CHEATHAM, Jr.
         Rice University, Houston, Texas, USA
Cochair: PAUL E.SENSENY
         RE/SPEC Inc., Rapid City, South Dakota, USA

A study on the validity of stress measurements in jointed crystalline rock

SCOTT BROWN, WILLIAM HUSTRULID & ARCHIE RICHARDSON
Colorado School of Mines, Golden, USA

1 INTRODUCTION

Block tests have recently become popular as part of the on going effort to characterize the host rock surrounding proposed repositories for storage of nuclear waste. Block tests have the advantage over laboratory and borehole tests in that a relatively large volume of rock is tested. This should diminish scaling considerations which often represent a major unknown when modeling parameters are derived from geomechanical test results. The disadvantage of block testing is the relative cost of these tests. For this reason, standard practice is to install as many instruments as possible in the block in the interest of maximizing information obtained from each test.

Stress measurements have been incorporated in most planned or completed block tests. Stresses are not measured directly, rather, strains or displacements are sensed and the stresses backcalculated. Typically, the calculations involve the familiar assumptions of linear elasticity, isotropy, and homogeneity. These assumptions may be reasonably good for crude modeling of overall excavation behavior. However, the extreme scatter in measured stresses indicate that they are not good for interpretation of borehole stress measurements in typical crystalline rocks which are nonhomogeneous, anisotropic and which contain numerous discontinuities on several scales.

The general problem can be broken down into two major aspects; (1) stress calculation requires an accurate knowledge of the tensor of elastic properties at the measurement point, which in itself is difficult to determine, and (2) the actual stress field is probably quite complex in itself. These two sources of variation in stress measurements are very difficult to separate employing the usual block test instrumentation setup. Typically elastic modulus values are determined from cores taken during drilling of stress measurement holes. These cores are then suitably instrumented with strain gages and tested in the laboratory. The resulting modulus is not generally reflective of the elastic tensor "seen" by the stress probe during subsequent testing. If the strain-relief overcoring method is used, some measure of anisotropy in elastic constants can be obtained by biaxial testing of the overcores. However, overcoring is not used in block tests because the high cost of excavating the block usually necessitates repeated testing of the same block. The impact of the overcoring holes on block geometry is not acceptable. Dilatometer

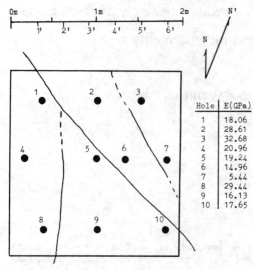

Hole	E(GPa)
1	18.06
2	28.61
3	32.68
4	20.96
5	19.24
6	14.96
7	5.44
8	29.44
9	16.13
10	17.65

Figure 1. Plan view of test block showing fracture orientation, EX holes tested and CSM cell results.(Sour, 1985)

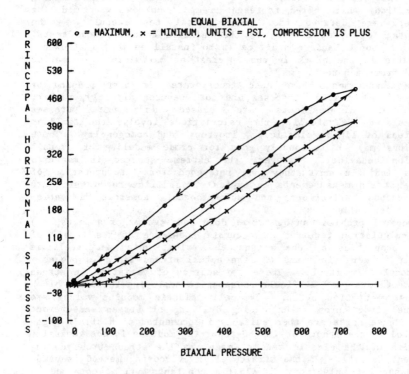

Figure 2. Typical plot of principal stress versus applied equal biaxial compression from a USBM gage.

testing of the measurement boreholes provides an average modulus value but no information on anisotropy. All of the present directional borehole modulus instruments suffer from major instrumental problems. (Hustrulid, 1976, Heuze and Salem, 1977).

Stress-field anisotropy presents similar difficulties when interpreting block-test stress measurements. The results of modeling a discontinuous system show large variations in the stress field due to the interaction of the various subblocks comprising the block (Lemos & Brady, 1983). In their model, Lemos and Brady used a hybrid model that enabled cost-effective modeling of discontinuities on several scales. They modeled a block assembly comprised of subblocks of elastic material dissected by a large, through going diagonal fracture. This geometry, though simple, is similar in concept to the CSM test block. They found that even hydrostatic loading caused a complex stress distribution which was strongly influenced by the major discontinuity. In a real block test the geometry of the subblocks and of boundary conditions may be even more complex. The anisotropy and inhomogeneity of the subblock rock material adds another level of complexity. Such a problem is certainly not amenable to characterization by perhaps a dozen point measurements.

2 TESTING

The present study was performed using an in-situ block excavated as part of an earlier study (Hardin, et al, 1981). Flatjacks on four sides of the block provide a controllable stress boundary condition on these sides. An attached block bottom and a free surface at the top of the block complete the picture.

Two types of borehole instruments were used in the block. For localized modulus determination, a CSM cell dilatometer system (Hustrulid and Hustrulid, 1972) was used. This instrument consists of an inflatable adiprene membrane, a screw-type pressure generator, and a pressure transducer. Using the instrument the EX boreholes can be internally pressurized, and through an appropriate calibration procedure an average modulus can be obtained. For localized stress determination, the USBM Borehole Deformation Gage was used. For a description of this instrument, see Merrill and Peterson (1962). Ten USBM gages were used in this investigation.

The ten USBM gages were set into vertical EX holes to a position at the block midplane, enabling a two-dimensional study of the stresses in a horizontal plane at that level. Each hole was carefully analyzed with a miniaturized borehole camera to determine the optimum locations for seating the displacement-sensing buttons.

The block was then subjected to four stress loading cycles, with σ (applied) peaking at 5.25 MPa in each cycle. Two of the tests were equal-biaxial tests ($\sigma_1 = \sigma_2$), and two were uniaxial ($\sigma_1 \gg \sigma_2$). Both NS and EW directions for P were employed.

3 RESULTS

3.1 CSM Cell

In each hole the CSM cell was centered at the location where a USBM gage was to be placed. The system was cycled 3 times and separate

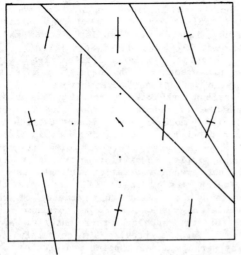

Hole	MPa P	Q	degrees Theta
1	2.92	0.00	350
2	3.73	0.39	359
3	6.22	0.80	16
4	2.21	0.76	16
5	1.17	-0.08	38
6	3.66	-0.09	356
7	3.40	0.87	-19
8	8.64	0.33	11
9	3.31	0.76	347
10	2.90	0.19	354

Theta is counter-clockwise positive from north.

Figure 3. Vector plot of principal stress distribution from a north-south uniaxial compression test. Nominal pressure is 5.25 MPa. Compression is positive.

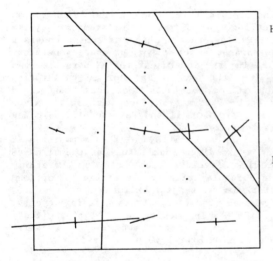

Hole	MPa P	Q	degrees Theta
1	1.87	0.25	104
2	3.81	0.67	73
3	5.02	0.16	101
4	1.76	0.27	68
5	3.21	-0.79	79
6	4.16	1.66	94
7	3.53	1.43	-50
8	13.95	1.09	93
9	2.98	0.15	106
10	4.19	0.67	92

Figure 4. Vector plot of principal stress distribution from an east-west uniaxial compression test. Nominal pressure is 5.25 MPa. compression is positive.

values were calculated for loading and unloading, resulting in 6 different modulus values for each hole. The average for these six values at each measurement location is shown in Figure 1 resulting in an overall average of 20.31 GPa for the entire block. An unusually low value was measured at hole 7. One explanation for this is the fact that hole 7 was located in a highly fractured area observed in the T.V. borehole logs.

3.2 Stress Determination

Data from the USBM gages was reduced using individual hole modulus corresponding to each gage. A typical plot of principal horizontal stresses versus applied flatjack pressure is shown in Figure 2. Of interest is the linearity of both principal stresses and that the calculated maximum stress, P is approximately equal to the calculated minimum stress, Q. In all cases notable hysteresis is evident with the down load curve being above the upload curve. Additionally, all cases return to the zero load conditions. A compilation of all the data results in the vector plots depicted in Figures 3 through 6.

When north-south (Figure 3) or east-west (figure 4) uniaxial loading was applied to the block, compressive principal stresses parallel to the applied stress field were calculated. Magnitudes were variable but in most cases they compared favorably with applied flatjack pressures throughout the load range.

The biaxial case (Figure 5) resulted in a complex calculated stress field that seems to be more affected by the discontinuities in the block. Of particular interest is the trend towards orthogonality of the principal compressive stresses to the nearest vertical fracture as applied load increases. At low stress levels, 0.70 MPa, (Figure

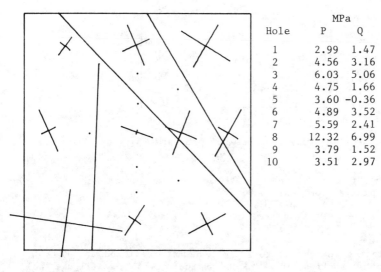

| Hole | MPa | | degrees |
	P	Q	Theta
1	2.99	1.47	−29
2	4.56	3.16	24
3	6.03	5.06	59
4	4.75	1.66	25
5	3.60	−0.36	70
6	4.89	3.52	−22
7	5.59	2.41	−30
8	12.32	6.99	82
9	3.79	1.52	−34
10	3.51	2.97	355

Figure 5. Vector plot of principal stress distribution from an equal biaxial compression test. Nominal pressure is 5.25 MPa. Compression is positive.

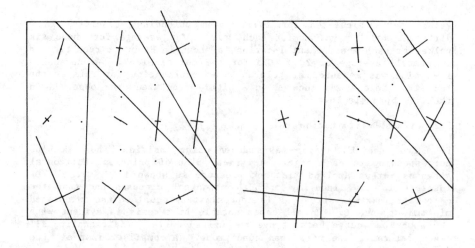

a.) 0.70 MPa nominal pressure   b.) 2.35 MPa nominal pressure

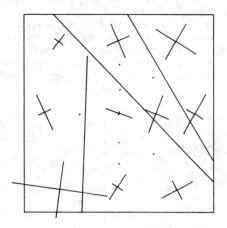

c.) 5.25 MPa nominal pressure

Figure 6. Vector plots of three different stress levels
in an equal biaxial compression test.

6a) the principal stress vectors are somewhat scattered and P >> Q.
Increasing the applied load to a nominal 2.35 MPa (Figure 6b)
resulted in rotations of the principal stresses towards orthagonality
with the nearest fracture and P approaching Q. Finally at the peak
load, 5.25 MPa (Figure 6c) further rotation is evident and the
measured stress field is increasingly hydrostatic.

4 CONCLUSIONS AND RECOMMENDATIONS

In conclusion, USBM gages seem to be a good way to measure stresses in crystalline-rock block tests. Principal stresses measured within the block align very well under uniaxial stress and appear to be related to the fracture orientation under biaxial stress. Better alignment with respect to the applied stress directions would be expected to develop if higher applied stresses were attainable. Flatjack construction precluded application of pressures above 5.6 MPa. Variation of stress magnitudes within the block result in part from the difficulty in separating modulus variation from stress field variation.

Determination of anisotropic elastic properties and their application in USBM gage reduction would probably improve measured stress results (Amadei, 1983). Further investigations in this area are currently being pursued at CSM, in conjunction with B. Amadei of University of Colorado.

5 NOTICE/DISCLAIMER

6 ACKNOWLEDGEMENTS

The financial support for the work reported was through contract E512-11800 with the Project Management Division of the Battelle Memorial Institute, Columbus, Ohio.

7 REFERENCES

Amadei, B. 1983. Rock anisotropy and the theory of stress measurements. New York, Springer-Verlag, 478 pp.

El Rabaa, A.W.M.A. 1982. Measurement and modeling of rock mass response to underground excavation. M.S. Thesis, Colorado School of Mines, 274 pp.

Hardin, E., Lingle, R. Board, M. and Voegel, M. 1981. A heated flatjack test series to measure the thermomechanical and transport properties of in situ rock masses. ONWI Report (ONWI-260), 193 pp.

Hueze, F.E. and Salem, A. 1977. Rock deformability measured in-situ problems and solutions. Proc. Int. Symp. on Field Meas. in Rock Mech. Zurich, A.A. Balkema, Rotterdam. pp. 375-387.

Hustrulid, W.A. and Hustrulid, A. 1972. CSM borehole device - assembly, calibration and use. Final Report to U.S.B.M. on extension to contract HO 101705.

Hustrulid, W.A. 1976. An analysis of the Goodman jack. Proc. 17th U.S. Symp. on Rock Mech. Showbird Utah. pp. 4B10-1 to 4B10-8.

Lemos, J. and Brady, B. 1983. Stress distribution in a jointed and fractured medium. 24th U.S. Symposium on Rock Mechanics. pp, 53–59.

Merrill, R. and Peterson, J. 1962. Deformation of a borehole in rock. U.S.B.M. Report, Investigation No. 5881.

Sour, L. 1985. Personal communication.

Load response of modelled underground structures

KHOSROW BAKHTAR, ALAN BLACK & ROBERT CAMERON
Terra Tek Inc., Salt Lake City, Utah, USA

ABSTRACT

A series of seven tests were conducted on circular cross-section modelled tunnels simulated in large blocks of jointed tuff-rock-simulant. Tests were performed under quasi-static and dynamic loading
conditions. Similitude laws were used for the design of models and
the fabrication of rock simulating material. The model material was
poured in steps in a large 1 cubic-meter mold to create planes of
discontinuities for simulating joints around modelled structures. A
scale factor of 27:1 was used for linear dimensions as well as
strength related parameters. Model tunnels were instrumented with
displacement transducers for monitoring deformation behavior. Each
instrumented model was subjected to a hydrostatic stress field prior
to increasing the load in axial direction. The stress-deformation
characteristics, as well as the rise time of loading, were used to
predict the behavior of prototype structures under different loading
conditions. For quasi-static tests, the peak vertical stress was
2.30 MPa which caused about 17 mm and 21 mm closure in horizontal and
vertical sides of the modelled tunnel. For dynamic tests, the peak
stress was computed to be 2.88 MPa which corresponded to a rise time
of 187 milliseconds and closures of 15 mm and 21 mm in the horizontal
and vertical sides of the modelled tunnel. Results of scaled-model
testing were used to predict prototype behavior subjected to similar
loading conditions.

INTRODUCTION

An experimental testing program was devised to study the behavior of
circular-cross section modelled tunnels constructed in jointed host
rock. The large size of samples (1m^3) was designed to extend the
data base beyond the usual limitations of laboratory test equipment.
The study consisted of physically modelling tunnels 4.57 m in diameter in tuff with parallel smooth joints at 2 m spacing with strikes
parallel to tunnel axis and dip at 45° to the horizontal.

The conditions of similarity between the prototype rock and modelling materials were applied using the basic theory of physical modelling to design and construct rock simulants. Granular and filler
materials cemented with Portland cement were used to simulate scaled

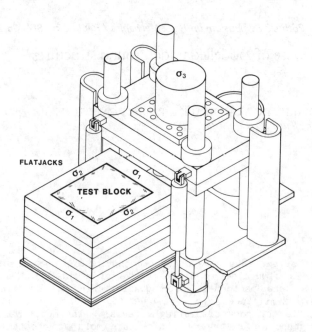

Figure 1.   Terra Tek's large polyaxial testing facility for loading
1m³ blocks of intact or jointed rock.   Horizontal stresses of σ_1 and
σ_2 are applied by flatjacks, with a maximum rating of 35 MPa.
Dynamic loads are applied by the (σ_3) actuator charged with gas.

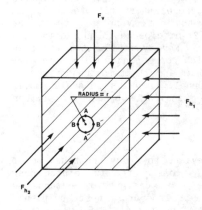

Figure 2. Schematic of model tunnel with associated joints subjected to hydrostatic stress-field.

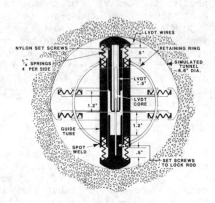

Figure 3.   Deformation gauge
for measuring model tunnel
load response.

properties of tuff. In order to control the mechanical and physical properties of the simulant, the cement agent, filler materials and water portions of the mix were adjusted and twenty different trial batches were prepared. Cylindrical test samples were cast from each batch and subsequently tested for their mechanical and physical properties to determine the most appropriate mix proportion. The main physical and mechanical properties which were important for the best choice of simulant for tuff were: unconfined compressive strength, tensile strength, Young's modulus, Poisson's ratio, angle of internal friction, and bulk density. Dimensionless properties, such as Poisson's ratio and angle of internal friction, were matched exactly for the model and prototype. Parameters such as linear dimensions and strength were scaled down such that a scale factor 27:1 was maintained between prototype and model. Equation 1 was used to design the tuff-simulant based on similitude laws.

$$\tau^* = \rho^* \, \ell^* \tag{1}$$

where: τ^* = stress scale factor (τ_p/τ_m)

ρ^* = density scale factor (ρ_p/ρ_m)

ℓ^* = geometry scale factor (ℓ_p/ℓ_m)

subscripts m and p refer to model and prototype, respectively. The density scale factor was kept at unity.

An aluminum mold with capacity of $1m^3$ was used for casting large blocks of test samples. The mold contained a heavy plastic tube at the center to simulate the tunnel. This tube was withdrawn following the completion of casting and curing operations. By tilting the mold and employing a step-by-step casting procedure, the orientation and spacing of joints were controlled. Each test block was cured for sixteen days prior to testing.

Terra Tek's large polyaxial testing facility was used to load the test blocks under quasi-static and dynamic loading conditions. From the seven large scale tests, three tests were performed under conditions of pseudo-static loading. The remaining four tests were performed at dynamic rates of loading. Peak axial loads of over 10,000 KN were obtained in about 180 milliseconds using a high pressure gas charged loading system. Figure 1 shows the overall view of the large polyaxial testing frame.

TESTING

Each test sample was initially subjected to a hydrostatic stress field prior to loading to failure in the axial direction, Figure 2. The load response in each case was measured in two orthogonal directions at three locations along the model tunnel axis using a deformation gauge (Figure 3) with the associated displacement transducers. Output of all transducers were monitored and subsequently stored using a dedicated computer system with the associated high rate data acquisition unit.

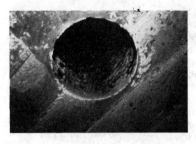

Figure 4. Sectional view of tunnel before quasi-static test.

Figure 5. Section view after quasi-static test.

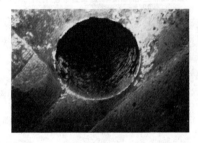

Figure 6. Sectional view of model tunnel before dynamic event.

Figure 7. Sectional view of model tunnel after dynamic test.

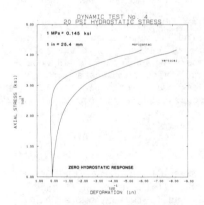

Figure 8. Load-deformation curves for tunnel tested under dynamic load.

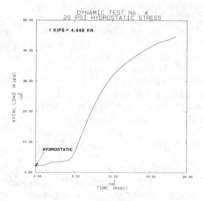

Figure 9. Load-risetime for dynamic test on modelled tunnel.

The initial hydrostatic field ranged between 0.00 to 1.034 MPa. Testing procedure consisted of pressurizing the flatjacks in the two horizontal directions while simultaneously applying the axial load to create the initial stress field and then increasing the axial load either quasi-statically or dynamically to cause structural failure.

ANALYSIS OF QUASI-STATIC AND DYNAMIC DATA

For the purpose of this study, the load response of the model tunnels was of interest. Furthermore, the effect of σ_{h2} (Figure 2), i.e. stress parallel to fracture plane, was only accounted for to plot the stress path and was ignored in subsequent analysis.

For quasi-static and dynamic tests, the following data was derived and plotted:

o   second stress deviator invariant, $(J_2')^{1/2}$ versus pressure, $(J_1/3)$, where J_1 is the first stress invariant - stress path.

o   load deformation curves:

  -   axial deformation
  -   transverse deformation

The first and second stress deviator invariants were computed using Equations 2 and 3

$$\text{pressure} = \frac{J_1}{3} = \frac{\sigma_{ii}}{3} = \frac{1}{3}(\sigma_v + \sigma_{h1} + \sigma_{h2}) \tag{2}$$

$$\sqrt{J_2'} = \frac{1}{2}S_{ij}S_{ij} = [\frac{(\sigma_v-\sigma_{h1})^2 + (\sigma_{h1}-\sigma_{h2})^2 + (\sigma_v-\sigma_{h2})^2}{6}$$

$$+ (\text{shear stress terms})]^{1/2} \tag{3}$$

TYPICAL RESULTS

Examples illustrating the load response of circular cross-section tunnels subjected to quasi-static and dynamic stress fields are given in this section. For all tests, increase in applied axial load resulted in subsequent pressure buildup in flatjacks, typical of proportional loading case. Figures 4 and 5 show sectional view of a modelled tunnel before and after a quasi-static test. Closures in both vertical and horizontal sides of the tunnel were observed following the completion of test. Figures 6 and 7 show sectional views of a tunnel prior to and after a dynamic test. The deformation curves as well as the load-risetime variation for these tests are also given in Figures 8 and 9. Load deformation curves for dynamic tests show that closures occurred in both directions in the model. However, the horizontal sides of the tunnel exhibited some expansion at the early stage of loading.

CONCLUSION

Results of seven large scale tests on model tunnels constructed in jointed tuff-rock-simulant are used to predict behavior of prototype structures subjected to similar loading conditions. The scale factor used for this study was 27:1, for geometry and stress related parameters. The density scale factor was kept at unity. In order to predict the prototype static load response, deformation and stress are magnified by a factor of 27. The tunnel deformations observed in models were less than what was expected based on the authors' previous experience with intact rock. The main reason for the small observed radial deformations could be the presence of uniformly spaced joints and the boundary conditions which prevented the stress trajectories to be transmitted across the interfaces.

ACKNOWLEDGEMENTS

The authors are indebted to the Defense Nuclear Agency for funding this project. We are also indebted to Mohamad Khodaverdian, Robert Hendrickson, Scott Woodhead, and Jerard Bohman of Terra Tek for their invaluable support. Special thanks are extended to Ms. Anne MacLeod for typing and editing the manuscript.

Physical model study of a longwall mine

DUK-WON PARK & DWAYNE C.KICKER
University of Alabama, Tuscaloosa, USA

1 INTRODUCTION

An integral facet of ground control in longwall coal mining is
understanding the stress distribution in the longwall panel and
surrounding chain pillars as the longwall face advances. There are
many available methods of study such as field measurement,
analytical solution, numerical simulation and physical modeling.
Usually these methods are combined for solving actual problems.

However, for complex conditions, extensive field instrumentation
requires a great expense, and both numerical modeling and the
analytical solution become extremely complicated. Provided that
essential variables are known and proper methods are used, physical
modeling can solve many problems quickly at considerably less cost.

Admittedly, rock mechanics modeling is not an easy task. It is
often necessary to lessen the strength of a model material and
change its physical properties in order to meet the law of
similitudes. A synthetic material which will satisfy all
requirements can probably never be created, therefore a compromise
is necessary for practical purposes (Obert & Duvall 1967). For
example, if shear strength is the dominant mode of failure in the
prototype, then that relationship in the model should be satisfied
with all other failure modes disregarded.

The major topics in this study include development of a new model
and model material, stress measuring technique and results of tests.

2 LONGWALL MINE MODEL

Harris (1974) simulated the European longwall mining method using a
sandbox model and examined the stress distribution around a longwall
face. In the sandbox, floor strips were installed and they were
lowered one by one, simulating gob development as a result of
longwall face advancing. Miniature load cells were emplaced on the
bottom of the box to monitor stress distribution in the panel and
rib around the longwall panel. It has to be noted that chain
pillars are not generally used in European coal mines.

In the earlier stages of the model development a similar concept
was used as Harris' model. The model utilized steel rods that would
slide or drop out of the bottom of the sandbox creating openings in

the sand to simulate the room and pillar mining method (Park et al., 1983). However, because of the differences in compliance values between model material and steel, an uneven initial stress distribution was created during the compaction. Therefore, a new concept was developed in which the mine openings are actually excavated in the sand with a special excavation tool. The tool is a steel rod with two types of excavation devices on either end of the rod (Figure 1). The right end allows excavation without compacting the sand, and the left end consists of a 2.54 cm (1 in.) wide scraper, which provides a clean, rectangular entry. This tool worked very effectively throughout the experiments using the improved models for chain pillar stress measurement and longwall panel front abutment.

Figure 1.   Excavation tool.

2.1 Model material

For the physical longwall mine model, model material is required to simulate coal, which does not react to stress as a perfect elastic material but behaves as an elasto-plastic material. During the period of yielding, stress transfers from one pillar to others and some of the amount of strength is retained after failure. After various model materials were tested, a sand and oil mixture was found well suited for simulating the behavior of coal.

Locally available quartz sand was used. The size distribution of the sand is shown in Table 1. Six different combinations of sand and oil mixtures were made using two types of heavy oil, 250 SAE and 90 SAE. The ratios of oil and sand and density are shown in Table 2. It was noticed that the density was influenced by the ratio of oil and sand. For both types of oil, the maximum density was attained when the ratio was 73.9 cc (2.5 oz.) of oil per 0.45 kg (1 lb.) of sand (mixtures No. 2 and 6).

Table 1.   Particle size distribution of sand used as model material

Size		Weight	Percentage
Mesh	Millimeters	(grams)	
>16	+1.4095	4	0.99
16-48	-1.4095 + 0.295	76	18.72
48-70	-1.2950 + 0.199	196	48.28
70-80	-1.1990 + 0.182	50	12.30
80-100	-0.1820 + 0.147	55	13.55
<200	-0.1470 + 0.074	25	6.16

Table 2. Composition of model material and density

Mixture No.	250 SAE Oil cc (ounce)	90 SAE Oil cc (ounce)	Sand kg (lb)	Density (g/cc)
1	44.4 (1.5)		0.45 (1)	1.70
2	73.9 (2.5)		0.45 (1)	1.82
3	94.5 (3.2)		0.45 (1)	1.66
4		44.4 (1.5)	0.45 (1)	1.50
5		29.6 (1.0)	0.45 (1)	1.63
6		73.9 (2.5)	0.45 (1)	1.78

A direct shear strength test was performed on each mixture with
various normal loadings, using a regular direct shear-testing
machine for soil. The typical relationship between horizontal
displacement and horizontal load for a constant normal load is shown
in Figure 2. The slope is steep during the first stage and it
becomes gentler, simulating the strain softening phenomenon. After
the maximum shear stress is reached, some strength is maintained for
a period of time and gradually decreases, showing quite a long
plastic failure. When four or five values were obtained using
different normal stresses, a graph of the shear strength versus
normal stress was plotted to obtain cohesion and the internal
friction angle. Most of them showed a linear relationship.

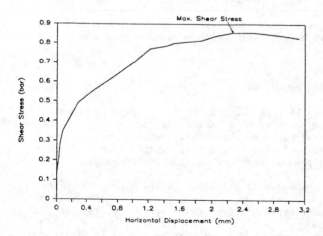

Figure 2. Shear stress versus horizontal displacement for
model material.

Both mixtures showed low cohesion; the 250 SAE mixture had an average cohesion of 0.28 bars (4.0 psi) and the 90 SAE mixture has 0.15 bars (2.0 psi). However, internal friction angles were 33.3 for the 250 SAE mixture and 39 for the 90 SAE mixtures. Slight variations were noticed in internal friction angles for the different oil/sand ratios. In summary, higher viscosity oil reduced the internal friction angle while increasing the cohesion.

Throughout this study, mixture No. 1 was used as the model material for the first layer.

2.2 Stress measuring techniques

For this model, it is critical to select adequate means of measuring stress distribution in the chain pillars or the longwall panel. Because of the fact that stress change in the model is quite small, the measuring device should be sensitive enough to detect extremely small stress changes, and the physical size of the device should be small enough so as not to disturb the stress distribution by emplacing them in the model pillars. Miniaturized load cells, the latest state-of-the-art technology, have provided excellent results. Each load cell incorporates semiconductor strain gages in a fully active Wheatstone bridge configuration. The load cells are powered by 15 V DC excitation and have built in temperature compensation, as well as individual calibration. They are 2.79 mm (0.11 inch) in thickness with a 12.7 mm (0.50 in) diameter, allowing the stress of a small point to be measured. The resolution of the load cells is 276 Pa (1/25 psi). The load cells are commercially available from Entran Devices, Inc. and further specifications are provided in Entran Bulletin ELF5005-881.

The model used a maximum of 12 load cells all of which are monitored by two switching and balancing units connected in series. A constant 15 V is supplied by a voltage regulator connected to the power terminals of one switch and balance unit, and the output voltage across the signal terminals is recorded by a voltmeter. By recording the output voltage from the load cell circuit and applying the calibration factor, the load on each cell can be calculated.

2.3 Chain pillar stress measurement

The model consists of a box constructed of 19 mm (3/4 in.) plywood, 74.9 x 120.6 x 50.8 cm, mounted on a table. The box rests on the table at its four corner posts so that a 12.7 mm (0.5 in.) slot is left around the bottom perimeter of the box. This allows a flexible layout of entries and panels, which are accessed through this opening.

To create entries, the excavating tool is guided along its desired path by metal plates, 1.3 mm (0.05 in.) in thickness, which are secured on the table top where pillars are to be created (Figure 3). The tool is then guided by the edge of the plates.

To effectively simulate stress distribution in the chain pillars, four entries were driven across the width of the model along its central area, so that a longwall panel is created on either side of the set of entries. Each panel actually represents only half of the total panel width, which is that portion of the panel affecting the

Figure 3. Sandbox longwall mine model.

stress in the chain pillars. Each pillar is 12.7 x 12.7 cm (5 x 5 in), and the half width of the panel is 35.6 cm (14.0 in). The width of the entry is 2.54 cm (1 in) and the height is 1.27 cm (0.5 in).

Each entry is cut from one side of the box and each crosscut is cut from the adjacent side. Therefore, the only access to the crosscuts is through the panel. To aid in the mining of the crosscuts, metal rods were placed on the table top extending from outside the box through the 12.7 m (0.5 in) slot to the pillar edge where each crosscut is to be made (Figure 3). Then, as the model is loaded, these rods are removed to create openings through the panel so that the excavating tool can begin cutting the crosscuts guided by the pillar plates.

The stress was chosen to be measured in three chain pillars parallel to the direction of the longwall face. Four load cells were mounted in each pillar as shown in Figure 4a. A thin plastic strip was first secured to the metal guide plates and the load cells were secured to the plastic strip to aid in careful removal of the load cells.

A series of three tests were completed with overburden depths of 34.3 (Test #1), 22.9 (Test #2), and 15.2 (Test #3) cm. Each test had a common 10.2 cm (4 in) layer of wet sand (sand/oil mixture) compacted to approximately the same pressure, and a second layer of dry sand varied to meet the desired overburden thickness.

The mining procedure was kept the same for each test. The entries were completed in 24 intervals, where at each interval, each load cell reading was recorded. As the mining activity neared the load cell area, more intervals were taken. Each longwall panel was mined in 14 intervals.

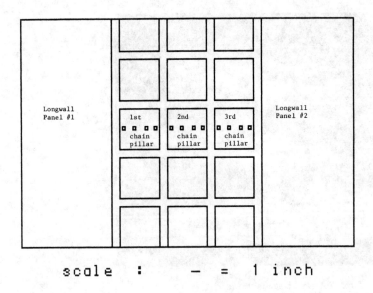

Figure 4a. Layout of chain pillar model.

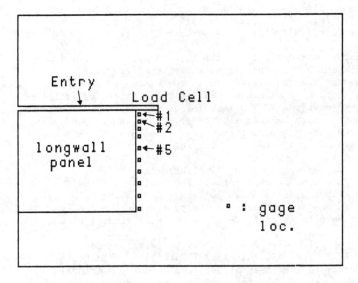

Figure 4b. Layout of front abutment model.

2.4 Longwall panel front abutment measurement

The same model used to measure chain pillar stress also was used to measure front abutment pressure in the panel. The layout was changed to simulate a 43.2 cm (17 in) wide panel with a 50.8 cm (20 in) advance over a portion of the model as shown in Figure 4b. Notice that the line of load cells at the end of the advance covers 30.5 cm (12 in) of the panel width. This represents half of the total panel width. The remaining 12.7 cm (5 in) width is there to reduce the effects of the model wall on the panel stress distribution. The inside boundary of the panel is the model wall and the outside edge is created by a single entry.

The first step in the procedure is to mine the single entry. The first 35.6 cm (14 in) of the entry is created by removing a steel rod. The excavating tool is then used to extend the entry another 15.2 cm (6 in) for a total length of 50.8 cm (20 in). The entry is excavated in this manner so that the rod does not produce any unrealistic stress distributions around the load cell area.

The next step is to mine the panel, which is advanced in approximately 2.54 cm (1 in) intervals until the face reaches the load cell line.

3 RESULTS OF TESTS

3.1 Chain pillar

The stress distribution in the chain pillars for each test was very similar, with reproducible trends occurring at each test run. As mining approached the load cell area, stress in that area generally increased. Once the mining activity reaches the load cell location, a sharp decrease occurs at the two load cells nearest the mining activity, while other areas continued increasing. Therefore, initial failure is occurring at the pillar edges. This affect is illustrated in Figure 5, which shows the stress distribution across the three chain pillars for different stages of mining. A negative sign indicates the face distance from the load cell area and a positive sign indicates the advance past the load cell area. This sign convention is used throughout each experiment. However, after this initial failure, the pillar edges generally begin to handle more stress as the face continues to advance. At the completion of the entries, higher stress along the pillar edge is more evident in the tests with low overburden pressures than in the tests with higher pressures. With high overburden pressures, drastic failure sometimes occurs along the pillar edge, in which low stress was continually measured throughout the period of entry development (Figure 5). Also, at the completion of the entries, the highest stress generally occurs in the middle pillar, indicating a stress transfer to this area (Figure 6).

As the longwall face approaches the load cell area, the stress in pillar nearest the panel begins to increase, though some fluctuation of stress level occurs across the width of the pillar. Then, as the face reaches the load cell area, a sharp decrease in stress occurs along the pillar edge, with progressively less decrease across the pillar width. As this decrease in stress, or pillar failure occurs in the first pillar, a slight stress increase occurs in the middle

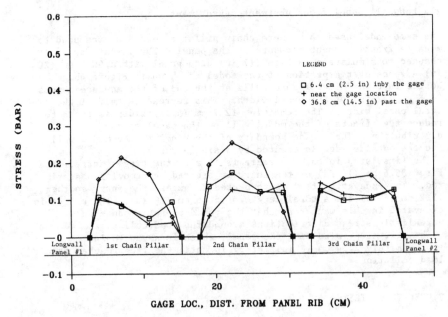

Figure 5.   Stress distribution during entry development.

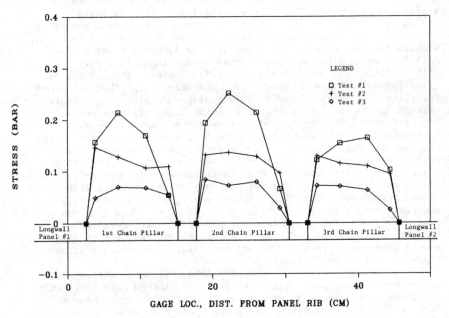

Figure 6.   Stress distribution across chain pillars at completion of entries.

pillar, indicating a stress transfer from the first pillar to the middle pillar. Little stress change is noted in the third pillar during this period (Figure 7).

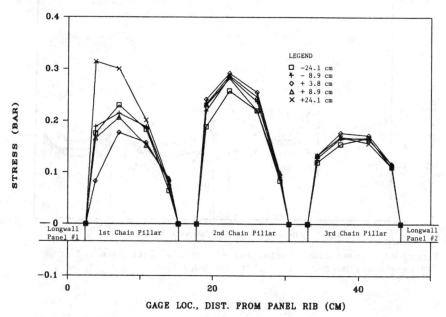

Figure 7. Stress distribution across chain pillars during advance of longwall panel #1.

These results agree with those obtained from a numerical modeling conducted by Park and Ash (1985). In their study, strain softening behavior of rock and coal layers around a coal mine opening was simulated using a quasi-elastic approach, which accounts for residual strength after failure. This simulation was achieved in such a way that material values were modified after each run according to stress distribution until it reached an equilibrium condition. The results agreed with the field measurement conducted in an Alabama coal mine. Three typical stages of stress re-distribution are shown in Figure 8, which can be compared with Figure 5.

The pillar nearest the panel continues to show a stress decrease for a face advance approximately 5 cm (2 in) past the load cell area. At this point, a stress increase occurs. Again, the stress increase is somewhat proportional across the pillar width, with the highest increase along the pillar edge nearest the panel and the lowest increase on the opposite pillar edge. As this happens, a slight decrease in stress occurs in the second and third pillars, indicating a stress transfer again, back to the first pillar (Figure 7). Apparently, as the roof is allowed to cave behind the face, a recompaction of the sand occurs over the pillar near the gob area, causing the stress transfer.

Similar effects are noticed as panel #2 is mined. The same type pattern of stress increase as face approaches the load cell area,

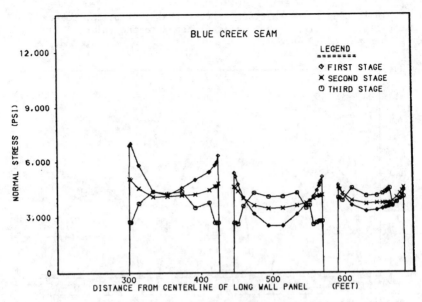

Figure 8. Stress distribution across chain pillars obtained from finite element method (after Park and Ash, 1985).

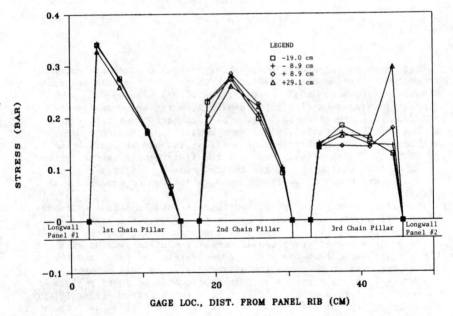

Figure 9. Stress distribution across chain pillars during advance of longwall panel #2.

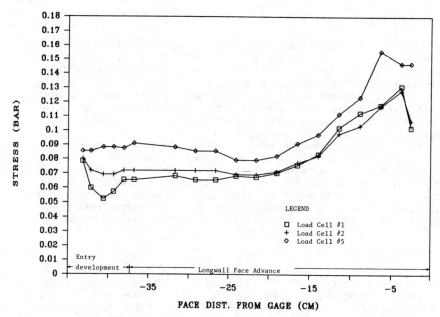

Figure 10. Development of front abutment stress.

sharp decrease in stress at the load cell area, then sharp increase as face continues to advance. The stress along the pillar edge farthest from the active panel still remains high, but a stress decrease is noticed (Figure 9).

A general trend in the manner of stress transfer is noticed in the models with higher overburden pressure. As stated, the stress in the pillar near the active panel shows an overall increase. The maximum stress decrease in the other two pillars occurs along the edge farthest from the active panel. This effect is illustrated in Figure 7.

3.2 Front abutment

As the model was loaded, the initial stress across the width of the panel varied slightly. However, the affects of mining produced similar stress changes in each load cell. During entry development, the load cells near the entry (cell #1 and #2) show a decrease just as in the chain pillar model, as shown in Figure 10. As the panel edge begins to fail, stress inside the panel (cell #5) increases. Then, as the face begins to advance, the stress remains fairly constant, even decreasing in some cases until a significant stress increase occurs at about 20 cm (8 in) ahead of the face. As mining continues, the stress in each load cell, though initially varied, begins to converge to the same level. The innermost load cell (#5) in Figure 10 reached the maximum stress at 6.4 cm (2.5 in) from the face. The two load cells near the panel edge also converged to the same maximum stress at 3.8 cm (1.5 in) from the face.

4 CONCLUSIONS

A new physical longwall mine model was developed to study stress
distributions around a longwall face in both the chain pillars and
panel. State-of-the-art stress detection devices combined with a
new excavation technique and model material have provided
reproducible results on the manner of stress re-distributions caused
by longwall mining. The model has successfully simulated the mode
of stress changes in the chain pillars and has measured the
development of the panel front abutment.

To increase the capability of the model, the laws of similitude
and dimensional analysis should be applied to the model to prototype
relationships. Many of the pertinent variables of this model study
are related to the model material. Therefore, the development and
application of other model materials should enhance the model. With
continued research and refinement, the model can become more
beneficial in the understanding of pillar stress distributions.

ACKNOWLEDGEMENT

The work was funded by the Bureau of Mines, U.S. Department of the
Interior, through Virginia Polytechnic Institute and State
University, as a research project of the Generic Mineral Technology
Center in Mine System Design and Ground Control.

REFERENCES

Harris, G.W. 1974. A sandbox model used to examine the stress
    distribution around a simulated longwall coal-face. Int. J. Rock
    Mech. Min. Sci. & Geomech. 11:325-335.
Langhaar, H.L. 1951. Dimensional analysis and theory of models, p.
    60-65. New York: John Wiley & Sons, Inc.
Murphy, G. 1950. Similitude in engineering, p. 57-66. New York: The
    Ronald Press Company.
Obert, L. & W.I Duvall 1967. Rock mechanics and the design of
    structures in rock, p. 387-401. New York: John Wiley & Sons, Inc.
Park, D.W. & N.F. Ash 1985. Stability analysis of entries in a deep
    coal mine using finite element method. Proc. 2nd Conference on
    the use of Computers in the coal industry. New York: AIME.
Park, D.W., Sanford, R.L., Simpson, T.A. & H.L. Hartman 1983.
    Pillar stability and subsidence study at a deep longwall coal
    mine. Proc., Annual Workshop, Generic Min. Tech. Center, Mine
    Systems Design and Ground Control, Blacksburg, VA: Virginia
    Polytechnic Institute and State University.

Modeling of coal mine roof reinforcement

H.C.PETTIBONE, S.M.DAR & T.W.SMELSER
Spokane Research Center, Bureau of Mines, Washington, USA

1 ABSTRACT

The Bureau of Mines is using a full-scale geotechnical model of a 4.6-m
wide (15-foot) coal mine entry in correlation with computer finite-
element analysis using the BMINES and ANSYS codes. This basic study on
roof-bolt support systems is being conducted at the Bureau's Spokane
Research Center. Physical and computer modeling of coal mine roof
reinforcement systems is being verified by underground tests. During
the last 4 years, 185 1-day tests have been performed on 5 different
roof-bolts in 2 sets of roof slabs on the coal mine entry model. Exact
correlation has been achieved between the results of BMINES and ANSYS
computer codes. Excellent correlation was obtained between the results
of computer modeling and the results of physical model tests.

2 INTRODUCTION

During the last 30 years, the use of roof bolts for the support and
stabilization of coal mining excavations has increased to become the
primary support system used in coal mining. During this period, the use
of roof-bolt support resulted in a great reduction in the number of
fatal roof-fall accidents in coal mines. However, roof-fall accidents
still occur frequently in areas of bolted roof. Roof-bolting plans are
based mostly on trial and error, which leads to underdesign or overdesign with regard to bolt length, spacing, tension, and bolt type.
Underdesign leads to safety problems, and overdesign is an unnecessary
financial burden to the coal mine operator. A set of comprehensive
industry guidelines is needed for the selection and design of optimum
roof-bolt plans that will maximize safety and minimize cost. These
guidelines need to consider the site-specific geology of coal mines and
instruct the operator as how to design an appropriate roof-bolting plan
that increases safety and reduces cost.

It is estimated that between 65 and 70 million bolts were used in the
United States during 1984. Despite this usage, the theory of roof
bolting remains underdeveloped. A basic understanding of how different
types of roof bolts perform their desired function is sadly lacking.
Underground tests designed to provide this knowledge have been only
partially successful due to the many uncontrollable geologic variables
present in underground mining situations. The authors believe that the
best approach is to conduct a laboratory model study in correlation with

Figure 1. Physical model of a coal mine entry.

finite-element analysis (FEA), along with field verification, in which
these variables can be tightly controlled and measured (Smelser 1982).
  The purposes of this study are to upgrade the basic understanding of
the ground support-and-rock interaction mechanics of bolted mine roof,
and to verify and improve computer finite-element modeling techniques;
then FEA can be used to predict roof-bolt structural behavior for a
range of complex geologic conditions encountered in underground mining.
This information, joined with the results of other Bureau projects, will
provide a basis for safer, more cost-effective roof-control plans and
help to establish guidelines for current and emerging bolting systems.
  Three hypotheses are being examined: (1) roof bolts strengthen a coal
mine roof, according to the beam building theory, (2) tensioned roof
bolts in a laminated roof create a zone of uniform compression, and
(3) untensioned fully grouted roof bolts strengthen a laminated roof by
increasing the interlaminar shear strength.
  The choice of using a physical laboratory model in conjunction with
computer modeling and field verification results was made because
underground testing yields limited results due to difficulties in
defining underground conditions and measuring parameters such as loads,
strains, and deflections. A physical model allows accurate measurement
of the performance of different bolt types as a function of a wide range
of precisely measured parameters. Although the model being used is
idealized and limited in size, it serves as a reliable basis for con-
firming the mechanism of rock reinforcement by bolting, and the accuracy
of the computer FEA approach to mining problems. The FEA approach will

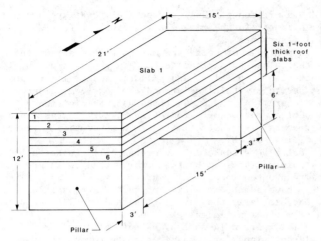

Figure 2. Dimensions of model coal mine entry.

serve as the basis for evaluating the extremely variable and complex
site-specific problems encountered in the underground environment in a
rapid and cost-effective manner. Underground tests to verify the
BMINES code will increase confidence in this analytical approach until
reliable guidelines emerge.

3 OBJECTIVE

The objective of computer and physical model testing and field verification of roof-bolting systems is to improve the basic understanding of
how and why roof bolts function in a coal mine roof. Also, this work
will help establish guidelines for safer, more cost-effective roof
bolting systems.

4 PHYSICAL MODEL TESTING

The physical model of a coal mine entry is shown in figure 1, and the
dimensions of the simulated entry are given in figure 2. This model
simulates a layered sedimentary deposit typical of underground coal
mining. The roof slabs and pillars are separated from each other by a
layer of 0.152-mm (6-mil) polyethylene to prevent bonding of the concrete and to produce a uniform coefficient of friction in the laminated
roof. A 34.5-MPa (5,000-psi) sand-portland cement grout was used to
simulate a competent shale. The simulated mine entry was cast in place
on the structural testing floor at the Bureau's Spokane Research Center
(Maus 1980).
    Surrounding the concrete model entry and tied into a structural
testing floor is a 1.33-MN (150-ton) structural steel reaction frame
supporting a servocontrolled hydraulic loading system. Loads from the
hydraulic cylinders, which simulate 30 m (100 ft) of overburden, are
distributed over the model surface through rubber-faced steel loading
pads, as shown in figure 3. This system is capable of applying forces
of about 13.3 MN (3 million pounds) vertical and 8 MN (1.8 million
pounds) horizontal, with vertical and horizontal shear capabilities of

2.2 and 4 MN (0.5 and 0.9 million pounds), respectively. Figure 4 shows a system of hydraulic supports in the mine entry capable of furnishing premining and postmining support.

The slabs with the installed roof bolts are extensively instrumented to monitor strain in the bolts, total load on certain types of bolts, slab deflection, strain within the slabs and pillars, interlaminar slip between the slabs, temperature within and around the model, movement of the model, and entry closure. A minicomputer and data acquisition system controls the model operation on a real-time basis. Instant data display keeps the test operators constantly informed of critical strains within the model or bolting system.

Three types of roof bolts were tested. The mechanically anchored bolt is tensioned to put a compressive load on the strata. The resin-grouted steel bolt is generally an untensioned, fully grouted steel dowel. The friction stabilizers do have some compressive or radial stress induced during installation, but basically they are untensioned steel tubes held in place by friction or mechanical interlock.

Roof-bolt holes on a 1.2 x 1.2 m (4-foot by 4-foot) pattern were drilled into the model roof slabs for comparison tests to be performed on 1.5-m (5-foot) long conventional, mechanically anchored steel bolts, resin-grouted steel bolts, and three friction stabilizers.

5 COMPUTER MODELING

Computer modeling of the full-scale model mine entry was done using the BMINES (Agbabian 1981) and ANSYS (Swanson 1982) computer codes. The BMINES code was specifically designed for mining problems, but was relatively new and unproved. The ANSYS code was chosen to serve as a check against the BMINES code. Both codes incorporate slip elements and are compatible with roof-bolt modeling.

The bedding and joint phenomenon of the mine entry was simulated by using six horizontal slip planes (joints). Characteristics of the mechanically anchored bolts and resin-grouted bolts were incorporated into the finite-element model. Computer modeling of multiple slip planes pierced by roof bolts is an area of limited work and required considerable research for accurate theoretical modeling (Dar 1985). Even in proposed codes, the options pertaining to the analytical modeling of slip planes and to various types of rock-bolt systems still remain unverified even when considered in the light of plane stress and plane strain (2-D cases). A three-dimensional analysis would involve considerable expense and time and a greater degree of uncertainty in comparison to a two-dimensional analysis. Assumptions of symmetry with respect to the vertical-longitudinal plane passing through the center of the mine entry make a three-dimensional analysis unnecessary.

Figure 3 shows an example of the finite-element mesh developed for the two-dimensional analysis of the model mine entry. The loading shown in figure 3 is estimated to be present at a depth of 30 m (100 feet).

6 PROJECT STATUS

More than 80 tests were completed on the first set of slabs in the physical model of the coal mine entry including proof and acceptance tests, load cylinder efficiency tests, unbolted load tests, resin-grouted bolt tests, and mechanically anchored bolt tests. Satisfactory correlations were obtained between the deflection of the physical model

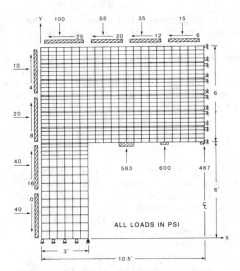

Figure 3. Finite element model mesh.

Figure 4. East side of physical model.

and finite-element predictions. Testing of Split-Sets was not accomplished in the first set of slabs because of excessive fatigue in the concrete structure (Reference to specific trade names does not imply endorsement by the Bureau of Mines). The significant contribution of the first set of slabs is that they served as a debugging and training phase for the physical model.

The six 0.3-m (1-foot) thick roof slabs in the model were removed and replaced in 1982. Steel fibers were added to the second set of slabs to retard the growth of shrinkage cracks that develop in the concrete and

1277

could propagate into a failure crack. Experience has shown that the fibers not only eliminated the propagation of cracks but also greatly reduced the number of shrinkage cracks in the model.

One hundred and two separate load tests have been performed on the second set of slabs including 19 calibration and unbolted load tests, 12 tests on resin-grouted steel bolts, 31 tests on mechanically anchored bolts, 9 tests on Split-Sets, 9 tests on Roof Supporter I, 10 tests on Swellex, and 12 unbolted load tests to recheck performance of the slabs.

7 TEST RESULTS

The BMINES and ANSYS programs give almost duplicate predictions for deflection in the unbolted and bolted cases. Figures 5 and 6 show examples of computer predictions for an unbolted case and a bolted case using mechanical bolts with 9 kips tension. These two graphs also show physical model results, which correlate very well with the BMINES and ANSYS theoretical results. All physical model test result curves are the average of three 1-day tests on the second set of slabs.

In figure 7, we see the predicted values from BMINES compared with resin-grouted steel bolts and three types of friction stabilizers (Split-Sets, Roof Supporter I, and Swellex). The shape of the curve is the same for the predicted and experimental values even though the maximum deflection at midspan differs.

The three kinds of friction stablizers show almost identical deflection results in the model. Pull test data from the model and associated test blocks show that the three types of friction stabilizers behave very differently. The Split-Sets and Roof Supporter I are steel tubes that are driven into a 35-cm (1-3/8-inch) diameter hole. For both fixtures, the pulling force is slightly higher than the driving force. An average from 16 of each type of fixture installed in the model shows a pulling force for Split-Set of 364 N/cm (208 pounds per inch) while the Roof Supporter I is 420 N/cm (241 pounds per inch). The Swellex is inflated with 27.6 MPa (4,000 psi) water pressure and hence conforms to all irregularities in the hole. Based on a 1-foot-long test in a sample block, the Swellex develops 1100 N/cm (625 pounds per inch) pull force. This value was derived from a single test and verified by field tests.

The physical model in which these bolts were tested is so stiff and insensitive that it only responds to the presence of a bolt when that bolt applies an active force to the model. This is shown by the deflection plots that imply mechanically anchored roof-bolts reduce deflection more than resin-grouted steel bolts or any of the three friction stabilizers. Experience in the field shows just the opposite to be true. Many Eastern U.S. coal mines with very bad top can only be mined by using resin-grouted steel bolts. Do not infer from the results of these tests in our geotechnical model that mechanically anchored roof-bolts are better than resin-grouted steel or any of the friction stabilizers.

We have noted increased flexibility of the slabs since the start of this test series. At the beginning, the unbolted slabs required 50 percent live load to produce a given deflection. After the resin and mechanical bolts were tested, the same slabs required only 40 percent live load to produce the same midspan deflection in the unbolted case.

Figures 5 through 7 graphically indicate that behavior of a model coal mine roof can be predicted with either the ANSYS or BMINES program. It also shows that good correlation is obtainable between the concrete

1278

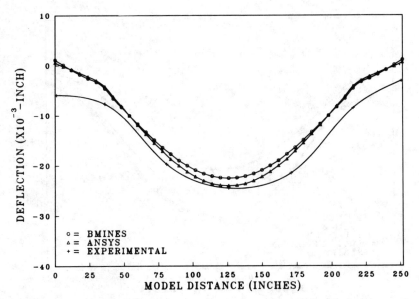

Figure 5. Vertical deflection, bottom of slab 6, 40% live load, unbolted.

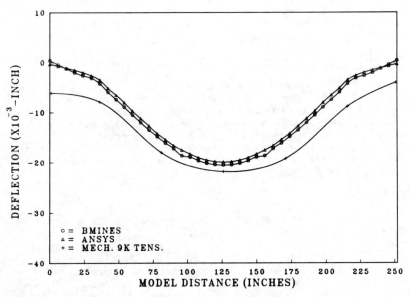

Figure 6. Vertical deflection, bottom of slab 6, 40% live load, mechanical bolts, 9 kip tension.

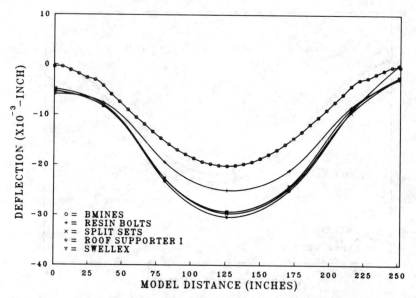

Figure 7. Vertical deflection, bottom of slab 6, 40% live load, resin bolts, three friction stabilizers.

geotechnical model and a mathematical program. These test results have given us enough confidence to take the mathematical model into the field and see if we can get the same excellent results in a working coal mine as we were able to achieve in the laboratory modeling situation.

8 CONCLUSIONS

The results of this research to date lead to the following conclusions:
    1. Full-scale model testing of a simplified mine entry with roof-bolt support was accomplished and is feasible and practical.
    2. Computer modeling of a layered mine roof with slip planes pierced by roof bolts was accomplished and is feasible and practical.
    3. Excellent correlation was obtained between physical model results and computer modeling results using BMINES and ANSYS codes.

REFERENCES

Agbabian Associates 1981. BMINES - Computer Code, El Segundo, CA.
Dar, S. M., H. C. Pettibone & T. W. Smelser 1985. Computer Modeling of Roof Support. Denver, CO. Proceedings of ASCE Spring Convention.
Maus, Charles W. 1980. Full-scale Model Roof-Bolt Test System. Evans City, PA. Final Report for Bureau of Mines Contract S0271014 by Mine Safety Appliances Company, Advanced Systems Division.
Smelser, Thomas W., Sidiq M. Dar, Howard C. Pettibone & Douglas D. Bolstad 1982. Modeling and Field Verification of Roof-Bolt Systems. Dallas, TX. Proceedings of SME-AIME Annual Meeting.
Swanson Analysis Systems Inc. 1982. ANSYS - Engineering Analysis System, Houston, PA.

Investigation of equivalent materials
for physical modeling of Utah coal seams

H.MOON & V.J.HUCKA
University of Utah, Salt Lake City, USA

1 INTRODUCTION

Better safety and higher productivity in coal mining require implementation of new mining systems, for example, longwall mining technology. The success of longwall mining, however, depends not only on the technology used but also on controlled caving in the longwall panel. Performing all the necessary investigation by full-scale experiments is too costly and generally not acceptable to the mining industry. A physical model made up of modeling (equivalent) materials can be used to simulate the strata behavior and the mining process planned. The safety and productivity of a proposed mining method thus can be analyzed by testing the physical model.

Three scale factors, geometry, unit weight and stress scale factors, were used to scale elastic deformation properties and strength properties of the coal and rock in selected Utah coal mines. Discussed are problems involved in the development of suitable modeling material as well as the limitations of small-scale physical modeling.

2 PRINCIPLES OF PHYSICAL MODELING

The conditions of similarity between prototype and model systems may be summarized as follows:
- (1) Geometric similarity
- (2) Dimensional homogeneity
- (3) Equality of dimensionless products
- (4) Similarity of the initial states
- (5) Similarity of the boundary conditions.

Conditions (1), (4) and (5) are mainly concerned with the construction and operation of the scale model while conditions (2) and (3) are relevant to the scaling of mechanical properties.

Application of condition (2) to the mechanical systems following Newton's law of motion results in a basic formula that describes the relation between the scale factors of stress, mass density, acceleration and geometry (Turchaninov, et al., 1979):

$$\overset{*}{\sigma} = \overset{*}{\rho}\,\overset{*}{g}\,\overset{*}{l} \tag{1}$$

where $\overset{*}{\sigma}$ = stress scale factor (σ_m/σ_p)

$\overset{*}{\rho}$ = mass density scale factor (ρ_m/ρ_p)

$\overset{*}{g}$ = gravitational acceleration scale factor (g_m/g_p)

$\overset{*}{l}$ = geometry scale factor (l_m/l_p) .

The subscripts p and m refer to the quantities in the prototype and model systems, respectively. Scale factor is defined as the ratio of the quantity in model system to the corresponding quantity in the prototype system. Centrifugal modeling and equivalent material modeling are branched from the above equation.

In the case of the same gravitational acceleration for both the prototype and model system, Eq. (1) takes the following form:

$$\overset{*}{\sigma} = \overset{*}{\gamma} \, \overset{*}{l} \tag{2}$$

where $\overset{*}{\gamma}$ = unit weight scale factor (γ_m/γ_p) .

Due to the dimensional homogeneity, the scaling of elastic modulus and strength depends on the stress scale factor. Linear displacements in the prototype and model systems are related by the geometry scale factor. Scale factors for strain, angular displacement, angle of internal friction and Poisson's ratio are all equal to one, satisfying the equality of dimensionless products.

3 MECHANICAL PROPERTIES OF THE COAL AND ROCK IN SOME UTAH COAL MINES

Longwall mining is planned for the Hiawatha seam located in Central Utah. The coal seam is a part of the Star Point Sandstone formation of Cretaceous age, which consists of sandstone and claystone layers. Mechanical properties of the coal and rock are summarized in Table 1.

Table 1. Mechanical properties of the coal and rock.

Prototype	Uniaxial Compressive Strength C (MPa)	Brazilian Tensile Strength T_i (MPa)	Young's Modulus E (GPa)	Angle of Internal Friction (degrees)
Sandstone	116	8.7	23	43-63
Claystone	129	7.3	25	44-59
Coal	23	1.5	4.9	--

Prototype	Strength Ratio C/T_i	Poisson's Ratio γ	Modulus Ratio E/C	Strain at Failure %
Sandstone	10-20	0.04-0.18	150-300	0.3-1.0
Claystone	10-30	0.02-0.28	150-300	0.3-1.0
Coal	10-20	0.18-0.39	100-300	0.3-0.4

4 EVALUATION AND TEST RESULTS OF MODELING MATERIALS

A great number of modeling materials were classified and summarized by Stimpson (1970) from the constituent material point of view. General guidelines on selection of a modeling material may be found in that paper. Granular material cemented with gypsum, plaster, cement or wax is generally accepted in physical model studies of geomechanics problems (slope stability, underground excavation, dam foundation, blasting, tunnel design, etc.).

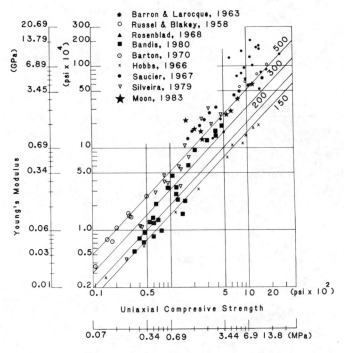

Figure 1. Young's modulus versus uniaxial compressive strength.

Due to the property change of cement with time and due to the high plasticity of wax, granular material cemented with gypsum or plaster is considered suitable to model elastic brittle prototypes. Mechanical properties of the gypsum plaster based modeling materials were analyzed with a special emphasis on the compressive strength, Young's modulus, modulus ratio, strength ratio (the ratio of uniaxial compressive strength to tensile strength), and the strain at failure. Depending on the constituents, mix proporation and curing process, the properties vary in a wide range (Figures 1, 2 and 3).

For our study the Hydrocal White gypsum cement and No. 1 Casting industrial plaster manufactured by the U. S. Gypsum Company were used as cementing agent. Compressive strengths of the gypsum cement and industrial plaster were 34.5 MPa and 13.8 MPa, and the consistency (parts of water by weight added to 100 parts of cementing agent for optimum work-

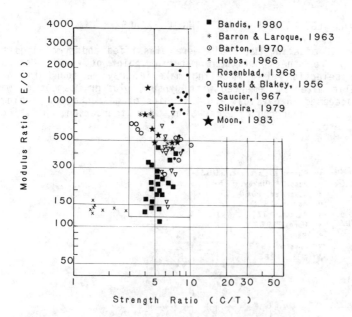

Figure 2. Modulus ratio versus strength ratio.

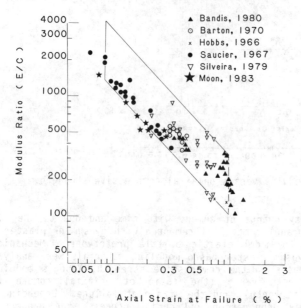

Axial Strain at Failure (%)

Figure 3. Modulus ratio versus axial strain at failure.

ability) were 45 to 70, respectively. The setting time was 25 minutes to 37 minutes in common. Sieved silica sand and glass beads were used as granular filler. The particle size of the silica sand was in between 0.2 and 0.8 mm. Two types of glass beads, MSML glass bead (particle size between 0.05 and 0.01 mm) and MSXP glass bead (particle size between 0.25 and 0.41 mm) were also used as granular filler.

The mixture of Hydrocal White gypsum cement, silica sand and water was tested as group A. Group B was a mixture of Hydrocal White gypsum cement, glass bead and water. Group C was composed of No. 1 Casting industrial plaster, glass bead and water. The weight percentage of the filler/ (cementing agent + filler) was increased from 0 to 60% with a 20% interval for group B, and from 20% to 80% with the same interval for group C (Table 2).

Table 2. Compositions of modeling materials.

Group	Cementing Agent	Filler	Water
B	Hydrocal White gypsum cement	MSXP glass bead and MSML glass bead 1:1 by weight	45% of the cementing agent by weight
C	No. 1 Casting industrial plaster	Ditto	70% of the cementing agent + 15% of the filler by weight

Specimens were cured in a laboratory oven for 24 hours at the temperature between 300 and 390 degrees Fahrenheit. Only results on the group B and C mixtures are presented in this paper (Table 3).

Table 3. Strength and deformation properties of group B and C mixtures.

Group	Uniaxial Compressive Strength C (MPa)	Direct Tensile Strength T_d (MPa)	Brazil Tensile Strength T_i(MPa)	Cohesion c (MPa)	Angle of Internal Friction (degree)	Strain at Failure (%)
B	3.8-8.3	0.5-1.2	0.5-1.2	0.7-1.6	47-53	0.2-0.3
C	1.1-1.8	0.2-0.3	0.2-0.3	0.2-0.4	43-47	0.1-0.2

Group	Young's Modulus E (GPa)	Poisson's Ratio ν	Strength Ratio E/T	Modulus Ratio E/C	Unit Weight γ (g/cm^3)
B	1.9-4.1	0.16-0.2	5.4-7.8	438- 556	1.2-1.7
C	0.9-1.5	0.17-0.24	4.2-5.0	485-1366	1.1-1.6

Details on specimen preparation and test procedures can be found elsewhere (Moon, 1983). Strengths and elastic moduli of the group B mixture are increased by adding more granular filler, while strengths of the group C mixture decrease with the increasing amount of the filler (Figure 4).

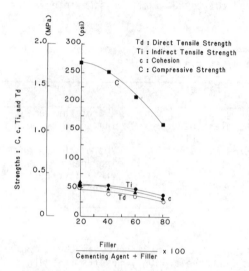

Figure 4. Strength properties of group C mixtures.

5 DISCUSSION

5.1 Effects of the Constituents

Water added into mixtures beyond the chemically required amount increases the porosity of the specimen and thus reduces its strength and unit weight. According to Eq. (2), the simultaneously decreasing strength and unit weight have a counterbalancing effect on the geometry scale factor. Fine granular fillers have a large specific surface area which requires more water to preserve the workability of mixtures. Increasing amount of granular filler increases the total surface area of the grain boundary as well as the unit weight of the specimen. Since set gypsum cement and plaster are weaker and more deformable than the granular filler and since they form a continuous matrix in the composite material, the cementing agents generally control the deformation and failure of the specimen. Group B mixtures resembles a composite material reinforced by stiff spherical particles, while group C may be compared to a two-phase composite medium weakened by the inclusion of voids.

5.2 Effects of mix proportions

The volume fraction of individual constituents were changed by the mix proportion design. Adding more granular filler makes the material less deformable, increases Young's modulus, reduces the strain at failure and decreases Poisson's ratio. The water-absorbing effect of the fine granular filler makes the set gypsum cement and plaster stronger. The bonding strength of the cementing agent can be reduced either by increasing the water proportion or by reducing the amount of cementing agent. For the group C mixtures, the increase of water proportional to the amount of filler prevents the increase of the bonding strength. Increased Young's modulus of the group C mixtures could be attributed partly to the addition of more filler and partly to the locally stiffened area under the strain gages attached to the porous specimen.

5.3 Effects of curing process

The process of removing moisture, the curing process, makes the material stable physically and mechanically. Completely dried specimens contain only the chemically bound water. The dissociation and rehydration of the set gypsum cement and plaster due to the moisture in the atmosphere do not have significant effects on mechanical properties. High curing temperature and prolonged curing period cause the transformation of the set gypsum cement (or plaster) from dihydrate $(CaSO_4 \cdot 2H_2O)$ to hemidrate $(CaSO_4 \cdot \frac{1}{2}H_2O)$. Bonding strength of the plaster may be reduced further by using such dissociation process.

5.4 Comparison of the modeling material with the prototype

Comparing the prototype and the modeling material, the following ranges of scale factors are obtained.
-Stress scale factor: 1/105 to 1/5
-Unit weight scale factor: 1/1   to 1/2
-Geometry scale factor: 1/105 to 1/2.5.
The angle of internal friction and Poisson's ratio were in a satisfactory range. However, the modulus ratio should be reduced, the strain at failure and the strength ratio must be increased (Figures 2 and 3).
   In order to change further the modulus ratio, strength ratio and the strain at failure, the constituents and the internal structure (i.e., void and crack distributions) of the material have to be changed. Strength and deformation behavior of the two-phase composite becomes complicated due to the complex relations between water and the cementing agent, water and the granular filler, water and workability of the mixtures, and water and porosity of the specimen. Although the individual elastic moduli and strengths may be controlled by such systematic changes of the mix proportion, it is difficult to change the dimensionless products.

6 SUMMARY

   Principles of physical modeling, mechanical properties of various modeling materials and the factors affecting the properties were reviewed and studied. The interrelation between three scale factors were discussed from the point of view of material study and model construction.

Three groups of mixtures consisting of gypsum cement, plaster, glass bead and silica sand were tested. Unsolved problems remain in the dimensionless quantities (i.e., modulus ratio, strength ratio). Unless convenient ways of controlling the material properties were developed, there exists quite a restricted degree of freedom in physical modeling technique, particularly when (i) the model includes a large number of different prototypes, (ii) many alternative designs are to be compared, (iii) the initial and boundary conditions are not simple, and (iv) the prototypes are not isotropic and linearly elastic. Complications did arise from the fact that the three scale factors are determined by different restrictions. Geometry scale factor depends on the size of the model frame available as well as the size of the area of mining to be modeled. Unit weight and stress scale factors are solely dependent on the modeling material for a given prototype. Thus, a physical model scaled correctly from the strength point of view may become a distorted model from the deformation point of view. A compromise between the scale factors is inevitable in this respect. Technical problems related to the construction, instrumentation, imposing the initial and boundary conditions and operation of the model are the subjects of a future study.

REFERENCES

Bandis, S. 1980. Experimental studies of scale effects on shear strength. Ph.D. Dissertation. The University of Leeds, U.K.
Barron, K., and Larocque, G.E. 1963. The development of a model for a mine structure. Proc. Rock Mechanics Symposium, McGill University, 145-189.
Barton, N.R. 1970. A low strength material for simulation of the mechanical properties of intact rock in rock mechanical models. Proc. 2nd Congr. Inter. Rock Mech. Belgrade, 2, Paper 3-15.
Hobbs, D.W. 1966. Scale model studies of strata movement around mine roadways. Apparatus, techniques and some preliminary results. Int. J. Rock Mech. Min. Sci. 3, 101-127.
Moon, H. 1983. Study of modeling materials for physical modeling of Utah coal mines. M.S. Thesis. University of Utah, June, p.117.
Rosenblad, J.L. 1968. Development of a rocklike model material. Proc. 10th Symp. on Rock Mech. University of Texas, Austin, 331-361.
Russell, J.J. and Blakey, F.A. 1956. Physical and mechanical properties of one cast gypsum plaster: Plaster AB/2. Aust. J. of Applied Sci., 7, 176-190.
Saucier, K.L. 1967. Development of material for modeling rock, Misc. Paper No. 6-934, U.S. Army Engineer Waterways Experiment Station, Corps of Engineers, Mississippi.
Silveira, A.F. 1979. High density and low strength materials for geomechanical models. Intnational Colloquium on Physical Geomechanical Models, Bergamo, Italy, 115-131.
Stimpson, B. 1970. Modeling materials for engineering rock mechanics. Int. J. Rock Mech. Min. Sci. 9,77-121.
Turchaninov, I.A., Lofis, M.S. and Kasparyan, E.V. 1979. Principles of rock mechanics. Rockville, Maryland, Terraspace, Inc.

Author index

Abramson, L.W. 675
Ahrens, Thomas J. 1055
Amadei, Bernard 859
Andersen, Mark A. 403
Aoki, Kenji 841
Arcamone, J. 1103
Ashworth, E. 797, 937
Ashworth, T. 797
Axelrod, M.C. 851

Bachus, Robert C. 1067
Bakhtar, Khosrow 1255
Bardet, Jean-Pierre 139
Barton, Nick 487, 1087
Bass, Jay D. 1055
Bauer, Eric R. 1075
Bauer, S.J. 89, 523, 1113
Bawden, W.F. 163
Beus, M.J. 1163
Bhattacharya, Swapan 977
Black, Alan 1255
Blandford, G.E. 231
Board, Mark P. 749
Bouteca, M.J. 643
Boyce, Glenn M. 1219
Brawner, C.O. 49
Brest van Kempen, C.J.H. 425
Brie, Alain 227
Brown, D.J. 41
Brown, S. 777, 1247
Brummer, Richard K. 113
Bryan, Jon B. 999
Burton, Donald E. 999
Bush, Daniel D. 1087
Butcher, B.M. 883
By, T.L. 281

Cameron, Robert 1255
Cao Wei 993
Carosso, G. 259

Carr, Frederick 693
Carr, James R. 613
Chan, T. 785
Cheatham, J.B., Jr. 947
Chekan, Gregory J. 1075
Chern, Shiann-Jang 659, 1015
Choquet, P. 19
Christensen, Richard N. 925
Chugh, Yoginder P. 413
Coffin, D.Todd 667
Coode, A.M. 163
Cook, N.G.W. 471, 565
Cook, R.F. 447
Corkum, D.H. 79
Cramer, Michael L. 759
Cravero, M. 259
Cregger, D.M. 79
Cui Guangping 573
Cundall, Peter A. 759
Cyrul, T. 601, 967

da Costa, Alvaro Maia 239
Daemen, Jaak J.K. 1141
Daily, W.D. 807
Dar, S.M. 1273
Darot, M. 463
Dearman, W.R. 81
DeMarco, M.J. 549
Denby, B. 41
Detournay, Emmanuel 131
Dischler, S.A. 363
Dowding, C.H. 731
Dusseault, M.B. 313
Dutta, Piyush K. 1043

El-Mherig, A. 31
Elsworth, D. 633

Fahrenthold, E.P. 947
Fairhurst, Charles 239, 269

Farmer, Ian W. 1095
Fejes, A.J. 197
Foglia, Mauro 659
Ford, L.M. 523
Fordham, C. 313
Fossum, A.F. 251
Fujiwara, T. 557

Galloway, L.M. 231
Gao Hang 985
Gardner, Bruce H. 693
Garritty, P. 1095
Gauna, Michael 695
Gazonas, George 341
Ghosh, Amitava 1141
Giani, G.P. 259
Glenn, H.David 999
Gokce, A.O. 79
Gooch, Richard P. 621
Goodman, Richard E. 121, 1219
Gorham-Bergeron, E. 151
Guangping, Cui 573
Gueguen, Y. 463
Guenot, A. 455

Haase, C.S. 341
Haghighi, R.H. 651
Haimson, Bezalel C. 1207
Hall, Michael E. 749
Haramy, K.Y. 549
Hardy, M.P. 425
Harpalani, Satya 831
Hart, Roger D. 759
Heasley, Keith A. 189
Heins, Robert W. 905
Herrick, Courtney G. 1207
Heuze, F.E. 333
Hill, J.J. 1151
Hill, John L., III 1075
Hladysz, Zbigniew 1023
Hokens, Daniel E. 289
Holcomb, D.J. 715
Holland, J.F. 1113
Holzhausen, Gary R. 341, 621
Hopkins, D. 565
Hsu, Kai 227
Hucka, V.J. 1281
Hudson, P.J. 1235
Hustrulid, W. 777, 873, 1247

Iabichino, G. 259
Ingraffea, A.R. 333
Irani, Fersheed K. 1057
Irvin, R.A. 1095
Isaac, A.K. 439, 685

Janardhanam, R. 395
Jones, A.K. 883
Jones, Frank O., Jr. 403
Jones, T.Z. 179
Josien, JP. 1103

Kaiser, P.K. 957
Kane, William F. 395
Karfakis, Mario G. 905
Kemeny, John 471
Khan, Akhtar S. 1057
Kicker, Dwayne C. 1261
Kikuchi, Shinji 1015
Kim, K. 363
King, Michael S. 739
Kirby, G.C. 497
Kliche, Charles A. 1023
Kohli, K.K. 179
Konya, C.J. 641
Krieg, Raymond D. 769
Kulacki, F.A. 817

Labreche, Duane A. 515
Labuz, J.F. 731
Lang, P.A. 785
Li Baiying 985
Li Jiaxiang 985
Lin, Dezhang 269
Lindner, E.N. 575
Lindsey, Patrick D. 1189
Liner, Y. 479
Liren, Yu 573
Liu Zongcai 985
Loset, Fredrik 487
Lovell, C.W. 305
Lundquist, R.G. 651

Madill, T. 1173
Makurat, Axel 487
Maleki, H.N. 425
Maloney, S.M. 957
Martin, Eddie 695
Martin, Edward 693
Martin, R.J., III 715
Matsumoto, Takashi 841
Mazur, C.J. 497
McCrae, R.W. 447
McLennan, John D. 323
McNabb, K.E. 531
McPherson, Malcolm J. 831
Michihiro, K. 557
Miller, H.D.S. 1173
Moebs, Noel M. 977
Moon, H. 1281
Morgan, Harold S. 769
Morris J.P.E. 927
Mottahed, P. 163

Mraz, D. 313
Myer, L.R. 565

Nakamura, Tetsuya 659
Nelson, D.P. 251
Newman, David A. 1181
Nguyen, V.U. 937
Nicholson, D.E. 297
Niou, Stephen 1015
Niyom, Deeswasmongkol 11
Nolting, Richard M. 1219

Oakland, M.W. 305
Ohnishi, Yuzo 841
Oravecz, K.I. 927
Osborne, Rodney L. 925

Paillet, F.L. 207
Pan Li-zhou 869
Panet, M. 455
Pakalnis, R. 1173
Park, Duk-Won 1261
Parrish, D.K. 1113
Patrick, W.C. 851
Payne, A.R. 439, 685
Peck, J.H. 79
Pettibone, H.C. 1273
Picardy, John C. 323
Piguet, JP. 1103
Plesha, Michael E. 387
Plumb, Richard A. 227
Preece, Dale S. 507
Price, Kenneth R. 695
Price, R.H. 89

Rajen, Gaurav 817
Ramirez, A.L. 807
Reeves, Malcolm J. 1033
Ren, N.-K. 1235
Repsher, Richard C. 707
Reuschlé, Th. 463
Revalor, R. 1103
Richards, D.P. 873
Richardson, A. 777, 1247
Rigby, G.L. 479
Russell, James E. 703

Sakurai, S. 11
Samama, L. 731
Saperstein, Lee W. 189
Savage, William Z. 1121
Schmitt, Douglas R. 1055
Schuch, Robert L. 749
Scott, Ronald F. 139
Senseny, P.E. 377
Serata, Shosei 659, 1227
Shaffer, R.J. 333

Shah, S.P. 731
Shi, Gen-hua 121
Shlyapobersky, J. 539
Shrinivasan, Krishnan 1227
Simonson, J.R. 377
Singh, Madan M. 977
Singh, R.N. 31, 41
Siriwardane, H.J. 171
Skudrzyk, Frank J. 97
Smelser, T.W. 1273
Smith, David R. 797
Snodgrass, James J. 1181
Soltani, Amir M. 723
Steblay, Bernard J. 707
Steed, C. 163
St.John, Christopher 131
Stone, Charles M. 769
Stow, S.H. 341
Sulem, J. 455
Summers, David A. 895
Sun Zhengpeng 985
Sutherland, Herbert J. 507
Swift, Robert P. 999
Swolfs, Henri S. 1121
Szwilski, A.B. 601

Tandanand, Sathit 591
Tan Xue Shu 993
Tanon, D.D.B. 19
Teufel, Lawrence W. 1199
Tharp, Thomas M. 667
Thomas, R.K. 523
Thompson, P.M. 785
Tijani, S.M. 643
Tinucci, John P. 121
Traeger, Richard K. 221
Turk, N. 81

Ubbes, W. 777
Udd, J.E. 69
Unrau, J. 313
Unrug, Kot F. 967

Van Stone, Larry J. 917
van Zyl, Dirk 1159
Vik, Gunnar 487

Wang, H. 69
Wang, S.T. 231
Wardle, L.J. 531
Watters, Robert J. 723
Whyatt, J.K. 1163
Wilkins, B.J.S. 479
Wilson, Michael L. 749
Wold, M.B. 1007
Worsey, Paul N. 1133

Xian Xue Fu 993

Yoshida, Hidenobu 841
Yoshioka, H. 557
Young, R.P. 1151
Yow, J.L., Jr. 851
Yu Liren 573
Yu Shijian 985

Zeng Ruihua 985
Zimmerman, Roger M. 749
Zimmerman, Robert W. 739
Zyvoloski, George 355